40

THE INTERNAL
CONSTITUTION
OF THE STARS

THE INTERNAL CONSTITUTION OF THE STARS

By

SIR A. S. EDDINGTON

WITH A NEW INTRODUCTION

By

LLOYD MOTZ

Associate Professor of Astronomy
Columbia University

DOVER PUBLICATIONS, INC.
NEW YORK

59-65135

Introduction To Dover Edition

WITH the rapid developments that are taking place in science today the advanced students and even the well established workers in a particular field find themselves under such pressure to keep abreast of the current literature that the great classics in the field remain unread and are soon forgotten. This is particularly true in the highly technical sciences such as physics and astronomy where the problem is aggravated by the difficulty one encounters in locating long-out-of-print treatises and where few publishers are willing to risk the losses that may be involved in re-issuing expensive books. This is unfortunate, for it leads the student to accepting completely formulated theories without seeing just how they grew out of the many conflicting ideas that were prevalent in the past. It is not enough for the serious physicist, for example, to know that there are such things as Maxwell's equations, or to know the mathematical nature of the Lorentz transformations. Names like Boltzmann, Kirchhoff, Einstein, Planck, etc. must be more than the names by which we designate certain theories or which we assign to important equations. Before we can properly understand the most recent scientific theories and developments, we must be well acquainted with the ideas, both false and true, of the men whose work laid the foundations for these theories. And it is not enough to study these ideas second hand, in the writings of later authors who give us the final product without showing us the gropings and speculations of the original thinkers. It is for this reason that we must welcome the re-issuance of such an important book as Eddington's *Internal Constitution Of The Stars*.

Although it is true that astrophysics is quite a youthful science as compared to physics, the great progress that has been made in this field in the last twenty years may give many students the impression that a book such as this one, first published in 1926 and revised in 1930, must be out of date, but this impression is incorrect. One need only glance briefly through its pages to see how many of the fundamental ideas that we still use today in investigating the interior of stars were correctly formulated by Eddington. Indeed, one can take the formalism developed here and, with appropriate corrections for the coefficient of opacity and with the proper expressions for the thermonuclear release of energy, obtain most of the results that we have today.

Sir Arthur Stanley Eddington's research work spanned the period that began with the Bohr theory of the atom and ended with the developments in nuclear physics just prior to World War II, and although in his later years he tended to devote more and more of his time to fundamental problems of physics, his early and middle work period was concerned primarily with the application of the newer physics (the quantum theory and relativity theory) to astronomy. It is to Eddington more than to any other one man that we owe the very rapid development of astrophysics that took place immediately after the work of Planck, Einstein, and Bohr, and we must certainly count him among the giants of that period. We owe a great debt to him for this book which presented for the first time a systematic development of astrophysics as we know it today, and which is written in a style so lucid, brilliant, and delightful that even those who have already read the book find its re-reading rewarding and entertaining.

Eddington's books, and especially this one, are characterized by a masterful welding together of the abstract formalism of a subject with the kind of informal exposition that illuminates its most obscure features. We are treated in this book to much more than a bare discussion of the equations that are at the basis of all investigations into the internal structure of stars. We see quite clearly the intimate relationship of the main stream of astrophysics to the great discoveries in atomic physics and in the theories of radiation that were taking place in the early decades of this century, and at the same time we are introduced to the important observational data that made it possible to evaluate the correctness of the theoretical developments.

The importance of this book for the student of astrophysics lies in the fact that it presents the first detailed exposition of the theory of radiative equilibrium for stellar interiors. Although K. Schwarzschild had developed the equations of radiative equilibrium in a form suitable for the outer portions of a star in 1906, and R. Emden referred to this work in his famous book on the behavior of gas spheres in 1907, most of the work on stellar interiors that was done before Eddington's researches into the problem was based on the ideas of convective equilibrium. Eddington's work grew out of an investigation into the problem of the pulsations of cepheid variables and what processes were responsible for the equilibrium of such stars. From 1916 until 1926 when the first edition of this book was published, Eddington wrote a series of fifteen papers which laid the foundations of modern astrophysics as it applies to deep stellar interiors and at the same time developed a complete theory of radiative equilibrium. It is among these papers that we find the famous "standard model" and the point source model of a star analyzed in detail; and here, too, for the first time we see a theoretical derivation of a mass luminosity law.

Although this book is concerned in a large measure with the author's own work, it deals with the important contributions of other astronomers and physicists as well, so that the reader is given a complete picture of the development of astrophysics and the related fields of physics during that period.

In terms of the material that is dealt with, the book may be divided into five parts. The first part, which is just the first chapter of the book, introduces the problem of stellar interiors and gives an excellent survey of the historical background, starting with Lane's investigations, which are contained in a paper published in 1870. Here we can see what Eddington's plan of attack is as he discusses the essential points that must be considered in a comprehensive investigation of the problem of stellar interiors; and we can already see from this introductory material that the important departure from the work of previous investigators will be in connection with the properties of radiation, ionization, opacity, and energy generation. When we read this preliminary survey, we are at once struck by the breadth of Eddington's vision and his amazing ability to express the essential features of a difficult subject with the use of a few simple concepts. This ability is perhaps best illustrated on pages 18, 19, and 20 by his brief analysis of the need to replace convective equilibrium by radiative equilibrium and by his word picture of the inside of a star.

The second part of the work, which is contained in the next two chapters, is concerned with the laws of thermodynamics, the quantum theory of radiation, and the Bohr theory of the atom. After a brief discussion of radiation pressure, Eddington develops the laws of thermodynamics and from these he derives the Stefan-Boltzmann law and Wien's law for radiation in thermal equilibrium. Chaper III is devoted to Einstein's derivation of the Planck radiation formula and a fairly detailed discussion of the Bohr theory of the atom and atomic spectra.

In Chapters IV to VIII, which we may consider as constituting the third part of this book, Eddington develops the main theme of the investigation starting with the classical theory of polytropic and isothermal gas spheres, and derives for the first time the theorems on the minimal values of the central pressure and the mean temperature in a gaseous configuration. The equations of radiative equilibrium are derived in Chapter V, and the importance of working with a properly evaluated mean coefficient of absorption (the Rosseland mean) is emphasized. In Chapter VI Eddington solves the interior equations for the standard and the point source models of a star, obtains his famous quartic equation relating the radiation pressure to the mass, and develops the mass luminosity relation. He devotes Chapter VII to a discussion of his theoretical results as applied to some typical stars and gives a detailed analysis of the comparison between his mass luminosity law and the empirical results. In Chapter VIII he concerns himself with variable stars and develops his theory of adiabatic oscillations of cepheid variables.

Eddington was fully aware of the deficiencies of the theory as it had been developed up to 1930 and realized that the most serious flaws involved the opacity, the state of ionization in stellar interiors, and the source of stellar energy. The fourth part of this book is concerned with these questions, and it is in his discussion of the coefficient of opacity in Chapter IX that Eddington first introduces the concept of the "guillotine factor," which has been so fruitful in the investigation of stellar interiors. Because of the influence that ionization has on the "guillotine factor" he devotes most of Chapter X to an analysis of the dependence of ionization on density and temperature. At the same time he is concerned with the variation of the ionization, and therefore the mean molecular weight, with varying distances from the center and concludes that such variations may be neglected.

Although the discussion of sources of stellar energy in Chapter XI is very groping and speculative, it is highly imaginative. When Eddington wrote this book neither the wave mechanics of radio-active decay nor the neutron had yet been discovered so that it was necessary for him to think of the formation of heavy elements in terms of protons and electrons coming together with just the right amount of energy and coalescing into nuclei. He correctly points out that, under these conditions, helium cannot be synthesized from hydrogen by purely thermal processes, and he therefore devotes some space to speculating about other processes that might be at work. He is also concerned in this chapter, under a heading called "Astronomical Difficulties", with the problem of the giant stars that has only recently been solved.

In Chapter XII Eddington develops the theory of stellar atmospheres and applies to it the analysis of the formation of absorption lines and to the structure of the continuous spectrum. Although many refinements in the study of atmospheres have been introduced since Eddington's work, the reader will find that very little of a fundamental nature has been changed. In this chapter all the tools that are required for the investigation of the atmosphere of a star are available. The last chapter of the book is devoted to interstellar matter. Here Eddington presented for the first time a detailed discussion of all the evidence that was available for the existence of diffuse matter in interstellar space. This was the beginning of a new and exciting branch of astronomy which has developed rapidly since then.

One cannot avoid a feeling of excitement as one reads these pages which unfold for us a truly heroic period in the field of astrophysics.

LLOYD MOTZ
Associate Professor of Astronomy
Columbia University

New York, New York
January, 1959

PREFACE

THE study of the mechanical and physical conditions in the deep interior of the stars is undertaken primarily in the hope that an understanding of the internal mechanism will throw light on the external phenomena accessible to observation. More than fifty years have gone by since the general mode of attack was first developed; and the scope of the inquiry has grown so that it now involves much of the recently won knowledge of atoms and radiation, and makes evident the ties which unite pure physics with astrophysics. It would be hard to say whether the star or the electron is the hero of our epic.

The reader will judge for himself whether solid progress has been made. He may, like Shakespeare, take a view less optimistic than my own—

> The heaven's glorious sun
> That will not be deep-searched with saucy looks;

but I hope he will not be so unkind as to continue the quotation—

> Small have continual plodders ever won
> Save base authority from others' books.

Re-reading this work I find passages where I have been betrayed into too confident assertion. It is only too true that the most patent clues may mislead, and observational tests of the rough kind here possible sometimes flatter to deceive. But the subject is a fair field for the struggle to gain knowledge by scientific reasoning; and, win or lose, we find the joy of contest.

The last two chapters trespass beyond the ground indicated by the title of the book. This extension can perhaps be justified; but I am aware that, whatever excuse I might make, the real reason was that I could not forgo a desire to collect and review some of the remarkable researches of those who have investigated the outer layers of a star.

The book was written between May 1924 and November 1925. Time was occupied by a number of minor investigations made to fill the gaps that disclosed themselves as the material was brought together. Anyone writing on a theme which many workers are actively investigating is liable to find his pen unable to overtake the rate of growth of the subject. During the above-mentioned period the theoretical papers on stellar constitution in the *Monthly Notices* alone amounted to more than 400 pages. It has been still more difficult to cope with modifications and progress in the theory of the atom, on which astronomical developments must rest. As we go to press a "new quantum theory" is arising which may have important reactions on the stellar problem when it is more fully developed.

An effort has been made to include everything judged important up to November 1925; but naturally the whole book could not be rewritten in the last month and late developments had to be grafted on to an earlier foundation. Further additions have been made in proof up to March 1926; footnotes in *square brackets* show information received too late to be used in the text.

The question of notation has caused me much perplexity since branches of physics ordinarily remote from one another are here brought together. Apart from the inadequacy of the alphabet, the abolition of overlapping symbols and adoption of a consistent notation throughout the book has been deemed impracticable. There are limits to our toleration of change of familiar symbols. A rose by any other name would smell as sweet, but the equation $p\omega = U_2 - U_1$ would lack the familiar savour of the quantum relation. The use of m for absolute magnitude and the mass of an electron, of R for Boltzmann's constant and the radius of a star, of a for a radiation constant and the semiaxis of an orbit, of e for the charge of an electron and the Napierian base, may cause momentary confusion but, it is hoped, no serious difficulty. Similarly we refer to the astronomical equation of areas in its most recognisable form in sections where $h^2 = \mu l$ is not likely to be misconstrued as a relation between Planck's constant and molecular weight. I would suggest to the reader in difficulty that there is a chance that the symbol which puzzles him is included in the list of natural constants in Appendix I.

I have derived help from many colleagues. Mr R. H. Fowler has generally been my referee in difficulties over points of theoretical physics, and I have similarly had recourse to Dr C. D. Ellis for experimental questions. I thank especially Prof. E. A. Milne who has read the proof sheets and eliminated a number of errors and obscurities. My acknowledgments are also due to the staff of the University Press for their care and attention in the printing.

A. S. E.

July, 1926

NOTE TO THE SECOND IMPRESSION

THE advances made since this book was first published are scarcely of sufficient importance to justify an extensive revision, and (except for correction of a few misprints) the text has been reprinted unchanged. The following seem to be the most important passages which are not in accord with later results:

p. 195. The argument giving an upper limit of ξ_1 between $\frac{1}{5}$ and $\frac{1}{6}$ is fallacious (as hinted in the footnote) owing to the neglect of terms involving the square of the amplitude. The correct condition excluding negative pressure is that the inward acceleration must never exceed g; this gives an upper limit 0·6 to 0·8, which is too high to be of interest.

p. 205. I have now proved that the retardation of phase of the flow of heat in passing through the non-adiabatic part of the star is much less than the quarter-period which observation seems to demand. The apparent discrepancy between observation and theory is not a difficulty peculiar to the pulsation theory of Cepheids, and we may perhaps infer that the problem is affected by some unrecognised factor which the present analysis fails to take into account. (*Monthly Notices*, **87**, p. 539.)

p. 275. According to recent results the radiation-pressure corresponding to photo-electric absorption acts primarily on the electrons (not on the ions). The first two paragraphs of § 193 should accordingly be deleted.

The reasons for believing that all stars except white dwarfs are in the condition of a perfect (or slightly superperfect) gas were stated fully in the book since the theory was novel at the time; and although the contrary view has since become prominent through the powerful advocacy of Sir James Jeans, the treatment does not seem to require revision. The condition of matter at the temperatures and densities admitted to prevail in the stellar interior is primarily a problem of atomic physics, and it does not seem to be disputed that, according to the laws at present accepted, physicists would predict rather confidently that the condition is gaseous. In support of "liquid stars" most stress has been laid on the fact that (1) it is difficult to devise a plausible law of liberation of subatomic energy which will not render a gaseous star unstable or throw it into pulsation (§ 211), and (2) there is a tenfold discrepancy between the physical and the astronomical calculation of opacity for a gaseous star (§ 172). Whilst we do not think that these difficulties should override the clear indications of atomic physics, we have from the first called attention to them prominently, and they are referred to as "two clouds obscuring the theory" in the concluding paragraph of the book.

A. S. E.

July 1930

CONTENTS

CHAP.   PAGE

I.   Survey of the Problem 1

II.   Thermodynamics of Radiation 27

III.   Quantum Theory 44

IV.   Polytropic Gas Spheres 79

V.   Radiative Equilibrium 97

VI.   Solution of the Equations 114

VII. The Mass-Luminosity Relation 145

VIII. Variable Stars 180

IX.   The Coefficient of Opacity 216

X.   Ionisation, Diffusion, Rotation 250

XI.   The Source of Stellar Energy 289

XII. The Outside of a Star 321

XIII. Diffuse Matter in Space 371

APP.

I.   Physical and Astronomical Constants 395

II.   References 397

INDEX 403

DIAGRAMS

FIG.

1.   Distribution of Temperature and of Mass in a Star . . 86

2.   The Mass-Luminosity Curve compared with Observations . 153

3.   Statistics of Absolute Magnitude and Spectral Type . . 175

4.   Schematic Type-Magnitude Diagram 176

5.   Spectral Energy Curve of the Sun 328

XV

TABLES

(This list includes only the Tables most likely to be used for reference)

TABLE		PAGE
4, 5, 6.	Solutions for Polytropes $n = 2, 2\frac{1}{2}, 3$	82–83
7.	Solution for Isothermal Gas Sphere	90
8.	Weights for Calculating Opacity with Rosseland's Correction	112
13 A.	Central Temperature and Mean Density for given Mass and Effective Temperature	136
14.	Calculation of Absolute Magnitude from Mass	137
16.	Reduction of Bolometric to Visual Magnitude. Surface Brightness	139
16 A.	Temperature Scale for Spectral Types	141
17, 18, 19, 20.	Comparison of Observations with the Theoretical Mass-Luminosity Law	154–155
23.	Data for Stars on the Main Series (Central Temperature 40,000,000°)	178
24, 25.	Observational and Theoretical Data for 18 Cepheids	182
30.	Atomic Numbers and Energy-Levels of the Elements	252
36.	Distribution Density of Free Electrons	263
38.	Electrostatic Correction to the Pressure	269
39.	Values of Ratio of Specific Heats for Stellar Material	270
41.	Radiation of Mass. Duration of Stages of Evolution	309
47.	Stellar Abundance of the Elements	370

CHAPTER I

SURVEY OF THE PROBLEM

1. At first sight it would seem that the deep interior of the sun and stars is less accessible to scientific investigation than any other region of the universe. Our telescopes may probe farther and farther into the depths of space; but how can we ever obtain certain knowledge of that which is hidden behind substantial barriers? What appliance can pierce through the outer layers of a star and test the conditions within?

The problem does not appear so hopeless when misleading metaphor is discarded. It is not our task actively to "probe"; we learn what we do learn by awaiting and interpreting the messages dispatched to us by the objects of nature. And the interior of a star is not wholly cut off from such communication. A gravitational field emanates from it, which substantial barriers cannot appreciably modify; further, radiant energy from the hot interior after many deflections and transformations manages to struggle to the surface and begin its journey across space. From these two clues alone a chain of deduction can start, which is perhaps the more trustworthy because it is only possible to employ in it the most universal rules of nature—the conservation of energy and momentum, the laws of chance and averages, the second law of thermodynamics, the fundamental properties of the atom, and so on. There is no more essential uncertainty in the knowledge so reached than there is in most scientific inferences.

We should be unwise to trust scientific inference very far when it becomes divorced from opportunity for observational test. We do not, however, study the interior of a star merely out of curiosity as to the extraordinary conditions prevailing there. It appears that an understanding of the mechanism of the interior throws light on the external manifestations of the star, and the whole theory is ultimately brought into contact with observation. At least that is the goal which we keep in view.

2. The gravitational field emanating from the interior and the radiant energy streaming out from the interior together control the conditions in the shallow layer or atmosphere examined with the telescope and spectroscope. We believe that they are by far the most important controlling factors. Spectrum analysis detects in the stellar atmospheres chemical substances which differ from one star to another; in some helium is prominent, in others oxygen, hydrogen, calcium, iron, titanium oxide, and so on. But it is not to be supposed that this is an indication of the relative abundance of the chemical elements—that a star showing strongly the iron spectrum is richer in that element than other stars; it is rather an indication of physical conditions of temperature and density favourable for exciting the respective spectra. Without entirely denying the possibility of differences of chemical composition, which may be necessary to account for some of the more unusual types of spectrum, we assume that in the main the observed differences of surface phenomena are not connected with chemical constitution.

We have thus to consider an atmosphere of material of fixed composition, with free upper surface and density increasing downwards. Its physical state—distribution of density, temperature and pressure; hence also its radiative and optical properties—will then depend entirely on the extraneous controlling influences to which it is subjected; and these extraneous influences are, as already stated, the force of gravity holding it down to the star and the stream of radiant heat poured into it from below. In order to remain in a steady state the atmosphere must adjust itself to let the radiant heat pass through. Thus the surface conditions depend on two parameters, viz. the value of g at the surface and the "effective temperature" T_e. The effective temperature is a conventional measure specifying the rate of outflow of radiant heat per unit area; it is not to be regarded as the temperature at any particularly significant level in the star.

By varying the controlling factors g and T_e the state of the stellar atmosphere can be varied in two directions. Accordingly we must expect that the possible varieties of stellar spectrum will form a twofold sequence, that is to say, will be capable of arrangement in two-dimensional order. This is in fact the case. For a long time only a one-dimensional order was recognised, viz. the well-known Draper sequence of types. But the spectroscopic method of determining absolute magnitudes, due to Adams and Kohlschütter in 1914, introduces a classification of spectra transverse to the Draper classification. Roughly speaking the Draper criterion follows the parameter T_e and the absolute magnitude criterion the parameter g; but the correspondence is probably not so close as was at one time supposed. The observational criteria divide the two-dimensional distribution of states into one system of meshes, and the parameters T_e and g into another system. There is no reason to anticipate any close coincidence of the two methods of partition.

The same twofold sequence of possible states appears when we consider the star as a whole. Evidently one sequence is obtained by considering stars of different mass. A transverse sequence is formed by stars of the same mass but different radius (or mean density). Thus a third way of dividing into meshes the two-dimensional distribution of states is obtained by taking the mass and radius of the star, M and R, as parameters.

3. Consider now the connection between our three pairs of parameters —g and T_e; Draper Type and Absolute Magnitude criterion; M and R— any pair defining a unique state of the star. The connection of the spectral criteria with g and T_e is a problem of great importance in which much recent progress has been made; but it is not a problem of the stellar interior and lies outside the main lines of our investigation. As regards the connection of g and T_e with M and R, the connection of g needs no comment; the main question is, How is T_e, or equivalently the rate of outflow of radiation, determined by the mass and radius of the star? That is the central problem of this book. Various branches of inquiry will diverge from it; but it supplies the continuous thread in the discussion, so long as we are studying the stellar interior.

This is essentially a problem of the stellar interior and not of superficial conditions. The sun does not radiate 6.10^{10} ergs per square centimetre per second *because* its photosphere is at $6000°$ C.; its photosphere is maintained at $6000°$ because 6.10^{10} ergs are streaming through it. It is under the temperature gradient in the interior that the radiant stream gathers way; the surface layers cannot dam the flow since their capacity for storing energy is insignificant; they can only adjust themselves to let it through. Qualitatively the radiant stream is greatly transformed in passing through the last few thousand kilometres of the star, and the actual waves that spread through space are born in the photospheric layers; but quantitatively it is one continuous stream passing from the interior into outer space.

The intensity of this outward flow of energy through the interior depends on two factors, the one helping and the other hindering. Heat flows from a higher to a lower temperature, and the cause of the flow within the star must be a gradually increasing temperature from the surface to the centre. The hindering factor is the obstruction opposed by matter to the transmission of this stream of heat. We shall find that in a star the heat is transmitted almost entirely by radiation, and the obstruction to the flow of radiation is the *opacity* or *absorption coefficient* of the stellar material. Our problem is, therefore, firstly to find the distribution of temperature inside a star so as to determine the temperature gradient urging the flow; secondly, to determine the opacity of matter under the physical conditions prevailing in the interior.

4. Here at the outset we must deal with a criticism urged by Nernst, Jeans and others. It has been argued that this procedure for calculating the outward flow of radiation is necessarily doomed to failure, because the star's output of heat energy is determined by entirely different considerations. The supply of heat replenishing that which the star radiates into space must come from the conversion of other forms of energy; and since the star remains apparently steady for exceedingly long periods of time, the radiation of the star must be just equal to the amount of energy converted in the interior. It is now believed that this conversion process is the liberation of subatomic energy. The critic contends that, since the outflowing heat represents the energy liberated by subatomic processes, the amount can only be calculated if we know the laws of liberation of subatomic energy, and any procedure which evades this difficult problem begs the question.

Now it is quite true that a theory of the rate of liberation of subatomic energy is a conceivable approach to the problem of stellar radiation. In the present state of our knowledge such theories are little more than guess-work and results are rudimentary. But it is unsound to argue that no other procedure is permissible. The amount of water supplied to a town is the amount pumped at the waterworks; but it does not follow that a calculation based on the head of water and diameter of the mains is fallacious because it evades the problems of the pumping station.

It may seem puzzling to understand how two radically different ways of calculating the theoretical radiation from a star can be made to agree. Appealing again to the analogy, the two modes of calculating the water supplied to a town may not agree; but in that case there will be a flood at the pumping station. Similarly in a star a disagreement would involve the blowing up or collapse of the star. Accepting it as a fact that the stars generally are in a nearly steady state, we must infer that for actual stars (but not necessarily for a model star of arbitrarily assigned constitution) the two modes of calculating the radiation would give the same result; and in Chapter XI we shall try to follow up the question how the adjustment has occurred by which the supply of subatomic energy just meets the demand. Meanwhile we note that, flood or no flood, the flow of water must conform to the pressure gradient and diameter of the pipe; and so also the radiation from a star must in any case conform to the temperature gradient and opacity in the interior.

We may thus proceed with our method of determining the expenditure of radiation by the star without reference to the supply of subatomic energy. How the star manages to accommodate its supply to balance its expenditure, and so avoid collapse or expansion, is an independent problem.

Lane's Theory.

5. The pioneer investigation of the distribution of temperature within a star is contained in a paper published in 1870 by J. Homer Lane entitled, "On the Theoretical Temperature of the Sun, under the Hypothesis of a Gaseous Mass maintaining its Volume by its Internal Heat, and depending on the Laws of Gases as known to Terrestrial Experiment*."

* *American Journ. of Sci. and Arts*, Series 2, **4**, p. 57.

This was followed and amplified by investigations on similar lines by A. Ritter*, Lord Kelvin†, and others, culminating in the systematic and exhaustive research of R. Emden. Although we find it necessary to break away from these earlier investigations on a fundamental point, viz. the mode of transfer of heat within the star, they contain much that is sufficiently general to be adapted to present theories. The calculations and tables in Emden's remarkable book *Gaskugeln* (Teubner, 1907) have been extensively used by the author.

Lane reached the striking result that if a star contracts the internal temperature rises so long as the material is sufficiently diffuse to behave as a perfect gas. Until recently it was believed that the gravitational energy converted into heat by contraction was the only important source of maintenance of a star's heat. In that case the star through radiating heat must contract, and the heat generated by the falling in of material must be sufficient not only to replace the radiation lost but to raise the internal temperature to a higher level. Lane's result thus took the paradoxical form that a star by losing heat automatically grows hotter.

Lane's investigation is not, however, bound up with any particular views as to the source of a star's heat. It sets forth the change of temperature necessary to preserve equilibrium. The star has the option to obey Lane's law or to collapse; it is obvious that actual stars have not chosen the latter alternative, but the reason lies outside Lane's theory. Accepting the modern belief that the heat is supplied by liberation of subatomic energy, we still suppose that stars are formed by gradual condensation of primordial matter; so that the course of evolution is from low to high density and therefore by Lane's law from low to high temperature. At least in the earlier stages the internal temperature of a star is gradually rising. If in the later stages of high density the material no longer behaves as a perfect gas the temperature may ultimately fall again.

6. In Lane's time there was no evidence that any star existed for which the theory of a perfect gas would be applicable. The mean density of the sun is 1·41 gm. per cu. cm., and long before reaching such a density terrestrial gases cease to conform to the perfect gas law. There was at that time no reason to doubt that the sun's density was typical of stars in general. But we now know that there exist stars ("giant stars") with mean densities comparable to that of air or even to the density in an ordinary vacuum tube. These at least can be treated as composed of perfect gas; so that there will be no lack of opportunity for application to actual stars of results obtained for perfect gas.

The existence of stars of low density is now a commonplace of astronomy, and it is unnecessary to survey the abundant proofs derived indirectly

---

* *Wiedemann's Annalen*, 1878–1889.
† *Phil. Mag.*, Series 5, **23**, p. 287 (1887).

from studies of absolute magnitude and spectral type and more directly from the calculated densities of eclipsing variables. The confirmation that is most easily grasped is afforded by the recent interferometer measurements of the angular diameters of stars at Mount Wilson. These show that certain stars such as Betelgeuse, Antares and o Ceti, are of enormous bulk, capable of containing the whole orbit of the earth inside them. We are therefore compelled to extend our ideas of the nature of stars beyond anything that would be suspected from knowledge of the sun.

The great bulk of these giant stars is due to low density rather than great mass. Betelgeuse for example has a radius of the order 250 million km. and a volume 50 million times greater than the sun. But the mass, or amount of matter contained in it, is probably between 10 and 100 times greater, so that the density is about a million times less. It is rather interesting to notice that Einstein's theory of gravitation has something to say on this point. According to it a star of 250 million km. radius could not possibly have so high a density as the sun. Firstly, the force of gravitation would be so great that light would be unable to escape from it, the rays falling back to the star like a stone to the earth. Secondly, the red-shift of the spectral lines would be so great that the spectrum would be shifted out of existence. Thirdly, the mass would produce so much curvature of the space-time metric that space would close up round the star, leaving us outside (i.e. nowhere). The second point gives a more delicate indication and shows that the density is less than 0·001; for even at that density there would be a red-shift of the spectrum too great to be concealed by any probable Doppler effect.

Lest this argument should be regarded by our more conservative readers as ultra-modern, we hasten to add that it is to be found in the writings of Laplace—

A luminous star, of the same density as the earth, and whose diameter should be two hundred and fifty times larger than that of the sun, would not, in consequence of its attraction, allow any of its rays to arrive at us; it is therefore possible that the largest luminous bodies in the universe may, through this cause, be invisible*.

7. For many years Lane's discovery had little effect on the accepted theories of stellar evolution. Sir Norman Lockyer accepted it and accordingly classified the stars in an ascending and descending temperature sequence; but he was almost alone in his views. Astrophysicists in general regarded the hottest stars as the earliest and the coolest stars as the latest in order of development†. Probably they did not realise that any of the

---

* Laplace, *Système du Monde*, Book 5, Cp. VI. I am indebted to Dr H. Jeffreys for this reference.

† The expressions "early" and "late" type of spectrum are still commonly employed for high-temperature types (*B* and *A*) and low-temperature types (*K* and *M*) respectively.

ordinary types of spectrum could be produced in bodies diffuse enough to behave as a perfect gas, and supposed that Lane's theory, if it had any astronomical significance, must refer to some pre-stellar stage of development.

About 1913 a revolution of ideas occurred and the "Giant and Dwarf Theory" of E. Hertzsprung and H. N. Russell soon gained general acceptance. Setting aside certain misgivings which have arisen since 1924, we shall summarise the main points of the theory. In principle it was a revival of the ideas of Lane and Lockyer; the novel point was the adaptation of these ideas to the observational data, so that each star could be assigned its particular place in the scheme. The stars start to be visible as cool red stars of type M with low density and enormous bulk. They contract and in obedience to Lane's condition rise in temperature*, passing up the spectral series K, G, F to A and B—i.e. the reverse of the previously accepted order. At some stage of the contraction the density becomes too great for the perfect gas laws to apply, the rise of temperature is checked, and ultimately the star cools down again as a solid or liquid would do; in this last stage it returns down the spectral series to type M and ends in extinction. On this theory the stars which had been classed together indiscriminately as type G, for example, must be divided into two groups, the one making the ascent, the other on the descent, the one a nearly perfect gas, the other a very imperfect gas behaving similarly to a liquid. The surface conditions being similar, as evidenced by the spectral type, the outstanding distinction is that the ascending series or *giants* have much greater volume than the descending series or *dwarfs*. The greater volume and surface of the giant stars gives them greater luminosity, and when the absolute magnitudes are studied the division into two groups is easily seen. The separation is shown in the types M, K, G and F; it is not to be expected in type A, which marks the turning-point for most stars. Naturally it is most striking in type M, where the stars in the most diffuse and most concentrated state are brought into contrast; the one group clusters about absolute magnitude $+ 1^{m}\cdot 5$, the other about $+ 10^{m}\cdot 5$, and there is a clear gap of about 6^{m} in which no M star has yet been detected.

According to the statistics there is little or no change of absolute brightness with type along the giant series; this would be expected since the rising temperature and decreasing surface area will keep the total light about the same. In descending the dwarf series the decreasing temperature and decreasing surface combine to give a rapid falling off of brightness.

---

* The theory applies to internal temperature, and it was generally taken for granted that the observed photospheric temperature would keep step; but this is by no means inevitable.

Much additional confirmation is obtained. The required bifurcation of density has been verified by the researches of Russell and Shapley on eclipsing variable stars. The sun and a number of other dwarf stars of type G have densities near that of water; but at least three eclipsing variables of type G are found to have densities less than that of air. There is evidence that this is not due to continuous range of density but is a definite bifurcation; intermediate densities belong to the higher types F, A, B which are traversed between the two stages of G. As already mentioned, the startling bulk ascribed by this theory to the giant stars has been verified by interferometer measurements.

The giants and dwarfs can now be distinguished by special differences in their spectra of a kind not considered in the Draper classification into types. This is a particular application of the spectroscopic method of determining absolute magnitude.

We shall find later that it is difficult to accept the giant and dwarf theory in its entirety. The ascending series presents no difficulty; but the descending series does not seem to be explicable in the manner that Lockyer, Russell and Hertzsprung supposed, because we now have evidence that the sun and other stars assigned to this branch behave as though constituted of perfect gas, notwithstanding that their densities are greater than water. In fact, the conditions in the stellar interior are such that the gas laws should continue to hold at much higher densities than under terrestrial conditions. The theory of stellar evolution is now in a very confused state, and the difficulties will be considered in due course.

8. The broad principles used by Lane in calculating the internal distribution of temperature have been followed in all later researches. We consider the case of a star composed of perfect gas. Then any one of the three variables, pressure (P), density (ρ), temperature (T), can be calculated from the other two by the law

$$P = \Re\rho T/\mu \qquad\qquad\dots\dots\dots\dots\dots\dots\dots(8\cdot1),$$

where $\Re$ is the universal gas constant $8\cdot26 \cdot 10^7$ and μ the molecular weight in terms of the hydrogen atom. Thus effectively there are only two independent variables determining the state of the material. The differential equations satisfied by them are obtained by expressing two conditions: (1) the *mechanical equilibrium* of the star, which requires that the pressure at any internal point is just sufficient to support the weight of the layers above, and (2) the *thermal equilibrium* of the star, which requires that the temperature distribution is capable of maintaining itself automatically notwithstanding the continual transfer of heat from one part of the star to another. It is necessary to formulate and integrate the two equations expressing these conditions; and they suffice to determine the two independent variables specifying the condition of the material at any point.

Hence the distribution of pressure, density and temperature is found. The general scheme of distribution is (in the first approximation) homologous from star to star; that is to say, all gaseous stars copy the same model each on its own appropriate scale of mass, length, temperature, etc. The heavy work of the solution can be done once for all, and it is then only a question of adapting it to the scale of the particular star considered. We do not here enter into details; the problem is fully treated in Chapter IV.

In order to obtain definite numerical values of the temperature inside a star according to Lane's theory it was necessary to have the following data—

M the mass,
R the radius,
μ the mean molecular weight of the material,
γ the ratio of specific heats of the material.

The first two define the star under consideration; but we might suppose that the values of the last two in any star could only be guessed by considering the probable chemical composition of the interior—as to which we know practically nothing. We shall explain how this difficulty has been surmounted.

Actually the value of γ gave no serious trouble. It cannot exceed $\frac{5}{3}$, the value for a monatomic gas; and it cannot be less than $\frac{4}{3}$ without rendering the star unstable—which we know it is not. The difference in temperature distribution corresponding to the limits $\frac{5}{3}$ and $\frac{4}{3}$ is of some account; but there is no important change in its general character, and either limit gives an approximation good enough for many purposes. The constant γ, however, no longer concerns us. We shall abandon that part of Lane's theory responsible for its introduction, replacing Lane's hypothesis of *convective* equilibrium by *radiative* equilibrium. In all the earlier researches it was supposed that heat was carried from the interior to the surface of the star by convection currents, so that the interior was kept thoroughly stirred and followed the same law of thermal equilibrium as the lower part of the earth's atmosphere. But it appears now that the heat is transferred by radiation and the temperature distribution is controlled by the flow of radiation; convection currents, if they exist, will strive to establish a different distribution, but the temperature continually slips back to radiative equilibrium since the transfer by radiation is much more rapid. Radiative equilibrium was first adopted by R. A. Sampson* in 1894; but it could not be developed fully without the more recent progress of thermodynamics. K. Schwarzschild† brought it into prominence in a famous paper on the condition of the sun's atmosphere. Our task is to apply the same principle to the interior of the sun and stars.

* *Memoirs R.A.S.*, **51**, p. 123. † *Göttingen Nachrichten*, 1906, p. 41.

With the substitution of radiative for convective equilibrium the constant γ disappears; its place is taken by the numerical constant $\frac{4}{3}$ which from one point of view can be regarded as the ratio of specific heats of the aether, aether having now replaced matter as the agent of transport of heat.

9. It remains to fix the appropriate value of μ, and it is necessary to do this with fair accuracy because μ is raised to a high power in many important formulae of the theory. We may assume that all chemical bonds are dissolved at the high temperature in the stellar interior, so that the atoms are isolated. Our first impulse is to adopt for μ the average atomic weight of the elements which we think likely to be most abundant. Since iron is often supposed to be the commonest element and is moreover an element of medium weight, a value about 50 is suggested. The author's first investigations* were made on this assumption. It was, however, suggested to him independently by Newall, Jeans and Lindemann that in stellar conditions the atoms themselves would break up to a considerable degree, many of the satellite electrons being detached.

The atom is often compared to a miniature solar system. Nearly all the mass is concentrated in a nucleus carrying positive charge; negative electrons of small mass, in number sufficient to balance the positive charge, describe orbits round the nucleus. At high temperatures a process known as ionisation occurs by which these satellite electrons are successively set free and travel about in the material as independent particles. The molecular weight μ appearing in our formulae (e.g. in (8·1)) is the average mass per independent particle. We use the term *molecule* to denote the particles moving independently of one another whether they are combinations of atoms or portions of atoms. If the ionisation is carried to the extreme limit a remarkable simplification occurs; *the molecular weight becomes approximately equal to 2 whatever the chemical composition of the material*, provided only that there is not an excessive proportion of hydrogen.

The number of satellite electrons is equal to the atomic number Z of the element, so that if all of them are set free there will be $Z + 1$ independent particles or molecules. Hence if A is the atomic weight

$$\mu = A/(Z + 1).$$

It is a well-known rule that the atomic number is about half the atomic weight, so that μ is near to 2. Some illustrations are given in Table 1.

Evidently the uncertainty of chemical composition is a much less serious matter when we realise that it is column 4 of the table which concerns us instead of column 3.

In the actual conditions of a star the ionisation is not quite complete, and for the heavier elements some of the satellite electrons remain undetached. This raises the molecular weight a little. It is now possible to

* *Monthly Notices,* **77,** p. 16.

make an approximate calculation of the degree of ionisation of the various elements under given conditions of pressure and temperature so that the amended molecular weights can be found. But the detached electrons are so large a proportion of the whole system that the correction is trifling; and if we adopt a molecular weight about 2·2 we cannot be far from the truth. As the ionisation will diminish with the diminishing temperature towards the outside of the star, we may as a refinement adopt a molecular weight increasing very slowly from the centre outwards.

Table 1.

Average Molecular Weight.

Element	Z	A	$A/(Z+1)$	Element	Z	A	$A/(Z+1)$
Hydrogen	1	1	0·50	Iron	26	56	2·07
Helium	2	4	1·33	Silver	47	108	2·25
Lithium	3	7	1·75	Barium	56	137	2·40
Oxygen	8	16	1·78	Gold	79	197	2·46
Calcium	20	40	1·91	Uranium	92	238	2·56

10. Having thus resolved the difficulty as to the two constants γ and μ, we can obtain numerical values of the temperature, density and pressure in a gaseous star of known mass and radius. It will help us to realise the conditions that will have to be considered if we now give the results obtained for a particular star. For this illustration we choose the brighter component of Capella. Capella is the only diffuse (giant) star for which the required observational data reach a high standard of accuracy; most of the first-class astronomical data refer to dense (dwarf) stars. It is also an advantage that Capella is a typical diffuse star, standing about mid-way in the spectral series. We take the opportunity of explaining (for those unfamiliar with double-star astronomy) how the data as to mass, luminosity, etc. have been obtained from astronomical observations.

Capella.

11. Capella was discovered to be a spectroscopic binary in 1899 by Campbell and Newall independently. The two components are not very unequal in brilliancy, so that lines due to both can be seen in the spectrum; the two sets of lines are observed to shift to and fro across one another owing to the changing Doppler effect as the components approach and recede in their orbits. The period is 104·022 days. The full knowledge obtained for Capella depends on the fact that it has also been observed as a visual double star, and the elements of the visual orbit are believed to be well determined. The separation of the two components is only about 0″·05, which is beyond the resolving power of the largest telescopes adapted for this kind of observation; but in 1920 Michelson's interferometer method of observation used in connection with the 100-inch reflector at Mount Wilson achieved its first striking success by measurements of the separation and position angle of Capella. These observations, begun by Anderson and continued by Merrill, have yielded a good visual orbit. It should be understood that the spectral lines of *both* components can be observed in only a small proportion of the spectroscopic binaries; and it is extremely rare for visual and spectroscopic orbits to be determined for the same star. Thus our knowledge of the system of Capella is unusually complete.

The line-of-sight velocity of the brighter component varies between + 4 and + 56 km. per sec., a range of 52; the fainter varies between + 63 and − 3 km. per sec., a range of 66. Neglecting eccentricity the mean velocity + 30 (necessarily the same for both components) is the motion of recession of the centre of mass of the system from the sun. The masses must be in the inverse ratio of the respective velocity ranges so that the brighter component has 66/52 or 1·26 times the mass of the fainter.

The eccentricity is found to be very small (·0086), so that we may treat the orbits as circular and the orbital speeds as constant. If the line of sight were in the plane of the orbit the orbital speed would be equal to the half-range of velocity, 26 and 33 km. per sec. respectively; to allow for projection these values must be multiplied by cosec i, where i is the inclination of the orbit plane to the plane of the sky. The circumference of the orbit is at once found by multiplying the orbital speed by the period. In this way we find that if a_1 and a_2 are the radii (or semiaxes) of the two orbits

$$a_1 \sin i = 36{,}800{,}000 \text{ km.,} \qquad a_2 \sin i = 46{,}400{,}000 \text{ km.}$$

We now turn to the visual observations. These treated in the usual way determine the inclination $i = 41°·1$. Hence

$$a_1 = 56{,}000{,}000 \text{ km.}$$

$$a_2 = 70{,}600{,}000 \text{ km.}$$

$$a_1 + a_2 = 126{,}600{,}000 \text{ km.} = 0·847 \text{ astronomical units.}$$

By Kepler's third law the mass of the system is

$$M_1 + M_2 = (a_1 + a_2)^3/P^2,$$

the unit of mass being the sun's mass, $a_1 + a_2$ being in astronomical units (i.e. in terms of the earth's distance from the sun), and the period P in years. We thus have

$$M_1 + M_2 = (·847)^3/(·285)^2 = 7·5,$$

and dividing this between the two components in the ratio 1·26 : 1 already found

$$M_1 = 4·18, \qquad M_2 = 3·32.$$

12. In the orbit determined from the visual measures the semiaxis of the relative orbit $(a_1 + a_2)$ is found to be $0''\cdot 0536$. We have seen that in linear measure this is equal to $0\cdot 847$ astronomical units. Hence 1 astronomical unit corresponds to $0''\cdot 0632$. Accordingly the parallax of Capella is

$$\varpi = 0''\cdot 0632.$$

A rough parallax had previously been found trigonometrically in close agreement with the above value, but the parallax furnished by the orbital data is presumably of much superior accuracy.

The observed visual magnitude of Capella is $0^{m}\cdot 21$. To reduce to absolute magnitude, i.e. magnitude at the standard distance of 10 parsecs or parallax $0''\cdot 1$, we must add

$$5 \log_{10} (\varpi/0''\cdot 1),$$

which gives $0\cdot 21 - 1\cdot 00 = -0^{m}\cdot 79$. This represents the sum of the light of the two components. It is estimated that they differ in visual magnitude by $0^{m}\cdot 5$. The absolute visual magnitudes are then found to be $-0^{m}\cdot 26$ and $+0^{m}\cdot 24$, since these would compound to give $-0^{m}\cdot 79$.

The spectral type of the bright component is classed as $G\,0$, the same as that of the sun. The sun's effective temperature is $5740°$, but it appears from theory and observation that the same spectral characteristics will appear at lower temperature in a diffuse star like Capella than in the sun. We shall therefore adopt $5200°$ for the effective temperature. This, of course, is only the marginal temperature of the great furnace, and affords no idea of the terrific heat within.

It is convenient to introduce the *bolometric magnitude*, which is a measure of the heat-intensity of a star in the same way that the visual magnitude is a measure of its luminous intensity or the photographic magnitude is a measure of its photographic intensity, the measures in each case being on a logarithmic scale. Black-body radiation has maximum luminous efficiency when it corresponds to a temperature of about $6500°$, and the zero of the scale of bolometric magnitude is chosen so as to agree with visual magnitude for stars of this effective temperature. At any other temperature a greater amount of radiant energy is required to produce the same intensity of light, so that the bolometric magnitude is brighter (numerically smaller) than the visual magnitude. At $5200°$ the reduction to bolometric magnitude is $0^{m}\cdot 10$, so that the absolute bolometric magnitude of the bright component of Capella is

$$-0\cdot 26 - 0\cdot 10 = -0^{m}\cdot 36.$$

Since the bolometric magnitude indicates the total radiation emitted from the star and the effective temperature indicates the radiation per sq. cm., we are able to calculate the area of the surface and hence the radius of Capella. The calculation is most conveniently made by using the sun (absolute bolometric magnitude $+ 4.9$; effective temperature $5740°$; radius $6.95 . 10^{10}$ cm.) as intermediary. The difference of absolute magnitude m is converted into ratio of total radiation L by the formula*

$$m - m_\odot = - \tfrac{5}{2} \log_{10} (L/L_\odot).$$

Also we have
$$\frac{L}{L_\odot} = \frac{R^2 T_e^4}{R_\odot^2 T_\odot^4},$$

the rate of radiation being proportional to the fourth power of the effective temperature. Hence

$$m - m_\odot = - 5 \log_{10} (R/R_\odot) - 10 \log_{10} (T_e/T_\odot) \ldots\ldots\ldots(12.1).$$

13. Applying the theory developed in the succeeding chapters to the observational data we obtain the following collected results†.

Capella (bright component).

Parallax $= 0''.0632$.
Apparent visual magnitude $= + 0^{m}.74$.
Spectral type $= G\,0$.
Effective temperature $= 5200°$.
Mass $= 4.18 \times \odot = 8.30 . 10^{33}$ gm.
Absolute bolometric magnitude $= - 0^{m}.36 = 5^{m}.26$ brighter than the sun.
Total radiation $= 127 \times \odot = 4.80 . 10^{35}$ ergs per sec.
Radius $= 13.74 \times \odot = 9.55 . 10^{11}$ cm.
Mean density $= .00227$ gm. per cu. cm.

At the centre—

Temperature $= 7.20 . 10^6$ degrees.
Density $\quad = .0547$ gm. per cu. cm.
Pressure $\quad = 2.23 . 10^{13}$ dynes per sq. cm. $= 22$ million atmospheres.

Of this pressure the fraction $.694$ is ordinary gas pressure and $.306$ is radiation pressure.

The mean temperature of the whole mass is $4\frac{1}{2}$ million degrees.

A sphere of radius 0.646 of the radius of the star contains 93.4 per cent. of the mass. At the surface of this sphere—

Temperature $= 1.89 . 10^6$ degrees.
Density $\quad = .00121$ gm. per cu. cm.
Pressure $\quad = 1.07 . 10^{11}$ dynes per sq. cm.

---

* By definition a change of five magnitudes signifies a hundredfold increase or decrease of light; one magnitude corresponds to a light ratio of $(100)^{\frac{1}{5}}$ or 2.512.

† These results are calculated for a *central* molecular weight 2.1, and to allow for the ionisation decreasing outwards the molecular weight has been taken to vary as $T^{-\frac{1}{3}}$ (§ 94).

A sphere of radius 0·831 of the radius of the star contains 99·5 per cent. of the mass. At a point on this sphere—

Temperature = 0·81 . 10^6 degrees.
Density   = ·000107 gm. per cu. cm.
Pressure   = 3·62 . 10^9 dynes per sq. cm.

All but 1 per cent. of the mass is at a temperature above a million degrees but the remainder is of very low density and occupies nearly half the volume of the star.

The maximum temperature gradient in the interior is 1°·1 per kilometre—very much less than the temperature gradient in our own atmosphere. This maximum occurs about $\frac{1}{3}$ of the way from the centre to the surface; it is a very flat maximum and the gradient throughout the greater part of the star is not much below the maximum value.

Gravity at the surface is 1/45·2 times that at the surface of the sun or about $\frac{3}{5}$ of gravity on the earth. The absolute value is 606 cm. sec.$^{-2}$. In the interior it rises to a maximum of 4 times this value and then falls to zero at the centre.

The average rate of liberation of heat in the interior required to supply that lost by radiation from the surface is 58 ergs per sec. per gm. By its radiation Capella is losing mass at the rate of about 500 million tons per second.

Radiation Pressure.

14. It is necessary to take account of a phenomenon ignored in the early investigations, which may have a considerable effect on the equilibrium of a star, viz. the pressure of radiation. It is well known that electromagnetic waves, including light waves, possess mass and momentum and exert a force on anything which obstructs their progress. Ordinarily the pressure of radiation is extremely minute and can only be demonstrated by very delicate terrestrial experiments; but the radiation inside a star is so intense that the pressure is by no means negligible as regards the conditions of equilibrium of the material. At a point in the interior the radiation pressure shares with the gas pressure the task of supporting the weight of the superincumbent layers of material. The radiation pressure is proportional to the fourth power of the temperature; it amounts to

2,550 atmospheres at 1,000,000°,

25,500,000 atmospheres at 10,000,000°.

The outward flowing radiation may thus be compared to a wind blowing through the star and helping to distend it against gravity. The formulae to be developed later enable us to calculate what proportion of the weight of the material is borne by this wind, the remainder being supported by the gas pressure. To a first approximation the proportion is the same at all parts of the star. It does not depend on the density nor on the opacity of the star*. It depends only on the mass and molecular weight. Moreover, the physical constants employed in the calculation have all been measured in the laboratory, and no astronomical data are required. We can imagine a physicist on a cloud-bound planet who has never heard tell of the stars calculating the ratio of radiation pressure to gas pressure for a series of globes of gas of various sizes, starting, say, with a globe of mass 10 gm., then 100 gm., 1000 gm., and so on, so that his nth globe contains 10^n gm. Table 2 shows the more interesting part of his results.

Table 2.

No. of Globe	Radiation Pressure	Gas Pressure
30	·00000016	·99999984
31	·000016	·999984
32	·0016	·9984
33	·106	·894
34	·570	·430
35	·850	·150
36	·951	·049
37	·984	·016
38	·9951	·0049
39	·9984	·0016
40	·99951	·00049

The rest of the table would consist mainly of long strings of 9's and 0's. Just for the particular range of mass about the 33rd to 35th globes the table becomes interesting, and then lapses back into 9's and 0's again. Regarded as a tussle between matter and aether (gas pressure and radiation pressure) the contest is overwhelmingly one-sided except between Nos. 33–35, where we may expect something interesting to happen.

What "happens" is the stars.

We draw aside the veil of cloud beneath which our physicist has been working and let him look up at the sky. There he will find a thousand million globes of gas nearly all of mass between his 33rd and 35th globes— that is to say, between $\frac{1}{2}$ and 50 times the sun's mass. The lightest known star is about $3 \cdot 10^{32}$ gm. and the heaviest about $2 \cdot 10^{35}$ gm. The majority are between 10^{33} and 10^{34} gm. where the serious challenge of radiation pressure to compete with gas pressure is beginning.

15. It is remarkable that the units into which the matter of the universe has aggregated primarily are so nearly alike in mass. The stars differ

* The independence of the opacity seems paradoxical at first, since for given flow of radiation transparent matter offers less obstruction and experiences less force than opaque matter. But this is compensated because the flow of radiation increases with the transparency of the material.

widely in brightness, density and physical condition, but they mostly contain about the same amount of material. It is as though nature had a standard model before her in forming the stars, and (except for occasional lapses of vigilance) would not tolerate much deviation. The extreme range (about $\frac{1}{6}$ to 100 times the sun's mass) does not give a fair idea of the general uniformity of mass; our methods of observation tend to select the more exceptional individuals—highly luminous stars which are especially massive, and double stars in which the original unit is subdivided—from many millions of stars of normal size. A mass range of 5 : 1 would, I believe, include more than 90 per cent. of the stars.

We can see in a general way the cause of this uniformity, though the details of the explanation are not clear. Gravitation is the force drawing matter together, and as it gathers in more and more material tends to build globes of enormous size. We must assume that, opposed to this, radiation pressure is the main disruptive force*. It is only when the mass has reached 10^{33} gm. that this check on the aggregating power of gravitation emerges from insignificance; but with further increase of mass it rapidly rises. The increase in the proportion of radiation pressure in Table 2 is a measure of the increasing peril to the unity of the star. The stability of a fluid mass subject to radiation pressure has not been investigated; but since a few stars are known in which the radiation pressure is found to amount to 80 or 90 per cent. of the whole, it is presumed that it does not of itself cause instability. But it may well render the star more liable to be broken up by a small rotation or disturbance of symmetry, so that the more massive the star the smaller the chance of survival. As plausible figures we might suggest that radiation pressure below 15 per cent. will not have an important effect; and gravitation will build up to the corresponding mass without much hindrance, unless the star divides under very rapid rotation according to the well-known theory; but a 50 per cent. radiation pressure would be a serious danger, and the corresponding mass could only be reached in circumstances of exceptional tranquillity.

We have not in our minds any definite idea as to the stage in the formation of the star at which the mass accumulation is limited by action or threat from radiation pressure. At present we can only point to the significant fact that stellar masses congregate just at the point where radiation pressure is beginning to endanger the safety of the star, and larger masses occur in rapidly diminishing numbers as though their con-

---

* There is no mathematical proof of this, and the speculation rests on the numerical agreement. We know that a star without radiation pressure is stable (unless the rotation is very rapid), but the stability of a star with radiation pressure has never been investigated. But since we observe that stellar masses cease abruptly when radiation pressure becomes important, we venture to forecast the answer.

tinuance were only permitted under rare conditions. It is this coincidence which leads us to think that radiation pressure is the agent which has cloven chaos into stars.

It may be remarked that if the molecular weight is decreased the same conditions occur at higher mass, so that low molecular weight favours greater masses. Reference to the last column of Table 1 shows that, whereas in general the average molecular weight does not depend much on the chemical constitution, abundance of hydrogen would lower it appreciably. It is just possible that the occasional stars of exceptionally great mass are those formed from material which happened to be rich in hydrogen.

It is necessary to add that in Table 2 (taken from a publication by the writer in 1923) the adopted molecular weight is 4, whereas the most likely value in normal stars is now considered to be 2·2. To change to weight 2·2 we must multiply the masses by $(4/2·2)^2 = 3·3$. This would make the numerical coincidence rather less impressive. But every star has passed through a cool diffuse (pre-stellar) stage in which the ionisation was less and the molecular weight higher, and it would seem proper to make the calculation for this stage as the most dangerous period*. The value 4 may thus be justified. There is also another possibility. It is now seriously debated whether the mass of a star may not diminish considerably during its life-time, thereby providing the energy which it radiates. If so, the present calculation should predict the initial masses, and allowance must be made for the wastage in any comparison with actual stars. This point is considered in § 214. It is there shown that the range of masses of stars *in the earliest diffuse stage* corresponds very closely to the critical range of radiation pressure.

16. As the pressure is partly that of aether waves and partly of material molecules, so also the store of heat in the star is partly aetherial and partly material. The ratio of aetherial to material heat is not widely different from the ratio of aetherial to material pressure; in fact, when the adiabatic constant of the material is $\gamma = \frac{4}{3}$, the two ratios are the same. Thus in masses exceeding 10^{33} gm. we encounter a new condition of things transcending anything in our terrestrial experience of hot bodies; instead of the heat being almost wholly contained in the motions and internal vibrations of molecules a large proportion is in the form of aether waves. These waves are hastening in all directions inside the star. They are encaged by the material as in a sieve, which prevents them leaking into outer space except at a slow rate. An aether wave making for freedom is caught and absorbed by an atom, flung out again in a new direction, and passed

---

* On the other hand, the disturbing effect of rotation would not become important until a later stage.

from atom to atom; it will thread the maze for hundreds of years until by accident it finds itself at the confines of the star, free now to travel through space indefinitely or until it reaches some distant world and perchance entering the eye of an astronomer makes known to him that a star is shining.

In any hot body the individual elements of heat-energy are continually changing from material to aetherial form and *vice versa*. In a red-hot mass of iron material heat must change to aetherial in order to be radiated. But in the hot metal the aetherial heat existing at any moment is less than a billionth part of the whole; only in the stars does the aetherial portion rise to equal importance with the material portion. Radiation by small masses is a hand-to-mouth procedure; but the star keeps a thousand years' supply always in readiness and emits its radiation by leaking aether waves from this store. This will perhaps help us to realise why it has been necessary to change from Lane's original theory of convective equilibrium to the theory of radiative equilibrium. The older investigators supposed that convection currents must exist to bring up fresh supplies of material heat to the surface, there to be turned into radiation. Now the problem is reversed; we have to explain how the star manages to dam back its store of aetherial heat so that the escape is no greater than we observe.

The Inside of a Star.

17. The inside of a star is a hurly-burly of atoms, electrons and aether waves. We have to call to aid the most recent discoveries of atomic physics to follow the intricacies of the dance. We started to explore the inside of a star; we soon find ourselves exploring the inside of an atom. Try to picture the tumult! Dishevelled atoms tear along at 50 miles a second with only a few tatters left of their elaborate cloaks of electrons torn from them in the scrimmage. The lost electrons are speeding a hundred times faster to find new resting-places. Look out! there is nearly a collision as an electron approaches an atomic nucleus; but putting on speed it sweeps round it in a sharp curve. A thousand narrow shaves happen to the electron in 10^{-10} of a second; sometimes there is a side-slip at the curve, but the electron still goes on with increased or decreased energy. Then comes a worse slip than usual; the electron is fairly caught and attached to the atom, and its career of freedom is at an end. But only for an instant. Barely has the atom arranged the new scalp on its girdle when a quantum of aether waves runs into it. With a great explosion the electron is off again for further adventures. Elsewhere two of the atoms are meeting full tilt and rebounding, with further disaster to their scanty remains of vesture.

As we watch the scene we ask ourselves, Can this be the stately drama of stellar evolution? It is more like the jolly crockery-smashing turn of a music-hall. The knockabout comedy of atomic physics is not very considerate towards our aesthetic ideals; but it is all a question of time-scale. The motions of the electrons are as harmonious as those of the stars but in a different scale of space and time, and the music of the spheres is being played on a keyboard 50 octaves higher. To recover this elegance we must slow down the action, or alternatively accelerate our own wits; just as the slow-motion film resolves the lusty blows of the prize-fighter into movements of extreme grace—and insipidity.

And what is the result of all this bustle? Very little. Unless we have in mind an extremely long stretch of time the general state of the star remains steady. Just as many atoms are repaired as are smashed; just as many bundles of radiation are sent out as are absorbed; just as many electrons are captured as are exploded away. The atoms and the electrons for all their hurry never get anywhere; they only change places. The aether waves are the only part of the population which do actually accomplish something; although apparently darting about in all directions without purpose they do in spite of themselves make a slow general progress outwards. This flow would if uncompensated lead to a gradual change in the whole state of the star, very slow but yet, we believe, too fast to accord with observational evidence. It is therefore necessary to assume that subatomic energy of some kind is liberated within the star, so as to replenish the store of radiant energy. This also involves a gradual transformation of the material of the star which, however, scarcely concerns the present discussion. The point which we wish here to explain is why this clash of atoms, electrons and aether waves is of practical concern to the astronomer, seeing that each process seems to be engaged in undoing the work of other processes. In particular, how does the absorption of aether waves produce any result, seeing that for each portion of radiation absorbed an equal quantity of radiation is being emitted?

We may think of the star as two bodies superposed, a material body (atoms and electrons) and an aetherial body (radiation). The material body is in dynamical equilibrium, but the aetherial body is not; gravitation takes care that there is no outward flow of matter, but there is an outward flow of radiation. If there were no interaction between the two bodies, the whole store of radiation would diffuse away in a few minutes; it is because it is tied to the material body by the processes of absorption and emission that it is restrained to a slow rate of diffusion. Absorption followed by emission, although it leaves the quantity of radiation unaltered, has this effect: radiation with a slight outward bias is taken from the aetherial body; it is quickly restored again with the outward bias removed. The quicker the succession of these transformations the more strictly the outward flow is curbed. That is in accordance with the conclusion we had already reached that the factor which resists the outward flow of radiation is the absorption coefficient or opacity of the material of the star.

Opacity of Stellar Material.

18. To determine the opacity—the hindering factor in the outward flow of radiation—we have to turn to physical theories of the process of absorption. The question put to the physicist runs somewhat like this— Given a layer of material a centimetre thick and of known density and temperature, what proportion of the radiation falling on one side will be transmitted? Before answering, the physicist might reasonably ask us, What kind of material? If he asks this, we are done; because we have little, if any, knowledge of the proportionate composition of the material in the star. There is no reason to suppose that spectroscopic observation of the superficial layers is any guide to the internal composition. Fortunately the physicist does not press this question but substitutes another, What kind of radiation? We can answer that. Radiation at any point in the interior is virtually in an enclosure with walls at constant temperature; in fact, the ideal conditions of an enclosure are approached far more closely in a star than in any possible terrestrial experiment. The constitution of radiation in an enclosure—the proportion of waves of different frequencies—depends only on the temperature, and is fixed by Planck's Law.

At the temperatures of several million degrees prevailing inside Capella and in all typical stars the radiation consists of X rays. A physicist would classify them as rather soft X rays, that is to say, of greater wave-length and less penetrating power than those usually employed in radiography. For example, at 10,000,000° the radiation is mainly between 3 Å and 9 Å wave-length, and it is the absorption coefficient of matter for radiation of this kind that we have to study. These X rays can be produced in the laboratory and their properties studied experimentally. It naturally suggests itself that we should compare the absorption coefficients of ordinary terrestrial substances with those found for stellar material by the present method. It will be remembered that our primary aim in this research is to find the temperature gradient and opacity in a star so as to derive the total outflow of radiation; conversely, if we know the temperature gradient and outflow of radiation, we can find the opacity. For Capella the temperature distribution has been found by the theory already outlined, and the output of radiation has been measured by the bolometer or (probably with greater accuracy) inferred from the light-power of the star. The opacity at an average point in the interior turns out to be about 100 c.g.s. units. To obtain an idea of what this value signifies, let us enter Capella and find a region where the density is the same as that of our atmosphere. Take a slab of gas there 6 inches thick. Of the radiation falling on one side of the slab, $\frac{2}{3}$ will be absorbed in the slab and only $\frac{1}{3}$ transmitted. This seems a very high opacity if we compare it with the transmission of light through gas; but the experimental physicist knows well the difficulty of getting the softer kinds of X rays to pass through a few centimetres of air.

In Table 3 we give a few examples of laboratory determinations of the absorption coefficients of X rays to compare with the value 100 found for Capella.

Table 3.

Mass Absorption Coefficients for X Rays*.

Wave-length	Air	Al	Cu	Ag
0·5	0·5	2·0	19	12
1·0	3·2	14	140	82
1·5	9·2	46	52	260
2·0	19	110	120	580
3·0	53	360	350	—
5·0	190	1600	—	—

The stellar value is thus of the same general order of magnitude as the laboratory determinations.

19. A closer study of the table shows that the relation of stellar opacity to terrestrial opacity is not so straightforward as it at first appears. It will be seen that the terrestrial opacity increases very rapidly with the wave-length; subject to certain discontinuities (illustrated in the column for Cu) the opacity varies approximately as the cube of the wave-length. Now the mean wave-length for Capella is considerably higher than any of those given in Table 3, and it is clear that if we took the values for, say, 7 Å the absorption coefficients would be higher than 100.

Moreover, the rapid change with wave-length suggests that the opacity of a star ought to change very rapidly with its internal temperature, since the mean wave-length of the radiation is inversely proportional to the temperature. This does not agree with astronomical observation; the whole series of giant stars from type M to type A though differing widely in internal temperature is found to show a fairly constant opacity.

There is thus some difference between stellar conditions and laboratory conditions which affects the absorption of X rays. It is not difficult to understand what this difference is. The primary dissimilarity is the exceedingly high temperature of the stellar material; and it is a natural (though fallacious) assumption that temperature will not much affect a process like absorption, which is performed by the atoms individually

* From M. Siegbahn, *The Spectroscopy of X Rays*, Appendix, Table III.

each contributing its share independently of the presence of the others. But are we dealing with the same kind of atoms in the two cases? It is a question of definition of the word *atom*. The atomic nucleus which we regard as characterising the element is unaltered, and for that reason we can say that the same elements are present in the stars as on the earth. But if the atom is taken to mean the whole system with its satellite electrons, then we must say that the atoms in the stars are not the same as those on the earth. Most of that circulating system is broken away. The "billiard-ball" atoms, about 10^{-8} cm. in radius, so familiar in our picture of terrestrial gases, do not exist in the stars; and in particular those properties of terrestrial gases which depend on the considerable size of the atoms (limit to compressibility) have no immediate application in the stars. In considering absorption and opacity the mutilation of the electron system of the atom is of vital importance, because it is just this system which contains the mechanism of absorption.

In elements of moderate atomic weight the X ray absorption is performed mainly by the ten innermost electrons which are classed in two groups, viz. 2 K-electrons and 8 L-electrons. The outer electrons of the system are concerned in absorption of greater wave-lengths, including visual light; the loss of these will not seriously alter the atom's power of absorbing X rays. But the mutilation extends to the inner ten electrons which would otherwise have been active in absorbing the X rays in the star; and this, of course, reduces the absorbing power as compared with terrestrial atoms. The absorption is itself the cause of the breaking away of electrons, so that if the circumstances are such that any absorbing mechanism is called strongly into play that particular mechanism will be especially broken down. There is in fact a saturation effect.

We may look at the difference between terrestrial and stellar absorption from another point of view. When aether waves fall on an atom they are not absorbed continuously. The atom lies quiet waiting a favourable chance and then suddenly swallows a whole quantum at once. The mouthful is too big for the atom's digestion; consequently the atom bursts. One of the satellite electrons shoots off at great speed carrying away the surplus energy which the atom could not assimilate. The atom is now done for so far as that particular absorption trap is concerned, and it has to let the quanta fly past without interfering. Evidently this bursting could not go on continually unless there were some counter-process of repair. The atom must capture one of the free electrons flying by, inducing it to stay and heal the breach. The absorption trap is then set again and the atom is ready for another quantum. The emission of radiation occurs during this process of repair, the free electron having surplus energy which must be radiated. For each burst there must be a repair; so for each absorption there must be an emission.

In the laboratory we can produce X rays of the quality occurring in the stars, but we cannot produce them with the same intensity. Thus we can only perform the experiment of feeding the atoms with quanta at a very slow rate. Long before the atom has the chance of a second mouthful it has had time to set its trap in order and is ready again. But in the stars the X rays fly by so fast that the atoms are gorged and cannot take advantage of their abundant chances. The moment the trap is ready it is sprung again. Only a small proportion of the absorption traps are in working order at any one moment and the absorption coefficient is proportionately reduced. This saturation effect is responsible for the stellar coefficient falling below the values derived by extrapolation of Table 3. In the main, terrestrial experiments are adapted to measure the atom's activity in catching X rays, and astronomical experiments to measure its power of recovery afterwards. The consumption of food by the hungry hunter depends on his skill in catching it; the consumption by the prosperous citizen depends on the strength of his digestion.

For stellar investigation we therefore find it best to fix attention not on the process of disruption but on the process of repair (electron capture). In other words, we turn from absorption coefficients to emission coefficients. In the equilibrium condition of a star absorption and emission must balance, so that it is indifferent which of them we study. It is only a question of following the line of greatest practical simplicity.

Details will be given later of attempts to calculate the emission or absorption at given temperature and density from a purely physical theory of the process of electron capture. As happened for molecular weight, the chemical composition of the material appears not to have a large influence on the result. If we could solve this problem fully we could extend the problem set to the cloud-bound physicist in § 14 and ask him to predict the heat and light emitted by his globes of given mass and density with no assistance from astronomical observation. The theory which seems most in keeping with our general physical knowledge leads to predictions pretty near the truth, but, I think, not so near as they ought to be. This part of our aim is still in the interesting state when we cannot help feeling that we are not far off the right track and the true solution is waiting just round the corner.

20. Jumping as well as we can the difficulties raised by the discordance above alluded to, we combine our helping and hindering factors and determine the theoretical rate of outflow of radiation from a star. The result is the mass-luminosity relation explained and compared with observation in Chapter VII. We shall not here anticipate the results which follow when at length the theory reaches direct contact with observation. The purpose of this preliminary survey is that in entering on the mathematical investigations we may be equipped with a general knowledge of the conditions to be studied and of the interplay of the various factors.

Other problems will arise in the course of our work. The Cepheid variables, considered to be pulsating stars, give opportunities for development and test of the theory. Of special interest is the theory of the White Dwarfs—incredible but apparently true. The problem of the source of a star's energy will be considered; by a process of exhaustion we are driven to conclude that the only possible source of a star's energy is subatomic; yet it must be confessed that the hypothesis shows little disposition to accommodate itself to the detailed requirements of observation, and a critic might count up a large number of "fatal" objections.

Those portions of thermodynamics and the quantum theory which are essential for our astronomical investigations are developed *ab initio* in Chapters II and III. It is not expected that these Chapters can take the place of a regular treatise; nor has it been our aim to give a particularly elementary exposition suitable for a first approach to the subject. It can probably be assumed that everyone interested in astrophysical problems has picked up sporadically the leading ideas of atomic structure and quanta, and is familiar with some of the numerous experimental applications. The systematic outline here offered may help him to arrange these ideas and fill up the gaps in their sequence. Although the discussion is given in the form of mathematical deduction, it must be understood that when, as in these two Chapters, the results at every stage are subject to close test by experiment, the purpose of the argument is to exhibit the inner connection of the various phenomena and not to persuade the sceptic that the phenomena must occur. Consequently, although a reasonable degree of rigour is required, the laborious exploration and closing of every possible loophole is of secondary importance and would be out of place in a brief survey.

Chapters IV–XI contain the main theme of investigation—the study of the internal condition of a star. The culminating point is Chapter VII, where the comparison with observation is made. Roughly speaking, the mechanics of the problem is placed before this, and the physics is placed afterwards. That is because the study of absorption, ionisation, electrical energy, etc., in the light of atomic physics would if undirected lead us far away from astronomical problems; and it is necessary first to ascertain what are the points of special astronomical importance, the doubts to be settled, and the difficulties to be discussed. We need to have a clear idea of how our results will react on observable properties of the stars. I do not think that any order of development would have avoided the numerous cross-references forward as well as backward.

In the last two Chapters we permit ourselves an excursion into outer space and observe how the complexity of the problem grows when the conditions of thermodynamical equilibrium in an enclosure are gradually relaxed. The "outside of a star" is a problem expanding indefinitely into the whole subject of stellar spectroscopy and stellar observation generally. For the most part we pursue only those branches of the subject which illustrate and amplify the methods and theories used for the stellar interior.

CHAPTER II

THERMODYNAMICS OF RADIATION

Radiation Pressure.

21. Radiant energy or radiation consists of electromagnetic waves in the aether. Maxwell's electromagnetic theory showed that these waves possess momentum. If E is the energy of the waves, c the velocity of light, the momentum is E/c in the direction in which the waves are travelling.

According to the modern view energy and mass are inseparable, c^2 ergs corresponding to 1 gm. This leads immediately to the same result. For the energy E ergs indicates a mass E/c^2 gm., and since the velocity is c the momentum is $(E/c^2) \times c = E/c$.

A material screen which absorbs the waves absorbs also their momentum. Thus the momentum of the screen changes, which is another way of saying that it is acted on by a force. Suppose that waves containing E ergs per cu. cm. impinge normally on a perfectly absorbing surface. A column of radiation of height c passes into and is absorbed by each sq. cm. of the surface per sec.; this column contains Ec ergs and the momentum is thus Ec/c or E units. The force on the screen is thus E dynes per sq. cm.

For imperfect absorbers we must deduct the proportion of the momentum which is not passed on to the material screen, viz. that of the transmitted, scattered or reflected waves. For example, a perfect reflector would experience a pressure $2E$; half of this is due to its stoppage of the incident waves and half is the recoil due to the projection of the train of reflected waves. Again, if the screen is semi-transparent and transmits waves of reduced energy-density E' the force per sq. cm. is $E - E'$. This may be analysed into a pressure E of the incident waves and a recoil pressure $- E'$ of the transmitted waves, as though the screen had wholly absorbed the incident beam and had itself originated the transmitted beam on the other side.

If we regard the incident, reflected, scattered, transmitted or emitted beams as each exerting its own pressure on the side of the screen at which it arrives or originates, we need not trouble to discriminate the different cases of absorption, reflection, etc. The pressure on either side of the screen is equal to the energy-density of the radiation on that side, and the force on the screen corresponds to the difference of the pressures on its two sides. For example, in the case of the perfect reflector the pressure is equal to the total energy-density $2E$ on one side of the screen, viz. the energy-density E of the incident waves + the energy-density E of the reflected waves. It makes no difference whether the waves are travelling towards or away from the screen, because on reversing the direction of conveyance of momentum we also reverse the sign of the momentum that is being conveyed; so that a wave-train conveying positive momentum away from the screen gives the same pressure as a wave-train conveying negative momentum into the screen. A pressure system cannot be represented by a vector; it may be associated with an axis but not with a direction.

The rule that

$$\text{pressure} = \text{energy-density}$$

applies only to radiation travelling normal to the surface; oblique incidence must be considered separately.

22. Consider as in the last section a column of radiation travelling in a fixed direction, and place in its track a screen of area S inclined so that the angle of incidence is θ. The cross-section of the column obstructed by the screen is $S \cos \theta$, and accordingly the force, which would be ES for normal incidence, is $ES \cos \theta$ for oblique incidence. This force is in the direction of the momentum of the beam; resolving it into components normal and tangential to the screen the force is

$$ES \cos^2 \theta \text{ normal}, \qquad ES \cos \theta \sin \theta \text{ tangential}.$$

An important case is when the radiation is isotropic, i.e. consists of waves of equal intensity in all directions. Since the average value of $\cos^2 \theta$ over a sphere is $\frac{1}{3}$ and of $\cos \theta \sin \theta$ is zero the force becomes in this case $\frac{1}{3}ES$ normal to the surface. Thus we have the important law—

The pressure of isotropic radiation is $\frac{1}{3}$ of its energy-density.

This pressure is exerted normally on any surface exposed to the radiation and is entirely analogous to the hydrostatic pressure of a fluid. In a gas the momentum is conveyed by the molecules; and a gas at rest, in which the velocities of the molecules are symmetrical as regards direction so that the momentum is being conveyed at the same rate in all directions, is analogous to isotropic radiation. In non-isotropic radiation or in a disturbed gas with unsymmetrical distribution of molecular velocities there is no longer a simple hydrostatic pressure; a stress-system with six different components is involved.

When the radiation is not isotropic the normal pressure on a surface is given by using the weighted mean of $\cos^2 \theta$ instead of the factor $\frac{1}{3}$. It is to be noted that an increase of flow in a particular direction θ at the expense of flow in the opposite direction does not alter the pressure. In the interior of a star we have often to consider radiation which is nearly isotropic but with a slight preponderant outward flow; this kind of asymmetry does not in itself affect the pressure, though it is likely to involve consequentially smaller asymmetrical effects which modify the pressure by second order terms.

The internal pressure, whether of radiation or of a fluid, may be defined without reference to the insertion of any extraneous material such as a screen. The isotropic pressure $\frac{1}{3}E$ signifies that across any unit surface, say, in the plane yz, momentum is being transferred so that the region on the positive side of the surface is gaining $\frac{1}{3}E$ units of positive x-momentum from the negative side; equivalently the negative side is gaining $\frac{1}{3}E$ units of negative x-momentum from the positive side. The internal pressure thus defines the boundary flow of momentum which it is necessary to take into account in applying the condition of conservation of momentum to any region.

23. The relations between the energy, momentum and pressure of aether waves can be brought into line with those of matter if we regard their energy as half kinetic and half potential. The mass E/c^2, velocity c, momentum E/c, and kinetic energy $\frac{1}{2}E$ are then related in the same way as the corresponding quantities

$$m, \quad V, \quad mV, \quad \tfrac{1}{2}mV^2$$

for matter. Also for isotropic radiation the internal pressure is $\frac{2}{3}$ of the kinetic energy-density $\frac{1}{2}E$, agreeing with the well-known result that the pressure of a gas is $\frac{2}{3}$ of the density of kinetic (translatory) energy of its molecules.

Accordingly the analogy between radiation and a gas will be rendered closer if we choose a gas in which the kinetic energy of the molecules is half their whole energy. Such a gas must (according to the elementary theory) have three internal or rotational degrees of freedom sharing equally in the equipartition of energy with the three external degrees of freedom for each molecule. The ratio of specific heats for such a gas is $\gamma = \frac{4}{3}$; and it is often convenient to regard radiation as a gas with ratio of specific heats $\frac{4}{3}$.

By this analogy we may anticipate some results proved more rigorously later. For $\gamma = \frac{4}{3}$ the pressure varies as T^4 in adiabatic expansion or compression; this law is also true for radiation (Stefan's Law). Again, in calculating the distribution of density and temperature inside a star we pass from the theory of convective equilibrium to radiative equilibrium by substituting the constant $\frac{4}{3}$ instead of the ratio of specific heats of the material. Since radiative equilibrium postulates that the heat is conveyed through the star by aether waves instead of by material transport it is appropriate that the ratio of specific heats for aether waves should appear instead of the ratio for the material.

Entropy.

24. Quantitatively energy is conserved; qualitatively there is a continuous unidirectional change in the character of the energy of the universe.

In the ultimate analysis this change appears to be in all cases a change from a more organised to a more chaotic condition. For example, a train of plane waves may by irregular reflection or scattering be converted into radiation moving in all directions at random. We cannot invert this process or discover an appliance which will automatically convert disorganised radiation into plane waves. Spherical waves can be converted into plane waves by a parabolic mirror and back again to spherical waves by another mirror. But spherical waves are in their way as highly organised as plane waves; no chance disturbances of regularity have befallen them. When once the random element has been introduced it cannot be eliminated by any natural process. If we construct a machine which receives chaotic radiation and sends it out again as trains of plane waves we must infer that the organisation has been given to the waves at the expense of other energy put through the machine; and this energy is drained of organisation and ejected from the machine in a more chaotic state than it was originally. Such a machine continually requires fresh supplies of energy not because it uses up energy but because it uses up organisation of energy.

Thus in the vicissitudes of things energy is liable to take a step down in rank which it cannot recover by any natural process. The potentiality inherent in organisation—which is of immense importance for the practical utilisation of energy—is lost to the universe, irrecoverably so far as we can see.

25. We introduce a numerical measure of the disorganisation caused by these irreversible steps. Such a measure should evidently be proportional to the quantity of energy disorganised; the other factor measuring the degree of disorganisation will consist of the difference of two terms dependent respectively on the initial and final states of the energy and therefore functions of the physical variables used to specify those states. The measure of disorganisation is thus expressed by a quantity S such that

$$dS = dQ\,(\theta_2 - \theta_1) \quad\ldots\ldots\ldots\ldots\ldots\ldots(25\cdot1),$$

where dQ is the quantity of energy passing from state 1 to state 2 and θ is a function of the physical variables describing the states.

When several such transfers are contemplated it is convenient to express the result in terms of the additions to the energy in the respective states. Thus, in the above example, energy in state 1 receives an addition

$dQ_1 = - dQ$, and energy in state 2 receives an addition $dQ_2 = dQ$. Accordingly (25·1) may be written

$$dS = \theta_1 dQ_1 + \theta_2 dQ_2.$$

Combining any number of transfers by summation or integration the total change of S will be

$$\delta S = \int \theta dQ \qquad \dots\dots\dots\dots\dots\dots\dots\dots\dots(25\cdot2),$$

where dQ is the infinitesimal addition to energy in the state for which the corresponding coefficient is θ.

In considering a system composed of several bodies A, B, C, ... we apportion S among the different bodies so that

$$S = S_a + S_b + S_c + \dots.$$

If the transfer above considered is from state 1 in body A to state 2 in body B we should write

$$dS_a = \theta_1 dQ_1, \qquad dS_b = \theta_2 dQ_2.$$

It follows that (25·2) applies to each body of the system separately, δS referring to that body only and dQ on the right being limited to energy transferred to or from or within that body.

In order that S may fulfil the purpose for which it was introduced, viz. to measure the progressive degradation of the energy of the universe, it must in any natural process satisfy the condition

$$\Sigma \delta S \geqslant 0 \qquad \dots\dots\dots\dots\dots\dots\dots\dots\dots(25\cdot3),$$

the summation being taken over all bodies concerned in the process under consideration. The coefficients θ must be determined by applying this condition.

The quantity S is called *entropy*. It is unique among fundamental physical quantities in having a one-sided conservation, that is to say, it is indestructible but not uncreatable. Since only the change of S has been defined the entropy of each body involves an arbitrary additive constant.

Mechanical work is taken as the standard from which increasing disorganisation of energy is measured, so that the coefficient θ is zero for energy dQ added to or taken from mechanical work. We need not exclude the possibility of forms of energy with negative entropy referred to this standard, although no such form has been recognised. Subatomic energy has been converted into heat but the converse process is unknown; it is conceivable (but unlikely) that the conversion of heat into subatomic energy involves a greater drain of organisation than its conversion into work.

26. A process involving creation of entropy cannot be reversed, since the reversal would involve destruction of entropy, which is impossible.

Thus if a process can be shown to be reversible we can be sure that the entropy is unaltered by it. Reversible processes are necessarily somewhat idealised because it is scarcely possible in practice entirely to safeguard the energy from disorganisation. But in thermodynamical arguments the practicability of the processes considered is not usually relevant. If we have a process which under certain practical conditions works irreversibly in one direction, and under very slightly altered conditions works irreversibly in the opposite direction, we may infer that there is a limiting intermediate condition for which the process in either direction involves no alteration of entropy.

An irreversible process of great importance is the spontaneous flow of heat (by conduction or by radiation) from a hot body to a cold body in proximity tending to equalise their temperatures. Since the transfer is spontaneous, i.e. its occurrence is not dependent on the provision of other sources of energy which might be drained of organisation, it may be treated as isolated. Consider two bodies A_1, A_2 at temperatures T_1, T_2. If T_2 is slightly less than T_1 a small quantity of heat will flow from T_1 to T_2; a slight alteration of the condition so that T_2 is a little greater than T_1 causes the process to occur in the reverse direction. Thus $T_2 = T_1$ is the limiting condition for which a transfer of a small quantity of heat from A_1 to A_2 or A_2 to A_1 involves no alteration of entropy. Hence setting $dS = 0$ in (25·1) we have

$$\theta_2 = \theta_1 \text{ whenever } T_2 = T_1 \quad \dots\dots\dots\dots\dots(26\cdot1).$$

Accordingly when dQ represents heat-energy the coefficient θ is a function of the temperature only.

Again, let the temperatures be unequal and $T_1 > T_2$. A quantity of heat dQ will then flow spontaneously from the temperature T_1 to the temperature T_2; and by (25·1)

$$dS = dQ \, (\theta \, (T_2) - \theta \, (T_1)).$$

Since dS cannot be negative, we have

$$\theta \, (T_2) > \theta \, (T_1) \text{ whenever } T_1 > T_2 \quad \dots\dots\dots\dots(26\cdot2).$$

Hence θ decreases as the temperature increases.

It must be understood that the coefficient $\theta \, (T)$ refers only to the transfer of an infinitesimal quantity of heat. When a finite quantity of heat is transferred from one limited reservoir to another the temperatures will alter during the progress of the flow and the consequent changes of θ must be taken into account.

The temperature referred to in this argument is *thermometric**. The

---

* No reference is made in this book to the so-called *thermodynamic temperature* introduced in some text-books.

principle of thermometry is that a test-body A_2 brought near enough to a body A_1 rises or falls to the temperature of A_1; it therefore requires that the spontaneous flow of heat shall be from A_1 to A_2 or the opposite according as $T_1 > T_2$ or the opposite—as assumed in our argument. The heat referred to (whether molecular motion or radiant energy) is "ordinary" heat-energy, that is to say the energy in the states 1 and 2 is assumed to have no special organisation beyond that defined by a single physical variable, viz. the temperature. It is possible for energy to possess organisation of a more specialised kind, in which case the coefficient θ will not be a function of the thermometric temperature only; for example, monochromatic radiation must be considered more highly organised than black-body radiation. But when such heat is allowed to flow into a test-body as in ordinary thermometry without specialised conditions, the excess organisation is inevitably wasted and there is no limiting condition of reversible flow with $dS = 0$. A transfer for which $dS = 0$ can only be arranged with special appliances (e.g. colour-filters), and the coefficient θ for such a state of organisation must be found from the behaviour with respect to these appliances and not with respect to ordinary thermometry.

27. Consider now a gram-molecule of perfect monatomic gas which obeys the law

$$pv = \Re T \quad\text{................................(27·1)},$$

where $\Re$ is the universal gas constant.

In an ideal monatomic gas the only heat-energy is kinetic energy of molecular motion. Since the pressure is $\frac{2}{3}$ of the kinetic energy per unit volume (§ 23) the heat-energy in the volume v is

$$Q = \tfrac{3}{2}p \cdot v = \tfrac{3}{2}\Re T \quad\text{.........................(27·2)}.$$

Now let the gas change from a volume and temperature v_1, T_1 to v_2, T_2. In general it will be necessary to supply or withdraw heat and mechanical work will be done by or against the pressure. In a change dv, dT the heat supplied must be

$$dQ = \tfrac{3}{2}\Re dT + p\,dv \quad\text{.........................(27·3)},$$

the first term raising the temperature in accordance with (27·2) and the second replacing the energy expended by the pressure in doing mechanical work.

The gas is supposed to have uniform temperature at each stage, and the heat dQ is to be added directly at each part of the gas—not poured in at one corner and allowed to flow to its destination. With this condition there is no limitation on the signs of dT, dv, dQ in (27·3) and the changes are therefore reversible. (If the above conditions were not postulated irreversible processes would evidently occur.)

By (25·2) the change of entropy of the gas is

$$S_2 - S_1 = \delta S = \int \theta(T)\, dQ \quad \dots\dots\dots\dots\dots(27\cdot4)$$

$$= \tfrac{3}{2}\Re \int \theta(T)\, dT + \int \theta(T)\, p\, dv$$

$$= \tfrac{3}{2}\Re \int_{T_1}^{T_2} \theta(T)\, dT + \Re \int_{v_1}^{v_2} T\theta(T)\, \frac{dv}{v} \quad \dots(27\cdot5).$$

Now $S_2 - S_1$ can depend only on the initial and final temperatures and volumes of the gas. This follows from the theory of gases according to which two specimens of the same gas at the same temperature and density are alike in all their properties. Or it can be deduced more generally from the reversibility. For if $S_2 - S_1$ were different according to the intermediate values of v and T, we could by taking the gas out by one route and back by another increase its entropy. Owing to the reversibility no entropy is created; hence the increase of entropy requires a decrease of entropy of our reservoirs of heat. The cycle could be repeated any number of times so that a small mass of gas would be able to furnish an infinite decrease of S (i.e. increase of organisation) to the rest of the universe.

The expression on the right of (27·5) must therefore depend only on the initial and final stages. The first term evidently satisfies this; and therefore the second integral must in spite of appearances be independent of the intermediate stages. This requires that $T\theta(T)$ shall be a constant. To prove this, the second integral can be written

$$\int_{\log v_1}^{\log v_2} T\theta(T)\, d(\log v).$$

Consider any elementary step $d(\log v)$. During this change of volume the gas can have any temperature we please; so that if it is possible to vary $T\theta(T)$ by varying T, we can vary the contribution made to the integral by this step. Thus the integral cannot be independent of the intermediate conditions of the gas unless

$$T\theta(T) = \text{const.}$$

By suitably connecting the units of entropy and temperature the constant may be set equal to unity so that

$$\theta(T) = 1/T \quad \dots\dots\dots\dots\dots(27\cdot6).$$

Here T is identified with the temperature on the scale of a perfect-gas thermometer; but, of course, the value of $\theta(T)$ here found is applicable to "ordinary" heat transferred from or to any kind of material in accordance with (26·1).

Equation (27·4) can now be written

$$S_2 - S_1 = \int dQ/T \quad \dots\dots\dots\dots\dots(27\cdot7).$$

28. Reverting to the monatomic gas, we obtain from (27·5) and (27·6)

$$S_2 - S_1 = \tfrac{3}{2}\Re \log (T_2/T_1) + \Re \log (v_2/v_1)$$
$$= \Re \{\log (v_2 T_2^{\frac{3}{2}}) - \log (v_1 T_1^{\frac{3}{2}})\},$$

so that the entropy of a gram-molecule of the gas is

$$S = \Re \log (vT^{\frac{3}{2}}) + C,$$

where C is a constant which may depend on the nature but not on the state of the gas. If the gas expands or contracts adiabatically, i.e. without transference of heat from or to the surroundings, the entropy remains constant since energy received or given up as mechanical work has zero entropy. Accordingly for adiabatic changes

$$vT^{\frac{3}{2}} = \text{const.} \quad \dots\dots\dots\dots\dots\dots\dots(28·1),$$

an equation which can also be obtained directly by setting $dQ = 0$ in (27·3).

More generally for a gas in which the whole heat energy is e times the translatory energy of the molecules, the pressure is $2/3e$ times the energy-density, and the adiabatic law is

$$vT^{\frac{3}{2}e} = \text{const.} \quad \dots\dots\dots\dots\dots\dots\dots(28·2),$$

which gives

$$\rho \propto T^{\frac{3}{2}e}, \qquad p \propto T^{1+\frac{3}{2}e}, \qquad p \propto \rho^{1+2/3e} \quad \dots\dots\dots(28·3).$$

The last equation is usually written $p \propto \rho^\gamma$, so that the adiabatic constant γ is given by

$$\gamma = 1 + 2/3e \quad \dots\dots\dots\dots\dots\dots\dots(28·4).$$

It can easily be shown that γ is equal to the ratio of the specific heat at constant pressure to the specific heat at constant volume.

Equilibrium of Radiation.

29. The spontaneous flow of heat from a hot body to a cooler body is a net transfer. Actually heat is flowing in both directions so that each receives heat from the other; but the hot body loses more than it gains and the cool body gains more than it loses. The inequality tends to right itself because a body as it loses heat will fall in temperature and the rate at which it sends out heat to the surroundings will decline; eventually it will reach a condition in which the loss of heat is just equal to the gain.

This "theory of exchanges" applies to flow of heat both by conduction and by radiation, but we are most concerned with radiation.

Consider an enclosure surrounded by walls maintained at a constant temperature. Radiation will be emitted from the walls into the enclosure, and radiation in the enclosure which falls on the walls will be wholly or partially absorbed by them. The greater the quantity of radiation inside the enclosure the greater will be the amount falling on the walls and the greater the amount absorbed. The quantity in the enclosure will thus decrease or increase until the loss by absorption just balances the steady emission from the walls. In practice the time required to reach this equilibrium condition is extremely short*.

The equilibrium distribution of radiation, both as regards density and quality (wave-length), is fixed entirely by the temperature T of the walls.

For suppose that by constructing the walls of different materials we could have two enclosures A and B with walls at the same temperature T but with the equilibrium density of radiation within a certain range of wave-length $\delta\lambda$ greater in A than in B. Let us open momentarily a passage between A and B crossed by a screen transparent only to radiation in the range $\delta\lambda$. More radiation of this quality will fall on the A side of the screen than on the B side and more will pass through from A to B than from B to A. Close the channel after a small but finite transfer has occurred. The enclosure B now contains more radiation than initially and therefore more than can be in equilibrium with its walls at temperature T; the surplus will pass into the walls which must accordingly rise in temperature. Similarly the walls of A will fall in temperature. We next bring the walls of B and A to the same temperature by allowing the necessary quantity of heat to flow from B to A. This flow of heat from a higher temperature T_1 to a lower temperature T_2 is irreversible and creates a quantity of entropy $dQ\left(\dfrac{1}{T_2}-\dfrac{1}{T_1}\right)$. But the whole system has returned exactly to its original condition so that it is impossible that entropy should have been created.

The contradiction can perhaps be realised more vividly if we suppose the passage to be opened and closed periodically. Then the temperature difference between A and B is continually renewed, and we can use B as the source and A as the sink of a heat-engine which develops mechanical work. This continuous conversion of heat originally at a uniform temperature T into mechanical work is obviously contrary to the principles of thermodynamics.

Since the energy-density of radiation in the enclosure depends only on the temperature it follows that the pressure of the radiation depends only on the temperature.

A word of explanation may be desirable as to the employment in thermodynamical arguments of ideal contrivances such as the screen transparent to an arbitrary range of wave-length. It is not at all essential to the argument that the processes referred to should be practicable; but it is essential that the ideal processes should not destroy entropy, if as usual the argument assumes that entropy is indestructible. The ideal

---

* In theoretical arguments we sometimes introduce walls which are perfect reflectors (for some or all frequencies). The approach to equilibrium then becomes infinitely slow.

process must not eliminate the random element in the state of the energy. If practicable processes are employed, we are on safe ground; with ideal processes we have to be on our guard against inadvertently introducing a "sorting demon." At first sight a screen transparent to one particular range of wave-length seems to be dangerously like a sorting demon; but since highly selective screens exist naturally, it is clear that such selection does not imply destruction of entropy; and although we may not be able to find a natural screen suitable for the particular range of wave-length $\delta\lambda$, the lack is due to irrelevant limitations of nature and not to any contravention of the laws of thermodynamics.

Radiation of the density and quality which would be in equilibrium with matter at temperature T is said to have the temperature T. A mixture of radiation of various wave-lengths in arbitrary proportions is not in general in equilibrium with matter at any temperature and has no unique temperature; but if it has the same total density as radiation at temperature T, T is called its "effective temperature." If such radiation is placed in an enclosure with walls at temperature T it is rapidly transformed into radiation with a true temperature T, that is to say, the enclosure becomes filled with an equal amount of energy with a true temperature and the walls neither gain nor lose heat on balance. Since this conversion is irreversible, entropy is increased by the conversion. The excess organisation of the radiation with no true temperature could in fact be utilised by means of selectively transparent screens to raise matter above its own effective temperature T. A notable illustration of this is afforded by the radiation traversing space due to the stars; its effective temperature is about 3° absolute, but it is capable of spontaneously raising selectively absorbent matter to far higher temperatures. Radiation at a true temperature of 3° could not transfer heat spontaneously to matter above 3°.

The coefficient θ for radiation having a true temperature T is the same as for molecular heat, viz. $1/T$. This follows because energy will pass from the radiation in an enclosure into the walls or *vice versa* according as its temperature is higher or lower than that of the walls; hence the limiting condition of transfer without change of entropy is when the temperatures are equal, and the equality of the coefficients θ follows from (25·1).

Having proved that radiation at temperature T has a definite density and composition, we have to discover the formulae for the density and composition. This investigation is made in several stages. First Stefan's law (30·3) is found determining the total density; next Wien's displacement law (32·1) which reduces the problem of determining the composition at all temperatures to the determination of the composition at any one temperature; then Planck's law (37·9) giving the form of the function left undetermined in Wien's law; and finally in (40·7) the identification of the physical constant contained in Planck's law.

Stefan's Law.

30. Consider radiation in an enclosure of adjustable volume, and change the volume from v_1 to v_2 and the temperature of the walls (and therefore of the enclosed radiation) from T_1 to T_2; the temperature at intermediate volumes is arbitrary. If E is the energy-density of the radiation, the heat added in a change dv, dT is

$$dQ = d(Ev) + p\,dv \qquad \ldots\ldots\ldots\ldots\ldots(30\cdot1),$$

or since $E = 3p$

$$dQ = 4p\,dv + 3v\,dp$$

$$= 4p^{\frac{1}{4}}d(p^{\frac{3}{4}}v) \qquad \ldots\ldots\ldots\ldots\ldots(30\cdot2).$$

Hence by $(27\cdot7)$ the change of entropy of the radiation is

$$S_2 - S_1 = 4\int \frac{p^{\frac{1}{4}}}{T}\,d(p^{\frac{3}{4}}v).$$

By the same discussion as in § 27 it follows that the integral on the right must be independent of the intermediate stages and hence that $p^{\frac{1}{4}}/T$ cannot be altered by varying T. But by § 29 p is a function of T only. Hence $p^{\frac{1}{4}}/T$ is a constant. Thus we can write

$$p = \tfrac{1}{3}aT^4, \qquad E = aT^4 \qquad \ldots\ldots\ldots\ldots\ldots(30\cdot3),$$

where a is a universal constant. The experimental value of a is $7\cdot64\ .\ 10^{-15}$ for C.G.S. units and degrees Centigrade.

The result $p \propto T^4$ is also obtained if we set $e = 2$ (the appropriate value for radiation) in $(28\cdot3)$. But it has a more general meaning for radiation than for a gas since it is not now confined to adiabatic changes. (The above argument if applied to a gas would break down at the statement "p is a function of T only.")

The result that *the energy-density of radiation is proportional to the fourth power of the absolute temperature* is known as Stefan's Law.

31. Subject to certain reservations the equilibrium distribution of radiation in an enclosure will not be upset by admitting molecules into the enclosure. The waves permeate freely the spaces between the molecules and in the interior of the molecules, and the reduction of the volume occupied by radiation is insignificant. The matter in the enclosure must take up the same temperature as the walls and the radiation. Thus radiation of density aT^4 will fill any region occupied by matter maintained at temperature T—except near the edges where the radiation is not properly "enclosed."

The reservation is necessary when the matter in the enclosure has an appreciable refractive index for radiation of the wave-lengths concerned. In this case the internal energy of the molecules and the energy of aether waves is so linked that the present argument is scarcely adequate. There does not appear to be any actual failure of Stefan's Law (or Planck's Law) in this case; but careful definition is required since the energy of material polarisation is in some applications appropriately grouped with the radiant energy whereas in other applications it is kept separate. Further reference to this point so far as it concerns stellar conditions is made in § 164.

The quantity of isotropic radiation passing in both directions through a plane area S is $\frac{1}{2}EcS$ per second. (The factor $\frac{1}{2}$ arises through taking the average of $\cos \theta$ over each hemisphere, the cross-section of an oblique beam through S being $S \cos \theta$.) The amount passing in one direction is $\frac{1}{4}EcS$. Hence if in a body at temperature T a cross-section is cut and suddenly exposed, radiation of amount $\frac{1}{4}Ec$ per sq. cm. per sec. will leave the body through this section. This is evidently the maximum intensity of radiation obtainable from a body maintained at a general temperature T. In practice it will be impossible to avoid a slight drop of temperature at the surface. This may be minimised by taking a good conductor of heat and coating it with a highly absorbent substance; the conductor is required to maintain the full temperature near the surface, and the absorber to secure that the radiation is "enclosed." Equilibrium radiation is often called *black-body radiation* in reference to this mode of experimenting on it. Another method of obtaining nearly the full black-body radiation is to make a small opening in a large enclosure maintained at the requisite temperature.

The full radiation of matter at temperature T is accordingly

$$\frac{1}{4}Ec = \frac{1}{4}acT^4 \text{ per sq. cm. per sec.} \quad \dots\dots\dots\dots(31\cdot1)$$

The constant $\sigma = \frac{1}{4}ac$ is called *Stefan's constant*, but we shall generally prefer to use the constant a.

Wien's Law.

32. We next deduce from thermodynamical considerations that the constitution of equilibrium radiation at temperature T satisfies Wien's displacement law

$$I(\nu, T) = \nu^3 f(\nu/T) \quad \dots\dots\dots\dots\dots\dots(32\cdot1),$$

where $I(\nu, T) d\nu$ is the energy-density of the radiation of frequency between ν and $\nu + d\nu$ and f is some definite function of ν/T. Since the form of f is not indicated by this investigation Wien's law does not determine the constitution; but if the constitution is known for any one temperature, it enables us to calculate the constitution for other temperatures.

LEMMA. *A chamber with perfectly reflecting walls initially contains equilibrium radiation. If the chamber expands or contracts, the radiation will be automatically converted into equilibrium radiation for the temperature corresponding to its new density.*

The perfect reflection has two consequences: (1) it ensures that no heat escapes from or is admitted to the chamber, so that the change is adiabatic ($dQ = 0$); (2) it eliminates the ordinary processes (absorption and emission) by which radiation in an enclosure attains equilibrium constitution, so that we have not the usual guarantee that after the alteration of volume there will be equilibrium radiation in the chamber.

Let us for the moment accept the first consequence, but evade the second by inserting in the chamber a speck of absorbing matter of negligible heat capacity; this re-introduces absorption and emission and the radiation will be brought into equilibrium with the matter just as though it formed the walls*.

Now let the chamber undergo any number of expansions and contractions and return to its original volume. As it is subject to the adiabatic condition the pressure is a function of the volume only; in fact, setting $dQ = 0$ in (30·2) we have $p^{\frac{3}{4}}v = $ constant. Hence the radiation has returned to its original pressure and therefore to its original energy-density; and as it is still equilibrium radiation it is exactly in its original state.

Thus the entropy of the radiation is unaltered. Since $dQ = 0$ no entropy has been removed from it to its surroundings. Therefore no entropy has been created in it.

The function of the speck of matter was to convert the radiation to equilibrium constitution as fast as any divergence was produced. But we have seen that this process is irreversible and that non-equilibrium radiation has less entropy than equilibrium radiation (§ 29), so that the conversion involves creation of entropy. Since no entropy has been created it follows that the speck of matter has not functioned at all—it has never in the whole process found any non-equilibrium radiation to convert. This shows that the adjustment is made automatically and reversibly by the reflecting walls without the help of any absorbing matter.

33. In these conditions the only cause of a change of constitution is the Doppler effect at the moving mirrors enclosing the radiation—moving when the chamber alters in size. When the walls recede the wave is reflected with lower frequency than the incident wave, so that there is a general conversion to lower frequencies accompanying the lowering of energy-density and temperature.

Let waves of energy-density E and frequency ν fall *normally* on a reflector receding with velocity V. Let E', ν' be the energy-density and frequency of the reflected waves. The well-known formula for the Doppler effect is

$$\frac{\nu'}{\nu} = \frac{c - V}{c + V} \qquad \qquad \dots\dots\dots\dots\dots\dots\dots\dots(33\cdot1).$$

* The argument is equally valid if the continual conversion of non-equilibrium into equilibrium radiation is accomplished by the *fiat* of the mathematician.

The pressure on the walls is $E + E'$ (§ 21). The work done on the walls per sq. cm. per sec. is therefore $(E + E') V$. This must be equal to the difference of energy of the incident and reflected waves, viz. $Ec - E'c$ per sq. cm. per sec. Hence

$$(E - E') c = (E + E') V \qquad \text{...............}(33\cdot2).$$

By (33·1) and (33·2)

$$\frac{v'}{v} = \frac{E'}{E} = \frac{c - V}{c + V} \qquad \text{.....................}(33\cdot3).$$

If the incidence is oblique the same result is obtained except that V must now be the velocity of the reflector resolved in the oblique direction.

We express the quantity E/v in units called *quanta**. By (33·3) $E/v = E'/v'$, that is to say, *the number of quanta is unaltered by reflection at moving walls*.

Consider a small change of volume of the chamber causing a change of temperature of the radiation from T to $T + dT$. During this change let a quantum of frequency v change to frequency v' by one or more reflections at the moving walls and write

$$v = v' (1 + s) \qquad \text{.......................}(33\cdot4).$$

Then by (33·3) s depends on the circumstances of the reflections, *but not on v*. Hence if we denote by $g(s) ds$ the proportion of the reflected quanta for which this coefficient lies between s and $s + ds$, $g(s)$ will be the same function whatever frequency v we are considering, since there is no correlation between v and s.

By definition

$$\left. \begin{array}{l} \displaystyle\int g(s)\, ds = 1 \\[2mm] \displaystyle\int s g(s)\, ds = s_0 \end{array} \right\} \qquad \text{.......................}(33\cdot5).$$

Let

Then s_0 is independent of v.

Let $J(v, T)\, dv$ be the number of quanta of frequency v to $v + dv$ in the chamber when the temperature is T, then

$$J(v', T + dT)\, dv' = \int g(s)\, ds\, J(v, T)\, dv,$$

where the integral on the right is taken over all values of s, and (for each value of s) v and dv are related to the fixed values v', dv' by (33·4). Hence substituting for v and dv

$$J(v', T + dT) = \int g(s)\, ds\, (1 + s)\, J(v'(1 + s), T).$$

---

* We use the modern nomenclature, but do not here introduce any of the principles of the quantum theory. The "number of quanta" is not assumed to be an integral number.

Expanding by Taylor's theorem, and neglecting squares of the infinitesimals s and dT

$$J\left(\nu', T\right) + dT \frac{\partial}{\partial T} J\left(\nu', T\right) = J\left(\nu', T\right) \int g\left(s\right) ds$$

$$+ \left\{ J\left(\nu', T\right) + \nu' \frac{\partial}{\partial \nu'} J\left(\nu', T\right) \right\} \int s g\left(s\right) ds.$$

Omitting the accents as no longer necessary, this reduces by (33·5) to

$$\frac{\partial J}{\partial T} dT = s_0 \left(J + \nu \frac{\partial J}{\partial \nu} \right),$$

or
$$\frac{\partial (\nu J)}{\partial T} = \frac{\nu s_0}{dT} \frac{\partial (\nu J)}{\partial \nu} \quad \dots\dots\dots\dots\dots\dots(33·6).$$

Now s_0/dT is independent of ν but we have no reason to suppose it independent of T and we must therefore take it to be an unknown function of T. Then (33·6) can be written

$$\frac{\partial (\nu J)}{\partial (\log f(T))} = \frac{\nu \partial (\nu J)}{\partial \nu} = \frac{\partial (\nu J)}{\partial (\log \nu)}.$$

The solution of this partial differential equation is

$$\nu J = F\left(\nu/f\left(T\right)\right) \quad \dots\dots\dots\dots\dots\dots(33·71),$$

where F is another unknown function.

The energy is obtained by multiplying the number of quanta by ν (according to our definition above). Hence

$$\nu J\left(\nu, T\right) = v I\left(\nu, T\right) \quad \dots\dots\dots\dots\dots(33·72),$$

where v is the volume of the enclosure and $I\left(\nu, T\right) d\nu$ the energy-density of radiation between ν and $\nu + d\nu$. Integrating for all values of ν and setting E for the whole energy-density

$$Ev = \int_0^\infty \nu J\, d\nu = \int_0^\infty F\left(\nu/f\left(T\right)\right) d\nu$$

$$= Cf\left(T\right) \quad \dots\dots\dots\dots\dots\dots\dots\dots(33·73),$$

where
$$C = \int_0^\infty F\left(x\right) dx.$$

Since the change is adiabatic, we have by setting $dQ = 0$ in (30·2)

$$p^{\frac{3}{4}} v = \text{const.},$$

or since $E = 3p$
$$E^{\frac{3}{4}} v = \text{const.} \quad \dots\dots\dots\dots\dots(33·74).$$

Hence by (33·73) and (33·74) $E^{\frac{1}{4}}$ is proportional to $f\left(T\right)$. But by Stefan's Law $E^{\frac{1}{4}}$ is proportional to T. Hence $f\left(T\right)$ is a constant multiple of T, and without loss of generality we can set in (33·71)

$$f\left(T\right) = T.$$

Hence by (33·71) and (33·72)

$$v\,I\,(v,\,T) = F\,(v/T).$$

By (33·74) $v \propto T^{-3}$, so that absorbing the constant of proportion in F

$$I\,(v,\,T) = T^3 F\,(v/T).$$

Finally, if
$$f_1\,(x) = F\,(x)/x^3$$

$$I\,(v,\,T) = v^3 f_1\,(v/T)$$

which proves the required theorem.

To review this rather lengthy investigation we note four steps: (1) Proof that the change of constitution of equilibrium radiation with temperature is brought about by reflection at moving walls independently of absorption and emission processes; (2) Proof that the number of quanta is unchanged; (3) Formulation and integration of the partial differential equation expressing the fact that there is no correlation between s and v; (4) Determination of one of the two functions introduced, by the condition that the total density of the radiation must agree with Stefan's law.

CHAPTER III

QUANTUM THEORY

Interaction of Radiation and Matter.

34. The theory of the equilibrium of matter and radiation at constant temperature depends on a principle which is a generalisation of the theory of exchanges (§ 29). After equilibrium is reached no visible change occurs; the density and constitution of the radiation, the proportion of atoms in various states of combination and ionisation, the number of free electrons, the proportion of molecular velocities between given limits, all remain steady; but beneath this statistical changelessness there is continual change happening to the individual atoms, electrons, and elements of radiation.

Consider the atoms of a particular element which are uncombined and in their normal neutral state. The number n of these atoms in the system will remain constant (apart from chance fluctuations) when equilibrium is reached. But the individuals composing this number continually change. New atoms appear in this state owing to the dissolution of chemical molecules containing them, neutralisation of ionised atoms by the capture of free electrons, relapse of excited atoms to the normal state. Atoms in the given state disappear owing to the converse processes—combination to form chemical molecules, ionisation by the expulsion of an electron, excitation by absorption of radiation or collision with electrons or atoms. The steadiness of n is due to an average balancing of gains and losses.

But the principle above mentioned is not content with formulating this general balance of gain and loss—a mere translation of the word "equilibrium." It asserts that the gain by any process balances the loss by the converse process. The gains due to capture of a free electron balance the losses due to expulsion of an electron, independently of the other sources of gain and loss. This principle of separate balancing extends to the smallest details. Gains due to capture of an electron to fill a vacancy at a particular level in an atom balance losses due to expulsion of an electron *from that level*; gains due to capture of an electron of particular speed balance losses due to expulsion of an electron *with that speed*.

We may put it in this way—Any statistical enumeration, however detailed, of the processes of change occurring in a system in equilibrium at constant temperature would remain true if the direction of time were reversed*. For our applications we state it in the form—

---

* The ultimate laws of nature (so far as known) leave the direction of time indeterminate and provide no test to distinguish the past from the future. The direction in which time is progressing can only be found by statistical tests depending

Law I. (*Generalised Principle of Exchanges.*) Every process of transformation occurring in a system in thermodynamical equilibrium is capable of direct reversal; and transformations in the two directions occur with equal frequency*.

No formal proof can be offered, but a little consideration will show how difficult it is to evade the law—to have the general balance occurring without the particular balance. The kind of phenomenon that would upset the balance is a cyclic series of processes. For example, an atom might become excited, then become ionised by expelling an electron in the excited state, and finally capture an electron at the normal level (i.e. without returning *via* the excited state). This will keep the number n constant although the individual processes are unbalanced. But that is not the whole effect. The exciting of the atom involves absorption of a quantum of radiation of particular frequency; its ionisation involves absorption of another quantum; and the recapture of the electron (taken for simplicity to have the same velocity as the expelled electron so as not to upset the distribution of electronic velocities) involves emission of a quantum of yet another frequency. Thus the effect of the cycle is to alter the constitution of the radiation of the field. To preserve the equilibrium of the radiation we must link with it another cycle occurring to the radiation and undoing the change. The trouble is—if we provide a separate mechanism for changing back the radiation, how are we to prevent it from working in the absence of the particular atoms we have considered? The mechanism will have the same distribution of radiation to operate on whether these particular atoms are present or not, because we have proved (§ 29) that the equilibrium distribution of radiation is independent of the chemical nature of the material present. Apparently the only way of securing that the mechanism will act when it is required and not when it is not required is to make the special atoms play an essential part in it; this they must do by absorbing the radiation previously emitted and liberating the radiation previously absorbed, with corresponding changes of their own energy. Except in very special cases this means that the linked cycle is the exact reverse of the first, so that each of the three processes of the cycle is now separately balanced by its opposite.

Looking at the question more generally we note that three types of energy come under consideration—

(1) Radiant energy.

(2) Kinetic (translatory) energy of electrons and molecules.

(3) Internal energy of molecules and atoms.

on enumerations of large assemblies. Entropy is the most convenient statistic, and the rule is that t must be measured so that dS/dt is positive. Our law asserts that when this test fails ($dS/dt = 0$) all other statistical tests fail to determine a direction of time.

* This is often referred to as the "principle of detailed balancing."

The first is distributed in a way which depends only on the temperature. The second is partitioned in a way depending only on the temperature, though the amount depends on the matter present. The third is distributed in a way peculiar to the chemical elements present. The uniform laws of distribution of the first two kinds and the arbitrary variability of the third makes it almost impossible to devise complex cycles for maintaining a balance*. The simple means of balancing proposed in Law I has at least great plausibility.

Many familiar experiments are performed in conditions far removed from thermodynamical equilibrium—in particular experiments on X rays and cathode rays. Unbalanced cycles are then prominent.

35. A second general principle is given by the quantum theory—

Law II. (*Quantum Law.*) Whenever radiant energy is transformed into other forms of energy or *vice versa* the transformation occurs in finite amounts called quanta; the amount of energy constituting a quantum is $h\nu$, where ν is the frequency of the radiation and h is a universal constant.

It is not necessary to regard the emission of a quantum as instantaneous or unanalysable. The essential point of Law II is that the absorption or emission of a quantum marks one "process of transformation" in the sense of Law I. If two quanta are emitted at the same time this is merely a chance coincidence, whereas the emission of the second half of a quantum is the inevitable sequel to the emission of the first half.

Einstein's Equation.

36. Consider two states of an atom with internal energy χ_1, χ_2 respectively ($\chi_2 > \chi_1$). The atom can pass from state 2 to state 1 by emitting radiation of energy $\chi_2 - \chi_1$, and the reverse process is a passage from state 1 to state 2 with absorption of a like amount of radiation. By Law II the frequency ν_{12} of the radiation emitted or absorbed is given by

$$\chi_2 - \chi_1 = h\nu_{12} \quad \dots\dots\dots\dots\dots\dots\dots\dots\dots(36\cdot1),$$

and by Law I the number of passages in the two directions in matter in thermodynamical equilibrium will balance independently of any other processes of transition involving the two states.

According to Bohr's theory of the atom, the possible values of χ_1 and χ_2 form a discontinuous series; but we make no use of this in our argument except to afford a verbal simplification, viz. that we may speak of the

---

* The argument apparently does not exclude a cycle involving only (1) and (2); but we believe we have sufficient knowledge of the law governing transformation of radiant into kinetic energy and *vice versa* (Compton Effect, § 52) to show that no such cycle occurs.

number of atoms with energy χ instead of the number in a range χ to $\chi + d\chi$.

Let n_1, n_2 be the number of atoms in states 1 and 2 and let $I(\nu_{12})$ be the energy-density of radiation of frequency ν_{12}. At present we do not assume equilibrium.

Passage from state 1 to 2 with absorption of radiation will be impossible unless radiation of the required frequency is present. The number of transitions will vanish if $I(\nu_{12})$ vanishes and presumably will increase proportionately to $I(\nu_{12})$; it will also be proportional to the number of atoms n_1 capable of this transition. We therefore set the number of transitions in time dt equal to

$$a_{12} n_1 I(\nu_{12}) dt \quad\text{...........................(36·21),}$$

where a_{12} is an atomic constant.

Passage from state 2 to state 1 with emission of radiation can occur spontaneously without the presence of extraneous radiation. The proportion of atoms spontaneously making this jump per unit time must be an atomic constant. We therefore set the number equal to

$$b_{21} n_2 dt \quad\text{..............................(36·22).}$$

It is conceivable that these passages may be hindered or stimulated by the presence of radiation of frequency ν_{12}. If so, the diminution or addition will presumably be proportional to the intensity of the radiation. We therefore set the number of additional passages equal to

$$a_{21} n_2 I(\nu_{12}) dt \quad\text{........................(36·23),}$$

where a_{21} may be positive or negative.

The constants a_{12}, a_{21}, b_{21} relate to processes in which the atoms act individually and do not depend on any statistical properties of the assemblage. In particular, they do not depend on the temperature—in fact as yet the assemblage is not supposed to have a temperature.

Apply these results to an assemblage in thermodynamical equilibrium at temperature T, the transitions (36·22) and (36·23) must balance (36·21) by Law I. The result is Einstein's equation

$$a_{12} n_1 I(\nu_{12}, T) = b_{21} n_2 + a_{21} n_2 I(\nu_{12}, T) \quad\text{.........(36·3),}$$

where I is no longer arbitrary but represents the distribution law of radiation in equilibrium at temperature T.

This gives

$$\frac{n_1}{n_2} = \frac{a_{21}}{a_{12}} \left(1 + \frac{b_{21}}{a_{21} I(\nu_{12}, T)} \right) \quad\text{.................(36·4),}$$

a formula giving the relative proportions of atoms in the two states in material at temperature T.

37. We now introduce a third state with energy χ_3 ($\chi_3 > \chi_2 > \chi_1$). Then since

$$\frac{n_1}{n_2} \cdot \frac{n_2}{n_3} = \frac{n_1}{n_3},$$

$$\frac{a_{21}}{a_{12}}\left(1 + \frac{b_{21}}{a_{21}I\,(\nu_{12},\,T)}\right)\frac{a_{32}}{a_{23}}\left(1 + \frac{b_{32}}{a_{32}I\,(\nu_{23},\,T)}\right) = \frac{a_{31}}{a_{13}}\left(1 + \frac{b_{31}}{a_{31}I\,(\nu_{13},\,T)}\right)$$
$$\dots(37\cdot1),$$

and by (36·1) $$\nu_{13} = \nu_{12} + \nu_{23} \quad\dots\dots\dots\dots\dots\dots(37\cdot2).$$

This holds for all temperatures T, and T only occurs in (37·1) in the way explicitly indicated by the notation. We may perhaps fairly assume that, for a fixed value of ν, $I\,(\nu,\,T)$ increases without limit as T increases to infinity*, so that by taking a sufficiently high temperature the second term in each bracket is made as small as we please. Hence taking T infinite

$$\frac{a_{21}}{a_{12}} \cdot \frac{a_{32}}{a_{23}} = \frac{a_{31}}{a_{13}} \quad\dots\dots\dots\dots\dots\dots(37\cdot3).$$

Substituting this in (37·1) we have

$$\left(1 + \frac{b_{21}}{a_{21}I\,(\nu_{12},\,T)}\right)\left(1 + \frac{b_{32}}{a_{32}I\,(\nu_{23},\,T)}\right) = \left(1 + \frac{b_{31}}{a_{31}I\,(\nu_{13},\,T)}\right).$$

Introducing Wien's Law (32·1) this becomes

$$\left(1 + \frac{c_{12}}{f\,(\nu_{12}/T)}\right)\left(1 + \frac{c_{23}}{f\,(\nu_{23}/T)}\right) = \left(1 + \frac{c_{13}}{f\,(\nu_{13}/T)}\right) \quad\dots\dots(37\cdot4),$$

where $$c_{12} = b_{21}/a_{21}\nu_{12}{}^3 \quad\dots\dots\dots\dots\dots\dots(37\cdot5),$$

and c_{12} is independent of T.

This may be written

$$\frac{1}{f\,(\nu_{12}/T)} \cdot \frac{1}{c_{23}} + \frac{1}{f\,(\nu_{23}/T)} \cdot \frac{1}{c_{12}} - \frac{1}{f\,(\nu_{12}/T + \nu_{23}/T)} \cdot \frac{c_{13}}{c_{12}c_{23}} = -\frac{1}{f\,(\nu_{12}/T)f\,(\nu_{23}/T)}$$
$$\dots\dots(37\cdot6).$$

Write this equation three times over, taking T equal to three temperatures T_1, T_2, T_3 successively. Eliminate $1/c_{12}$ and $c_{13}/c_{12}c_{23}$ between the three equations. We then obtain c_{23} expressed as a function of six arguments $\nu_{12}/T_1, \nu_{12}/T_2, \nu_{12}/T_3, \nu_{23}/T_1, \nu_{23}/T_2, \nu_{23}/T_3$. These reduce to four independent arguments

$$\nu_{12}/T_1, \qquad \nu_{12}/T_2, \qquad \nu_{12}/T_3, \qquad \nu_{12}/\nu_{23}.$$

Obviously c_{23} cannot depend on the first three of these; not can it depend on the fourth since ν_{12} can be taken arbitrarily without affecting c_{23}. Since c_{23} does not depend on any of its arguments it must be a definite

---

* $I\,(\nu,\,T)$ cannot *decrease* with T; for if it did, heat could be transferred from the cooler to the hotter of two enclosures by opening a window transparent only to ν. But it does not seem possible to show by thermodynamics alone that it increases without limit (see § 40).

natural constant involved in the unknown function $f(\nu/T)$. We have accordingly

$$c_{12} = c_{23} = c_{13} = C \quad \dots\dots\dots\dots\dots(37\cdot7)$$

Hence (37·4) becomes

$$\left(1 + \frac{C}{f(\alpha)}\right)\left(1 + \frac{C}{f(\beta)}\right) = \left(1 + \frac{C}{f(\alpha + \beta)}\right) \quad \dots\dots\dots(37\cdot8),$$

where $\alpha = \nu_{12}/T$, $\beta = \nu_{23}/T$.

It is well known that the only solution of this equation is the exponential function

$$1 + \frac{C}{f(\alpha)} = e^{k\alpha},$$

where k is a constant. Hence

$$f(\alpha) = C/(e^{k\alpha} - 1).$$

Wien's Law thus reduces to

$$I(\nu, T) = \frac{C\nu^3}{e^{k\nu/T} - 1} \quad \dots\dots\dots\dots\dots\dots(37\cdot9).$$

The radiation law is thus fully determined except for the two constants C and k which must later be identified. The form (37·9) is Planck's Law.

38. We can now find the relative proportions of atoms in states 1 and 2 at temperature T. By (36·4)

$$\frac{n_1}{n_2} = \frac{a_{21}}{a_{12}}\left(1 + \frac{C}{f(\nu_{12}/T)}\right) = \frac{a_{21}}{a_{12}} e^{k\nu_{12}/T} = \frac{a_{21}}{a_{12}} e^{(\chi_2 - \chi_1)/RT},$$

where

$$R = h/k \quad \dots\dots\dots\dots\dots\dots\dots\dots\dots(38\cdot1).$$

And generally

$$\frac{n_r}{n_s} = \frac{a_{sr}}{a_{rs}} e^{(\chi_s - \chi_r)/RT} \quad \dots\dots\dots\dots\dots\dots(38\cdot2).$$

Let $q_1, q_2, \dots q_r$ be the proportions of atoms in states 1, 2 ... r at *infinite temperature*. Then by (38·2)

$$a_{sr}/a_{rs} = q_r/q_s \quad \dots\dots\dots\dots\dots(38\cdot25),$$

so that, reverting to finite temperature,

$$n_1 : n_2 : \dots : n_r = q_1 e^{-\chi_1/RT} : q_2 e^{-\chi_2/RT} : \dots : q_r e^{-\chi_r/RT} \dots(38\cdot3).$$

The factors $q_1, q_2, \dots$ are called the *weights* of the respective states. The theory of these weighting factors will be considered later. They are determined when the constitution at any given temperature is known; and (38·3) then shows how the constitution changes with temperature. The result (38·3) is called Boltzmann's formula.

In Einstein's original paper* Boltzmann's formula (38·3) was quoted as a result established in statistical mechanics and the derivation of

---

* *Phys. Zeits.* **18**, p. 122 (1917). Einstein was following the converse procedure so as to deduce the quantum law (36·1) from his equation.

Planck's Law correspondingly shortened. We have here preferred to avoid this excursion into an extraneous subject, and in the present derivation Boltzmann's formula is obtained from pure quantum theory.

By (37·5)

$$C = \frac{b_{21}}{a_{21} \nu_{12}{}^3} = \frac{b_{21}}{a_{12}} \frac{q_2}{q_1} \cdot \frac{1}{\nu_{12}{}^3},$$

so that

$$\frac{b_{21}}{a_{12}} = C \frac{q_1}{q_2} \nu_{12}{}^3 \quad\dots\dots\dots\dots\dots(38\cdot4),$$

giving the relation between the coefficients of absorption and of spontaneous emission.

Also, considering the atoms in state 2, the emission per atom at temperature T is to the emission per atom at temperature zero in the ratio

$$b_{21} + a_{21} I (\nu_{12}, T) : b_{21}$$

by (36·3). This is equal to

$$C\nu_{12}{}^3 + \frac{C\nu_{12}{}^3}{e^{h\nu_{12}/RT} - 1} : C\nu_{12}{}^3 = (1 - e^{-h\nu_{12}/RT})^{-1} \dots\dots\dots(38\cdot5).$$

The ratio is greater than unity, so that emission is stimulated by the presence of radiation in the field. This stimulated emission is called by Einstein *negative absorption*.

As an example of this formula consider a radio-active process consisting of a simple readjustment of the nucleus of an atom with emission of a γ ray of frequency ν_{12}. The effect of raising the temperature is to increase the radio-activity in the ratio given by (38·5). The frequency of γ rays is so high that even a temperature of 10^7 degrees (in the interior of a star) makes no appreciable difference to the radio-activity.

When the atoms are crowded together in dense material, the absorbing and emitting power of the individual atom may be to some extent modified by the proximity of its neighbours, so that a_{12}, a_{21} and b_{21} are then not purely atomic constants. The extent of the interference will depend on ρ and T, and there is a breakdown of the foregoing argument which assumes that a_{12}, etc. are independent of T. This does not in any way affect the proof of Planck's Law, because we have proved that the distribution law is the same for diffuse and dense matter; we determine once for all the form of the universal function f by considering a diffuse distribution which lends itself to simple treatment. But Boltzmann's formula is deduced only for diffuse matter in which the atoms are so far apart as to act independently; it becomes inaccurate in dense matter.

39. The present investigation is not confined to transitions in which the atom remains intact. It applies also to transitions in which an electron is expelled from or captured by an atom with absorption or emission of radiation. If, as usual, we measure the energy of the system from a zero level with the electron just free of the atom and without kinetic energy, χ_1 will denote the energy of the electron in its orbit within the atom in the first state (a negative quantity) and χ_2 will denote the positive kinetic energy of the free electron. If the free electron is in a region of zero potential and has velocity (u, v, w)

$$\chi_2 = \tfrac{1}{2}m\,(u^2 + v^2 + w^2) \quad\ldots\ldots\ldots\ldots\ldots\ldots(39\cdot1).$$

By Law I we may particularise the description of the states as minutely as we please. We shall take a system in state 2 to consist of an atom which has lost an electron, together with a free electron with velocity in the range u, v, w to $u + du, v + dv, w + dw$ in an element of volume $dx\,dy\,dz$ at zero potential located in a specified manner with respect to the atom. Then the energy of a system in state 2 is given by (39·1).

By (38·3)
$$\frac{n_2}{n_1} = \frac{q_2 e^{-m(u^2 + v^2 + w^2)/2RT}}{q_1 e^{-\chi_1/RT}}.$$

If n' is the number of ionised atoms in the system, and dN is the average number* of free electrons in a range $dx\,dy\,dz\,du\,dv\,dw$

$$n_2 = n'dN,$$

so that
$$dN = \left(\frac{n_1}{n'}\frac{e^{\chi_1/RT}}{q_1}\right).q_2 e^{-m(u^2 + v^2 + w^2)/2RT} \quad\ldots\ldots\ldots\ldots(39\cdot2).$$

The factor in the bracket remains constant for different values of u, v, w, so that we obtain Maxwell's law of velocities

$$dN \propto e^{-m(u^2 + v^2 + w^2)/2RT}\,du\,dv\,dw\,dx\,dy\,dz \quad\ldots\ldots\ldots(39\cdot3),$$

except that we have not yet shown that the weight factor q_2 for the range of states considered is proportional to $du\,dv\,dw\,dx\,dy\,dz$. It might well have been a function of u, v, w.

Meanwhile the comparison of (39·2) with (39·3) shows that the constant R hitherto unidentified is the same constant (Boltzmann's constant) which occurs in the theory of gases. Assuming (39·3) the average value of u^2 is

$$\int_{-\infty}^{\infty} u^2 e^{-mu^2/2RT}\,du \div \int_{-\infty}^{\infty} e^{-mu^2/2RT}\,du$$
$$= RT/m.$$

Hence the average kinetic energy $\tfrac{1}{2}m\,(u^2 + v^2 + w^2)$ is equal to

$$\tfrac{3}{2}RT \quad\ldots\ldots\ldots\ldots\ldots\ldots\ldots\ldots\ldots\ldots\ldots(39\cdot4).$$

Thus R is identified as $\tfrac{2}{3}$ of the average kinetic energy of a molecule at $1°$ absolute.

* The number dN is an infinitesimal fraction. When an infinitesimal range of a continuous distribution of states is considered, so that there is no longer a large number of systems in state 2, it becomes necessary to consider time-averages (or alternatively, probabilities) in order to smooth out the accidental fluctuations.

The same law can be deduced for the distribution of velocities of atoms and molecules. The argument is the same if there is any process of dissociation and combination of atoms analogous to the ionisation and capture of electrons, provided that radiation is involved. It is not necessary that this process should play an important part in distributing velocities; the argument from Law I is that the distribution of velocities however controlled must be such that this process will not under any circumstances disturb it. Alternatively we can proceed as follows. In any assemblage there will be some free electrons. Let n_r, n_s be the numbers of electrons with kinetic energies χ_r, χ_s; and n_r', n_s' be the numbers of atoms with these kinetic energies. Let a_{rs} be the probability that 1 marked atom in a cu. cm. with energy χ_r meets 1 marked electron in a cu. cm. with energy χ_s and that the two energies are interchanged. Then balancing direct and reverse processes in equilibrium

$$a_{rs} n_r' n_s = a_{sr} n_s' n_r$$

so that as far as the factor involving temperature is concerned

$$n_r'/n_s' = n_r/n_s.$$

Again nothing is discovered as to the weight factor.

The deduction of Maxwell's Law from Einstein's equation indicates that radiative processes alone would drive an assemblage to take up the Maxwellian distribution of velocities apart from the collisions investigated in the usual proofs. It should be stated, however, that the great length and difficulty (and perhaps imperfect rigour) of the usual proofs arises in connection with the weight factor $du\,dv\,dw$, which is not considered here.

40. If we prefer not to make the assumption leading to (37·3) the factor

$$a_{123} = \frac{a_{31}}{a_{13}} \frac{a_{12}}{a_{21}} \frac{a_{23}}{a_{32}},$$

must be inserted on the right of (37·4). The proof that c_{23} is a definite natural constant C proceeds as before except that four equations corresponding to four different temperatures must be used to eliminate the other unknowns.

It then follows by taking T infinite that

$$a_{123} = 1 + C/f(0),$$

so that instead of (37·8) we have

$$\{1 + C/f(\alpha)\}\{1 + C/f(\beta)\} = \{1 + C/f(0)\}\{1 + C/f(\alpha + \beta)\}.$$

And the solution is

$$\{1 + C/f(\alpha)\} = ae^{k\alpha},$$

where a and k are constants. Wien's Law then gives

$$I (\nu, T) = \frac{C\nu^3}{ae^{k\nu/T} - 1} \quad\quad\quad\quad\quad\quad\quad (40{\cdot}1)$$

but Boltzmann's Law $(38{\cdot}3)$ is unchanged.

It is curiously difficult to justify the choice of 1 for the constant a so as to obtain Planck's Law, thereby making $I (\nu, \infty)$ infinite instead of having a finite limit. In § 37 we begged the question by assuming as obvious that $I (\nu, \infty) = \infty$. The proof cannot be completed without introducing some additional assumption as to the laws of interaction between matter (or electric charges) and radiation.

For this assumption we may take the Correspondence Principle, which asserts that the classical laws of dynamics and electrodynamics represent the limit towards which the quantum laws (the actual laws) tend asymptotically when the number of quanta involved is very great—that, in fact, the older theories are statistically true provided there is sufficient material for statistical treatment to be appropriate. Now according to the classical law of equipartition of energy $I (\nu, T)$ should be proportional to T, just as the average energy of a molecule is proportional to T. At sufficiently high temperature this classical energy will represent a very large number of quanta $h\nu$, and therefore by the correspondence principle it should agree with the true law $(40{\cdot}1)$. There is no such agreement if $a \neq 1$; but if $a = 1$ we have as $T \to \infty$

$$I (\nu, T) = \frac{CR\nu^2}{h} T \quad\quad\quad\quad\quad\quad\quad (40{\cdot}2)$$

so that it is proportional to T as in the classical theory.

Alternatively we may obtain Planck's Law by considering the mechanism of a particular process of transfer, e.g. the scattering of radiation by free electrons, since if $I (\nu, T)$ is determined from any one process all other processes must give the same result. But all recognised quantum theories of particular processes have been developed in accordance with the Correspondence Principle, and it is this feature of the processes which settles the value $a = 1$.

The constant C in Planck's Law can be determined by the Correspondence Principle. Consider the radiation in a cubical enclosure of side l. At a given initial instant the electromagnetic vector throughout the enclosure can be expressed by a triple Fourier series of which the typical term is

$$A_{n_1, n_2, n_3} \frac{\sin}{\cos} 2\pi n_1 x/l \cdot \frac{\sin}{\cos} 2\pi n_2 y/l \cdot \frac{\sin}{\cos} 2\pi n_3 z/l \quad\quad (40{\cdot}3),$$

where n_1, n_2, n_3 take all integral values. This gives rise to waves of the form

$$\sin 2\pi \left(\pm n_1 \frac{x}{l} \pm n_2 \frac{y}{l} \pm n_3 \frac{z}{l} + \nu t \right),$$

where, since c is the velocity of propagation,

$$\nu^2 = c^2 (n_1{}^2 + n_2{}^2 + n_3{}^2)/l^2 \quad\ldots\ldots\ldots\ldots\ldots(40\cdot4).$$

Since the waves contain two independent components polarised in perpendicular planes, we have (allowing for the double signs) 16 independent waves for each set of positive integral values of n_1, n_2, n_3.

The number of combinations of integers satisfying

$$n_1{}^2 + n_2{}^2 + n_3{}^2 < n^2$$

approximates when n is large to the volume of an octant of a sphere of radius n, viz.

$$\tfrac{1}{6}\pi n^3.$$

Hence by (40·4) the number of independent waves of frequency less than ν becomes

$$16 \times \tfrac{1}{6}\pi \, (\nu l/c)^3,$$

and the number between frequencies ν and $\nu + d\nu$ is thus

$$\frac{8\pi l^3}{c^3} \nu^2 d\nu.$$

According to the classical law of equipartition of energy each of these independent vibrations of the aether will receive on the average the energy RT*. Hence the energy in the enclosure of frequency ν to $\nu + d\nu$ is

$$8\pi RT l^3 \nu^2 d\nu/c^3.$$

By the Correspondence Principle this must agree with the limit of Planck's formula which by (40·2) gives

$$l^3 C RT \nu^2 d\nu/h.$$

Hence $\qquad\qquad\qquad C = 8\pi h/c^3 \quad\ldots\ldots\ldots\ldots\ldots\ldots\ldots(40\cdot5).$

Having evaluated C we can now give more explicitly the relation between the coefficients of absorption and emission resulting from Einstein's equation. By (38·4)

$$\frac{b_{21}}{a_{12}} = C \cdot \frac{q_1}{q_2} \nu_{12}{}^3 = \frac{q_1}{q_2} \cdot \frac{8\pi h \nu_{12}{}^3}{c^3} \quad\ldots\ldots\ldots\ldots\ldots(40\cdot61).$$

By (36·21) $a_{12} n_1 I \, (\nu_{12})$ is the number of quanta absorbed per unit time, and therefore $a_{12} n_1 I \, (\nu_{12}) \cdot h\nu_{12}$ is the energy absorbed per unit time—a time during which a quantity of monochromatic radiant energy $cI \, (\nu_{12}) \, d\nu$ has passed through a square centimetre. Hence if the n_1 atoms (in state 1) form an absorbing screen of area 1 sq. cm. the fraction absorbed is

$$a_{12} n_1 h\nu_{12}/cd\nu.$$

The atomic absorption coefficient, or absorption coefficient per atom per sq. cm. for the monochromatic radiation, is thus

$$\alpha = a_{12} h\nu_{12}/cd\nu \quad\ldots\ldots\ldots\ldots\ldots\ldots(40\cdot62).$$

* I.e. $\tfrac{1}{2}RT$ kinetic + $\tfrac{1}{2}RT$ potential. A free particle receives $\tfrac{1}{2}RT$ kinetic for each of its three degrees of freedom (39·4).

Hence by (40·61)

$$\alpha = \frac{q_2}{q_1} \frac{c^2}{8\pi\nu_{12}^2} \frac{b_{21}}{\delta\nu} \qquad\dots\dots\dots\dots\dots\dots(40\cdot63),$$

where $1/b_{21}$ is interpreted simply as the average duration of state 2 before a spontaneous relapse occurs, and $\delta\nu$ is the width of the spectral line emitted by such relapses*.

The number of atoms in a gram is $1/A_H$, where A is the atomic weight and H the mass of a hydrogen atom. Hence the mass absorption coefficient k, or absorption coefficient per gm. per sq. cm. is

$$k = \frac{\alpha}{A_H} = \frac{q_2}{q_1} \frac{c^2}{8\pi\nu_{12}^2} \cdot \frac{b_{21}}{A_H\,\delta\nu} \qquad\dots\dots\dots\dots\dots(40\cdot64).$$

The coefficients in (40·63) and (40·64) refer to the absorption of monochromatic radiation of frequency ν_{12} by material composed wholly of atoms in state 1. Also if the atom has more than one electron which by excitation can absorb frequency ν_{12}, the coefficients become multiplied by the corresponding factor.

Planck's Law (37·9) can now be given fully as

$$I\,(\nu,\,T) = \frac{8\pi h\nu^3}{c^3} \frac{1}{e^{h\nu/RT} - 1} \qquad\dots\dots\dots\dots\dots(40\cdot7).$$

By Stefan's Law

$$aT^4 = \int_0^\infty I\,(\nu,\,T)\,d\nu = \frac{8\pi h}{c^3}\left(\frac{RT}{h}\right)^4 \int_0^\infty \frac{x^3 dx}{e^x - 1} \qquad (x = h\nu/RT).$$

The integral is equal to $\pi^4/15$, so that

$$a = \frac{8\pi^5}{15} \frac{R^4}{c^3 h^3} \qquad\dots\dots\dots\dots\dots\dots(40\cdot8).$$

Some of the chief properties of Planck's Law may be stated here for reference. The mean frequency of the radiation is given by

$$\bar{x} = \int_0^\infty \frac{x^4 dx}{e^x - 1} \div \int_0^\infty \frac{x^3 dx}{e^x - 1}$$

$$= 24\,(1^{-5} + 2^{-5} + 3^{-5} + \dots) \div 6\,(1^{-4} + 2^{-4} + 3^{-4} + \dots)$$

$$= 3\cdot8322,$$

so that $\quad h\bar{\nu} = 3\cdot83RT \qquad\dots\dots\dots\dots\dots\dots\dots\dots(40\cdot91).$

The number of quanta per cubic centimetre is

$$8\pi \left(\frac{RT}{hc}\right)^3 \int_0^\infty \frac{x^2 dx}{e^x - 1}.$$

---

* More precisely α is the average absorption coefficient over any width $\delta\nu$ sufficient to cover the absorption line, so that $\alpha\delta\nu$ gives the whole absorption of the line. If we were to take $\delta\nu$ to cover only part of the absorption line the coefficient b_{21} would refer to a fraction only of the emissions and would not then be equal to the reciprocal of the duration of the excited state.

The integral is equal to 2·40411. Hence we find*

$$\text{number of quanta per cu. cm.} = 20·62T^3 \quad ......(40·92).$$

Average energy of a quantum is

$$aT^4 \div 20·62T^3 = 2·70RT \quad ....(40·93).$$

The maximum value of $I(\nu, T)$ is at a frequency given by

$$h\nu = 2·821RT \quad ....(40·94).$$

On the other hand, if Planck's Law is expressed in terms of λ instead of ν, so that $I'(\lambda, T)\, d\lambda$ is the energy-density between λ and $\lambda + d\lambda$, the maximum value of $I'(\lambda, T)$ is at a frequency given by

$$h\nu = 4·965RT \quad ....(40·95).$$

For comparison it may be added that yellow light is just perceptible when 500 quanta per second enter the eye.

41. The argument by which we reached Einstein's equation is plausible; but it is not contended that the truth of the equation can be demonstrated by *a priori* reasoning. The particular assumption which might be challenged is that $I(\nu_{12})$ is involved linearly in (36·21) and (36·23); it is conceivable that the number of transitions might not be simply proportional to the intensity of the radiation. But evidently if squared or higher powers of $I(\nu_{12})$ had appeared in the equation we should not have reached Planck's Law which is experimentally confirmed. It appears therefore that the assumptions are true in nature, and the whole discussion gives an illuminating idea of how a diversity of processes leads quite simply to a uniform law of distribution of radiation.

It is remarkable that Einstein's equation is in a certain sense a violation of Law I. Consider the transitions represented by $a_{21}n_2 I(\nu_{12})$, the number being jointly proportional to the number of suitable atoms and to the amount of radiation of relevant frequency. The natural interpretation is that when a quantum of radiation meets an excited atom, there is a certain definite probability that a transition will occur leaving us with a normal (or a less excited) atom and two quanta of radiation receding from it, viz. the original quantum and an emitted quantum. Clearly the reverse process consists in two quanta approaching the normal atom simultaneously, the final state being an excited atom with one quantum of radiation leaving it. The probability of two quanta colliding with the atom simultaneously should be proportional to $\{I(\nu_{12})\}^2$ if the quanta represent independent elements of radiation. But in Einstein's equation we do not balance the transitions $a_{21}n_2 I(\nu_{12})$ against a term in $\{I(\nu_{12})\}^2$, we balance them against a portion of the term arising from impacts of single quanta. Formally at least we are balancing a cycle of processes instead of a direct and reverse process.

* Numerical values of all the physical constants are given in Appendix I.

By way of contrast, consider what happens when an atom emits an electron instead of a quantum of radiation. If an electron encounters a normal atom there is a certain probability that the atom will be ionised so that two electrons (the original electron and an additional one) leave the atom. The converse process occurs when two electrons meet an ionised atom simultaneously and one of them (which would have escaped if it had been alone) is captured through the confusion caused by the entrance of the other. In that case we apply Law I, and deduce that the ionisations by electronic impact must be balanced by the captures due to the combined encounter of two electrons simultaneously.

This striking difference of treatment of electrons and radiation is justified experimentally. It strongly suggests that free radiation has no atomicity of constitution. If it consisted of independent atoms it would scarcely be possible to avoid effects due to simultaneous action of two atoms of radiation, the frequency of such effects being proportional to the square of the intensity. It is not sufficient to suppose that these combined effects are too small to be observed; in Einstein's equation the place which should have been theirs is definitely assigned by default to other agencies.

The modern quantum theory appears to incline to this view that free radiation is continuous, and that the quantum is only called into being in the process of interaction of radiation and matter.

As the general conception of the quantum theory has undergone some modification in recent years, it will be well to indicate how it is now regarded. We start with an electromagnetic field to which Maxwell's equations rigorously apply. This is the tensor $F_{\mu\nu}$ of the relativity theory or $(X, Y, Z, \alpha, \beta, \gamma)$ of the classical theory; and Maxwell's equations assert (1) that it is the curl of an electromagnetic potential, (2) that its divergence is the electric charge and current vector. By Maxwell's theory disturbances of this vector are electromagnetic waves propagated with the fundamental velocity c, and showing the phenomena of interference, diffraction, etc. in accordance with the undulatory theory. There is no discontinuity or quantum structure involved in this field. We have next to consider how the field and its waves become amenable to experimental detection—nothing having been yet said on this point. The detection is consequent on energy-changes provoked in material systems. The electric and magnetic forces are not in themselves observable; the observable effects arise from the mechanical or ponderomotive force of the field which is represented by another vector ($F_{\mu\nu}F_{\sigma}^{\nu\sigma}$ in the relativity theory). The simplest statement on the classical theory of the observable effects arising from the electromagnetic field is that it involves a flux of energy measured by the Poynting vector, or vector-product of the electric and magnetic forces, together with a flux of momentum represented by the well-known Maxwellian stresses; thus the energy and momentum led into any material system is computed and the observable response of the system is indicated. Here the quantum theory makes a change. According to it the Poynting vector does not measure the flux of energy but the probability of a flux. Considering a surface where the energy is passing into or out of a material system the flux can only occur in complete quanta; and where the classical theory gives a flux of a fraction p of a quantum, the quantum theory gives a probability p of the flux of a whole quantum.

The reasons for this view are very strong. Firstly, it leaves the wave theory of propagation of light in vacuum entirely undisturbed; interference bands will appear where the undulatory theory predicts. At the same time the energy units are preserved from weakening by spreading, because it is not the energy which is spread by the waves but a state of the aether which measures the probability of a jump of energy. Secondly, it modifies the classical theory at a point where the classical theory was already obscure. One of the still outstanding problems of the relativity theory is why a particular tensor formed from $F_{\mu\nu}$ should represent energy, momentum and stress; because (so to speak) the tensor does not *look like* energy, momentum and stress and no investigation has been able to make the connection appear unartificial. According to the quantum view the tensor measures a probability and is not the actual energy-tensor of the field. Thirdly, it accounts for the absence of quantisation of free radiation implied in the postulates of Einstein's equation; and it agrees with the Correspondence Principle that the classical formulae represent the limit when large numbers of quanta are involved, since for large numbers the probabilities become equivalent to averages.

None the less, the progress thus made is quite rudimentary, and if this key opens one door it is only to reveal other firmly locked doors ahead.

Quantisation of the Hydrogen Atom.

42. Consider a nucleus of charge Ze attended by a single electron of mass m and charge $-e$ which describes a Keplerian ellipse around it. The mass of the nucleus is regarded as infinitely great compared with m.

The acceleration of the electron is Ze^2/mr^2 so that the motion is under a central acceleration μ/r^2, where

$$\mu = Ze^2/m \quad\text{............................}(42\cdot1).$$

The position of the electron may be described by the canonical variables of Delaunay's planetary theory, viz.

$$q_1 = l_0 - \varpi, \qquad q_2 = \varpi - \Omega, \qquad q_3 = \Omega \quad\Big\}$$
$$p_1 = m\,(\mu a)^{\frac{1}{2}}, \qquad p_2 = m\,(\mu a)^{\frac{1}{2}}\,(1-\epsilon^2)^{\frac{1}{2}}, \qquad p_3 = m\,(\mu a)^{\frac{1}{2}}\,(1-\epsilon^2)^{\frac{1}{2}}\cos i\,\Big\}$$
$$\text{......}(42\cdot2),$$

where l_0 is the mean longitude of the electron regarded as a planet, ϵ the eccentricity, a the semiaxis major, ϖ the longitude of perihelion, i the inclination, Ω the longitude of the node. These variables are so chosen that p_1, p_2, p_3 are the momenta associated with the coordinates q_1, q_2, q_3 by the Hamiltonian equations

$$\frac{dq_r}{ds} = \frac{\partial H}{\partial p_r}, \qquad \frac{dp_r}{ds} = -\frac{\partial H}{\partial q_r} \quad \ldots\ldots\ldots\ldots\ldots(42\cdot3),$$

the Hamiltonian function H being expressed as a function of these six variables and the time s.

The principle of quantisation is that for variables satisfying $(42\cdot3)$

$$\int p_r \, dq_r = n_r h \quad \ldots\ldots\ldots\ldots\ldots\ldots\ldots\ldots(42\cdot4),$$

where n_r is an integer (or zero), h Planck's constant, and the integral is taken over a complete period of the coordinate q_r.

With the variables $(42\cdot2)$ p_1, p_2, p_3 are constants, and q_1, q_2, q_3 are angular variables which accordingly have period 2π. Hence the conditions $(42\cdot4)$ become

$$\left.\begin{array}{l} 2\pi m \, (\mu a)^{\frac{1}{2}} = nh \\[4pt] 2\pi m \, (\mu a)^{\frac{1}{2}} (1 - \epsilon^2)^{\frac{1}{2}} = n'h \\[4pt] 2\pi m \, (\mu a)^{\frac{1}{2}} (1 - \epsilon^2)^{\frac{1}{2}} \cos i = n''h \end{array}\right\} \quad \ldots\ldots\ldots\ldots(42\cdot5),$$

where n, n', n'' are integers. In order that ϵ and i may be real we must have

$$n \geqslant n' \geqslant n''.$$

We shall call n the principal quantum number of the orbit, and n', n'' subsidiary quantum numbers*.

The negative energy of the system is (as in an astronomical orbit)

$$-\chi = \frac{m\mu}{2a} \quad \ldots\ldots\ldots\ldots\ldots\ldots(42\cdot61).$$

Or by $(42\cdot1)$ and $(42\cdot5)$

$$-\chi = K/n^2, \qquad K = 2\pi^2 m Z^2 e^4/h^2 \quad \ldots\ldots\ldots\ldots(42\cdot62).$$

Accordingly the energy is determined by the principal quantum number and is independent of n', n''.

The possible eccentricities and inclinations of the quantised orbits are given by

$$1 - \epsilon^2 = \frac{n'^2}{n^2}, \quad \cos i = \frac{n''}{n'} \quad \ldots\ldots\ldots\ldots(42\cdot7).$$

* n' is also called the *azimuthal* quantum number, $n - n'$ the *radial* quantum number and n the *total* quantum number. From the magnetic properties of the hydrogen atom it is known that a fourth quantum number must be involved which has no representation in the usual atomic model.

Since n'' can take any value from 0 to n' and n' can take any value from 1 to n there should be $\frac{1}{2}n(n+3)$ different orbits of principal quantum number n. We have in this book taken the number to be $n(n+1)$ following the chief authorities. (But see *footnote*, p. 70).

43. In the undisturbed system here considered the coordinates q_2 and q_3 never describe their periods. Does the corresponding quantisation nevertheless occur?

The question as it stands is meaningless, since no observable effects would proceed from the quantisation if it did occur. The Bohr model is not so literal a picture of the atom as to possess an intrinsic truth independent of the observable effects it embodies. The importance of the quantisation is that it determines the change of energy, and therefore the frequency of the emitted radiation, when passage from one state to another occurs; but in the present simple system the energy does not depend on either n' or n'', so that it is indifferent whether these quantisations occur or not.

If we consider the slightly disturbed Keplerian motion which results from taking account of change of mass with velocity ("relativity correction") or from the presence of other electrons in the system, the apse-line revolves; q_2 now describes its period 2π and the second quantisation should be effective. At the same time the calculated energy of the system receives a correction involving n' and the quantisation can thus betray itself to observation by a discrete series of values of the energy corresponding to the integers n'. Again an extraneous electric or magnetic field causes the node to revolve; q_3 now describes its period and introduces the third quantisation. At the same time the external field provides a plane of reference (previously lacking) for i, and there is a small correction to the energy involving $\cos i$ and therefore n''. The discrete values of the energy corresponding to the integers n'' betray the quantisation. The existence of quantisation is only doubtful when it could give no observable effects.

In a slightly modified form the question becomes significant. In actual atoms the quantisation is not perfectly sharp, that is to say, the energy may have values extending over a small range about the mean value, and the spectral lines emitted in transitions to other states have a small but finite width. There is no doubt that the sharpness of the quantisation is connected with the number of periods described by the corresponding coordinate; accordingly as q_2 and q_3 move slower and slower the subsidiary quantisations will fade into indefiniteness. In this sense we can say definitely that when q_2 and q_3 are stationary only the principal quantisation remains. We can picture the quantisation as a kind of resonance effect which operates the more strongly the greater the number of cycles described without interruption; or the revolutions of the coordinate correspond to the lines of a grating (in time dimension) which has higher resolving power in proportion to the number of waves that it superposes.

Orbits of Large Quantum Number.

44. Material at high temperature contains in addition to the electrons bound to the atoms a number of free electrons broken loose from the atoms and moving as independent molecules. Statistics of the bound electrons are naturally given in the form—number with orbits of such and such quantum specification. Statistics of free electrons are given in the form —number within given limits of position and velocity. Now there is an important continuity between the statistics of bound and free electrons which is hidden when they are classified on different principles. Our purpose in this section is to transform the statistics of the most loosely bound electrons so as to make them comparable with those of the free electrons.

We have seen that the numbers of systems in two states with energies χ_1, χ_2 are in the ratio

$$q_1 e^{-\chi_1/RT} : q_2 e^{-\chi_2/RT},$$

where the weights q_1, q_2 depend on the states but not on the temperature. Hence in any assemblage we may set the number of systems in a state with energy χ_n equal to

$$Bq_n e^{-\chi_n/RT} \dots\dots\dots\dots\dots\dots\dots\dots(44\cdot1),$$

where B is a constant depending on the extent of the assemblage.

We shall assume that the weight of every quantised orbit is the same. The general coherence of this assumption with the ideas of statistical mechanics will appear later. The weight of each quantised orbit is taken to be unity, thus fixing the unit of q which was previously left undefined.

Consider as in the last section the system consisting of a nucleus attended by a single electron. There are $n(n+1)$ different orbits with principal quantum number n, hence the number of systems with energy χ_n will be

$$Bn(n+1) e^{-\chi_n/RT} \dots\dots\dots\dots\dots\dots(44\cdot2),$$

where by $(42\cdot62)$ $\quad -\chi_n = K/n^2, \qquad K = 2\pi^2 me^4 Z^2/h^2 \dots\dots\dots\dots(44\cdot3).$

Electrons with very small negative energy correspond to large values of n. We shall consider n so large that the series of values of the energy fades into a practically continuous range. Then by $(44\cdot3)$

$$d\chi_n = \frac{2K}{n^3} dn,$$

so that the number of integral values of n in a range $d\chi_n$ approaches

$$n^3 d\chi_n/2K \dots\dots\dots\dots\dots\dots\dots\dots(44\cdot4).$$

Let $$\epsilon'^2 = 1 - \epsilon^2,$$
so that by (42·7) $$\epsilon' = n'/n \quad\dots\dots\dots\dots\dots\dots\dots(44\cdot5).$$

For every integral value of n' there are $n' + 1$ orbits (corresponding to the values of n'' from 0 to n'), or with sufficient accuracy n' orbits. Thus for each integral value of n there are $n'dn'$ orbits in the range dn'. But by (44·5)

$$n'dn' = n^2\epsilon'd\epsilon' \quad\dots\dots\dots\dots\dots\dots\dots(44\cdot6).$$

By (44·4) and (44·6) the number of orbits in a range $d\chi\,d\epsilon'$ is

$$\frac{n^3}{2K}\,d\chi_n \cdot n^2\epsilon'd\epsilon',$$

and the number of systems having electrons describing orbits in this range is by (44·1)

$$B\,\frac{n^5}{2K}\,e^{-\chi_n/RT}\,\epsilon'd\epsilon'd\chi_n \quad\dots\dots\dots\dots\dots(44\cdot7).$$

45. By the theory of elliptic motion the constant of areas is

$$r^2\frac{d\theta}{dt} = \{\mu a\,(1 - \epsilon^2)\}^{\frac{1}{2}} = (\mu a\epsilon'^2)^{\frac{1}{2}},$$

so that if w is the transverse velocity

$$w^2 = \left(r\frac{d\theta}{dt}\right)^2 = \frac{\mu a\epsilon'^2}{r^2}.$$

Let V be the total velocity and u the radial component (dr/dt). Then

$$u^2 = V^2 - w^2 = V^2 - \frac{\mu a\epsilon'^2}{r^2},$$

so that at a fixed distance r from the nucleus and for fixed energy χ_n

$$u\,du = -\frac{\mu a}{r^2}\,\epsilon'd\epsilon' \quad\dots\dots\dots\dots\dots\dots(45\cdot1).$$

Note that V is independent of ϵ' since the energy does not involve n'.

Now the time spent at each passage in a spherical shell r to $r + dr$ is $dt = dr/u$; and by Kepler's Law the time of a half-revolution is $\pi a^{\frac{3}{2}}/\mu^{\frac{1}{2}}$. Hence each electron spends in the shell a fraction of its time

$$\mu^{\frac{1}{2}}dr/\pi a^{\frac{3}{2}}u.$$

Multiplying the number of electrons (44·7) by the fraction of their time spent in the shell we obtain the average number in the shell at any moment. Using (45·1), this number is

$$-\frac{Bn^5}{2K}\,e^{-\chi_n/RT}\,d\chi_n \cdot \frac{r^2dr}{\pi\mu^{\frac{1}{2}}a^{\frac{5}{2}}}\cdot du \quad\dots\dots\dots\dots(45\cdot2).$$

We notice first that the number in a range du is proportional to du. *This shows that the distribution of velocities at r has spherical symmetry.* The total velocity V is the same for all electrons of energy χ_n. We may assume that there is circular symmetry about the radius*. Then for complete spherical symmetry the number of velocities in any zone of directions θ to $\theta + d\theta$ (measured from the radial direction) is proportional to the area of the zone $2\pi \sin \theta d\theta$, i.e. to $d(\cos \theta)$ and therefore to du, since $u = V \cos \theta$.

Now integrate with respect to u. As n' goes from 0 to n, ϵ' goes from 0 to 1; w goes from 0 as far as it can, viz. to V—the premature stoppage being due to the fact that orbits of too low eccentricity lie wholly outside r. Thus $\pm u$ goes from V to 0, and allowing for the double sign the integral of du is $2V$. Hence the integrated result is

$$\frac{Bn^5}{2K} e^{-\chi_n/RT} d\chi_n \cdot \frac{2Vr^2 dr}{\pi \mu^{\frac{1}{2}} a^{\frac{5}{2}}} = 4\pi\rho r^2 dr \dots\dots\dots\dots(45\cdot3),$$

where ρ is the density† of the electrons at r with energy in a range $d\chi_n$.

By (42·61) and (42·62)

$$n^5/a^{\frac{5}{2}} = (2K/m\mu)^{\frac{5}{2}},$$

and using the values of μ and K (42·1) and (42·62) the result (45·3) reduces to

$$\rho = B \frac{4\pi m^2}{h^3} e^{-\chi_n/RT} V d\chi_n.$$

If $-\psi(r)$ is the potential energy of an electron at r due to the field of the nucleus

$$\chi_n = -\psi(r) + \tfrac{1}{2}mV^2,$$

so that

$$d\chi_n = mV dV.$$

Hence

$$\rho = B \frac{m^3}{h^3} e^{-\chi_n/RT} 4\pi V^2 dV \dots\dots\dots\dots(45\cdot4).$$

Since the distribution of velocities has been shown to have spherical symmetry we can divide the shell $4\pi V^2 dV$ of "velocity-space" uniformly into its rectangular elements $du\,dv\,dw$ just as a spherical shell $4\pi r^2 dr$ is split into its elements $dx\,dy\,dz$; so that the density of electrons with velocities between u, v, w and $u + du, v + dv, w + dw$ is

$$B \frac{m^3}{h^3} e^{-\chi_n/RT} du\,dv\,dw,$$

and the number in a range of space and velocity $dx\,dy\,dz\,du\,dv\,dw$ is

$$B \frac{m^3}{h^3} e^{-\chi_n/RT} dx\,dy\,dz\,du\,dv\,dw \dots\dots\dots\dots(45\cdot5).$$

---

* This could be proved by considering the distribution of $\cos i$, but it appears to be sufficiently obvious.

† The use of the term density is convenient, but it must be understood that the shell r to $r + dr$ is for each electron referred to a different nucleus. These shells are here thought of as superposed. Or, if preferred, instead of considering a large number of different atoms we can deal with the time-average for one atom.

By comparison with (44·1) it follows that the weight to be attributed to this range is

$$\frac{m^3}{h^3}\,dx\,dy\,dz\,du\,dv\,dw\,\dots\dots\dots\dots\dots\dots(45\cdot6).$$

We have thus connected the weight of states specified by a space and velocity distribution of electrons with the weight of states specified by quantum orbits.

Writing in (45·5) $\chi_n = -\psi + \tfrac{1}{2}m\,(u^2 + v^2 + w^2)$, we see that these electrons with small negative energy obey Maxwell's Law just as free electrons with positive energy do.

Ionisation.

46. Suppose that in the foregoing assemblage there are free electrons which in regions of zero potential are distributed with density σ_0. By Maxwell's Law the number in a range $dx\,dy\,dz\,du\,dv\,dw$ is*

$$\left(\frac{m}{2\pi RT}\right)^{\frac{3}{2}} \sigma_0 e^{-m\,(u^2+v^2+w^2)/2RT}\,dx\,dy\,dz\,du\,dv\,dw,$$

and generally at places where the potential is not zero the number is

$$\left(\frac{m}{2\pi RT}\right)^{\frac{3}{2}} \sigma_0 e^{-\chi/RT}\,dx\,dy\,dz\,du\,dv\,dw\,\dots\dots\dots\dots(46\cdot1),$$

where χ is the kinetic and potential energy.

We have now two formulae (45·5) and (46·1) for calculating the distribution of electrons of *zero energy*, according as zero energy is considered to be the limit of small negative or small positive energy. It is reasonable to assume that the two formulae must agree. Hence we have a means of determining the constant B in terms of σ_0. When the constants in the two formulae agree, we have complete continuity at zero energy. The classical formula (46·1) does not at first fail when applied to bound electrons subjected to quantum restrictions; only when n becomes small is the deviation manifested. This is an example of the Correspondence Principle which asserts that as n increases the quantum laws approach the classical laws as a limit.

In formulating this continuity we have to proceed carefully because our discussion of bound electrons has been confined to the case in which there is only one electron attached to the nucleus. We have therefore to consider the continuity between the number of systems consisting of a nucleus and a single bound electron in a given volume-element and the number of systems consisting of an *ionised* nucleus and a free electron in a corresponding volume-element. Let N be the number of nuclei with not more than 1 bound electron and Nx the number (out of these) with

---

* The constant $(m/2\pi RT)^{\frac{3}{2}}$ is found by equating the integral for all values of u, v, w to $\sigma_0\,dx\,dy\,dz$.

no bound electron. Then the number with no bound electron but with a free electron in the range $dx\,dy\,dz\,du\,dv\,dw$ is by (46·1)

$$Nx.\left(\frac{m}{2\pi RT}\right)^{\frac{3}{2}}\sigma_0 e^{-\chi/RT}dx\,dy\,dz\,du\,dv\,dw,$$

and this must be continuous with the number given by (45·5) as having only a single bound electron in this range. Accordingly

$$B\,\frac{m^3}{h^3} = Nx\left(\frac{m}{2\pi RT}\right)^{\frac{3}{2}}\sigma_0 \quad \dots\dots\dots\dots\dots(46\cdot2).$$

The number of systems with just one bound electron $N(1-x)$ is obtained by summing (44·2) for all possible orbits of that electron. Thus

$$N(1-x) = B\{2e^{-\chi_1/RT} + 6e^{-\chi_2/RT} + \dots + r(r+1)e^{-\chi_r/RT} + \dots\}$$
$$\dots\dots(46\cdot3).$$

From (46·2) and (46·3)

$$(1-x)/x = \sigma_0\left(\frac{h^2}{2\pi mRT}\right)^{\frac{3}{2}}\{2e^{-\chi_1/RT} + 6e^{-\chi_2/RT} + \dots\} \quad \dots(46\cdot4),$$

which determines the ionisation x when the temperature T and free electron density σ_0 are given

47. Although we have considered only one peculiarly simple system the formula (46·2) derived from it is valid always. There may be no such system in the assemblage considered—no atom ionised down to the last electron or none sufficiently free from disturbance by free electrons or neighbouring atoms. But there is always a chance of such a system, and the chance however infinitesimal is sufficient to justify the formula. There can be only one equation determining B in terms of σ_0 however many different kinds of systems may be involved, so that all systems must give the same result as the simple system which we have been able to work out fully. This requires in particular that in any kind of atom the weight of a space-velocity range for bound electrons approaches the limit (45·6) when the negative energy approaches zero.

To make the argument specific, define a system of class A to be one in which there is a nucleus and a bound electron with coordinates x, y, z to $x+dx$, $y+dy$, $z+dz$ relative to the nucleus and velocity in a range $du\,dv\,dw$ corresponding to small negative energy, provided that there is no other nucleus or electron within a distance δ of the nucleus. Let a system of class B be one in which there is a nucleus and a free electron with coordinates similarly specified and with velocity in an equal range but corresponding to small positive energy, provided that there is no other nucleus or electron within a distance δ. The postulate is that the numbers of systems of classes A and B must be continuous. The factor representing the proportion of systems spoiled by the intrusion of other matter within the distance δ will be the same for both classes. Since δ may be taken as large as we please the calculation for undisturbed systems is valid.

For more complex systems (46·3) is modified, and we must write (46·4) in the more general form

$$(1 - x)/x = \sigma_0 \, (h^2/2\pi m RT)^{\frac{3}{2}} \, \{q_1 e^{-\chi_1/RT} + q_2 e^{-\chi_2/RT} + \ldots\} \quad \ldots(47\cdot1).$$

Here x refers to the removal of a particular electron, the energy of its removal from the normal and successive excited orbits being $-\chi_1$, $-\chi_2$, etc. Strictly speaking $q_1, q_2 \ldots$ are all unity since in the complex system no two orbits will have precisely the same energy; but in practice we often group together the orbits with the same principal quantum number, ignoring the slight differences of χ. Also we ought strictly to treat separately the systems in which electrons other than the one whose removal is being considered are excited, because their excitation will make some difference to the energies $\chi_1, \chi_2 \ldots$; but in practice this is scarcely worth considering. The excitation of the other electrons occurs whether the particular electron is present or not, that is to say, both $N(1 - x)$ and Nx include excited systems; the approximation does not omit the excited systems, though it treats them not quite rigorously by amalgamating their energy-changes with those of the normal systems.

When a number τ of electrons in symmetrical orbits require the same energy $-\chi$ for their removal it would be inconvenient to treat the removal as τ distinct ionisations. For example, let N be the number of atoms stripped of their M and higher electrons. Dividing these into $N(1 - x)$ atoms retaining a *marked* L electron and Nx ionised as to this electron, x is given by (47·1); but we are more concerned to divide them into $N(1 - y)$ retaining all the L electrons and Ny ionised as to an *unmarked* L electron.

Considering the $N(1 - y)$ un-ionised atoms the proportion of these with a highly excited L electron in given space-velocity range becomes multiplied by τ, since any one of the τ electrons of the group which happens to be in this range will count. To secure the former continuity with the systems consisting of ionised atoms and free electrons, we must also have τ times as many of these systems. Evidently if we write σ_0/τ instead of σ_0 in the former equations the balance will be secured. (Virtually we assign to each of the L electrons a partial pressure of the free electrons equal to $1/\tau$ of the whole electron pressure, so that its highly excited states grade continuously into its share of the free electron distribution.) Accordingly making this substitution in (47·1)

$$\frac{1 - y}{y} = \frac{\sigma_0}{\tau} \, (h^2/2\pi m RT)^{\frac{3}{2}} \, (q_1 e^{-\chi_1/RT} + \ldots) \quad \ldots\ldots\ldots(47\cdot2).$$

In the complex systems the calculation of $\chi_1, \chi_2 \ldots, q_1, q_2 \ldots$ is no longer straightforward, and theoretical estimates of these quantities are partly guess-work. But a certain amount of experimental knowledge is available for most elements. In particular the values of χ for the principal energy-levels in the complete atom are known from measurements of the frequency of the radiation emitted during transitions in accordance with (36·1). The extent to which these are modified in the incomplete ions must be estimated by us as best we can.

An apparent difficulty arises because the series on the right of (46·4) is divergent, the exponentials tending to unity for large values of n so that the series behaves like $\Sigma n \, (n + 1)$. But the later terms of the series are fictitious. The semiaxis of the orbit increases proportionately to n^2 so that in any practical problem the orbit for large values of n will extend into regions no longer under the predominant attraction of the nucleus. The series in (47·1) is therefore not really infinite but stops at an outermost orbit beyond which the electron would be regarded as belonging to another atom. The arbitrary convention employed in fixing this limit applies also to the left side of the equation, since we cannot say whether an atom is ionised or not unless we have a definite rule for assigning each distant electron of negative energy to its proper atom. The simple calculation breaks down in three ways: (1) the field of the nucleus is shielded by the electrons (free or bound) surrounding it, (2) the periodicity becomes imperfect so that the quantisation fades away, (3) it reckons any region of space many times over as part of the field of every nucleus in the assemblage*.

Examples of the use of (47·1) for calculating the degree of ionisation at given temperature and density are given in Chapter x.

Theory of Weights of States.

48. Let $q_1, q_2 \ldots, p_1, p_2 \ldots$ be Hamiltonian coordinates specifying the state of a system at time s and satisfying (42·3). For convenience we consider six variables as in § 42 but the investigation is the same for any number of degrees of freedom.

Consider the states comprised in a range q_1 to $q_1 + \delta q_1, \ldots, p_3$ to $p_3 + \delta p_3$. Such a range will be called a *cell* and the volume of the cell is defined to be

$$V = \delta q_1 \delta q_2 \delta q_3 \delta p_1 \delta p_2 \delta p_3,$$

or more generally for a cell of any shape

$$V = \iiiiii dq_1 \, dq_2 \, dq_3 \, dp_1 \, dp_2 \, dp_3 \quad \ldots\ldots\ldots\ldots(48\cdot1).$$

---

* It will be understood that the failure of (46·4) does not stand in contradiction to what we have already said as to the universal validity of (46·2). Equation (47·1) is universally valid provided that the ionisation energies $\chi_1, \chi_2 \ldots$ are calculated with reference to the actual circumstances of the atoms; they may be different from the values for isolated atoms.

When there is perfect quantisation we can divide the whole domain of the coordinates into *unit cells* such that each unit cell contains just one quantum orbit. This may be done by taking δq_1 to correspond to a complete cycle of q_1 and δp_1 to correspond to an increase of 1 in the associated quantum number (preferably chosen so that the integral number corresponds to the middle of the cell). Thus

$$\iint dp_1 dq_1 = \int (p_1 + \delta p_1)\, dq_1 - \int p_1 dq_1$$
$$= (n_1 + \tfrac{1}{2})\, h - (n_1 - \tfrac{1}{2})\, h, \text{ by } (42\cdot4)$$
$$= h.$$

Hence for a unit cell $\qquad\qquad V = h^3$ ....(48·2).

We have already made the hypothesis that each quantum orbit has the same (unit) weight. We shall now regard this as a particular case of the more general hypothesis that each cell of volume h^3 has equal (unit) weight; so that for large cells

$$q = V/h^3 \ \ ....(48\cdot3).$$

When there is no quantisation (as in non-periodic motion) the states and the weight are spread through the cell. When there is imperfect periodicity the weight concentrates towards the quantum orbits in it. For perfect periodicity it is wholly concentrated in the quantum orbits.

For an electron moving in an electric field the rectangular coordinates x, y, z and the associated momenta mu, mv, mw satisfy Hamilton's equations and may be taken as the variables $q_1 \ldots p_3$. Thus by (48·1)

$$V = m^3 \iiint\!\!\iiint dx\, dy\, dz\, du\, dv\, dw,$$

and hence $\qquad q = \dfrac{m^3}{h^3} \iiint\!\!\iiint dx\, dy\, dz\, du\, dv\, dw$ ....(48·4).

This is the same as (45·6) but it is not restricted to the particular type of system there considered. In consequence of our more general assumption (48·4) applies generally both to bound and to free electrons, except that where there is periodicity the cell must be large enough to average out the *ridginess* in the distribution of weight induced by the quantisation.

49. It is necessary to show that the volume of a cell is invariant, that is to say, that it does not depend on the particular choice of coordinates $q_1 \ldots p_3$, provided that they satisfy Hamilton's equations. If it were not invariant the weights based on it would be ambiguous, and so also would be the quantisation. For readers familiar with the tensor calculus the following proof is probably the simplest.

We write q_4, q_5, q_6 for p_1, p_2, p_3 so that Hamilton's equations (42·3) become

$$\frac{dq_1}{ds} = \frac{\partial H}{\partial q_4}, \qquad \frac{dq_4}{ds} = -\frac{\partial H}{\partial q_1}, \quad \ldots$$

or in tensor notation

$$\frac{\partial H}{\partial q_\mu} = a_{\mu\nu} \frac{dq_\nu}{ds} \quad \dots\dots\dots\dots\dots\dots(49 \cdot 1),$$

where
$$a_{\mu\nu} = \tfrac{1}{3}(\mu - \nu) \text{ if this is } \pm 1$$
$$a_{\mu\nu} = 0 \text{ otherwise} \qquad \dots\dots\dots\dots(49 \cdot 2).$$

Consider a general transformation of coordinates (not confined to Hamiltonian coordinates) and let $a_{\mu\nu}$ be a covariant tensor with the values $(49 \cdot 2)$ in our original system. Since H and s are invariants, $\partial H / \partial q_\mu$ and dq_ν / ds are covariant and contravariant vectors respectively. Thus $(49 \cdot 1)$ is a tensor equation and holds in all coordinate systems. Of these the possible Hamiltonian systems are given by the condition that $a_{\mu\nu}$ has transformed to its original values. If $|a_{\mu\nu}|$ denotes the determinant formed with the elements $a_{\mu\nu}$, we have*

$$\int \sqrt{|a_{\mu\nu}|}\, dV \text{ is invariant for all coordinate systems.}$$

And since $|a_{\mu\nu}|$ has the same value for all Hamiltonian systems

$$\int dV \text{ is invariant for all Hamiltonian coordinates,}$$

which proves the theorem.

It may be noted that in mechanics Hamiltonian coordinates are distinguished from general coordinates in much the same way as in geometry Galilean coordinates (unaccelerated rectangular coordinates and time) are distinguished from general coordinates, viz. that a fundamental tensor characterising the continuum takes certain simple numerical values.

The K and L levels.

50. When the nucleus is attended by more than one electron mutual perturbations occur according to laws which have not yet been formulated. The atomic model cannot be worked out in detail, but a certain amount of knowledge of the arrangement of the electrons has been ascertained with the aid of experimental data.

Considering normal atoms unexcited by high temperature, the first two electrons go into 1-quantum orbits and the next eight into 2-quantum orbits. These are called K and L electrons respectively. This structure is completed in Neon $(Z = 10)$ and remains an undisturbed foundation in all higher elements. The M electrons in 3-quantum orbits start with Sodium (11) and reach a complement of 8 in Argon (18), after which 4-quantum orbits begin. But unlike the K, L structure the M structure is modified later and extended to 18 electrons in Copper (29) and all higher elements. Similarly the N electrons in 4-quantum orbits stop temporarily at 8, afterwards extended to 18, and then to 32.

* Eddington, *Mathematical Theory of Relativity*, §§ 48, 49.

In a star the ionisation is so intense that few nuclei are able to retain more than 10 electrons. Our interest is therefore confined to the K and L structure. With regard to the L electrons it must be recalled that there are two kinds of 2-quantum orbits according as the subsidiary number n' is 2 or 1. We accordingly distinguish the 2_2 or circular orbits and the 2_1 or elliptic orbits. The full complement consists of 2 electrons in elliptic and 6 in circular orbits*. The K orbits are necessarily circular (1_1 orbits).

To remove, say, a K electron from an atom a certain amount of work W_K is needed, and W_K can be deduced from experiment. For if radiation of frequency ν is passing through the material the quantum $h\nu$ will have sufficient energy to remove the electron provided that $h\nu > W_K$. If the removal is effected the quantum of radiation is absorbed, any surplus energy being communicated to the freed electron as kinetic energy. But if $h\nu < W_K$ the removal cannot be effected and the radiation passes through unabsorbed—so far as this absorption-mechanism is concerned. The critical frequency $\nu_K = W_K/h$ is marked in the spectrum by a sharp absorption edge; so that by spectral measurement ν_K and W_K can be found. Except for the lightest elements ν_K and ν_L are in the X ray region. The vacancy left at the K level by such an ionisation may be filled by capture of a free electron with a corresponding emission of radiation. But in laboratory conditions free electrons are scarce, and usually before there is time for such a capture an electron falls in from an upper level and fills the vacancy. This will usually be succeeded by further falls from higher levels until the vacancy is at the uppermost level where it remains until filled by a capture. If the first fall is from the L level the difference of energy of the atom before and after the fall is $W_K - W_L$ and this must be radiated as a quantum of frequency $(W_K - W_L)/h$. The lines corresponding to the various possible falls constitute the (emission) X ray spectrum of the element. Measurements of these lines constitute additional material for determining the energy-constants W_K, W_L, etc.

The apparent dissymmetry between absorption and emission of X rays is a consequence of the artificial production of X rays at low temperature in terrestrial experiments. Inside the stars there is thermodynamical equilibrium; ionisations and captures, falls and ascents, occur with equal frequency. There is line absorption as well as line emission, and continuous

* [The rule given by Pauli is that every possible orbit must have a different quantum specification. In addition to the quantum numbers n, n' there are two others (imperfectly represented in the Bohr model) of which one has only two possible values (usually called $\frac{1}{2}$ and $-\frac{1}{2}$) and the other takes integral or zero values from $-(n'-1)$ to $+(n'-1)$. This gives $4n'-2$ combinations. Accordingly the number of different (n, n') orbits is now believed to be $4n'-2$ instead of the number $n'+1$ given by the Bohr model. Evidently the change should be carried through into the formulae for ionisation, but it has come too late to adopt in this book.]

emission with emission edges as well as continuous absorption with absorption edges.

The energy required to remove an L electron from an atom is slightly different according as it is taken from a circular or elliptic orbit. Consequently there will be two L levels. Observation shows that there are actually three L levels which are denoted by L_1, L_2, L_3—L_3 being the lowest, i.e. nearest to K. There has for some time been considerable doubt as to the proper classification of the L levels; but at the time of writing the difficulty seems to have been cleared up. It appears that L_3 corresponds to the elliptic orbits; and L_1, L_2 both belong to the circular 2_2 orbits, being discriminated from one another by a third quantum number. Formerly the classification was L_1 circular and L_2 elliptic, whilst L_3 was a redundant elliptic orbit of obscure significance.

A detail which may be of importance in astronomical applications should be noted. Electrons falling to the K level from the L_1 and L_2 levels produce a pair of emission lines, the line due to L_1 being the more intense. If we adhere to the old classification this means that an electron in a circular orbit is quicker to seize an opportunity of falling than an electron in an elliptic orbit. With the new classification we reach the same conclusion for a different reason. There is no emission line corresponding to L_3, and falls from the elliptic orbit seldom if ever occur. This is in accordance with the "selection principle" which governs optical spectra (§ 51) and molecular spectra (§ 244), viz. that in all transitions the second quantum number must change by ± 1, so that a fall from 2_1 to 1_1 orbits is excluded. Use is made of this result in § 166.

The following example will give an idea of the amount of perturbation exercised by the electrons in an atom on one another. Consider an iron nucleus attended by one K electron, the other electrons being absent. The ionisation energy is obtained by setting $n = 1$, $Z = 26$ in (42·62). The corresponding wave-length is found to be 1·35 Å. But the K absorption-limit for iron is 1·74 Å. The difference is due to our dealing in the first case with the iron nucleus alone and in the second case with the complete iron atom. Now for copper ($Z = 29$) the observed limit is 1·38 Å, i.e. practically the same as the theoretical limit for the iron nucleus; hence we can regard the satellite electrons in copper as shielding the positive charge of the nucleus to the extent of approximately 3 units so far as the motion of a K electron is concerned. Again, consider a platinum nucleus ($Z = 78$) with two K electrons and one L electron. The K electrons being comparatively close to the nucleus may be treated as effectively reducing its charge by 2 units and the ionisation energy of the L electron is then found approximately by setting $n = 2$, $Z = 76$ in (42·62). The corresponding wave-length is 0·63 Å; the observed value for the complete platinum atom is 1·07 Å, so that the shielding is considerable.

In one sense the ionisation energy W is not particularly associated with the electron which is being removed; it is the difference of energy of the whole atom before and after the removal. We might suppose that a considerable part of this difference would be due to the other electrons requantising their orbits in the modified field of force. There is, however, an important principle in the quantum theory—the *adiabatic* principle—which shows that this requantisation is brought about automatically during the removal of the electron and is not an after-adjustment. If, for example, a field of uniform magnetic force is established slowly, the classical electromagnetic forces acting during its establishment will transform the orbits of the electrons into the new orbits required by the rules of quantisation for the new condition; the action of the magnetic field is not divided into two effects, a classical perturbation + a requantisation. Similarly the effect of removal of an electron is not to be divided into a progressive disturbance + a final adjustment.

Finally, it must be remembered that the Bohr atom is only a model and is not a literal description of the atom, although we accept it as such for most purposes. No one has insisted on this limitation more strongly than Prof. Bohr himself. Some progress has been made in the attempt to free the theory from its geometrical bondage but as yet we cannot afford to dispense with the model.

Optical Spectra.

51. The inert gases helium, neon, argon, etc. mark the completion (temporary or permanent) of the $K, L, M, \ldots$ groups of electrons. The elements immediately succeeding the inert gases have one rather loose electron starting the new group; this is called a *valency electron* and is responsible for their chemical behaviour as monovalent elements. They are succeeded by divalent elements with two loose electrons, and so on.

Usually the lines constituting the optical spectrum of an element are absorbed and emitted by transitions of a valency electron from one quantised orbit to another. The complexity of the spectrum increases with the number of valency electrons, and the account here given refers especially to elements or ions with one or two valency electrons.

As in § 42 we describe the orbit of an electron by two quantum numbers n and n' with $n' \leqslant n$. The third number n'' is neglected for the present. The orbit in the normal atom is assigned the numbers $n, n' = (1, 1), (2, 1), (3, 1) \ldots$ according as the valency electron is starting the $K, L, M, \ldots$ group. The possible orbits fall into a number of series. Taking, for example, Sodium in which the normal orbit of the valency electron is a $(3, 1)$ orbit, the series with their conventional nomenclature are—

S series	(3, 1),	(4, 1),	(5, 1),	(6, 1),	(7, 1) ...
P series	(3, 2),	(4, 2),	(5, 2),	(6, 2),	(7, 2) ...
D series	(3, 3),	(4, 3),	(5, 3),	(6, 3),	(7, 3) ...
F series		(4, 4),	(5, 4),	(6, 4),	(7, 4) ...
—			(5, 5),	(6, 5),	(7, 5) ...

The possible transitions between these orbits are governed by the *selection principle*, to which reference has already been made, viz. that n' must change by $+1$ or -1. It follows that there can be no transitions between orbits in the same series; the electron must pass to an orbit in the line next above or below.

In practical investigations we study primarily emission spectra. When through electrical bombardment the electron finds itself in one of the excited orbits enumerated above, it will usually prefer to fall to the lowest possible energy level consistent with the selection principle. Evidently (3, 1) is the lowest level reachable from the P series; (3, 2) is reachable from the S and D series, and (3, 3) from the F series. Although other lines (*combination* lines) due to a fall to an energy level which is not the lowest permissible may occur, the strongest lines have as their terminal orbits (3, 1), (3, 2), (3, 3), etc.

Atoms in their normal unexcited state can absorb only the P series (principal series) since the only permissible transition from (3, 1) is into an orbit in the line below.

The frequency of the radiation absorbed or emitted on account of a transition is given by the fundamental quantum relation (36·1). But except for a nucleus attended by only one electron (H and He$_+$) the energies of the orbits cannot yet be calculated theoretically. The manner in which the classical perturbations of the electrons on one another are modified by quantisation has not yet been made out. We must still resort to the clumsy expedient of observing the spectra.

When the quantum number is very large the excited electron is throughout most of its orbit remote from the rest of the atom, which then behaves approximately as a point charge of strength $+e$ for a neutral atom, $+2e$ for a singly ionised atom, $+3e$ for a doubly ionised atom, etc. The energy then converges towards the values given by (42·62) with $Z = 1, 2, 3, \ldots$, or to χ_n, $4\chi_n$, $9\chi_n$, $\ldots$, where χ_n is the energy of the nth orbit in the hydrogen atom. When a few lines of a series have been observed it is generally easy to see whether the difference of frequency of successive lines is converging towards once, 4 times, or 9 times the corresponding frequency difference in the hydrogen series, and the series can be assigned to the appropriate ion.

The common nomenclature* of the lines of the spectrum is based on

* I follow the nomenclature in A. Fowler's *Report on Series in Line Spectra*, p. 87.

the empirical series relations, and is not directly connected with the quantum interpretation in terms of n and n'. The letters S, P, D, F are used for $n' = 1, 2, 3, 4$, and the orbits are thus denoted by mS, mP, mD, mF, where m is an integer. The lowest orbits are denoted by $1S$, $1P$, $2D$ respectively, so that the four chief series are—

Sharp Series	...	...	...	$mS \rightarrow 1P$.
Principal Series	...	...	...	$mP \rightarrow 1S$.
Diffuse Series	...	...	...	$mD \rightarrow 1P$.
Fundamental (or Bergmann) Series		$mF \rightarrow 2D$.

An exception however arises in the following way. Consider, for example, ionised calcium Ca_+; the normal orbit $1S$ has the quantum specification $(4, 1)$; and as usual the $(4, 2)$ orbit is denoted by $1P$, and the $(4, 3)$ orbit by $2D$. It must be understood that in these complex systems the principal quantum number is only a vague indicator of the energy of the system, and there is no close correspondence of the energies in $(4, 3)$ and $(4, 1)$ orbits. In the elements immediately following calcium an extension of the M group of electrons (3-quantum orbits) begins; and the coming event casts a shadow before in so much that a $(3, 3)$ orbit although still of energy greater than a $(4, 1)$ orbit has less energy than a $(4, 3)$ orbit*. Hence the orbit of lowest energy in the D series is a $(3, 3)$ orbit denoted by $1D$; the fundamental series is accordingly $mF \rightarrow 1D$.

In the above case the $1D$ orbit is *metastable*, that is to say, the electron cannot (ordinarily) get out of it without first *absorbing* a quantum. By the selection principle it can only go from $1D$ to an orbit in the P or F series, and the lowest orbits in these series, $(4, 2)$ and $(4, 4)$, have greater energy.

A third quantum number n'' (known as the inner quantum number) also plays an important part in optical spectra. The energy depends on it to only a slight extent, so that two orbits differing only in n'' give a pair of lines close together—a doublet. The quantum theory of doublets is, we believe, undergoing a fundamental revision at the time of writing, and we shall not here pursue the subject of doublet and multiplet structure.

Scattering of X Rays by Electrons.

52. It is not possible for a solitary electron to absorb a quantum of radiation and add the energy to its own kinetic energy. This is made clear by the theory of relativity. We cannot say whether the kinetic energy of a particle has increased or decreased until we have decided on our axes of reference; but we can say whether a quantum of radiation has disappeared independently of frames of reference. Hence there can be no association

---

* An element often builds a new group of electrons not because there is "no room" in the lower group but because by so doing it obtains a configuration of less energy. Thus normal calcium contains $(4, 1)$ orbits although there are still ten 3-quantum orbits available; the valency electrons can pass into these by excitation.

between the disappearance of a quantum of radiation and a change of energy of an electron arbitrarily called an increase or decrease according to the standpoint of the observer. The absorption of a quantum of radiation signifies that the waves of some frequency ν have less energy by the amount $h\nu$ than they had previously. If we change to axes moving with a different velocity the frequency will change in accordance with Doppler's principle and the measurement of the radiant energy will be affected by the change of time reckoning and space reckoning; we shall now report that the waves of frequency ν' have less energy by an amount $h\nu'$. But it is still a disappearance of radiant energy, and there is no question of turning absorption into emission by a change of axes. On the other hand, the question whether the speed of the electron has increased or diminished depends entirely on the motion of the frame of reference adopted.

An electron can only be concerned in absorption or emission when it is in the field of a nucleus or another electron—unless indeed it is capable of altering its internal energy. Mutual energy or internal energy can be increased by absorption of a quantum, and we can say definitely that the change is an increase, not a decrease, independently of frames of reference. Or, to put the argument in another form, the field of the nucleus provides the frame of reference with respect to which the kinetic energy of the electron may be reckoned unambiguously.

Interaction between solitary electrons and radiation occurs by a slightly more complex process called scattering. A quantum of radiation of frequency ν_1 is replaced by a quantum of frequency ν_2, and the difference $h(\nu_1 - \nu_2)$ is added to the kinetic energy of the electron so that the law of conservation of energy is satisfied. Since ν_1 and ν_2 are altered by the Doppler effect we can have $\nu_1 > \nu_2$ in some frames of reference and $\nu_1 < \nu_2$ in others; thus the increase of kinetic energy in some frames of reference and the decrease in others are provided for. In order to secure this consistency it is necessary that the second quantum should be travelling in a direction different from the first, otherwise the Doppler effect would always alter ν_1 and ν_2 in the same ratio. This change of direction of the radiation is more conspicuous than the minute changes of energy and frequency, and hence the process is called "scattering."

Consider an electron initially at rest in the frame of reference considered. Let a quantum of energy E_1 travelling in the direction of the x-axis be incident on the electron; and let the scattered quantum of energy E_2 travel in a direction inclined at an angle θ to the x-axis. Let u, v be component velocities of the electron after scattering, along and perpendicular to the x-axis. Let

$$\beta = (1 - (u^2 + v^2)/c^2)^{-\frac{1}{2}} \quad \ldots\ldots\ldots\ldots\ldots\ldots (52\cdot1).$$

The mass of the electron changes with the change of velocity from m

to βm, and its whole energy accordingly changes from mc^2 to βmc^2. Equating this to the change of energy of the radiation

$$E_1 - E_2 = (\beta - 1)\, mc^2.$$

Conservation of momentum gives

$$\frac{E_1}{c} - \frac{E_2}{c} \cos \theta = \beta m \,.\, u,$$

$$- \frac{E_2}{c} \sin \theta = \beta m \,.\, v.$$

Hence

$$(E_1 - E_2 + mc^2)^2 - (E_1 - E_2 \cos \theta)^2 - E_2{}^2 \sin^2 \theta = (\beta mc)^2 (c^2 - u^2 - v^2) = m^2 c^4$$

which reduces to

$$- 2E_1 E_2 (1 - \cos \theta) + 2mc^2 (E_1 - E_2) = 0 \quad \ldots\ldots\ldots(52\cdot2).$$

Now $$E/c = h\nu/c = h/\lambda,$$

so that, if λ_1, λ_2 are the wave-lengths of the incident and scattered quanta, $(52\cdot2)$ gives

$$\lambda_2 - \lambda_1 = \frac{h}{mc}\, (1 - \cos \theta) \quad \ldots\ldots\ldots\ldots(52\cdot31),$$

or inserting numerical values

$$\lambda_2 - \lambda_1 = 0\cdot0242\ \text{Å} \times (1 - \cos \theta) \quad \ldots\ldots\ldots(52\cdot32).$$

The constant can be interpreted as the wave-length of a quantum containing as much energy as goes to constitute an electron.

Radiation scattered by electrons at rest is thus of longer wave-length by an amount dependent on the angle of scattering but not on the incident wave-length. This reddening is known as the Compton Effect. It is not possible to obtain any considerable quantity of free electrons to experiment on in the laboratory; but it appears that when X rays of high frequency are used the more weakly bound electrons of ordinary matter can be regarded as sufficiently free to scatter according to this formula. It has thus been possible to prove it experimentally.

The corresponding formula for scattering by a moving electron can be obtained by applying the Lorentz transformation. The wave-length is not always increased. If the electrons are moving with speeds such as to be in thermodynamical equilibrium with the radiation there must be just as much shortening of wave-lengths as lengthening. A proof of Planck's Law can be obtained by following up this condition in detail*.

53. To find the amount of scattering by free electrons, we consider first the classical formulae.

* Pauli, *Zeits. für Physik*, **18**, p. 272.

Denote the electric force in the electromagnetic oscillations which constitute the radiation by X. Acting on an electron of charge $-e$ and mass m, it will produce an acceleration

$$\Gamma = -eX/m.$$

Now according to classical electromagnetic theory an accelerated electron should radiate energy at the rate

$$\tfrac{2}{3}e^2\Gamma^2/c^3 = \tfrac{2}{3}e^4X^2/m^2c^3 \quad \dots\dots\dots\dots\dots(53{\cdot}1).$$

This radiation is not in the direction of the incident beam and is scattered radiation. By the conservation of energy it must be supplied at the expense of the incident beam.

If we have a screen containing N electrons per sq. cm. the radiation scattered per second will be

$$\frac{2}{3}\frac{Ne^4}{m^2c^3}\,\overline{X^2} \quad \dots\dots\dots\dots\dots\dots(53{\cdot}2),$$

where the mean value of X^2 is to be taken. This assumes that the conditions are such that the electrons scatter independently, and that there is no systematic phase relation of the wavelets from the separate electrons. The energy of the incident radiation is $\overline{X^2}/4\pi$ per cu. cm. (half electric and half magnetic); hence the amount incident on the N electrons in 1 second is

$$c\overline{X^2}/4\pi \quad \dots\dots\dots\dots\dots\dots(53{\cdot}3).$$

Dividing (53·2) by (53·3), the fraction of the incident radiation scattered by the screen is

$$\frac{8\pi}{3}\frac{Ne^4}{m^2c^4} = \frac{8\pi}{3}Nb^2 \quad \dots\dots\dots\dots\dots(53{\cdot}4),$$

where $b = e^2/mc^2 = 2{\cdot}81 \,.\, 10^{-13}$ cm.*

The usual definition of a scattering coefficient is the proportion scattered by a screen containing 1 gm. per sq. cm.; but since we are not likely to meet with a screen composed wholly of free electrons we prefer to modify the definition in this case. Instead of a gram of electrons we take the electrons contained in 1 gm. of matter, assuming (as is roughly true for all elements except hydrogen) that there is one electron for every two units of atomic weight, and therefore $3{\cdot}01 \,.\, 10^{23}$ electrons per gm. The scattering coefficient is then by (53·4)

$$s = 3{\cdot}01 \,.\, 10^{23} \times \frac{8\pi}{3}b^2 = 0{\cdot}200 \quad \dots\dots\dots\dots(53{\cdot}5).$$

As with the Compton effect this scattering coefficient has been verified experimentally by using hard X rays which act on the bound electrons of the lighter elements practically as if they were free. When the wavelength is comparable with the diameter of the atom the scattering is much.

* The radius of an electron is supposed to be $\tfrac{2}{3}b$ so that (53·4) signifies that each electron forms an obstruction equivalent to 6 times its own cross-section.

increased; because then the Z electrons of the atom give rise to scattered waves more or less in the same phase; thus the amplitude of the resultant is proportional to Z and the intensity is proportional to Z^2.

We do not suppose that free electrons scatter continuously in the manner here investigated. Actually some electrons scatter whole quanta and others are idle. But by the correspondence principle (53·1) is the limit to which the true formulae must tend when each electron is scattering many quanta; and it is customary to entertain the optimistic view that such formulae will apply without grave inaccuracy a long way short of the limit.

For very short wave-lengths (e.g. γ rays) the scattering coefficient is less than 0·2. This is associated with the fact that the electron acquires a velocity comparable with the velocity of light when it scatters a quantum of such radiation; its inertia increases, and other complications of the problem ensue.

CHAPTER IV

POLYTROPIC GAS SPHERES

54. We shall consider the equilibrium of an isolated mass of gas held together by its own gravitational attraction. In the absence of rotation or other disturbing causes the mass will settle down into a distribution with spherical symmetry. In view of the intended application of the results, such a gas sphere will be referred to as a "star."

At any point in a fluid in equilibrium there is a hydrostatic pressure P, the same in all directions. If any closed surface is drawn in the fluid the reaction of the fluid outside the surface on the fluid within consists of a force P per unit area along the inward normal; and for equilibrium these surface forces must balance the body forces such as gravitation acting on the interior.

Let ρ be the density at any point and g the acceleration of gravity. Since there is spherical symmetry P, ρ and g will depend only on the distance r from the centre.

The gravitational force at r is due entirely to the mass M_r interior to r, since the symmetrical shell outside r exerts no resultant attraction in its interior. Hence

$$g = GM_r/r^2 \quad\text{................................(54·1)},$$

where G is the constant of gravitation $6\cdot66 \cdot 10^{-8}$ in C.G.S. units. Also if ϕ is the gravitational potential, we have by definition

$$g = -\,d\phi/dr \quad\text{...........................(54·2)}.$$

The first condition to be satisfied is the well-known hydrostatic equation

$$dP = -\,g\rho\,dr \quad\text{...........................(54·3)},$$

expressing the increase of pressure as we descend in a column of fluid.

From (54·2) and (54·3)

$$dP = \rho\,d\phi \quad\text{...............................(54·4)}.$$

A second condition is given by Poisson's equation in the theory of attractions

$$\nabla^2\phi = -\,4\pi G\rho \quad\text{...........................(54·5)},$$

which for spherical symmetry takes the form

$$\frac{d^2\phi}{dr^2} + \frac{2}{r}\frac{d\phi}{dr} = -\,4\pi G\rho \quad\text{....................(54·6)}.$$

55. We have now two relations (54·4) and (54·6) between the three unknown functions of r, namely, P, ρ, ϕ. For further progress a third relation is necessary. The search for this will lead us far into the study of the thermodynamics of the star. In this Chapter we content ourselves with laying down an arbitrary connection between P and ρ and tracing the consequences. In general, whether the gas is perfect or imperfect, any value of the pressure can be made to correspond to given density by assigning an appropriate temperature; our procedure thus amounts to imposing a particular temperature distribution on the star. This will only correspond to possible actual conditions if the temperature distribution is such that it can maintain itself automatically.

The third relation is taken to be of the form

$$P = \kappa\rho^\gamma \quad\dotfill(55\cdot1),$$

where κ and γ are disposable constants. By taking different values of γ a variety of temperature distributions are brought under survey, and among these the actual distribution or one closely approximating to it will be included.

When the equation $(55\cdot1)$ is obeyed the distribution is called *polytropic*.

By differentiation, we have

$$dP = \gamma\kappa\rho^{\gamma-1}\,d\rho.$$

Hence by $(54\cdot4)$

$$\gamma\kappa\rho^{\gamma-2}\,d\rho = d\phi,$$

and on integration

$$\frac{\gamma}{\gamma - 1}\,\kappa\rho^{\gamma-1} = \phi + \text{const.} \quad\dotfill(55\cdot2).$$

The zero from which the gravitation potential ϕ is measured, is arbitrary. The usual convention is to make ϕ vanish at an infinite distance from all matter. But in this subject it is more convenient to take the zero of ϕ at the boundary of the star; the additive constant in $(55\cdot2)$ is then zero. Write

$$\gamma = 1 + 1/n \quad\dotfill(55\cdot3).$$

Then by $(55\cdot2)$

$$\rho = \left\{\frac{\phi}{(n + 1)\,\kappa}\right\}^n \quad\dotfill(55\cdot41),$$

and

$$P = \frac{\rho\phi}{n + 1} \quad\dotfill(55\cdot42).$$

Equation $(54\cdot6)$ accordingly becomes

$$\frac{d^2\phi}{dr^2} + \frac{2}{r}\frac{d\phi}{dr} + \alpha^2\phi^n = 0 \quad\dotfill(55\cdot5),$$

where

$$\alpha^2 = \frac{4\pi G}{\{(n + 1)\,\kappa\}^n} \quad\dotfill(55\cdot6).$$

The procedure will consist in solving this differential equation so as to determine ϕ as a function of r. Then ρ and P are found by $(55\cdot41)$ and $(55\cdot42)$. In order to standardise the solution we introduce two new variables

u and z proportional respectively to ϕ and r. Let ϕ_0 be the value of ϕ at the centre, and let

$$\phi = \phi_0 u, \qquad r = z/\alpha\phi_0^{\frac{1}{2}(n-1)} \quad\ldots\ldots\ldots\ldots\ldots(55\cdot7).$$

On substituting in (55·5) we obtain

$$\frac{d^2u}{dz^2} + \frac{2}{z}\frac{du}{dz} + u^n = 0 \quad\ldots\ldots\ldots\ldots\ldots\ldots(55\cdot8),$$

with the central conditions

$$u = 1, \qquad du/dz = 0, \text{ when } z = 0.$$

The change of variables from ϕ, r to u, z is merely a change of units introduced in order to bring the differential equation and its limiting conditions to a standard form. The condition $du/dz = 0$ at the centre follows from the vanishing there of $g = -\,d\phi/dr$.

56. The equation (55·8) can be solved without quadratures when $n = 0$, 1 or 5 (§ 61). For other values of n we obtain a start by assuming that for small values of z, u can be expanded in an infinite series which will run

$$u = 1 - \tfrac{1}{6}z^2 + a_3 z^3 + a_4 z^4 + \ldots$$

determining the coefficients so as to satisfy (55·8). This will not carry the solution very far, since it will presently diverge. But beginning with the values of u and du/dz at a point conveniently reached by the series we can now carry the solution step by step outwards through the star by quadratures. When u becomes zero the density vanishes, so that the boundary of the star is indicated.

Extensive tables of the solution for a number of values of n have been calculated by R. Emden*. We select here three of the tables which will ultimately concern us most. The values of z, u, du/dz are the direct result of quadratures; the remaining columns are calculated from these and are required for various applications.

The successive columns give the following physical quantities, expressed in each case in terms of a unit which will depend on the star considered—

1. Distance from centre.
2. Gravitation potential. Temperature (for a perfect gas of constant molecular weight).
3. Density.
4. Pressure.
5. Acceleration of gravity.
6. Reciprocal of mean density interior to the point considered.
7. Mass interior to the point considered.

* *Gaskugeln* (Teubner, 1907), Chapter v.

Equations (55·41) and (55·42) show that for different points in the same star $\rho \propto \phi^n$ and $P \propto \rho\phi \propto \phi^{n+1}$. Hence

$$\phi/\phi_0 = u, \qquad \rho/\rho_0 = u^n, \qquad P/P_0 = u^{n+1} \quad \ldots\ldots\ldots(56\cdot1).$$

Thus columns 2, 3, 4 of the tables give the potential, density and pressure in terms of the central potential, density and pressure*.

Polytropic Solutions.

Table 4.

$(n = 2, \quad \gamma = 1\cdot5.)$

z	u	u^n	u^{n+1}	$-du/dz$	$-z\,dz/3du$	$-z^2 du/dz$
0·00	1·00000	1·00000	1·00000	·00000	1·0000	·0000
0·25	·98969	·97950	·96940	·08247	1·0105	·0052
0·50	·95937	·92040	·88302	·15865	1·0750	·0388
0·75	·91128	·83042	·75675	·22386	1·1168	·1259
1·00	·84864	·72018	·61117	·27453	1·2142	·2745
1·25	·77533	·60114	·46609	·30937	1·3468	·4834
1·50	·69531	·48346	·33615	·32825	1·5232	·7386
1·75	·61238	·37501	·22965	·33307	1·7514	1·0200
2·00	·52974	·28062	·14866	·32640	2·0425	1·3056
2·50	·37463	·14035	·05258	·29023	2·8713	1·8140
3·00	·24166	·05840	·01411	·24067	4·1550	2·1660
3·50	·13379	·01790	·002395	·19169	6·0863	2·3482
4·00	·04866	·002368	·000115	·15040	8·8653	2·4064
4·25	·01326	·000176	·000002	·13346	10·615	2·4106
4·3518	·00000	·000000	·000000	·12729	11·396	2·4107

Table 5.

$(n = 2\cdot5, \quad \gamma = 1\cdot4.)$

z	u	u^n	u^{n+1}	$-du/dz$	$-z\,dz/3du$	$-z^2 du/dz$
0·00	1·00000	1·00000	1·00000	·00000	1·0000	·0000
0·25	·98971	·97450	·96447	·08226	1·0130	·0051
0·50	·95961	·90202	·86560	·15676	1·0632	·0392
0·75	·91242	·79520	·72555	·21798	1·1469	·1226
1·00	·85196	·66997	·57079	·26282	1·2683	·2628
1·25	·78246	·54156	·42375	·29036	1·4350	·4537
1·50	·70809	·42192	·29876	·30213	1·6549	·6798
1·75	·63246	·31811	·20119	·29532	1·9753	·9044
2·00	·55961	·23428	·13111	·28614	2·3298	1·1446
2·50	·42473	·11756	·04993	·25080	3·3227	1·5675
3·00	·31000	·05351	·01659	·20793	4·8093	1·8714
3·50	·21752	·02207	·004800	·16783	6·9517	2·0560
4·00	·14300	·007733	·001106	·13445	9·9170	2·1512
4·50	·08263	·001963	·000162	·10813	10·539	2·1896
5·00	·03384	·000211	·000007	·08796	18·948	2·1990
5·4172	·00000	·000000	·000000	·07500	24·076	2·2010

* In this Chapter we denote central values by the suffix 0; elsewhere in the book the suffix c is generally used.

Table 6.

$$(n = 3, \quad \gamma = 1\cdot3333.)$$

z	u	u^n	u^{n+1}	$-du/dz$	$-z\,dz/3du$	$-z^2\,du/dz$
0·00	1·00000	1·00000	1·00000	·00000	1·0000	·0000
0·25	·98975	·96960	·95966	·08204	1·0158	·0051
0·50	·95987	·88436	·84886	·15495	1·0756	·0387
0·75	·91355	·76242	·69650	·21270	1·1754	·1196
1·00	·85505	·62513	·53451	·25219	1·3218	·2522
1·25	·78897	·49111	·38747	·27370	1·5224	·4276
1·50	·71948	·37244	·26797	·27993	1·7862	·6298
1·75	·64996	·27458	·17847	·27460	2·1243	·8410
2·00	·58282	·19796	·11538	·26149	2·5495	1·0450
2·50	·46109	·09803	·04520	·22396	3·7210	1·3994
3·00	·35921	·04635	·01665	·18393	5·4370	1·6553
3·50	·27629	·02109	·005828	·14859	7·8697	1·8203
4·00	·20942	·009185	·001923	·11998	11·113	1·9197
4·50	·15529	·003746	·000582	·09748	15·387	1·9740
5·00	·11110	·001371	·000152	·08003	20·826	2·0007
6·00	·04411	·000086	·000004	·05599	35·720	2·0156
6·80	·00471	·000001	·000000	·04360	51·987	2·0161
6·9011	·00000	·000000	·000000	·04231	54·360	2·0150

57. Usually our problem will take the form of finding the internal distribution of density and pressure in a star of assigned mass and radius (or mean density). Thus the known data will be the mass M and radius R (or mean density ρ_m) together with the parameter n (or γ) defining the assumed law of dependence of pressure on density. We have therefore to find expressions in terms of M and R.

Since the boundary of the star is indicated by $u = 0$, we have

$$R = (r)_{u=0}, \qquad GM = (-r^2 d\phi/dr)_{u=0} \quad\ldots\ldots\ldots(57\cdot11).$$

Let
$$R' = (z)_{u=0}, \qquad M' = (-z^2 du/dz)_{u=0} \quad\ldots\ldots\ldots(57\cdot12).$$

The values of R' and M' will be found in the last line of each table. Then by (55·7)

$$\frac{R}{R'} = \frac{1}{\alpha\phi_0^{\frac{1}{2}(n-1)}}, \qquad \frac{GM}{M'} = \frac{1}{\alpha\phi_0^{\frac{1}{2}(n-3)}} \quad\ldots\ldots\ldots\ldots(57\cdot2),$$

whence
$$\left.\begin{aligned} &\frac{GM}{M'}\cdot\frac{R'}{R} = \phi_0 \\[4pt] &\left(\frac{GM}{M'}\right)^{n-1}\left(\frac{R'}{R}\right)^{n-3} = \frac{1}{\alpha^2} = \frac{\{(n+1)\,\kappa\}^n}{4\pi G} \end{aligned}\right\} \quad\ldots\ldots\ldots\ldots(57\cdot3).$$

Thus ϕ_0 and κ can be found from the given data, and the values of ρ_0 and P_0 are obtained from (55·41) and (55·42).

A more convenient way of obtaining ρ_0 is to express it in terms of the mean density ρ_m. We have

$$\rho_m = \frac{M}{\frac{4}{3}\pi R^3} = \frac{1}{G}\left(-\frac{1}{\frac{4}{3}\pi r^3}\cdot r^2\frac{d\phi}{dr}\right)_{u=0}.$$

But by (55·7)

$$\frac{1}{r}\frac{d\phi}{dr} = a^2\phi_0{}^n\cdot\frac{1}{z}\frac{du}{dz}.$$

Hence

$$\rho_m = \frac{3a^2\phi_0{}^n}{4\pi G}\left(-\frac{1}{z}\frac{du}{dz}\right)_{u=0} \quad\quad\quad\quad\quad\quad\text{......................(57·4)}.$$

But by (55·41) and (55·6)

$$a^2\phi_0{}^n = 4\pi G\rho_0 \quad\quad\quad\quad\quad\quad\text{..........................(57·5)},$$

a relation which is also evident by comparing (54·6) and (55·5). Hence

$$\frac{\rho_m}{\rho_0} = \left(-\frac{3}{z}\frac{du}{dz}\right)_{u=0} \quad\quad\quad\quad\text{........................(57·6)}.$$

The ratio ρ_0/ρ_m will be found at the foot of the sixth column in the tables. Other entries in the same column give the ratio of the central density to the mean density interior to the point considered.

The last column of the tables gives numbers proportional to the mass M_r within a sphere of radius r. The unit is found at once since the concluding entry (M') corresponds to the whole mass of the star. Similarly the first column gives the distance from the centre in terms of a unit which is ascertained from the condition that the concluding entry R' corresponds to the radius of the star.

58. We shall have to consider particularly stars composed of perfect gas. The temperature is then determined from P and ρ by the gas equation

$$P = \frac{\Re}{\mu}\rho T \quad\quad\quad\quad\text{..............................(58·1)},$$

where $\Re$ is the universal gas constant $8 \cdot 26 \cdot 10^7$, and μ is the molecular weight in terms of the hydrogen atom[*].

But before using this equation we must notice that in it P represents the gas pressure only, whereas in our analysis P has been used to denote the whole pressure of every description acting across a surface drawn in the star (cf. § 54, where P is first introduced). The pressure of radiation is therefore to be included in P. If β is the ratio of the gas pressure p_G to the whole pressure P the corrected equation runs

$$p_G = \beta P = \Re\rho T/\mu \quad\quad\quad\quad\quad\text{........................(58·2)}.$$

Then by (55·42)

$$\frac{\rho\phi}{n+1} = P = \frac{\Re\rho T}{\beta\mu}.$$

Hence

$$T = \frac{\beta\mu}{(n+1)\,\Re}\phi \quad\quad\quad\quad\text{........................(58·3)}.$$

---

[*] Unless otherwise stated the molecular weight will be measured in terms of the hydrogen atom in this book. If, however, μ is measured in grams the constant in the numerator is Boltzmann's constant $R = 1 \cdot 372 \cdot 10^{-16}$. The relation is $\Re = R/H$, where H is the mass of a hydrogen atom in grams.

By (57·3) the central temperature is determined by

$$T_0 = \frac{R'}{(n+1)M'} \frac{G}{\Re} \frac{\beta\mu M}{R} \quad \dots\dots\dots\dots(58\cdot4).$$

Provided that $\beta\mu$ is constant through the star (which is actually a fair approximation) we have by (58·3) $T \propto \phi$. Hence

$$T/T_0 = u \quad \dots\dots\dots\dots\dots(58\cdot5).$$

59. To show the method of using these formulae and tables we give calculations for the bright component of Capella. For the assumed relation between pressure and density we take $P \propto \rho^{\frac{4}{3}}$ so that $n = 3$ and the appropriate table is Table 6. The mass and radius of Capella (§ 13) are

$$M = 8\cdot3 \cdot 10^{33} \text{ gm.}, \qquad R = 9\cdot55 \cdot 10^{11} \text{ cm.},$$

whence the mean density is

$$\rho_m = \cdot00227.$$

From Table 6, column 6, the ratio ρ_0/ρ_m is 54·36. Hence

$$\rho_0 = \cdot1234 \text{ gm. per c.c.}$$

Also from the last line of Table 6

$$M' = 2\cdot015, \qquad R' = 6\cdot901.$$

Hence by (57·3)

$$\phi_0 = \frac{6\cdot66 \cdot 10^{-8} \times 8\cdot3 \cdot 10^{33} \times 6\cdot901}{2\cdot015 \times 9\cdot55 \cdot 10^{11}} = 1\cdot982 \cdot 10^{15},$$

and by (55·42)

$$P_0 = \tfrac{1}{4}\rho_0\phi_0 = \tfrac{1}{4} \times \cdot1234 \times 1\cdot982 \cdot 10^{15} = 6\cdot11 \cdot 10^{13} \text{ dynes per sq. cm.}$$

To determine the central temperature we must assume a molecular weight, and, if radiation pressure is not neglected, a factor β. We take $\mu\beta = 2\cdot0$ which is probably fairly near the truth, then by (58·3)

$$T_0 = \frac{2\cdot0 \times 1\cdot982 \cdot 10^{15}}{4 \times 8\cdot26 \cdot 10^7} = 1\cdot20 \cdot 10^7 \text{ degrees.}$$

To find the conditions at another point in the star, take for example the line $z = 3\cdot5$ in Table 6. This relates to a distance from the centre given by

$$\frac{r}{R} = \frac{z}{R'} = \frac{3\cdot5}{6\cdot901} = \cdot507,$$

or a little more than half-way from the centre to the surface. Here

$$T = \cdot27629T_0 = 3\cdot32 \cdot 10^6,$$
$$\rho = \cdot02109\rho_0 = \cdot00260,$$
$$P = \cdot005828P_0 = 3\cdot56 \cdot 10^{11}.$$

Also at this point

$$\frac{M_r}{M} = \frac{1\cdot8203}{2\cdot0150} = 0\cdot90,$$

so that although only about one-eighth of the volume is within this radius it contains 90 per cent. of the mass*.

In Fig. 1, we show a star divided into shells corresponding to (a) ten equal steps of temperature, (b) ten equal masses; that is to say, the circles on the left correspond to $T/T_0 = 0.9, 0.8, 0.7$, etc. and the circles on the right correspond to $M_r/M = 0.1, 0.2, 0.3$, etc. These diagrams are for the polytrope $n = 3$, which is believed to correspond nearly to the actual conditions of the stars.

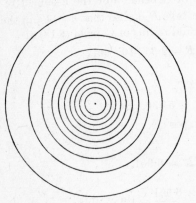

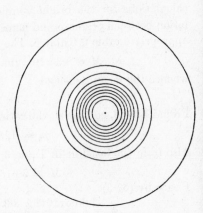

Fig. 1a. Ten equal steps of temperature.   Fig. 1b. Ten shells of equal mass.

Potential Energy.

60. We can determine the negative potential energy of a polytropic star, i.e. the work done by gravitation in drawing together the material from a state of infinite diffusion. The analysis is due to Emden.

Consider two concentric shells of masses dM_r and dM_s. The inner shell attracts the outer but not *vice versa*. The mutual potential energy (negative) is thus

$$\frac{G\,dM_r\,dM_s}{r},$$

where r is the radius of the *outer* shell.

The mutual energy of dM_r and of all shells interior to it is accordingly

$$\frac{G\,dM_r}{r} \int_0^M dM_s = \frac{G M_r\,dM_r}{r}.$$

---

* It will be understood that we are here merely illustrating the mode of using the formulae, and the results (although probably fairly near the actual values) are not intended to be our final conclusions as to the state of Capella (cf. § 13).

Hence the negative potential energy of the whole star is

$$\Omega = G \int_0^M \frac{M_r dM_r}{r} \quad\dots\dots\dots\dots\dots\dots(60\cdot11)$$

$$= \tfrac{1}{2} G \int_0^{M^2} \frac{d\,(M_r{}^2)}{r}$$

$$= \tfrac{1}{2} G \frac{M^2}{R} + \tfrac{1}{2} G \int_0^R \frac{M_r{}^2}{r^2}\, dr,$$

by integration by parts. Or since $GM_r/r^2 = -\, d\phi/dr$

$$\Omega = \tfrac{1}{2} G \frac{M^2}{R} - \tfrac{1}{2} \int M_r d\phi \quad\dots\dots\dots\dots(60\cdot12).$$

Again since $GM_r = -\, r^2 d\phi/dr$ and $dM_r = 4\pi r^2 \rho dr$,

(60·11) gives $\qquad \Omega = -\, 4\pi \int_0^R r^3 \rho \frac{d\phi}{dr}\, dr.$

Writing $\rho = \lambda\phi^n$ in accordance with (55·41)

$$\Omega = -\, \frac{4\pi\lambda}{n+1} \int_{r=0}^{\phi=0} d\,(\phi^{n+1})\, r^3$$

$$= \frac{12\pi\lambda}{n+1} \int \phi^{n+1}\, r^2 dr \quad \text{by integration by parts}$$

$$= \frac{3}{n+1} \int \phi \,.\, 4\pi\rho r^2 dr \quad\dots\dots\dots\dots\dots(60\cdot21)$$

$$= \frac{3}{n+1} \int \phi \, dM_r \quad\dots\dots\dots\dots\dots\dots(60\cdot22)$$

$$= -\, \frac{3}{n+1} \int M_r d\phi \quad\dots\dots\dots\dots\dots(60\cdot3)$$

by integration by parts.

Comparing (60·12) and (60·3)

$$\Omega = \tfrac{1}{2} G \frac{M^2}{R} + \frac{n+1}{6}\, \Omega.$$

Hence $\qquad\qquad \Omega = \frac{3}{5-n}\, G \frac{M^2}{R} \quad\dots\dots\dots\dots\dots(60\cdot4).$

We note for reference that

$$\Omega = 3 \int_0^R P \,.\, 4\pi r^2 dr = 3 \int P dv \quad\dots\dots\dots(60\cdot5),$$

where dv is the element of volume. This follows from (60·21) and (55·42).

Uniform density is given by $n = 0$ and (60·4) then gives the usual expression for a uniform sphere $\Omega = \tfrac{3}{5} GM^2/R$. For other distributions the numerical coefficient is greater, the mass being more concentrated to the centre.

61. The result (60·4) shows that there must be some break-down in the analysis when $n > 5$. The failure occurs because such distributions have no boundary; the "star" extends to infinity and the mass is infinite. These distributions are of no interest to us here.

In the critical case $n = 5$, the differential equation (55·8) is soluble, the solution being

$$u = (1 + \tfrac{1}{3}z^2)^{-\frac{1}{2}}.$$

The distribution thus extends to infinity and R is infinite. The whole mass, however, is finite, since $(-z^2 du/dz)_{z=\infty}$ is equal to $\sqrt{3}$.

Another simple solution occurs when $n = 1$, viz.

$$u = \sin z / z.$$

The boundary of the star is then at $z = \pi$. We have

$$R' = \pi, \qquad M' = \pi, \qquad \rho_0/\rho_m = \pi^2/3.$$

The solution for $n = 0$ is also simple since it corresponds to a uniform sphere.

62. If the material is a perfect gas and $\beta\mu$ is constant the mean temperature of the star can be calculated. The mean temperature T_m averaged with respect to mass is given by

$$T_m = \int_0^M T \, dM_r \div M.$$

Hence since
$$T/T_0 = \phi/\phi_0,$$

$$\begin{aligned}
\frac{T_m}{T_0} &= \frac{1}{M\phi_0} \int_0^M \phi \, dM_r \\
&= \frac{(n+1)\,\Omega}{3M\phi_0} \qquad \text{by (60·22)} \\
&= \frac{n+1}{5-n} \frac{GM^2}{R} \cdot \frac{1}{M\phi_0} \\
&= \frac{n+1}{5-n} \frac{M'}{R'} \qquad \text{by (57·3)} \dots\dots\dots\dots(62·1).
\end{aligned}$$

For $n = 3$ this gives
$$T_m/T_0 = 0.584.$$

Substituting for T_0 from (58·4)

$$T_m = \frac{1}{5-n} \frac{G}{\Re} \frac{\beta\mu M}{R} \dots\dots\dots\dots\dots\dots(62·2).$$

It is of considerable interest to have obtained at this early stage a simple formula for the mean temperature of the material of a star. If we are definitely assured that the temperature is some millions of degrees we know the kind of conditions with which the more detailed theory will have to deal. At present the chief point left in suspense is the value of n which will ultimately be found from the theory of radiative equilibrium. Equation (62·2) shows to what extent the mean temperature is affected by this determination. By changing the value of n we obtain a series of models with different degrees of concentration of mass to the centre. The following results (derived from Emden's tables) show the progression—

$n =$	0	$\frac{1}{2}$	1	$1\frac{1}{2}$	2	$2\frac{1}{2}$	3	4	$4\frac{1}{2}$	4·9
$\rho_0/\rho_m =$	1	1·84	3·29	6·00	11·40	24·08	54·36	623·4	6378	934800
$5/(5-n) =$	1	1·11	1·25	1·43	1·66	2·00	2·50	5·00	10·0	50·0

The last line shows how the mean temperature increases with the concentration (the mass, radius and molecular weight being fixed).

Unless the density decreases inwards, there is a minimum value of the mean temperature given by the form $n = 0$. This is proved more generally in § 66 where the discussion is not limited to polytropic models. The actual mean temperature is not inordinately higher than the minimum unless we have extreme concentration of mass to the centre as shown in the second line of figures; but in that case there is practically no density in the outer part of the star so that we are virtually dealing with a star of smaller radius.

The high temperatures inside the stars are often considered rather startling and it is well to realise that they are not dependent on the more advanced developments of the theory.

The Isothermal Gas Sphere.

63. A mass of perfect gas at uniform temperature is the limit of the polytropic distribution for $n = \infty$. Certain modifications of the analysis are necessary for this case. Although it has no direct application to actual stars a study of the isothermal distribution is useful for purposes of comparison.

By (58·2)
$$P = \kappa\rho, \qquad \kappa = \Re T/\mu\beta \quad\dots\dots\dots\dots(63\cdot1),$$

and (54·4) gives
$$d\phi = dP/\rho = \kappa d (\log \rho).$$

Hence integrating,
$$\rho = \rho_0 e^{\phi/\kappa} \quad\dots\dots\dots\dots\dots\dots(63\cdot2),$$

where ρ_0 is the density at $\phi = 0$. Since $n > 5$ the distribution extends to infinity and the mass is infinite. Previous conventions fixing the zero of ϕ at the boundary of the star or at infinity therefore break down. For convenience we now take ϕ to be zero at the centre, so that ρ_0 denotes the central density as before.

Poisson's equation becomes

$$\frac{d^2\phi}{dr^2} + \frac{2}{r}\frac{d\phi}{dr} + 4\pi G\rho_0 e^{\phi/\kappa} = 0 \quad\dots\dots\dots\dots(63\cdot3).$$

Write
$$\phi = \kappa u, \qquad r = \left(\frac{\kappa}{4\pi G\rho_0}\right)^{\frac{1}{2}} z \quad\dots\dots\dots\dots(63\cdot4).$$

Then (63·3) reduces to the standard form

$$\frac{d^2u}{dz^2} + \frac{2}{z}\frac{du}{dz} + e^u = 0 \quad\dots\dots\dots\dots\dots\dots(63\cdot5),$$

with the central conditions $u = 0$, $du/dz = 0$.

The solution calculated by Emden is given in Table 7. The successive columns are proportional to (1) distance from centre, (2) potential, (3) density and pressure, (4) acceleration of gravity, (5) central density divided by mean density interior to r, (6) mass interior to r.

Table 7.

Isothermal Gas Sphere.

z	$-u$	e^u	$-du/dz$	$-z\,dz/3du$	$-z^2\,du/dz$
0·00	·00000	1·00000	·00000	1·000	·0000
0·25	·01037	·98969	·08290	1·005	·0052
0·50	·04113	·95971	·16225	1·027	·0406
0·75	·09113	·91290	·23819	1·050	·1340
1·00	·15903	·85296	·30370	1·097	·3037
1·25	·24225	·78486	·36045	1·156	·5632
1·50	·33847	·71285	·40432	1·237	·9097
1·75	·44488	·64090	·44390	1·314	1·3595
2·00	·55967	·57140	·47286	1·410	1·8914
2·5	·80584	·44671	·50694	1·644	3·1684
3	1·06226	·34537	·51625	1·937	4·6462
3·5	1·31937	·26730	·51006	2·287	6·2483
4	1·57071	·20790	·49403	2·699	7·9045
4·5	1·81246	·16325	·47234	3·176	9·5650
5	2·04264	·12968	·44813	3·719	11·203
6	2·46598	·08493	·39879	5·015	14·353
7	2·84160	·05833	·35334	6·604	17·214
8	3·17489	·04180	·31372	8·500	20·078
9	3·47128	·03108	·27989	10·718	22·670
10	3·73646	·02384	·25121	13·269	25·121
100	8·59506	·000175	·01843	1808·6	184·3
1000	13·09847	·000002	·002045	163000	2045·1

Minimal Problems.

64. Up to the present we have restricted the investigation to distributions arranged according to a polytropic model. In the following theorems no such restriction is imposed, but we postulate that the density does not decrease as we go inwards. The new limitation is scarcely likely to exclude any case deserving serious consideration in application to the stars. It is not likely that a distribution could be stable with $d\rho/dr$ positive.

In Problem II we shall also postulate that the temperature does not decrease inwards. This limitation is entirely innocuous. A positive value of dT/dr at any point in a star would require a sink of energy within the star, since heat must flow in the direction of the temperature gradient.

Problem I. *To find the minimum value of the central pressure in a star of mass M and radius R subject only to the condition that the density does not decrease inwards.*

First consider an arbitrary distribution of density satisfying the condition $d\rho/dr \leqslant 0$. Remove a small part $\delta\rho_1$ of the density in the shell r_1 to $r_1 + dr_1$, and add the matter to the shell between r_2 and $r_2 + dr_2$, thereby increasing the density by $\delta\rho_2$. If δM is the mass transferred

$$\delta M = 4\pi r_1^2 dr_1 \delta\rho_1 = 4\pi r_2^2 dr_2 \delta\rho_2 \quad\ldots\ldots\ldots\ldots(64\cdot1).$$

The temperature distribution must, of course, be altered in the way necessary to maintain the new distribution of density in equilibrium.

We take $r_2 < r_1$. The pressure at any point within r_2 will be increased for two reasons. Firstly, the matter between r_1 and r_2 is now under the attraction of the mass δM, whereas formerly δM exerted no resultant force on it. Its weight is thus increased and contributes more pressure. Secondly, δM in its new position contributes more pressure, viz. $g_2 \delta\rho_2 dr_2$ instead of $g_1 \delta\rho_1 dr_1$. By (64·1) these are in the ratio

$$g_2/r_2^2 : g_1/r_1^2$$

which is greater than

$$1/r_2 : 1/r_1$$

because g cannot increase faster than r when the density does not increase outwards.

Thus any transfer of matter inwards increases the central pressure. The minimum pressure occurs when the matter is as far from the centre as is consistent with the limitations of the problem. We can go on reducing the central pressure by transferring matter outwards until we arrive at uniform density. The central pressure has then the value for a uniform sphere

$$P = \frac{3}{8\pi} \frac{GM^2}{R^4},$$

which is the required minimum value.

65. Problem II. *To find the minimum value of the central temperature in a star of mass M and radius R composed of perfect gas of constant molecular weight μ, subject only to the condition that density and temperature do not decrease inwards.* (*Radiation pressure is neglected.*)

We first show that in the distribution giving the minimum central temperature *either* the density gradient *or* the temperature gradient vanishes at every point.

For, if not, consider three consecutive spherical shells with densities $\rho_1 > \rho_2 > \rho_3$ and temperatures $T_1 > T_2 > T_3$. Remove a small mass from the second to the third shell. Since $\rho_2 > \rho_3$ it will be possible to treat a small mass in this way without reversing the density gradient. It was shown in Problem I that this transfer reduces the pressure interior to the shell ρ_2 by a constant amount. Since $\delta P = \Re \rho \delta T / \mu$, the reduction of temperature will be inversely proportional to the density and therefore least at the centre and increasing (or stationary) outwards. Thus the temperature gradient interior to ρ_2 will not be reversed; moreover, the temperature distribution outside ρ_3 is unaffected. The temperatures in the two shells will change in a more complicated way but since $T_1 > T_2 > T_3$ there is a small margin for such changes without reversal of the temperature gradient.

This shows that it will always be possible to reduce the central temperature without violating the conditions by making a small transfer at a point where both $\rho_1 > \rho_2 > \rho_3$ and $T_1 > T_2 > T_3$. Hence when the central temperature is an actual minimum one of these inequalities must be replaced by equality (not necessarily the same one in all parts of the star).

The central part of the star must be isothermal. For if a mass δM is taken from the outer part and distributed uniformly through a small sphere of radius r_1 at the centre, the increase of pressure tends to infinity like $\delta M / r_1$ whilst the increase of density is proportional to $\delta M / r_1^3$. Hence if r_1 is taken small enough the temperature falls. If, however, the central part of the star is isothermal, this transfer is ruled out because it would make the central temperature less than surrounding temperatures. The isothermal region must be limited because a completely isothermal star has no boundary. We have shown that where the star is not isothermal it must be of uniform density.

Hence the star of minimum central temperature consists of a region of uniform temperature surrounded by a region of uniform density. It remains to determine the extent of these regions.

Let T_1 be the temperature of the isothermal region, ρ_1 the uniform density in the outer region. Then the pressure P_1 at the transition is

$$P_1 = \frac{\Re T_1}{\mu} \rho_1.$$

Let R_1 be the radius of the transition sphere and let ρ_m be the mean density within this sphere. Let

$$\frac{R_1}{R} = \alpha, \qquad \frac{\rho_m - \rho_1}{\rho_1} = \beta \quad \dots\dots\dots\dots\dots(65\cdot1).$$

We have
$$M = \tfrac{4}{3}\pi\rho_1 R^3 + \tfrac{4}{3}\pi (\rho_m - \rho_1) R_1^3$$
$$= \tfrac{4}{3}\pi\rho_1 R^3 (1 + \alpha^3\beta) \quad \dots\dots\dots\dots\dots(65\cdot2).$$

At a point in the outer region
$$g = \tfrac{4}{3}\pi G\rho_1 r + \tfrac{4}{3}\pi G (\rho_m - \rho_1) R_1^3/r^2,$$
so that by (54·3) $-dP = \tfrac{4}{3}\pi G\rho_1^2 dr (r + \beta\alpha^3 R^3/r^2).$

Hence integrating between αR and R

$$P_1 = \tfrac{2}{3}\pi G\rho_1^2 R^2 \{1 - \alpha^2 + 2\beta\alpha^2 (1 - \alpha)\} \qquad \ldots\ldots\ldots(65\cdot3).$$

By (65·2) and (65·3)

$$\frac{\Re T_1}{\mu} = \frac{P_1}{\rho_1} = \frac{GM}{2R} \frac{(1 - \alpha)(1 + \alpha + 2\beta\alpha^2)}{1 + \beta\alpha^3} \ldots\ldots\ldots\ldots(65\cdot4).$$

The quantities α and β are connected by the theory of the isothermal part of the star. With the notation of § 63

$$\rho_1/\rho_0 = e^u, \qquad \rho_m/\rho_0 = -\frac{3}{z}\frac{du}{dz}.$$

Hence
$$\beta = -\frac{3}{z}\frac{du}{dz} e^{-u} - 1 \qquad\ldots\ldots\ldots\ldots\ldots(65\cdot51).$$

Also since $\alpha R = (\kappa/4\pi G\rho_0)^{\frac{1}{2}} z$ and $P_1 = \kappa\rho_0 e^u$, (65·3) gives

$$\frac{6}{z^2 e^u} = \frac{(1 - \alpha)(1 + \alpha + 2\beta\alpha^2)}{\alpha^2} \qquad\ldots\ldots\ldots\ldots(65\cdot52).$$

Choosing an arbitrary value of z we find e^u and du/dz from Table 7. Then β and α can be found from (65·51) and (65·52), and the factor

$$S = (1 - \alpha)(1 + \alpha + 2\beta\alpha^2)/(1 + \beta\alpha^3) \qquad\ldots\ldots\ldots\ldots(65\cdot6)$$

is calculated. The following results are found—

z	β	α	S
4	·782	·663	·646
4·5	·929	·673	·641
5	1·073	·680	·640
6	1·348	·687	·645

We see that S has a minimum value about ·640 at about $\alpha = \cdot676$. Hence by (65·4) a star with an isothermal region extending to $\cdot676R$ surrounded by a region of uniform density has the minimum central temperature, viz.

$$T_1 = 0\cdot32 \frac{G\mu}{\Re} \frac{M}{R} \qquad\ldots\ldots\ldots\ldots\ldots(65\cdot7).$$

It may be noted that for a star of constant density throughout the factor is 0·5, and for the polytrope $n = 3$ (the model chiefly used in this book) the factor is 0·856. Thus the temperatures which we find in the detailed investigation are not greatly above the minimum values.

66. Problem III. *To find the minimum value of the mean temperature in a star of mass M and radius R of perfect gas of molecular weight μ, subject only to the condition that the density does not decrease inwards. (Radiation pressure is neglected.)*

If T_m is the mean temperature

$$MT_m = \int T \cdot 4\pi\rho r^2 dr = \frac{\mu}{\Re} \int P \cdot 4\pi r^2 dr$$

$$= -\frac{\mu}{\Re} \int \tfrac{4}{3}\pi r^3 \cdot dP \qquad \text{by integration by parts}$$

$$= \frac{\mu}{3\Re} \int 4\pi r^3 g\rho dr \qquad \text{by (54·3)}$$

$$= \frac{G\mu}{3\Re} \int \frac{M_r}{r} dM_r = \frac{G\mu}{6\Re} \int \frac{d(M_r)^2}{r} \quad \dots\dots\dots\dots(66\cdot1).$$

This is a minimum when, for each step of $(M_r)^2$, r is as great as possible. This evidently leads to the uniform sphere. Hence by (62·2), the minimum value is

$$T_m = 0\cdot2 \frac{G\mu}{\Re} \frac{M}{R} \qquad \dots\dots\dots\dots\dots\dots(66\cdot2).$$

It is interesting to compare this with (65·7).

Incomplete Polytropic Regions.

67. A class of problems arises in which the polytropic condition (55·1) applies only to part of the star.

If the non-polytropic region is *interior* to the polytropic region Tables 4–7 are not applicable. For they give a particular solution of the general differential equation which conforms to certain boundary conditions at the centre; when the central region is excluded these conditions are no longer effective and another solution of the differential equation must be taken. The gravitational field which controls the polytropic part is modified by the excess or defect of mass in the central non-polytropic part.

An example of this would be afforded by a star obeying (55·1) only so long as its material can be treated as a perfect gas. Then, if the density is great enough, the equation breaks down near the centre. Tables 4–7 are not applicable even to the outer part which satisfies (55·1); and a new solution of the differential equation must be found by numerical calculation *de novo*. There is little of a general character to be said about this class of problem; but progress in particular cases that arise can usually be made by numerical calculation.

If the non-polytropic region is on the *outside*, Tables 4–7 can be used for the interior polytropic part. An instance of this has been treated in § 65 where Table 7 was used. A more important problem of this type arises in the following way. We can scarcely expect that in an actual star any simple physical law will hold uniformly from a central temperature of 10,000,000° to an outside temperature of 10,000°. Making use of the simplified properties of matter at temperatures of several million degrees we shall deduce laws which may be expected to hold with reasonable accuracy from say 10,000,000° to 1,000,000°. We do not know much about matter at temperatures below a million degrees, and therefore can give little or no consideration to what happens in the rest of the star.

Suppose then we have satisfied ourselves that between 10,000,000 and 1,000,000 degrees stellar material obeys the polytropic law with $n = 3$. Table 6 will apply to the part of the star above 1,000,000 degrees, because the break-down occurs in the region exterior to it and does not affect the field of gravitation within. Actually we perform the whole solution as though the same condition held good up to the surface—not because we think it likely to be satisfied at the lower temperatures, but because it does not much matter what happens in this outer part and (within reasonable limits) any law will do for our purpose. As this may seem a somewhat light-hearted procedure we examine the justification for it here.

Consider a star for which the central values are

$$T_0 = 10^7, \qquad \rho_0 = 0 \cdot 1,$$

with $\mu\beta = 2$, $n = 3$.

We find

$$P_0 = 4 \cdot 13 \, . \, 10^{13}, \quad \phi_0 = 1 \cdot 65 \, . \, 10^{15}, \quad \kappa = 8 \cdot 84 \, . \, 10^{14}, \quad \alpha = 4 \cdot 31 \, . \, 10^{-27},$$

and $(57 \cdot 2)$ gives

$$R = 1 \cdot 405 \, . \, 10^{11} R' = 9 \cdot 70 \, . \, 10^{11} \text{ cm.},$$

$$M = 3 \cdot 48 \quad . \, 10^{33} M' = 7 \cdot 02 \, . \, 10^{33} \text{ gm.}$$

These would be the mass and radius if the star were completed on the polytropic model. If, however, the model fails at temperatures below a million degrees, we stop the solution at $z = 5$. Denoting values at this point by suffix 1, we obtain by Table 6

$$T_1 = 1 \cdot 111 \, . \, 10^6, \quad \rho_1 = \cdot 0001371, \quad P_1 = 6 \cdot 29 \, . \, 10^9, \quad R_1 = 7 \cdot 02 \, . \, 10^{11},$$

$$M_1 = 6 \cdot 96 \, . \, 10^{33}.$$

Around this a distribution of some kind has to be added sufficient to produce the pressure P_1 of 6290 atmospheres. If M and R are the mass and radius of the complete star

$$P_1 = \int_{R_1}^{R} g\rho dr = \frac{G}{4\pi} \int_{M_1}^{M} \frac{M_r}{r^4} \, dM_r < \frac{G}{4\pi} \frac{M}{R_1{}^4} \int_{M_1}^{M} dM_r,$$

so that
$$\Delta M = M - M_1 > \frac{4\pi P_1 R_1{}^4}{GM} \quad \ldots\ldots\ldots\ldots(67 \cdot 1).$$

This gives
$$\Delta M > 0 \cdot 041 \, . \, 10^{33} \text{ gm.}$$

The additional mass will be greater than this lower limit very nearly in the ratio of $R_1{}^{-4}$ to the average value of r^{-4} for the added material. Although no upper limit for this factor can be given, it would be difficult to imagine its exceeding 2 or 3 without extravagant assumptions.

A wide range of conditions will be covered if we take the material beyond R_1 to conform to a new polytropic law $P = \kappa_1 \rho^{(1+1/s)}$, where s differs from n, and κ_1 from κ. The gravitational force in this region can be set equal to GM_1/r^2 since its own mass is very small compared with that of the rest of the star. Then, as in (55·42), we shall have

$$\frac{P}{\rho} = \frac{GM_1}{s+1}\left(\frac{1}{r} - \frac{1}{R}\right),$$

since ϕ is now $GM_1/r - GM_1/R$. Hence, setting $r = R_1$,

$$\left(\frac{1}{R_1} - \frac{1}{R}\right) = \frac{(s+1)\,P_1}{GM_1\rho_1} = 9·90.10^{-14} \times (s+1) \quad \ldots\ldots(67·2),$$

so that R can be found. We find for the added mass beyond R_1

$$\Delta M = 4\pi\rho_1 R^3 \int_{a_1}^{1} \left(\frac{1}{\alpha} - 1\right)^s \alpha^2 d\alpha \div \left(\frac{1}{\alpha_1} - 1\right)^s \ldots\ldots\ldots(67·3),$$

where $\alpha_1 = R_1/R$.

From (67·2) and (67·3) the following results are obtained—

s	R	ΔM
0	$7·54.10^{11}$	$·0479.10^{33}$
1	$8·15$	$·0508$
3	$9·72$	$·0534$
5	$12·04$	$·0549$
7	$15·81$	$·0561$

Whereas in the range $s = 0$ to 7 the radius of the star is doubled, the consequent change in mass $(M_1 + \Delta M)$ is not much more than 1 part in 1000.

The mass is thus very insensitive to conditions in the low temperature part of the star, and our procedure is amply justified so far as the mass is concerned. We must be prepared to admit an uncertainty of, say, 30 per cent. in the radius. It should be remembered that when there is wide diffusion of the outer material, e.g. with the law $s = 7$, the radius of the photosphere may be considerably smaller than the radius R representing the extreme limit of the stellar atmosphere; by taking higher values of s, R could be increased without limit, but I do not think that the photosphere (which in practice is regarded as the surface of the star) would be much increased.

CHAPTER V

RADIATIVE EQUILIBRIUM

68. Energy in the form of radiant heat and light is continually flowing from the surface of a star into space. The surface layers of material cannot continue to provide this energy for long unless their heat is replenished from below. We are thus led to consider the process of transfer of energy from the interior to the surface.

There are two modes of transfer of heat in material in static equilibrium, viz. *conduction* and *radiation*. In both the net flow is in the direction of the temperature gradient from high to low temperature. In both this flow is the resultant of streams of energy in both directions; the stream from the high-temperature region is rather more intense than the stream from the low-temperature region, and the difference constitutes the net flow. In conduction molecules of the hotter region transmit their energy by diffusion and collision to surrounding regions; in radiation the hot material emits aether waves which are absorbed in the surrounding regions. In both cases this transmission is largely neutralised by a similar transmission from the surrounding regions, and the resultant transfer depends on the slight preponderance of the flow from the hotter region.

A third mode of transfer is possible if the limitation to static equilibrium is abandoned. There may be a system of ascending and descending currents in the star by which the material is kept stirred. Heat-energy is then carried from one region to another by actual movement of the matter carrying it—as in the lower part of our own atmosphere. If matter through proximity to the surface loses more heat than can be replaced by radiation and conduction so that it cools below the normal temperature at its level, it will sink and be replaced by fresh unexposed material from below. This mode of transfer is called *convection*.

It was recognised early that the conductivity of matter is much too small to pass the necessary quantity of heat through the star. In the first investigations of the stellar interior the importance of transfer by radiation was not realised. Accordingly a system of convection currents was assumed to be present, and processes of transfer other than convection were considered negligible. The star was said to be in convective (or adiabatic) equilibrium.

69. On the hypothesis of convective equilibrium a definite relation between the pressure, density and temperature at different levels can be found. Consider an ascending current of material. By hypothesis there is no appreciable gain or loss of heat by conduction or radiation; it therefore expands without gain or loss of heat, i.e. adiabatically. For a perfect gas the relation between pressure and density in adiabatic expansion is

$$P = \kappa\rho^\gamma \quad\dots\dots\dots\dots\dots\dots\dots\dots\dots\dots(69\cdot1),$$

where γ is the ratio of the specific heat at constant pressure to the specific heat at constant vòlume (§ 28). Since the different levels are continuously connected by ascending and descending currents the equilibrium condition must be such that (69·1) holds throughout the interior. The hypothesis that loss of heat by radiation is negligible must evidently break down near the surface, so that the equation could not be exact in the extreme outer layers.

Since (69·1) is the relation discussed in Chapter IV the solution for a perfect gas in convective equilibrium is given by the formulae and tables there explained. The value of γ for the stellar material must be estimated or guessed; but the range of uncertainty from this cause is not very great. It is impossible for γ to exceed the value $\frac{5}{3}$ which corresponds to a monatomic gas; and it can be shown that if γ is less than $\frac{4}{3}$ the distribution is unstable (see § 104). Hence the solution is limited to values of γ between $\frac{5}{3}$ and $\frac{4}{3}$ or to values of n between 1·5 and 3.

We shall not enter further into the historic problem of convective equilibrium since modern researches show that the hypothesis is untenable. In stellar conditions the main prccess of transfer of heat is by radiation and other modes of transfer may be neglected.

We may remark that transfer by convection stands on a different footing from radiation and conduction. Radiation and conduction must always occur in a mass at non-uniform temperature, although their effects may be negligibly small. But convection need not occur at all. It will only be present if the conditions are such as to generate and maintain circulating currents.

70. Since the density of radiation is proportional to T^4 its importance is enormously enhanced at the high temperatures in the stellar interior, and it is not surprising to find that it ousts the other vehicles of energy. But whilst great intensity of radiation strengthens its control over the temperature distribution, it is not essential. I think that an isolated mass of gas at quite low temperature* would take up radiative rather than convective equilibrium.

Consider a gas stratified in radiative equilibrium. As explained in § 23 radiation behaves as though it had a ratio of specific heats $\gamma = \frac{4}{3}$ and accordingly P and T are related by

$$P \propto T^4.$$

* But not so low that conduction becomes comparable with radiation.

Let there be a circulatory current conveying heat between two pressure levels. As the mass rises to a level of lower ·pressure its temperature changes according to the adiabatic law

$$P \propto T^{\gamma/(\gamma-1)}.$$

For stability $\gamma > \frac{4}{3}$, so that $P \propto T^{(<4)}$. Hence the material which has ascended is cooler than its surroundings and receives heat from them; the material which has descended is hotter than its surroundings and gives up heat to them*. The circulatory current transfers heat *against* the temperature gradient, and by the second law of thermodynamics it can only do this at the expense of its mechanical energy. The currents therefore tend to die out, and there is nothing to restart them†.

Radiative equilibrium has a natural precedence over convective equilibrium, since in radiative equilibrium convection ceases, whereas in convective equilibrium radiation remains and tends to destroy it. In fact convective equilibrium is only approached automatically from one side; to reach it from the other side extraneous mechanical energy of stirring must be supplied.

Equation of Radiative Equilibrium.

71. We admit now that the only mode of transfer of heat is by radiation, and develop the equation of radiative equilibrium. We require three results reached in Chapter II—

(1) The momentum of radiation is E/c, where E is the energy and c the velocity of light. The momentum is in the direction in which the waves are travelling.

(2) Radiation in an enclosure with absorbing walls maintained at uniform temperature T is isotropic as regards direction of flow and has an energy-density

$$E = aT^4,$$

where $a = 7 \cdot 64 \cdot 10^{-15}$ in C.G.S. units and degrees Centigrade.

(3) With the same conditions radiation exerts a hydrostatic pressure

$$p_R = \tfrac{1}{3}E = \tfrac{1}{3}aT^4.$$

To a very high degree of approximation the last two results are immediately applicable to the interior of a star. It is true that the radiation

* E.g. let $\gamma = \frac{5}{3}$, and let a current ascend from a level where the pressure and temperature are P and T to a level where they are $\frac{1}{10000}P, \frac{1}{10}T$; under the diminished pressure the temperature of the convected material falls adiabatically to

$$(\tfrac{1}{10000})^{\frac{2}{3}} T = 0 \cdot 025T,$$

so that it is much below the temperature $0 \cdot 1T$ of its surroundings. Cf. H. N. Russell, *Astrophys. Journ.* 54, p. 293.

† Except that in a rotating star a small circulation is maintained as explained in § 199.

is not in an ideal enclosure with opaque walls at constant temperature; but the stellar conditions approach the ideal far more closely than any laboratory experiments can do. The material of a star is very opaque to the kind of radiation existing there. According to the figures deduced for Capella a screen containing 0·1 gm. per sq. cm. would let through e^{-12} or ·000006 of the radiation falling on it; at the average density in Capella such a screen would be 50 cm. thick. If then we draw a sphere of radius 50 cm. round a point in Capella the radiation at this point will be practically isolated from everything outside the sphere. The temperature gradient in Capella is about 1° per kilometre so that the enclosing walls with which we have surrounded the point are at constant temperature to within 0°·001—a uniformity scarcely likely to be attained in laboratory conditions.

Take the axis of x in the direction of the temperature gradient and consider a thin slab of stellar material at right angles to Ox having 1 sq. cm. area and thickness dx. Let the temperatures of the two faces be T and $T + dT$. The radiation pressure acting normally on the two faces will give forces $+ p_R$ and $- (p_R + dp_R)$, so that the resultant force in the direction Ox is

$$- dp_R.$$

This resultant gives the amount of momentum which is being acquired per second in the region occupied by the slab owing to the flow of radiation.

Since there is equilibrium this momentum must be got rid of; and it can only be got rid of by being first passed on to the matter of the slab. (The ultimate fate of the momentum does not concern us here, but it may be explained that when handed over to the matter it helps to neutralise the momentum communicated to the matter by gravitation.) The momentum passes into the matter by the process of absorption (including scattering).

Let k be the mass coefficient of absorption. The definition of k is that a thin screen of material of mass w per sq. cm. absorbs the fraction kw of the radiation passing through it normally. In our problem $w = \rho dx$, and accordingly if H ergs of radiation per sq. cm. per sec. are travelling along Ox the amount absorbed will be $Hk\rho dx$ and its x-momentum will be $Hk\rho dx/c$ per sq. cm. per sec.

Consider next H ergs per sec. passing obliquely through a sq. cm. of the slab at an angle of incidence θ. The distance travelled through the slab is now $dx \sec \theta$ and the absorption is increased proportionately. The momentum absorbed is now $Hk\rho dx \sec \theta/c$; but multiplying by $\cos \theta$ to obtain the x-component, the absorption of x-momentum is as before

$$Hk\rho dx/c$$

for any angle of incidence up to 90°. Of course, if the angle is greater than 90° so that the radiation passes in the other direction through the slab, the sign is reversed. Note that H is reckoned per sq. cm. of the slab, not per sq. cm. of cross-section of the beam.

In general radiation will be flowing both ways through the slab. Corresponding to the flow H_+ through a square centimetre from the negative to the positive side of the slab there will be an absorption of $H_+ k\rho\,dx/c$ units of positive momentum, and corresponding to the flow H_- from the positive to the negative side there will be an absorption of $H_- k\rho\,dx/c$ units of negative momentum. Hence for a net positive flow $H = H_+ - H_-$, there will be a net gain of $H k\rho\,dx/c$ units of positive momentum by the matter in the slab.

We have seen that the x-momentum $-dp_R$ acquired in the region per second must all be transferred to the matter by this process. Hence

$$- dp_R = H k\rho\,dx/c,$$

or
$$H = - \frac{c}{k\rho} \frac{dp_R}{dx} \quad\dots\dots\dots\dots\dots\dots(71\cdot1).$$

Writing for p_R its value $\tfrac{1}{3}aT^4$,

$$H = - \frac{ac}{3k\rho} \frac{dT^4}{dx} \quad\dots\dots\dots\dots\dots\dots(71\cdot2).$$

Equation $(71\cdot1)$ shows that the net flow of radiation is, as we should expect, proportional to its internal pressure gradient and inversely proportional to a factor $k\rho$ measuring the obstructive power of the material screen through which it is being forced. The equation is analogous to that governing the flow of a material fluid through a channel or sieve.

The equation breaks down under the same circumstances as the corresponding equation for a material fluid, viz. when the flow is so rapid that the pressure gradient can no longer be calculated hydrostatically. This happens near the surface of a star. The argument cannot apply to any part of the star which we can *see*; for the fact that we see it shows that its radiation is not "enclosed." But at a small depth below the photosphere the equation becomes a tolerable approximation; and throughout the main interior its accuracy is so far beyond all requirements that it may be used without hesitation*.

72. A certain amount of controversy has occurred with regard to the derivation of this equation which reflects the time-long difference of view between the physicist and the mathematician. Perhaps a short digression on this antagonism may be permitted, for it is likely to give rise to many misunderstandings in problems of the kind we have to consider. I conceive that the chief aim of the physicist in discussing a theoretical problem

---

* Rather unexpectedly the equation remains a good approximation even in the extreme outer layers. The "first approximation," described in § 226 and used generally throughout Chapter XII, gives $(71\cdot2)$ immediately. Comparison with the "second approximation" developed in § 230 shows that the inaccuracy is not large.

is to obtain "insight"—to see which of the numerous factors are particularly concerned in any effect and how they work together to give it. For this purpose a legitimate approximation is not just an unavoidable evil; it is a discernment that certain factors—certain complications of the problem—do not contribute appreciably to the result. We satisfy ourselves that they may be left aside; and the mechanism stands out more clearly, freed from these irrelevancies. This discernment is only a continuation of a task begun by the physicist before the mathematical premises of the problem could be stated; for in any natural problem the actual conditions are of extreme complexity and the first step is to select those which have an essential influence on the result—in short, to get hold of the right end of the stick. The correct use of this insight, whether before or after the mathematical problem has been formulated, is a faculty to be cultivated, not a vicious propensity to be hidden from the public eye. Needless to say the physicist must if challenged be prepared to defend the use of his discernment; but unless the defence involves some subtle point of difficulty it may well be left until the challenge is made.

I suppose that the same kind of insight is useful to the mathematician as a tool; but he is careful to efface the tool marks from his finished products—his proofs. He is content with a rigorous but unilluminating demonstration that certain results follow from his premises, and he does not generally realise that the physicist demands something more than this. For the physicist has always to bear in mind a thousand and one other factors in the natural problem not formulated in the mathematical problem, and it is only by a demonstration which keeps in view the relative importance of the contributing causes that he can see whether he has been justified in neglecting these. As regards rigour, the physicist may well take risks in a mathematical deduction if these are no greater than the risks incurred in the mathematical formulation. As regards accuracy, the retention of absurdly minute terms in a physical equation is as clumsy in his eyes as the use of an extravagant number of decimal places in arithmetical computation.

Having said this much on the one side we may turn to appreciate the luxury of a rigorous mathematical proof. If the results obtained do not agree with observation the fault must assuredly lie with the premises assumed. The mathematician's power of narrowing down the possibilities supplements the physicist's power of picking out the probabilities. If space were unlimited we might try to duplicate investigations where necessary so as to satisfy both parties. But if one investigation must suffice I do not think we should usually give way to the mathematician. Cases could be cited where physicists have been led astray through inattention to mathematical rigour; but these are rare compared with the mathematicians' misadventures through lack of physical insight.

The point to remember is that when we *prove* a result without understanding it—when it drops unforeseen out of a maze of mathematical formulae—we have no ground for hoping that it will apply except when the mathematical premises are rigorously fulfilled—that is to say, never, unless we happen to be dealing with something like aether to which "perfection" can reasonably be attributed. But when we obtain by mathematical analysis an *understanding* of a result—when we discern which of the conditions are essentially contributing to it and which are relatively unimportant—we have obtained knowledge adapted to the fluid premises of a natural physical problem.

I think the idea that the purpose of study is to arrive at a string of proofs of propositions is a little overdone even in pure mathematics. Our purpose in studying the physical world includes much that is not comprised in so narrow an ideal. We might indeed say that, whereas for the mathematician insight is one of the tools and proof the finished product, for the physicist proof is one of the tools and insight the finished product. The tool must not usurp the place of the product, even though we fully recognise that disastrous results may occur when the tool is badly handled.

73. We now give an alternative derivation of the fundamental equation (71·1) which enables some points of detail to be discussed.

In isotropic radiation of density E the density of that part travelling in directions included within a solid angle $d\omega$ is

$$E \frac{d\omega}{4\pi}.$$

Since the flow of energy in a star is not perfectly isotropic but depends on the angle θ between $d\omega$ and the direction of the radius we shall denote the energy-density of radiation within the solid angle $d\omega$ by

$$E(\theta) \frac{d\omega}{4\pi}.$$

Consider a small cylinder of length ds and cross-section dS with its length in the direction θ. The infinitesimal $d\omega$ is considered to be small compared with dS/ds^2, so that the divergence of the beam in the cylinder is negligible and the radiation within $d\omega$ travels along the cylinder.

The amount entering the cylinder per second through the base is

$$E(\theta) \frac{d\omega}{4\pi} . cdS \quad \dots\dots\dots\dots\dots\dots(73 \cdot 1).$$

The amount leaving at the top is

$$\left(E(\theta) + \frac{d}{ds} E(\theta) . ds \right) \frac{d\omega}{4\pi} . cdS \dots\dots\dots\dots\dots(73 \cdot 2).$$

The amount absorbed in the cylinder is

$$E(\theta)\frac{d\omega}{4\pi}cdS.k\rho ds \quad\text{..........................(73·3)}.$$

Finally, a certain amount will be emitted by the material in the cylinder. This will be emitted indiscriminately in all directions so that the amount within $d\omega$ is the fraction $d\omega/4\pi$ of the whole. So far as ordinary thermal emission is concerned the amount will depend on the temperature; but we must here include also any sub-atomic energy liberated in the form of aether waves. If j is the total radiation emitted per gram per second, the amount from the mass $\rho\,ds\,dS$ in the cylinder emitted within $d\omega$ is

$$j\frac{d\omega}{4\pi}.\rho\,ds\,dS \quad\text{...........................(73·4)}.$$

Balancing the gains (73·1) and (73·4) and the losses (73·2) and (73·3) by the cylinder in a steady state, we have

$$\frac{d}{ds}E(\theta)=\frac{j\rho}{c}-k\rho E(\theta) \quad\text{.....................(73·5)}.$$

When $E(\theta)$ is a function of r and θ only, as in a star, we have

$$\frac{d}{ds}=\cos\theta\frac{d}{dr}-\frac{\sin\theta}{r}\frac{d}{d\theta}.$$

The second term on the right takes account of the fact that proceeding along ds the axis of the cylinder meets successive radii at a diminishing angle. Hence

$$\cos\theta\frac{d}{dr}E(\theta)-\frac{\sin\theta}{r}\frac{d}{d\theta}E(\theta)=\frac{j\rho}{c}-k\rho E(\theta) \quad\text{......(73·6)}.$$

74. First consider the case when r is large and the curvature of the stratification in the star can be neglected. Then (73·6) reduces to

$$\cos\theta\frac{d}{dr}E(\theta)=\frac{j\rho}{c}-k\rho E(\theta) \quad\text{..................(74·1)}.$$

Let E be the total energy-density of the radiation, H the net outward flow per second across unit surface perpendicular to r, and p_R' the actual pressure of the radiation in the radial direction (allowing for the imperfect isotropy). Then

$$\left.\begin{aligned}E&=\frac{1}{4\pi}\int E(\theta)\,d\omega\\[4pt]H/c&=\frac{1}{4\pi}\int E(\theta)\cos\theta\,d\omega\\[4pt]p_R'&=\frac{1}{4\pi}\int E(\theta)\cos^2\theta\,d\omega\end{aligned}\right\} \quad\text{..................(74·2)}.$$

The proof of the last two equations follows at once from the discussions in §§ 31 and 22 respectively.

Multiply (74·1) first by $d\omega/4\pi$ and integrate, and secondly by $d\omega \cos\theta/4\pi$ and integrate. We obtain

$$\frac{1}{c}\frac{dH}{dr} = \frac{j\rho}{c} - k\rho E \quad\dotfill(74\cdot3),$$

$$\frac{dp_R'}{dr} = -\frac{k\rho H}{c} \quad\dotfill(74\cdot4).$$

The second equation agrees with (71·1) except that the actual operative stress-component p_R' appears instead of the hydrostatic approximation p_R. Reference to (74·2) shows that the error caused by using p_R does not depend on the fore-and-aft asymmetry arising from the presence of a net flow H, but on the much smaller radial-transverse asymmetry which makes the weighted mean value of $\cos^2\theta$ differ slightly from $\tfrac{1}{3}$.

Equation (74·3) can be written

$$cE = \frac{j}{k} - \frac{1}{k\rho}\frac{dH}{dr}.$$

In strict thermodynamical equilibrium with no outward flow H this becomes

$$cE = j/k,$$

or

$$j = kacT^4 \quad\dotfill(74\cdot5),$$

giving the well-known law that the emission coefficient is proportional to the absorption coefficient for different kinds of matter at the same temperature.

75. Let $E(\theta)$ be expanded in zonal harmonics, viz.

$$E(\theta) = A + BP_1(\cos\theta) + CP_2(\cos\theta) + DP_3(\cos\theta) + \dots \quad(75\cdot1).$$

By integration over a sphere,

$$E = \frac{1}{4\pi}\int E(\theta)\, d\omega = A.$$

Multiplying the series by $\cos\theta$ and integrating,

$$H/c = \frac{1}{4\pi}\int E(\theta)\, P_1(\cos\theta)\, d\omega = \frac{B}{4\pi}\int \{P_1(\cos\theta)\}^2\, d\omega = \tfrac{1}{3}B.$$

Multiplying by $P_2(\cos\theta) = \tfrac{3}{2}\cos^2\theta - \tfrac{1}{2}$, and integrating,

$$\tfrac{3}{2}(p_R' - p_R) = \frac{1}{4\pi}\int \{\tfrac{3}{2}E(\theta)\cos^2\theta - \tfrac{1}{2}E(\theta)\}\, d\omega$$

$$= \frac{C}{4\pi}\int \{P_2(\cos\theta)\}^2\, d\omega$$

$$= \tfrac{1}{5}C.$$

Hence the first three coefficients in the expansion have the interpretation

$$A = E, \qquad B = 3H/c, \qquad C = \tfrac{15}{2}(p_R' - p_R) \quad\dots\dots(75\cdot2).$$

Using the exact formula (73·6) in which curvature is taken into account we have

$$\left(\cos\theta\,\frac{d}{dr} - \frac{\sin\theta}{r}\,\frac{d}{d\theta}\right)(A + BP_1 + CP_2 + \ldots) = \frac{j\rho}{c} - k\rho\,(A + BP_1 + CP_2 + \ldots).$$

By the properties of zonal harmonics

$$\cos\theta\,.\,P_n = (nP_{n-1} + (n+1)\,P_{n+1})/(2n+1),$$

$$-\sin\theta\,\frac{dP_n}{d\theta} = \frac{n\,(n+1)}{2n+1}\,(P_{n-1} - P_{n+1}).$$

Hence equating coefficients of the corresponding harmonics on both sides, we obtain the following series of equations

$$\frac{1}{3}\frac{dB}{dr} + \frac{2}{3}\frac{B}{r} = -k\rho A + \frac{j\rho}{c} \quad\ldots\ldots(75\cdot31),$$

$$\frac{dA}{dr} + \left(\frac{2}{5}\frac{dC}{dr} + \frac{6}{5}\frac{C}{r}\right) = -k\rho B \quad\ldots\ldots\ldots(75\cdot32),$$

$$\left(\frac{2}{3}\frac{dB}{dr} - \frac{2}{3}\frac{B}{r}\right) + \left(\frac{3}{7}\frac{dD}{dr} + \frac{12}{7}\frac{D}{r}\right) = -k\rho C \quad\ldots\ldots(75\cdot33),$$

$$\left(\frac{3}{5}\frac{dC}{dr} - \frac{6}{5}\frac{C}{r}\right) + \ldots \qquad = -k\rho D \quad\ldots\ldots\ldots(75\cdot34).$$

We have already seen that the opacity of stellar material is such that a typical point in the interior of a star is cut off almost completely from any direct radiation from matter differing in temperature by more than $0°\!\cdot\!001$ (§ 71). Allowing a full difference of $0°\!\cdot\!001$ we can have the point illuminated from one direction by the radiation from matter at say $4{,}000{,}000\!\cdot\!001$ degrees and from another direction from matter at $4{,}000{,}000\!\cdot\!000$ degrees. It is this unequal illumination which is responsible for the asymmetry of $E\,(\theta)$. With the above numbers the proportional difference of intensity of the radiation in the two directions is 1 part in 10^9. Hence none of the coefficients $B, C, D, \ldots$ in (75·1) can exceed $10^{-9}\,A$.

Choose a unit of length comparable with the radius of the star and consider a point not unduly near the centre so that dB/dr and B/r are of the same order of magnitude as B; and so on for the other coefficients. Since in (75·32) dC/dr and C/r are of order not greater than $10^{-9}\,A$, it follows that $k\rho B$ is of the same order as dA/dr or A. Hence $k\rho$ must be of order 10^9 (as can be verified directly from the values we have given for the stellar opacity). Then from (75·33) we see that $k\rho C$ is of order $10^{-9}\,A$, so that C is of order $10^{-18}\,A$. It can now easily be shown that $D, (E), \ldots$ are of orders $10^{-27}\,A$, $10^{-36}\,A$, etc.*

---

* Since the equations show that $k\rho C$, $k\rho D$, $k\rho\,(E)$ are of order not greater than $10^{-9}\,A$, C and *all* subsequent coefficients are not greater than $10^{-18}\,A$. This being proved the equations now show that $k\rho D$, $k\rho\,(E)$, etc. are not greater than $10^{-18}\,A$; hence D and *all* subsequent coefficients are not greater than $10^{-27}\,A$; and so on. (The symbol (E) is used to avoid confusion with the energy-density E.)

For the region within a few thousand kilometres of the centre the argument needs modification because then B/r is of much greater magnitude than B. But in this region where the asymmetry is just beginning to manifest itself and the temperature gradient is falling to zero B is much less than $10^{-9} A$. The equations in fact show the manner in which the coefficients B, C, D, etc. tend to zero with r.

By neglecting C in comparison with A, and B in comparison with $k\rho A$, we shall introduce errors of order 1 part in 10^{18} in normal applications in the interior of a star. Hence the following results from (75·31) and (75·32) are generally true to about 18 significant figures

$$\left.\begin{aligned} k\rho A &= j\rho/c \\ dA/dr &= -k\rho B \end{aligned}\right\} \quad \dotfill (75\cdot4),$$

and by (75·2)

$$p_R' = p_R.$$

Or since $A = E$, $B = 3H/c$, we obtain

$$\left.\begin{aligned} cE &= \frac{j}{k} \\ H &= -\frac{c}{3k\rho}\frac{dE}{dr} \end{aligned}\right\} \quad \dotfill (75\cdot5).$$

These agree with previous results, but we have now indicated the degree of accuracy of the approximation.

76. We may ask further how near to the surface of the star the equations (75·5) can be used without risk of failure of the approximation. Our error is of order $(B/A)^2$. At small distances below the surface H represents the flow of radiation which will shortly emerge from the surface of the star so that $H = \frac{1}{4}acT_e^4$ by (31·1), where T_e is the effective temperature of the star. Hence by (75·2) $B = \frac{3}{4}aT_e^4$; $A = aT^4$. Thus roughly

$$(B/A)^2 = (T_e/T)^8.$$

Thus the approximation is good down to a temperature about three times the effective temperature of the star.

The possible* failure of the equation of radiative equilibrium at temperatures below say 30,000° does not concern us in the investigations we shall make. As explained in § 67 we stop working long before this point is reached, and are able to dispense with knowledge of the conditions much below 1,000,000°.

The ratio $(T_e/T)^8$ may generally be taken as a measure of the accuracy of the equations in other parts of the star. It is true that H may decrease† before arriving at the surface where its value is directly related to T_e but

---

* Actually no serious break-down occurs (§ 231).

† The spreading of the spherical wave may more than compensate for its reinforcement by supplies of liberated energy in the region traversed.

the factor is unimportant. It will be seen from this that the claim to a general accuracy of 1 part in 10^{18} is by no means an overstatement.

In the exact equation (75·31) the left side is equal to

$$\frac{1}{3r^2}\frac{d}{dr}(Br^2) = \frac{1}{cr^2}\frac{d}{dr}(Hr^2).$$

Now $4\pi r^2 H$ is the net outward flow of radiation across the sphere of radius r. It would be constant for successive spheres if no contribution to the flow were made by liberation of sub-atomic energy or other sources. Actually there must be some such liberation in order to maintain a steady state so that $d(Hr^2)/dr$ is positive. Hence (75·31) shows that $k\rho A < j\rho/c$, or

$$cE < j/k,$$

the difference being due to the inclusion in j of emission other than ordinary thermal emission.

A number of subtleties arise when we attempt to retain terms of order 10^{-18} over which we might linger for a long while if they were of any conceivable importance. For instance, a question arises as to the exact definition of the temperature. The effective temperature of the radiation is *defined* by $E = aT^4$ (§ 29). How closely will this agree with the temperature of the matter defined by the mean speed of the molecules? If sub-atomic energy is being liberated in the form of aether waves there must be a net passage of energy from aether to matter so that the radiation temperature is slightly the higher. If gravitational energy is being liberated by contraction this appears first as energy of molecular motion and the material temperature is the higher. Since the equilibrium relation $cE = j/k$ is only in error by at most 1 part in 10^{18} the two temperatures cannot differ by more than 10^{-11} of a degree.

Since energy of gravitational contraction is not liberated in the form of radiation it is not to be included in j. On the other hand, if the star is contracting the balance (73·5) is not exact; and if terms of order 10^{-18} are retained, allowance must be made for the radiation accumulating in the cylinder in consequence of the slowly changing temperature of the star. Further elaboration of these points may be left to the reader. If a sense of confusion arises from the ramifications of the inquiry, we may always return to the alternative investigation in § 71 which goes straight to the point and shows the problem in clearer perspective.

Absorption and Opacity.

77. In the foregoing work we have assumed that the absorption coefficient k is independent of the direction θ of the beam of radiation. This would only be strictly true if the composition of the radiation travelling in different directions was the same. Actually the inward-flowing radiation is of slightly lower average frequency than the outward-flowing, because it is made up of emissions from matter at slightly lower temperature. Since k varies according to the character of the radiation that is being absorbed the coefficient to be used for each stream should be that appropriate to its composition.

It has been pointed out by S. Rosseland* that this has important consequences. Consider the equations (75·5)

$$\left. \begin{aligned} j &= ckE \\ H &= -\frac{c}{3k\rho}\frac{dE}{dr} \end{aligned} \right\} \quad \dots\dots\dots\dots\dots\dots(77\cdot1).$$

If the quantities j, H, E refer to the amount of radiation between narrow limits of frequency ν to $\nu + d\nu$ these equations will be correct since k is then a constant k_ν. They are therefore correct in the differential form

$$\left. \begin{aligned} dj &= ck_\nu I\,(\nu)\,d\nu \\ dH &= -\frac{c}{3k_\nu\rho}\frac{dI\,(\nu)}{dr}\,d\nu \end{aligned} \right\} \quad \dots\dots\dots\dots\dots(77\cdot15),$$

where as usual we write $dE = I\,(\nu)\,d\nu$ for the energy-density between ν and $\nu + d\nu$. Hence integrating

$$\left. \begin{aligned} j &= c\int_0^\infty k_\nu\,I\,(\nu)\,d\nu \\ H &= -\frac{c}{3\rho}\int_0^\infty \frac{1}{k_\nu}\frac{dI\,(\nu)}{dr}\,d\nu \end{aligned} \right\} \quad \dots\dots\dots\dots\dots(77\cdot2).$$

Putting (77·2) in the form of (77·1) we write

$$j = ck_1E \quad \dots\dots\dots\dots\dots\dots(77\cdot31),$$

$$H = -\frac{c}{3k_2\rho}\frac{dE}{dr} \quad \dots\dots\dots\dots\dots\dots(77\cdot32),$$

where

$$\left. \begin{aligned} k_1 &= \int k_\nu I\,(\nu)\,d\nu \div \int I\,(\nu)\,d\nu \\ \frac{1}{k_2} &= \int \frac{1}{k_\nu}\frac{\partial I\,(\nu)}{\partial T}\,d\nu \div \int \frac{\partial I\,(\nu)}{\partial T}\,d\nu \end{aligned} \right\} \quad \dots\dots\dots\dots(77\cdot4),$$

the latter being obtained since

$$\frac{dI\,(\nu)}{dr} = \frac{\partial I\,(\nu)}{\partial T}\frac{dT}{dr}.$$

The result in brief is that the two equations (77·1) require that k shall be averaged in a different manner and if we use them simultaneously our results will be in error by an averaging factor. To distinguish the two mean values we call

k_1 the mean coefficient of absorption,

k_2 the coefficient of opacity.

* *Monthly Notices*, **84**, p. 525.

Since (77·32) is the fundamental equation used in astronomical theory, the astronomical researches lead directly to a determination of the coefficient of opacity. Attempts to calculate the absorption by a consideration of the physical processes occurring in the matter at given temperature and density usually depend on (77·31) and lead naturally to the mean coefficient of absorption. Thus the physical and the astronomical results are not strictly comparable until the averaging factor has been allowed for. We shall, of course, take account of Rosseland's correction when practicable. But in some cases the theories discussed are not sufficiently detailed to give dj for separate frequencies and only the total emission can be found; exact correction is then impossible. Averaging factors very commonly occur in statistical investigations and they are not usually so large as to disturb the rough kind of agreement which is the most we can hope for in these problems. Rosseland's factor is, however, liable to be of surprising importance and we must discuss it in some detail.

78. Since k_2 has the character of a harmonic mean and k_1 of an arithmetic mean k_2 is likely to be smaller than k_1. This prediction is not certain in all cases because the weighting is not the same for k_1 and k_2.

The fact that k_2 is a *harmonic* mean is highly important because it restricts the range within which we must seek for sources of absorption which contribute importantly to stellar opacity. Suppose, for example, that we have studied exhaustively a range of frequency ν_1 to ν_2 which contains $\frac{2}{3}$ of the whole weight of k_2; that is to say, such that

$$\int_{\nu_1}^{\nu_2} \frac{\partial I\,(\nu)}{\partial T}\, d\nu = \frac{2}{3} \int_0^\infty \frac{\partial I\,(\nu)}{\partial T}\, d\nu.$$

Let the weighted mean value of $1/k_\nu$ for this range be $1/k'$. We can now set an upper limit to k_2, because—to take the worst possible case—even if k_ν is infinite outside this range (77·4) gives

$$\frac{1}{k_2} = \frac{2}{3} \cdot \frac{1}{k'} + \frac{1}{3} \cdot \frac{1}{\infty},$$

so that $k_2 = \tfrac{3}{2} k'.$

Whatever happens beyond the limits ν_1 and ν_2, the opacity cannot be increased more than 50 per cent.

An *upper* limit to k_2 is especially valuable because the danger is that we may be unaware of some important mechanism of absorption and emission. Indeed at the present moment physical theory apparently does not indicate sufficient absorption to agree with astronomical observation and we should be glad to find an additional mode of absorption. The result just proved shows that we can narrow down our search to processes capable of absorbing and emitting frequencies between ν_1 and ν_2, and relieves us from an exhaustive discussion of very low and very high frequencies, which might be difficult and uncertain. Of course we cannot ignore the regions beyond ν_1 and ν_2 entirely, since anything like a transparent gap, wherever it occurred, might make k_2 very much less than k'. But it is easy to convince ourselves that all such windows are blocked up by the study of a single process of absorption without exhaustive treatment.

The contrast between an arithmetic mean k_1 and a harmonic mean k_2 is that, roughly speaking, in an arithmetic mean we have to fear infinite values and in a harmonic mean infinitesimal values. The latter fear is much more easily allayed than the former.

As an application of this, it has been pointed out by Rosseland that fine line absorption has no important effect on the opacity. For taking together the spectral lines (of all the elements) in the range ν_1 to ν_2—chiefly K and L lines of the X ray spectrum which are not unduly numerous—they will if of the usual narrowness cover up only a small part of the range. However opaque they may be they can only increase the mean opacity proportionately to the area, or more strictly the weight, which they block out. This leads us to expect that continuous absorption due to ionisation, and not line absorption due to excitation, will be the main cause of stellar opacity. But it is doubtful if we ought to dismiss line absorption quite so summarily. It is well known that in certain conditions spectral lines may become very broad; and although the theory of the broadening is not at present well understood we may suspect that in the stellar interior the L lines of the elements are broad. In that case the lines of the various elements may together cover the whole frequency range.

79. By Planck's Law

$$I\,(\nu) = \frac{C\nu^3}{e^{h\nu/RT} - 1},$$

so that

$$\frac{\partial I\,(\nu)}{\partial T} = \frac{Ch}{RT^2}\frac{\nu^4 e^{h\nu/RT}}{(e^{h\nu/RT} - 1)^2}.$$

Writing $h\nu/RT = x$, the weight of any range dx to be used in forming the mean value k_2 is proportional to

$$\frac{x^4 e^x dx}{(e^x - 1)^2} \quad \dots\dots\dots\dots\dots\dots\dots\dots\dots(79\cdot1).$$

From this Table 8 has been calculated giving in the second column the relative weight for each value of x and in the third column the weight of the range from 0 to x.

We see from the third column that 69 per cent. of the weight is contributed by frequencies between

$$2\cdot5RT/h \text{ and } 7RT/h.$$

At 10 million degrees the frequency RT/h corresponds to wave-length 14·3 Å, so that 69 per cent. of the weight is between 6 and 2 Å. For elements of moderate atomic weight this corresponds to L radiation. It is this region that we must search particularly for sources of stellar opacity.

When dealing with sources of continuous absorption which operate chiefly in the above stretch of spectrum, we shall often drop the distinction between absorption and opacity for approximate treatment. The correction necessary to reduce k_1 to k_2 will be referred to as Rosseland's correction.

Table 8.

Weights for Calculating Opacity.

$x = h\nu/RT$	Weight at x	Weight 0 to x
0	·000	·0000
$\frac{1}{2}$	·244	·0016
1	·921	·0121
$1\frac{1}{2}$	1·872	·038
2	2·897	·084
$2\frac{1}{2}$	3·806	·150
3	4·467	·230
4	4·864	·413
5	4·270	·591
6	3·229	·736
7	2·194	·840
8	1·375	·908
9	·810	·949
10	·454	·973
∞	·000	1·000

80. Consider two frequencies ν' and ν'', the first in a strong absorption line or band and the second in a region of little absorption. If we were considering the outer atmosphere of a star the absorption would cause the radiation to be lacking in the constituent ν'. But it is not so in the interior of the star, where thermodynamic equilibrium is nearly perfect. Strong absorption is compensated by strong emission, and ν' and ν'' are present in the ordinary proportions indicated by Planck's Law. The difference is that whereas the ν'' radiation is on the whole flowing outwards the ν' radiation is practically brought to a standstill.

If, for example, ν'' is on the average absorbed and re-emitted once in 100 cm. path and ν' once in 1 cm. path, the difference of intensity of the outward and inward streams of ν'' corresponds to the difference of temperature of the points from which these streams were emitted, viz. the temperature drop in 200 cm. The difference of intensity of the outward and inward

ν' radiation corresponds to the temperature drop in 2 cm. The net outward flow for ν' is thus only one-hundredth of that of ν''.

If ν' represents 1 per cent. of the radiation and ν'' the remaining 99 per cent., the absorption-line at ν' will double the total amount of absorption and emission going on; although constituting but a small part of the radiation it does as much business as all the rest put together. This means that k_1 is doubled. But as regards opacity the effect is that 1 per cent. of the radiation suffers an almost complete check, and the rest flows through as before. Hence k_2 is only increased 1 per cent.

CHAPTER VI

SOLUTION OF THE EQUATIONS

81. The fundamental equations of the theory of the interior of a star are the hydrostatic equation (54·3) and the equation of radiative equilibrium (71·1), viz.

$$\frac{dP}{dr} = - g\rho \qquad \qquad (81\cdot1),$$

$$\frac{dp_R}{dr} = - \frac{k\rho H}{c} \qquad \qquad (81\cdot2).$$

The whole pressure P is made up of gas pressure p_G and radiation pressure p_R, so that

$$P = p_G + p_R \qquad \qquad (81\cdot3).$$

From (81·1) and (81·2)

$$dp_R = \frac{kH}{cg}\, dP \qquad \qquad (81\cdot4).$$

In a steady state the amount of radiation $4\pi r^2 H$ flowing per second outwards across a sphere of radius r must be equal to the amount of energy liberated within the sphere, probably from subatomic sources. Denoting by L_r the liberation of energy per second within the sphere, we have

$$H = L_r/4\pi r^2, \qquad g = GM_r/r^2,$$

so that

$$\frac{H}{g} = \frac{1}{4\pi G}\frac{L_r}{M_r} \qquad \qquad (81\cdot5).$$

The quantity L_r/M_r is the average rate of liberation of energy per gram for the region interior to r. Presumably this liberation is greater at the hot dense centre than in the outer parts, and L_r/M_r will decrease as r increases and the successively cooler layers are brought into the average. But we do not anticipate that the decrease will be rapid. The rate of generation of energy may decrease rapidly with temperature, but the change of L_r/M_r will be much less marked since it is toned down by the averaging.

Let M be the mass of the star, and L the total emission of energy per second from its surface. (The observed bolometric magnitude is determined by L.) Then L/M is the boundary value of L_r/M_r. We set

$$\frac{L_r}{M_r} = \frac{\eta L}{M} \qquad \qquad (81\cdot6),$$

so that η increases from 1 at the boundary to some unknown but not very large value at the centre. The form of the function η depends on the unknown law of liberation of subatomic energy, but it may be expected to be approximately the same for all stars.

Substituting in (81·4) we have

$$dp_R = \frac{L}{4\pi cGM} \cdot \eta k \, dP \quad \dotfill (81\cdot7).$$

82. We are about to introduce an approximation with regard to the behaviour of ηk; but before doing so we note that the exact equation (81·7) enables us to set an upper limit to the opacity k in any star (perfect gas or not) for which L and M are known by observation.

The temperature must in any case increase inwards and it seems extremely unlikely that the density can diminish inwards. If both temperature and density increase the material pressure p_G must increase. Hence for an inward step dp_G is positive, so that by (81·3)

$$dp_R < dP.$$

Then by (81·7)

$$\frac{L\eta k}{4\pi cGM} < 1,$$

and, since $\eta > 1$,

$$k < 4\pi cGM/L$$
$$< 25100 M/L.$$

For Capella (§ 13), $M = 8\cdot3.10^{33}$, $L = 4\cdot8.10^{35}$. Hence

$$k < 435 \text{ c.g.s. units.}$$

Similarly for Sirius we find $k < 630$, and for the sun $k < 13,200$. Note that k cannot rise above these values *in any part* of the star unless there is a reversal of the density gradient.

The physical explanation of these upper limits is that the radiation observed to be emitted must work its way through the star, and if there were too much obstruction it would blow up the star.

The upper limits found for Capella and Sirius are sufficiently low to narrow the field of speculation. Absorption coefficients higher than these have been measured in laboratory experiments. The upper limits in fact are only 4 or 5 times greater than the definitive values of k found later.

83. We shall now work out the case in which ηk is constant throughout the star. This requires that the absorption coefficient should be nearly constant, decreasing a little towards the centre to counterbalance the increase of η. Reasons will be given in due course for believing that the absorption coefficient does behave in this way, and that $\eta k = $ const. is a very close approximation. One simplification resulting from the assumption that ηk is constant is that radiation pressure and gas pressure are in the same ratio throughout the star.

Accordingly let

$$\eta k = \text{const.} = k_0 \quad \dotfill (83\cdot1),$$

so that k_0 is in a sense the boundary value of k. But it must be understood that the value of k in the photosphere may be widely different from k_0.

As explained in § 67 we have not much concern with the outer regions of the star, and there is no need to extend the assumption (83·1) into the low-temperature part of the star.

Integrating (81·7) $$p_R = \frac{Lk_0}{4\pi cGM}\, P \dotfill (83\cdot 2).$$

Strictly speaking, there is a small constant of integration of the order 1 dyne per sq. cm., since radiation pressure does not vanish at the surface. We neglect this in comparison with the pressure of the order 10^{12} dynes per sq. cm. in the main part of the interior.

Introduce a constant β, defined by

$$\left.\begin{array}{l} p_R = (1-\beta)\, P \\ p_G = \beta P \end{array}\right\} \dotfill (83\cdot 3).$$

Then by (83·2) $$L = \frac{4\pi cGM\,(1-\beta)}{k_0} \dotfill (83\cdot 4).$$

The important equation (83·4) does not require any serious consideration of the low-temperature part of the star. We have written L/M for the boundary value of L_r/M_r; but it is not necessary that our "boundary" should coincide with the surface of the star. The only object in taking it at or near the surface is in order to have in our equation quantities determined directly by observation; but this is sufficiently provided for if our "boundary" is taken where the temperature is say $\frac{1}{10}$ of the central temperature. By the method of § 67 it is shown that the mass up to this point is practically the whole mass of the star. Also the radiation flowing through this boundary is practically the radiation which flows out of the star since the small mass beyond can form no appreciable sink or source of energy. Thus it is sufficient to develop the theory so far as to obtain the expression for L/M for the high-temperature part of the star; it is then justifiable to substitute for this in practice the observed surface value of L/M.

So far the formulae are valid whether the material is a perfect gas or not.

Perfect Gases.

84. Now consider a star for which the material is a perfect gas so that it obeys the gas law

$$p_G = \frac{\mathfrak{R}}{\mu}\, \rho T.$$

Since also $$p_R = \tfrac{1}{3}aT^4,$$

we have by (83·3) $$P = \frac{\mathfrak{R}\rho T}{\beta\mu} = \frac{aT^4}{3\,(1-\beta)} \dotfill (84\cdot 1).$$

Eliminating T we obtain

$$P = \kappa \rho^{\frac{4}{3}} \qquad \dots\dots\dots\dots\dots\dots\dots(84\cdot2),$$

where

$$\kappa = \left\{ \frac{3\mathfrak{R}^4 (1 - \beta)}{a\mu^4\beta^4} \right\}^{\frac{1}{3}} \qquad \dots\dots\dots\dots\dots\dots(84\cdot3).$$

The distribution is thus one of the polytropic forms discussed in Chapter IV, viz. that given by $\gamma = \frac{4}{3}$, $n = 3$ (Table 6). Setting $n = 3$ in the second equation of (57·3)

$$\left(\frac{GM}{M'}\right)^2 = \frac{(4\kappa)^3}{4\pi G}$$

$$= \frac{4^3}{4\pi G} \frac{3\mathfrak{R}^4 (1 - \beta)}{a\mu^4\beta^4}.$$

Hence

$$1 - \beta = CM^2\mu^4\beta^4 \qquad \dots\dots\dots\dots\dots\dots(84\cdot4),$$

where

$$C = \frac{4\pi G^3 a}{3 \cdot 4^3 \mathfrak{R}^4 M'^2} = 7\cdot83 \cdot 10^{-70} \qquad \dots\dots\dots\dots(84\cdot5).$$

Here the mass of the star is expressed in grams and the molecular weight in terms of the hydrogen atom. It is more convenient to express the mass of the star in terms of the sun's mass ($\odot$). Since $\odot = 1\cdot985 \cdot 10^{33}$ gm., (84·4) becomes

$$1 - \beta = \cdot00309 \, (M/\odot)^2 \, \mu^4\beta^4 \qquad \dots\dots\dots\dots(84\cdot6).$$

The value of β is found by solving this quartic equation; it can then be substituted in (83·4). We notice that β depends only on the mass and mean molecular weight of the star and is independent of its radius and opacity.

Estimates of μ depend on a discussion of the ionisation in the interior (Chapter X). For most stars the value is probably about 2·2; it may be slightly modified according to the temperature and density of the particular star considered.

Table 9, containing the values of $1 - \beta$ for various masses and assumed molecular weights, is given for the purpose of forming a general idea of the conditions. A more extensive table intended for use in practical calculations will be found in § 100.

Table 9.

Values of $1 - \beta$.

Mass (Sun = 1)	$\mu = 2\cdot2$	$\mu = 3\cdot5$	$\mu = 30$
$\frac{1}{4}$	·004	·026	·738
$\frac{1}{2}$	·017	·082	·810
1	·057	·195	·864
2	·151	·344	·903
4	·292	·492	·931
8	·444	·620	·951
50	·747	·836	·980

85. The quantity $1 - \beta$ represents the ratio of radiation pressure to the whole pressure. We have seen in § 15 that this has probably an intimate connection with the aggregation of the material of the universe into stars of a standard mass. We there suggested that stars would be likely to form with radiation pressure between 15 per cent. and 50 per cent. of the whole—the idea being that greater radiation pressure would be highly dangerous to the stability of the star, whilst the aggregations would naturally reach a mass at which the risk began.

With this criterion, $\mu = 2 \cdot 2$ gives a standard mass from 2 to 10 times the sun's mass, and $\mu = 3 \cdot 5$ a mass $\frac{3}{4}$ to 4 times the sun's mass. The latter is nearer to the general average of the stars; perhaps a rather higher molecular weight would fit still better. We have suggested two possible explanations of this (1) that the critical period occurs early in the aggregation of the matter into stars when temperature and ionisation are low, so that μ is higher than in fully developed stars, (2) that stellar masses decrease somewhat in the course of evolution. Judging from their luminosity, stars in the earliest stage (K and M giants) seldom have masses below 2. In any case, we are scarcely in a position to attach importance to a factor of 2 or 3, and may well feel satisfied with the general coincidence in order of magnitude between stellar masses and the critical range for radiation pressure.

If there were any doubt as to the existence of strong ionisation inside a star, the third column of Table 9 could be appealed to. For undissociated atoms we should expect a molecular weight 30 or higher and the table shows that very intense radiation pressure would result. It would be difficult to accept the conclusion that in Capella 93 per cent. of the weight of the material is supported by pressure of the outrushing radiation; and it is satisfactory that the ionisation predicted by thermodynamical theory renders the state of the star much less precarious.

Luminosity and Opacity.

86. Neglecting possible small changes of μ dependent on the temperature and density, $1 - \beta$ is a function of the mass only. Hence by (83·4)—

For gaseous stars of the same mass the total radiation L is inversely proportional to the opacity k_0.

This fundamental result can be established on a wider basis without using the approximation $\eta k = \text{const.}$

Consider two homologous stars in which corresponding regions contain the same mass but differ in linear scale. We shall assume (1) that the relative distribution of the source of energy is the same for both so that L_r/L is the same at corresponding points, and (2) that k varies with ρ and T according to some law of the form $\rho^x T^y$, so that the distribution of k is homologous if the distribution of ρ and T is homologous in the two stars.

Alteration of the linear dimensions in the ratio l will alter ρ in the ratio l^{-3} and g in the ratio l^{-2}. To preserve homology p_G and p_R at corresponding points must keep the same ratio to one another. This means that ρT must change in the same ratio as T^4. Hence T changes in the ratio l^{-1}, and p_R and p_G in the ratio l^{-4}. Inserting these changes in the equations of equilibrium (81·1) and (81·7), the first continues to be satisfied and the second is satisfied if

$$\eta k L$$

is unaltered at every point. The assumptions stated above secure that η is unaltered and that k is altered in the same ratio at every point. Hence the sufficient condition is that kL is unaltered, or that L is inversely proportional to k.

In putting forward the giant and dwarf theory of evolution Russell and Hertzsprung laid stress on the fact that observational statistics show a series of bright (giant) stars which have about the same luminosity from type M to type A, as well as a series of rapidly diminishing brightness from A to M (dwarfs). The giants all have low density so that our results for a perfect gas are unquestionably applicable to them. Assuming that there is no important change of average mass along the giant series*, the approximate constancy of L shows that k_0 must also be approximately constant along the series.

This evidence is admittedly rough. In Russell's type-luminosity diagram the giant series lies along a fairly horizontal line indicating constant absolute visual magnitude. This must be corrected to reduce to bolometric magnitude and also for effects of selection of the data. Then the weak point arises that we have very little direct evidence as to how constant is the average mass along the line. Perhaps also allowance should be made for a slightly smaller molecular weight at the hotter end of the series.

But rough as it is this indication is remarkably suggestive, because between type M and type A there is a great change in the internal condition of the star and, as we shall presently see, the internal temperature rises tenfold. It would be something to the good to be able to say definitely that the change of k_0 is not more than in the ratio 20 : 1. In physical experiments X ray absorption is a rapidly varying function of the wavelength of the radiation and therefore of the temperature; a range of 1000 : 1 is by no means excluded.

87. To proceed further we must be able to compare the internal temperatures of stars of different spectral types. The fundamental formulae so far obtained in this chapter are

$$1 - \beta = \cdot00309 \, (M/\odot)^2 \, \mu^4 \beta^4,$$
$$L = 4\pi c G M \, (1 - \beta)/k_0.$$

* We have purposely stopped short at type A since beyond this (in types B and O) the average mass is known to be considerably greater.

To these may be added

$$\frac{T^3}{\rho} = \frac{3\Re \,(1 - \beta)}{a\mu\beta} \qquad \dots\dots\dots\dots\dots\dots(87\cdot1),$$

which is contained in (84·1). This shows that T^3/ρ, which is constant throughout any one star, is also constant for all stars of the same mass. (As usual we neglect possible small differences of μ.)

Hence in stars of the same mass *the temperature at homologous points in the interior varies as the cube root of the mean density*.

The effective temperature follows a different law. The levels where the temperature is equal to T_e (somewhere in the photosphere) are not at homologous points; in fact as the density and temperature of the star increase, the photosphere comes relatively nearer to the surface. By (31·1) the black-body radiation of matter at temperature T is

$$\tfrac{1}{4}acT^4 \text{ per sq. cm. per sec.}$$

hence from a sphere of radius R the radiation per second is

$$L = 4\pi R^2 . \tfrac{1}{4}acT^4 = \pi acR^2T^4.$$

Accordingly the effective temperature of a star is *defined* by

$$L = \pi acR^2T_e{}^4 \qquad \dots\dots\dots\dots\dots\dots\dots(87\cdot2),$$

since this gives the temperature of the black body giving the same amount of radiation as the star.

The mean density of the star is

$$\rho_m = \frac{M}{\tfrac{4}{3}\pi R^3} = \frac{3\sqrt{\pi}}{4} \,(ac)^{\frac{3}{2}} \frac{M}{L^{\frac{3}{2}}} \,T_e{}^6 \qquad \dots\dots\dots\dots(87\cdot3)$$

by (87·2). The central density being a constant multiple of ρ_m we have

$$\rho_c \propto ML^{-\frac{3}{2}} T_e{}^6,$$

so that by (87·1) we have for stars of fixed mass

$$T_c \propto L^{-\frac{1}{2}} T_e{}^2 \qquad \dots\dots\dots\dots\dots\dots(87\cdot4).$$

We may take the effective temperature for type M to be 3000°, and for type A 10,500°. Hence if L is constant (as the observations appear to indicate) the range of central temperature is 12 : 1. The range of mean density should be the cube of this—about 2000 : 1—and this is in accordance with our general knowledge of the densities of these types.

For the reasons already stated it is difficult to judge how closely the rule that L is constant for stars of the same mass is supported by observation. As bias may enter into our estimates it may be best to quote an opinion formed by the writer before he had arrived at any theory as to what the variations of k_0 ought to be*. He then concluded from the observations that k_0 might vary as rapidly as $T^{\frac{1}{2}}$ or $T^{-\frac{1}{2}}$ but was not likely to pass beyond these limits. This corresponds to a range of 3·5 : 1

* *Zeits. für Physik*, 7, p. 368.

in k_0 for the series of stars from M to A, and therefore to an equal range of L. This is equivalent to a range of 1·4 bolometric magnitudes. No idea was formed as to which direction of variation was the more likely.

Having found that k_0 is tolerably constant throughout a 12-fold range of temperature it would seem natural to conclude that at stellar temperatures it tends to a constant value independent of physical conditions altogether. The opacity would then be the same for all stars whatever their masses. This conclusion, which was accepted in the writer's earlier papers, turns out to be fallacious. We are now convinced that k does indeed vary rapidly with the temperature, but it also varies with the density. The major part of the variation is proportional to ρ/T^3 which is a constant for stars of the same mass (and also within any one star). Thus the main variation conceals itself in our first study of the observational data, and it springs a surprise on us when we begin to compare stars of different masses.

88. The approximate constancy of k_0 from star to star in the giant series which we have *found* must be distinguished from the approximate constancy of k (and more strictly of ηk) within a single star which we have *assumed*. A little consideration will show that there has been no vicious circle. If ηk is variable within a star we may still expect that some kind of average value of it will be determined by (83·4); then comparison with observation gives us the unexpected result that nearly the same average value holds in other stars in spite of great differences of physical condition.

But having now found that the absorption changes very little from star to star notwithstanding great differences of temperature, it seems so much the more likely that we were right in assuming that its variations within a single star could be neglected. A tenfold range of temperature covers all the interior of a star with which it is necessary for us to deal, and we have verified the approximate constancy over a tenfold range of temperature from star to star. We have verified it for stars presumed to be of the same mass and therefore subject to the limitation $\rho/T^3 = \text{con-}$ stant; but that is just the condition satisfied by different parts of the same star. Thus we have already evidence that our first wild shot is likely to be a tolerable approximation. We now turn to some results which suggest that it may be an especially good approximation.

The Approximation $\eta k = constant$.

89. Anticipating the results of the theoretical investigation of absorption in Chapter IX we accept as the law of absorption

$$k \propto \rho/\mu T^{\frac{7}{2}} \qquad \dots \dots \dots \dots \dots \dots (89 \cdot 1),$$

which when applied to the different parts of a single star (or to stars of the same mass) reduces by (87·1) to

$$k \propto T^{-\frac{1}{2}} \quad ....(89\cdot2).$$

This coincides with one of the limits suggested in § 87 as being consistent with the observed magnitudes of the giant series. At present the physical theory of absorption is not definitive, and we must not lay undue stress on the odd half power of the temperature. But (89·1) is the law which appears most likely according to our limited knowledge and it is appropriate to develop its consequences fully for comparison with astronomical observation.

The function η depends on the relative distribution in different parts of the star of the source of stellar energy—a distribution at present unknown. What makes progress possible is that η is comparatively insensitive to very great changes in the assumed distribution of the source. The general effect of such changes can be seen in the following way. The temperature gradient in a star achieves two purposes: it gives a pressure gradient great enough to distend the mass M of the star against gravity and it drives the radiation L through the obstructing opacity to the surface. Now L comes from varying depths according to the distribution of the source. If we concentrate the source of L to the centre a greater proportion of L comes from the deeper parts and more temperature gradient is required near the centre to drive it through. Or, if the temperature drop at our disposal is limited by the known mass and distension of the star (i.e. to the amount required to achieve the first purpose) we must be content with less L. Hence in general L/M will be decreased by concentrating the source to the centre. What concerns us is the average optical depth of the source of energy below the surface. To evaluate this precisely we must know the law of distribution of the source. But it is clear that, whether the source is spread uniformly over the mass or whether it is strongly concentrated to the centre, the difference in average depth will be a factor of the order 2 or 3 of no great consequence for a first approximation.

90. Let ϵ be the rate of liberation of energy per gram. We can represent various degrees of concentration of the source to the centre by taking ϵ to vary as T^s within a single star.

First consider the law $\epsilon \propto T$. Then the average value of ϵ within a sphere of radius r will be proportional to the average temperature within the sphere. Comparing $r = 0$ and $r = R$, we have

$$\frac{\eta_c}{1} = \frac{T_c}{T_m},$$

since the ratio of the η's for two spheres is the ratio of the average values of ϵ in the two spheres. (Central values are denoted by the suffix c.) By (62·1) $T_m/T_c = 0·584$. Hence

$$\eta_c = 1·7.$$

If we proceed from the centre to a distance including 95 per cent. of the mass the temperature drops in the ratio 1 : 0·21 (Table 6). Hence by (89·2) k increases in the ratio 1 : 2·2. Meanwhile η undergoes practically its full decrease in the ratio 1·7 : 1. Evidently ηk keeps remarkably steady in the main part of the mass of the star. A more detailed calculation for intermediate points is given in Table 10.

The law $\epsilon \propto T$ represents a moderate concentration of the source of energy to the centre*. If the source is subatomic we can well imagine that a much stronger concentration occurs. It is desirable therefore to consider $\epsilon \propto T^2$ and $\epsilon \propto T^4$. Results obtained by rough calculation of η are given for four different laws in Table 10. The star is divided into 10 shells of equal mass, and the values of T, η and $\eta T^{-\frac{1}{2}}$ are given for the limit of each shell, the central temperature being taken as unity†.

Table 10.

Test of constancy of $\eta T^{-\frac{1}{2}}$.

M_r/M	T	$\epsilon = \text{const.}$	$\epsilon \propto T$		$\epsilon \propto T^2$		$\epsilon \propto T^4$	
		$\eta T^{-\frac{1}{2}}$	η	$\eta T^{-\frac{1}{2}}$	η	$\eta T^{-\frac{1}{2}}$	η	$\eta T^{-\frac{1}{2}}$
0·0	1·00	1·00	1·70	1·70	2·57	2·57	4·71	4·71
0·1	0·88	1·07	1·57	1·68	2·18	2·32	3·38	3·60
0·2	0·80	1·12	1·49	1·67	1·97	2·20	2·81	3·14
0·3	0·73	1·17	1·41	1·65	1·81	2·12	2·40	2·81
0·4	0·66	1·23	1·36	1·67	1·67	2·06	2·07	2·55
0·5	0·60	1·29	1·31	1·69	1·54	1·99	1·80	2·33
0·6	0·53	1·37	1·25	1·72	1·41	1·94	1·58	2·17
0·7	0·46	1·47	1·19	1·76	1·31	1·93	1·40	2·06
0·8	0·38	1·62	1·13	1·84	1·20	1·95	1·24	2·02
0·9	0·23	1·89	1·07	2·02	1·10	2·08	1·11	2·10
Mean		1·32		1·74		2·12		2·75

The constancy of $\eta T^{-\frac{1}{2}}$ is best for $\epsilon \propto T$, but it is also reasonably close for the other laws. In Table 10 T_c has been taken as unit, so that

$$T^{-\frac{1}{2}} = k/k_c.$$

* The law $\epsilon \propto T$ also corresponds to the contraction theory of stellar energy if the star passes through a series of homologous states.

† The solution based on the approximation $\eta k = \text{const.}$ is used to calculate these values; so that, for example, the values of $\eta T^{-\frac{1}{2}}$ are only to be trusted if they turn out to be reasonably constant. The table tests the first approximation; it would be a dubious procedure to use it as a starting-point for a second approximation.

Hence $$\eta T^{-\frac{1}{2}} = \eta k/k_c = k_0/k_c,$$

where k_0 is the constant introduced in § 83.

If $\eta T^{-\frac{1}{2}}$ is not quite constant the closest approximation to k_0/k_c will be given by using the mean value of $\eta T^{-\frac{1}{2}}$ given at the foot of the table. Hence (83·4) may be written

$$L = \frac{4\pi cGM (1 - \beta)}{\alpha k_c} \ldots\ldots\ldots\ldots\ldots(90·1),$$

where $\qquad \alpha = 1·32 \qquad 1·74 \qquad 2·12 \qquad 2·75$

for $\qquad \epsilon \propto$ const. $\qquad T \qquad T^2 \qquad T^4$

respectively. The brightness diminishes as the concentration of the source to the centre increases, as already foreseen. When numerical results are required we shall generally adopt $\alpha = 2·5$ representing a fairly strong concentration to the centre.

Point-source of Energy.

91. It will appear in later Chapters that the observed brightness of the stars is less than that predicted by present physical theories and that it is very difficult to find a plausible explanation of the discordance. The predicted brightness is decreased by concentrating the source of energy towards the centre and the discordance thereby lessened. We inquire what is the maximum possible change that can be made in this way on the most extreme suppositions. We therefore consider now the limit when the concentration is complete and the source of stellar energy is a point-source at the centre*.

This problem can only be solved by very laborious numerical calculations; but it seems worth while to carry out an accurate calculation for this limiting case in order that we may know the extreme margin of error entailed by our present ignorance of the laws of liberation of subatomic energy.

The differential equations of the theory are

$$dp_R = - k\rho Hdr/c \ldots\ldots\ldots\ldots\ldots(91·1),$$
$$dP = - g\rho dr \ldots\ldots\ldots\ldots\ldots(91·2).$$

For a point-source at the centre emitting the whole of the energy L ultimately radiated by the star

$$H = L/4\pi r^2,$$

and the adopted law of absorption is

$$k = k_1\rho/T^{\frac{1}{2}},$$

* *Monthly Notices*, **85**, p. 408.

where k_1 is a constant. We take μ constant throughout the star, the effect of varying μ being reserved for discussion in § 94. Hence (91·1) becomes

$$dp_R = -\frac{k_1 L}{4\pi c}\frac{\rho^2}{r^2 T^{\frac{1}{2}}}dr \dots\dots\dots\dots\dots(91\cdot3).$$

With (91·2) and (91·3) we carry on a quadrature for P and p_R. After each step we find T and ρ from P and p_R. The mass of the added shell is computed from the values of ρ and added to the current total; hence the new value of g is found. We are then ready to determine dp_R and dP for the next step dr. The usual devices of quadrature are employed, including the guessing of half-way values to be subsequently checked.

The only serious trouble arises with regard to starting values. The mass M and radius R of the star are only found at the end of the calculation; in their place we must have two disposable initial conditions at the start. Unfortunately we can only make a beginning by fixing *three* disposable constants, viz. the constant $k_1 L$ for the star and the temperature T and density ρ at the starting-point*. We thus over-condition the problem and generally fail to reach a solution. The failure betrays itself by p_G falling to zero whilst p_R is still large or *vice versa*, thus violating the boundary condition that both vanish almost simultaneously. In that case we must modify one of the initial quantities, say T, and try again. After many trials we contrive to straddle the true solution sufficiently closely. Of course a great amount of calculation is wasted on unsuccessful trials.

The following value was taken

$$\log_{10} k_1 L = 62\cdot6590,$$

and the solution began at $r = 0\cdot9.10^{11}$ cm. with an adopted density $0\cdot01$. These values ultimately fix M and R. The temperature at the starting-point was varied until two solutions were obtained which kept close together until reasonably near the edge of the star, and then failed in opposite ways, i.e. p_G ran off to zero prematurely in one case and p_R in the other. The solutions gave respectively $9\cdot687.10^{33}$ and $9\cdot706.10^{33}$ for the mass M_r up to $r = 8\cdot1.10^{11}$; and as little mass remained to be added the limits were close enough to fix the mass with ample accuracy.

Finally, as a complete check suitable† starting values of P, p_R and M_r at $r = 8\cdot1.10^{11}$ were interpolated, and the solution carried backwards towards the centre with double the number of intermediate steps. Working in this direction the mass M_r is stripped off in successive shells and the test is that M_r must just reach zero at the centre. The test was well

---

* The density at the centre is zero, the mass being driven away by the intense radiation pressure; so we start at some fixed distance from the centre where the density is still very low and the interior mass is just beginning to be of account.

† I.e. suitable for carrying the solution considerably further outwards before p_G or p_R ran off to zero.

fulfilled and it was possible to go beyond the original starting-point to $r = 0.5 \cdot 10^{11}$; the small mass then remaining would fill the interior with mean density ·0038 which is (as nearly as we can judge) in the proper relation to the actual density ·0065 at the point reached. There were 76 steps in this final calculation and the results at every fourth step are given in Table 11. The adopted value of μ was 2·2.

Table 11.

Solution for a Point-source.

r	M_r	ρ	T	p_R	p_G
·5	·0020	·652	6·93	5·889	1·697
·9	·0234	·989	6·68	5·065	2·477
1·3	·0941	1·273	6·43	4·344	3·070
1·7	·2536	1·501	6·16	3·675	3·473
2·1	·5435	1·659	5·88	3·043	3·660
2·5	·997	1·726	5·57	2·452	3·609
2·9	1·628	1·697	5·24	1·916	3·336
3·3	2·422	1·578	4·88	1·448	2·892
3·7	3·337	1·391	4·51	1·058	2·356
4·1	4·313	1·166	4·14	·7489	1·811
4·5	5·286	·934	3·77	·5144	1·321
4·9	6·198	·719	3·41	·3441	·9202
5·3	7·012	·535	3·07	·2250	·6162
5·7	7·707	·388	2·74	·1443	·3990
6·1	8·278	·274	2·44	·0909	·2511
6·5	8·734	·1895	2·17	·05641	·1543
6·9	9·088	·1288	1·92	·03448	·09268
7·3	9·356	·0861	1·69	·02071	·05456
7·7	9·554	·0567	1·48	·01215	·03146
8·1	9·699	·0372	1·28	·00675	·01780
Unit 10^{11}	10^{33}	10^{-2}	10^6	10^{12}	10^{12}

We see from the trend of the column M_r that not much mass remains to be added after the last line of the table. The small amount to come, computed by the methods of § 67, is found to be $\Delta M = 0.26 \cdot 10^{33}$ gm. The additional radius, which is not required with any great accuracy, is also approximately calculated to be $\Delta R = 3.25 \cdot 10^{11}$ cm.

92. Our result then is that a star for which

$$M = 9.96 \cdot 10^{33} \text{ gm.} = 5.02 \times \odot,$$
$$R = 11.35 \cdot 10^{11} \text{ cm.}$$

emits radiation at a rate given by

$$\log_{10} k_1 L = 62.6590.$$

For comparison we calculate by our previous methods the radiation L'

from the same star if the source obeys the law $\epsilon \propto T$, this being the law for which our ordinary method is most accurate. The result is

$$\log_{10} k_1 L' = 63 \cdot 0467,$$

so that $\qquad\qquad \log (L'/L) = 0 \cdot 388,$

corresponding to a magnitude difference $0^{\mathrm{m}} \cdot 97$.

The point-source gives the lowest possible brightness and we may take the law $\epsilon \propto T$ as giving the greatest possible brightness, since the concentration of the source to the centre can scarcely be less than this. We could split the difference by adopting $\alpha = 2 \cdot 75$ in $(90 \cdot 1)$. The extreme uncertainty (not the probable uncertainty) due to ignorance of the law of subatomic energy would then be $\pm \, 0^{\mathrm{m}} \cdot 5$.

The foregoing numerical solution applies only to stars of mass $5 \cdot 02 \times \odot$, but it can be adapted to any assigned radius of the star since it is easily proved that an alteration of radius leaves the solution homologous. The magnitude difference $0^{\mathrm{m}} \cdot 97$ between L and L' does not depend on the radius. It will no doubt change with the mass of the star, presumably being less for the less massive stars. This could only be tested by repeating the whole work with other constants. But our main purpose is achieved by calculation for a single mass since the discrepancy referred to at the beginning of § 91 is shown by all stars. In particular it was desired to investigate the problem for a mass near that of Capella for which the best observational data are available*.

Attention may be called to a few points of interest in Table 11. The ratio of p_R to p_G in the outer parts settles down to a value near $0 \cdot 37$; for the usual solution for the same star the ratio $(1 - \beta)/\beta$ is $0 \cdot 52$ throughout. In the main part of the mass the point-source gives slightly more uniform temperature and considerably more uniform density than the usual solution.

93. The numerical results obtained in the trial solutions bring home to us very vividly the fact that the general internal conditions determine the surface conditions and not *vice versa*. We find that two solutions which are scarcely distinguishable to four significant figures through $\frac{9}{10}$ of the mass of the star will diverge rapidly in opposite directions before the boundary is reached. Practically any kind of distribution in the outer layers can be tacked on to the same solution for the main part of the mass (i.e. the same to the number of significant figures commonly employed).

At first sight it might be thought that the solution must depend on the surface conditions because we actually employed a boundary condition, viz. that p_R and p_G vanish together, to decide the value of T corresponding to $r = 0 \cdot 9$, $\rho = 0 \cdot 01$; other trial values of T were rejected because they

---

* It was also thought best to choose a star with fairly large radiation pressure, since this brings in a complication which makes it less easy to prophesy the result.

failed to satisfy this. But here "vanish" must be understood in the ordinary physical sense, i.e. "become insignificant"; and p_R and p_G are insignificant for the present purposes when they become less than, say, 10^8 dynes per sq. cm. Any more refined expression of the boundary condition is quite superfluous. It is after all only commonsense that we shall not seriously disturb the internal condition of a star by applying a trivial radiation pressure or gas pressure of the order 100 atmospheres to its surface; but it is interesting to trace in the numerical calculations how rapidly the effects of such surface disturbances fade out as we descend.

Variable Molecular Weight.

94. Ionisation of the atoms is favoured by high temperature and by low density. In general, the influence of temperature predominates and we must expect the ionisation to increase as we go towards the centre of the star. This involves a gradual decrease of molecular weight towards the centre, the same atomic weight representing an increasing number of independently moving particles or "molecules."

In order to study a molecular weight decreasing inwards we consider laws of the form

$$\mu = \mu_1 T^{-s},$$

and find the modification of our former results for constant μ in § 84. We use the approximation $\eta k = \text{const.}$

Equation (84·1) now becomes

$$P = \frac{\Re \rho T^{1+s}}{\beta \mu_1} = \frac{a T^4}{3 (1 - \beta)} \quad \dots\dots\dots\dots\dots(94\cdot1),$$

so that

$$\rho = \frac{a \mu_1 \beta}{3 \Re (1 - \beta)} T^{3-s} \quad \dots\dots\dots\dots\dots(94\cdot21).$$

Hence

$$P = \kappa \rho^\gamma \quad \dots\dots\dots\dots\dots(94\cdot22),$$

where

$$\gamma = 4/(3 - s) \quad \dots\dots\dots\dots\dots(94\cdot23),$$

$$\kappa = \frac{a}{3 (1 - \beta)} \left\{ \frac{3 \Re (1 - \beta)}{a \mu_1 \beta} \right\}^\gamma \quad \dots\dots\dots\dots\dots(94\cdot24).$$

Setting as usual

$$\gamma = 1 + 1/n,$$

$$n = \frac{3 - s}{1 + s} \quad \dots\dots\dots\dots\dots(94\cdot3),$$

and the distribution is of the polytropic type treated in Chapter IV.

By (57·2)

$$\left(\frac{GM}{M'} \right)^2 = \frac{1}{a^2 \phi_0^{n-3}} = \frac{(n + 1)^n \kappa^n}{4\pi G} (n + 1)^{3-n} \left(\frac{P_0}{\rho_0} \right)^{3-n}$$

by (55·6) and (55·42). The suffix 0 here indicates central values. Hence

$$\left(\frac{GM}{M'}\right)^2 = \frac{(n+1)^3}{4\pi G}\left\{\frac{a}{3(1-\beta)}\right\}^n\left\{\frac{3\Re(1-\beta)}{a\mu_1\beta}\right\}^{n+1}\left\{\frac{\Re T_0^{1+s}}{\beta\mu_1}\right\}^{3-n}$$

$$= \frac{(n+1)^3}{4\pi G}\frac{3(1-\beta)}{a}\left(\frac{\Re}{\beta\mu_1}\right)^4 T_0^{4s}$$

$$= \frac{(n+1)^3}{4\pi G}\frac{3(1-\beta)}{a}\left(\frac{\Re}{\beta\mu_0}\right)^4.$$

This gives

$$1-\beta = C_n (M/\odot)^2 \mu_0^4\beta^4 \qquad\qquad (94\cdot4),$$

where

$$C_n = \frac{4\pi G^3 a \odot^2}{3\Re^4 (n+1)^3 M_n^2} \qquad\qquad (94\cdot5),$$

and M_n is the value of M' for the law $P \propto \rho^{1+1/n}$.

We have thus a quartic equation (94·4) for β analogous to (84·4), the coefficient C_n depending on the law adopted for the change of molecular weight by (94·3). Constant molecular weight corresponds to $n = 3$. But (94·4) contains the central (minimum) molecular weight μ_0. It would make a fairer comparison with the results for constant molecular weight if we used an average value of μ, instead of the minimum value.

The effect of varying molecular weight can best be appreciated if we use in all cases the standard formula

$$1-\beta = \cdot00309 (M/\odot)^2\mu^4\beta^4 \qquad\qquad (94\cdot6),$$

and indicate how to choose the average value μ so that this may be exact. The condition reconciling (94·4) and (94·6) is

$$C_n\mu_0^4 = C_3\mu^4 \qquad\qquad (94\cdot71),$$

since $\cdot00309 = C_3$. The required value of μ occurs at a point in the star where the temperature T_n is such that

$$\mu_0 T_0^s = \mu T_n^s \qquad\qquad (94\cdot72),$$

so that

$$\frac{T_n}{T_0} = \left(\frac{C_3}{C_n}\right)^{\frac{1}{4s}} \qquad\qquad (94\cdot8).$$

In Table 12 results are given for various laws $\mu \propto T^{-s}$. The columns M_n and ρ_c/ρ_m are taken from Emden's tables, except for $s = \frac{1}{6}$ which is a rough interpolation. We have included a range of laws much wider than is likely to be required, including laws in which μ decreases outwards. The fourth column gives the coefficient to be used in place of ·00309 in (94·4). Alternatively if we use (94·6) μ must be calculated for a point in the star where the temperature T_n is as given in the sixth column. It will be seen that if we use the value of μ appropriate to a region of the star where the temperature is $\frac{2}{3}$ of the central temperature, the result will serve for any law between $s = 0$ and $s = \frac{1}{3}$.

The value $s = \frac{1}{6}$ would give a reasonable representation of the expected effect. With this law a molecular weight 2·1 (iron retaining 1 or 2 electrons) at 10,000,000° would become 3·3 (iron with K and L rings complete) at 1,000,000°, and 8·3 (iron with 6 electrons missing) at 10,000°. If the elements are mainly lighter than iron this may be an over-correction of the effect. It is possible that there may be a compensation due to the elements of high atomic weight tending to concentrate towards the centre, but according to present knowledge this seems unlikely (§ 196). In obtaining the results for Capella (§ 13) the value $s = \frac{1}{7}$ has been assumed which is perhaps nearly as probable as $s = \frac{1}{5}$*.

Table 12.

Molecular Weight varying as T^{-s}.

s	n	M_n	C_n	ρ_c/ρ_m	T_n/T_c
$-\frac{3}{11}$	4·5	1·7357	·00160	6377	·548
$-\frac{1}{5}$	4	1·8064	·00197	623	·570
0	3	2·0150	·00309	54·36	—
$\frac{1}{7}$	2·5	2·2010	·00387	24·08	·675
$\frac{1}{5}$	2·33	(2·27)	·00421	(20)	·679
$\frac{1}{3}$	2	2·4107	·00512	11·40	·685
$\frac{3}{5}$	1·5	2·7176	·00696	6·00	·713
1	1	3·1416	·01002	3·29	·742

It will be seen that the central density is about 20–25 times the mean density when allowance is made for variable μ as compared with 54 times the mean density on the usual assumption of constant μ. The central temperatures will also be reduced a little. The change is not so very important, because there is in any case an uncertain factor of about 2 in the central density owing to our ignorance of the low temperature part of the star (§ 67). Also, although it is convenient to give the central temperature and density for comparative purposes, we are really more concerned with mean conditions than with these extreme values.

Dense Stars.

95. According to the giant and dwarf theory the dwarf series of stars is due to the material of a star ceasing to behave as a perfect gas when the density becomes great. The theory assumes that the deviations set in at about the same density under stellar conditions as in terrestrial gases. In the author's earlier papers the theory of imperfect gases was developed in considerable detail for application to dwarf stars.

---

* Results for $s = \frac{1}{5}$ could not be given with so much detail since Emden's tables do not include this value. Fowler and Guggenheim's calculations indicate that the value $s = \frac{1}{7}$ is quite large enough (§ 180).

It now appears very unlikely that any of the stars, except probably the mysterious "white dwarfs," deviate appreciably from a perfect gas, so that these early attempts to treat the dwarf stars have lost interest. But we cannot ignore the study of imperfect gases entirely. It is part of our task to set forth the astronomical evidence that leads to the conclusion that the dwarf stars obey the gas laws, and for this it is necessary to discuss what would happen if they did not.

Van der Waals' equation for an imperfect gas is

$$(p + a/v^2)(v - b) = \Re T/\mu,$$

the volume v being the reciprocal of the density. The term a/v^2 can be neglected in comparison with the enormous pressures in the stars. The equation can then be written

$$p_G = \frac{\Re}{\mu} \rho' T \qquad \dots\dots\dots\dots\dots\dots(95\cdot1),$$

where

$$\rho' = \rho (1 - \rho/\rho_0)^{-1} \qquad \dots\dots\dots\dots\dots(95\cdot2),$$

and ρ_0 represents the limiting density when the pressure is infinite.

It would be idle to discuss the validity of this equation in actual stellar conditions because our ultimate conclusion will be that it does not apply at all, the supposed deviations due to the finite size of the atoms having no existence. We take $(95\cdot1)$ as giving a model star deviating from a perfect gas in a way similar to terrestrial gas.

It is assumed as before that ηk is constant.

The results $(84\cdot1)$, $(84\cdot2)$ and $(84\cdot3)$ apply if ρ is replaced by ρ'; and the equations of equilibrium are accordingly

$$\frac{dP}{dr} = -g\rho, \qquad P = \kappa \rho'^{\frac{4}{3}}.$$

Hence

$$\frac{1}{\rho} d(\rho'^{\frac{4}{3}}) = -\frac{g}{\kappa} dr.$$

The left side can be integrated, giving

$$d\{4\rho'^{\frac{1}{3}}(1 + \rho'/4\rho_0)\} = -(g/\kappa) dr \qquad \dots\dots\dots\dots(95\cdot3).$$

We choose ρ_0 according to the extent of the deviation from a perfect gas which we wish to consider. We then start at the centre of the star with arbitrarily chosen values of κ and central density ρ_c and build up a solution of $(95\cdot3)$ by quadratures. The mass M and radius R are found at the end of the quadratures, when ρ has been brought down by steps to zero. Unlike the problem of the point-source (§ 91) the solution presents no difficulty and the quadrature is of the simplest kind.

If in any solution of $(95\cdot3)$ all masses are altered in the ratio M and all lengths in the ratio $M^{\frac{1}{3}}$, densities will be unaltered and the left side of the equation is unaltered. Since $g\,dr$ is then altered in the ratio $M^{\frac{2}{3}}$, κ must be altered in the ratio $M^{\frac{2}{3}}$.

Thus, having found any pair of corresponding values of M and κ we can find κ for any other star of different mass but of the same mean density. To pass to another mean density a new quadrature is necessary.

From κ we find $1 - \beta$ by (84·3).

Results of a number of such calculations are given in Table 13*.

Table 13.

Solution for Dense Stars ($\kappa = 2\cdot22 \cdot 10^{-8}$).

ρ_c/ρ_0	R	M	ρ_m/ρ_0	$\log_{10} \kappa \, (M = \odot)$
0·9	2·294	29·70	0·587	13·5564
0·8	1·800	8·325	0·340	13·9247
0·7	1·717	4·112	0·194	14·1289
0·6	1·790	2·592	0·1078	14·2625
0·5	1·958	1·884	0·0600	14·3549
0·4	2·223	1·483	0·0322	14·4241
0·3	2·616	1·245	0·0166	14·4748
0·0	—	0·884	—	14·5739

The values used in the calculations for this table were $\kappa = \frac{1}{3}G$ and $\rho_0 = 1$. These give "stars" of mass only a few grams, but the results can afterwards be transformed to the stellar scale. Columns 2 and 3 give the radius in centimetres and the mass in grams resulting from the quadratures. From these we find at once the mean density tabulated in column 4. We can now find κ for any other mass by the rule $\kappa \propto M^{\frac{2}{3}}$, and the last column contains the values of κ corresponding to the sun's mass, e.g. in the first line, raising the mass from 29·70 gm. to $1\cdot98 \cdot 10^{33}$ gm. involves raising κ from $2\cdot22 \cdot 10^{-8}$ to the value shown.

If ρ_0 and all densities† are altered in the same ratio by altering lengths, leaving the masses unchanged, (95·3) continues to be satisfied with the same value of κ. Hence the table is applicable for any value of ρ_0, except that the auxiliary column R should be altered in the appropriate ratio. In practical applications of the table we are concerned only with the last two columns.

96. As an example, let us calculate what deviation from a perfect gas would be necessary to decrease the brightness of the sun 3 magnitudes below that of a perfectly gaseous star of the same mass. (This is about the difference assumed on the giant and dwarf theory.) Assume first that k is the same for both. The reduction in L corresponding to 3 magnitudes is in the ratio 1 : 16, and hence by (83·4) we must suppose $1 - \beta$ decreased

* *Zeits. für Physik*, **7**, p. 379. The later values of the constants (Appendix I) would increase all the entries in the last column of Table 13 by ·0096.

† The previous statement that alteration of mean density involves a new quadrature referred to problems in which ρ_0 is unaltered.

in this ratio. By Table 9 the value of $1 - \beta$ for a perfect gas is ·05*, so we must decrease it to ·0031 for the sun.

By (84·3) κ is proportional to $(1 - \beta)^{\frac{1}{3}}/\beta^{\frac{4}{3}}$; hence we find that the reduction in $\log_{10} \kappa$ is 0·4280. The value of $\log_{10} \kappa$ for a perfect gas and for the sun's mass is given in the last line of Table 13 as 14·5739; the reduced value 14·1459 is seen to correspond very nearly to the third line of the Table. By a slight interpolation the corresponding value of ρ_m/ρ_0 is 0·18. Since ρ_m for the sun is 1·41 it follows that $\rho_0 = 7\cdot8$.

The result is that if the limiting density of stellar matter under extreme pressure is 7·8 the sun's brightness will fall 3 magnitudes below that predicted for a perfect gas owing to the purely mechanical effect on the equilibrium.

But in addition there will be a further reduction of brightness owing to reduced transparency, which we can roughly estimate.

Failure of the gas laws would somewhat modify the distribution of density in the sun, but this effect is of minor importance since the mean density is prescribed. The main effect is a decrease of internal temperature; with reduced compressibility a lower temperature is sufficient to withstand the compressing force of gravity. The outward stream of radiation proportional to the gradient of T^4 is accordingly reduced, and it is this effect which has been calculated above. But according to our absorption law if the temperature is decreased without changing the density the opacity is increased proportionately to $T^{-\frac{7}{2}}$. The factor hindering the outflow is increased very nearly as much as the factor causing the outflow is reduced. The full reduction of brightness is thus about double that stated above, and if $\rho_0 = 7\cdot8$ the sun will be about 6 magnitudes fainter than a perfectly gaseous star of the same mass.

97. Further illustrations of the use of Table 13 will be found in the author's earlier papers† where curves are traced showing the rise to a maximum of the effective temperature and subsequent fall as a star of constant mass contracts. The values of k and ρ_0 (both assumed constant) were fixed by observational data for the sun and for a typical giant star. An oft-quoted result that a star of mass less than $\frac{1}{4}$ that of the sun cannot rise to the temperature of type M, must now be regretfully consigned to oblivion. In a somewhat later paper‡ in which the variation of k with temperature and density was taken into account, it was seen that the permissible

---

* The calculation is here made for $\mu = 2\cdot1$.

† *Monthly Notices*, **77**, p. 605; *Zeits. für Physik*, **7**, p. 377.

‡ *Monthly Notices*, **83**, p. 98. See especially Table 2, p. 104, where $\rho_0 = 13$ was selected as corresponding to Eggert's value $\mu = 3\cdot3$ which was then current; but it was noted that ρ_0 was very sensitive for changes of μ, and the same table gives $\rho_0 = 83$ for the modern value $\mu = 2\cdot2$. Moreover it now becomes unnecessary to adopt a different μ for Sirius.

deviations from the gas laws were much smaller. The reader who cares to examine the development of the ideas may perhaps be interested to trace how by progress of the theory and improvement of the observational data ρ_0 was raised from 4 to 13 to 83 and then practically to infinity*; otherwise there is not much profit in going over the old ground. Our concern here has been to show that if the dwarf stars were affected by deviations from the perfect gas law as large as those affecting terrestrial gases the consequent effect on their luminosities should be easily detectable by observation.

Principal Results.

98. We now resume the main discussion from the point reached in § 88, adopting the approximations $\eta k = \text{const.}$, $\mu = \text{const.}$, and the perfect gas condition. Accepting the law of absorption suggested by physical investigations (Chapter IX)

$$k = C\rho/\mu T^{\frac{7}{2}} \quad\dots\dots\dots\dots\dots\dots\dots\dots(98\cdot1),$$

where C is a constant, we have by (87·1)

$$k = \frac{Ca}{3\Re}\frac{\beta}{1-\beta}\frac{1}{T^{\frac{1}{2}}} \quad\dots\dots\dots\dots\dots\dots(98\cdot2),$$

so that by (90·1)

$$L = \frac{4\pi cG}{\alpha}\frac{3\Re}{Ca}\frac{M(1-\beta)^2}{\beta}T_c^{\frac{1}{2}}\dots\dots\dots\dots\dots\dots(98\cdot3),$$

where α may be taken to be about 2·5†.

By (84·6) the factor $M(1-\beta)^2/\beta$ is a function of M and μ only.

The radius of the star need only be known roughly, the main dependence of L being on M. The radius is involved because it settles the internal temperature which appears directly in the factor $T_c^{\frac{1}{2}}$; also a general knowledge of internal temperature and density is needed as a guide to the ionisation to be expected, and is a basis for estimating the best value of μ to adopt, but we can scarcely go far wrong over this. As regards the factor $T_c^{\frac{1}{2}}$, in order to change L by as much as 1 magnitude it would be necessary to change T_c from, say, 25 million to 4 million degrees; hence it is not likely that our calculations of internal temperature can be so much in error as to affect L seriously‡. Granting this, our calculation of L for a star of accurately known mass should be trustworthy to well

---

* *Monthly Notices*, **84**, p. 308.

† Whatever the actual central temperature may be, the value of T_c to be used in (98·3) should be calculated on the assumption that the distribution is that of the polytrope $n = 3$. Different models of internal structure are then represented by slightly modifying the factor a. For example, in the point-source model treated in § 91 the actual central temperature is infinite; but using the fictitious T_c, equation (98·3) applies if we put $a = 4\cdot2$.

‡ In this connection the calculations of minimal temperature in §§ 65, 66 are of interest.

within a magnitude, since it rests only on indubitable laws of physics together with the following conditions—

    (*a*) constancy of ηk;

    (*b*) constancy of μ;

    (*c*) the condition of a perfect gas;

    (*d*) the adopted absorption law.

The first three conditions have been passed in review in §§ 89–97. The conclusions are that the uncertainty due to ignorance of η is at most $\pm$ 0^{m}·5 for a star of ordinary mass. Possible variations of μ are eliminated by using the average value of μ corresponding to $\frac{2}{3}$ the central temperature. Deviation from perfect gas laws in the sense observed in terrestrial gases would cause a decrease of L, deviations of the order occurring in terrestrial gases being sufficient to produce a marked effect.

It would seem then that any discrepancy between theory and observation must be attributed to—

    (*a*) a wrong physical prediction of the absorption coefficient;

    (*b*) a wrong estimate of the value of μ to be employed;

    (*c*) a failure of the condition of a perfect gas.

If we are not mistaken all other loopholes have been explored and blocked up.

99. In practice a star is generally described by its mass M and effective temperature T_e. It is desirable to understand how its other properties vary with these. Collecting a number of formulae already obtained, we have

$$\left.\begin{aligned}
&L \propto R^2 T_e^4 \propto M(1-\beta)/k_c \\
&T_c^3/\rho_c \propto (1-\beta)/\mu\beta \\
&k_c \propto \rho_c/\mu T_c^{\frac{7}{2}} \propto \beta/(1-\beta)\,T_c^{\frac{1}{2}} \\
&\rho_c \propto M/R^3 \\
&T_c \propto \beta\mu M/R \\
&1-\beta \propto M^2\beta^4\mu^4
\end{aligned}\right\} \quad \ldots\ldots\ldots\ldots(99\cdot1).$$

From these are derived

$$\left.\begin{aligned}
&R \propto M^{\frac{7}{10}}(1-\beta)^{\frac{3}{4}}\mu^{\frac{2}{5}}T_e^{-\frac{3}{5}} \\
&T_c \propto M^{-\frac{1}{5}}(1-\beta)^{-\frac{1}{2}}\mu^{-\frac{2}{5}}T_e^{\frac{3}{5}} \\
&\rho_c \propto M^{-\frac{11}{10}}(1-\beta)^{-\frac{9}{4}}\mu^{-\frac{6}{5}}T_e^{\frac{24}{5}} \\
&L \propto M^{\frac{7}{5}}(1-\beta)^{\frac{3}{2}}\mu^{\frac{4}{5}}T_e^{\frac{4}{5}}
\end{aligned}\right\} \quad \ldots\ldots\ldots\ldots(99\cdot2).$$

The variation with μ has been retained here for completeness, but the primary intention of these formulae is the comparison of stars with fixed value of μ. In that case $(1-\beta)$ is a function of M increasing with M.

The most important result from (99·2) is that for stars of the same effective temperature, and therefore roughly of the same spectral type, T_c and ρ_c decrease as M increases. *Type for type, the more massive stars are the cooler and more rarefied.*

We add here for reference the formulae for calculating central temperature, density and pressure when M and R are given. These are obtained by substituting the numerical values for $n = 3$ in (58·4) and (57·6).

$$\left.\begin{array}{c} T_c = 0{\cdot}856\, \dfrac{G}{\Re}\, \dfrac{\mu\beta M}{R} \\[2mm] \rho_c = 12{\cdot}98\, \dfrac{M}{R^3} \\[2mm] P_c = 11{\cdot}11\, G\, \dfrac{M^2}{R^4} \end{array}\right\} \quad \dots\dots\dots\dots\dots(99{\cdot}3).$$

Table 13 A gives the mean density and central temperature of stars of masses 3, 10, 40 respectively and of various effective temperatures (with roughly equivalent spectral types). The values are calculated from (99·2), the constant being chosen to fit the mass and luminosity of Capella. The mass 3 may be taken as typical of ordinary giant stars, and the progression of mean density with spectral type shown in the table is of considerable interest. It agrees very well with the densities generally attributed to these types on observational grounds.

Table 13 A.

Mean Density and Central Temperature ($\mu = 2{\cdot}11$).

Effective Temperature	Type	Mass = 3 × ⊙		Mass = 10 × ⊙		Mass = 40 × ⊙	
		ρ_m	T_c	ρ_m	T_c	ρ_m	T_c
deg.			million deg.		million deg.		million deg.
3,000	M	·000446	4·65	·000020	2·45	·000002	1·52
4,000	K	·00177	7·36	·000078	3·88	·000007	2·40
5,500	G	·0082	12·3	·000360	6·48	·000032	4·01
7,500	F	·0363	20·1	·00159	10·6	·000140	6·57
10,500	A	·182	34·5	·00800	18·2	·00070	11·3
18,000	B	(2·42)	(81·7)	·106	43·0	·0093	26·6
27,000	O	(17·4)	(156)	(·763)	(82·1)	·067	50·8

It is probable that actual stars (other than white dwarfs) do not have temperatures above 40 million degrees, so that the last two entries for a star of mass 3 are fictitious. This was expected on the giant and dwarf theory, since the density on reaching type A was considered appropriate for the turning-point into the dwarf series. According to present views the failure of stars of mass 3 to reach types B and O is more mysterious, and the limit of 40 million degrees will be discussed at a later stage.

100. The last formula of (99·2) is so frequently used that we have constructed an extended table for applying it. For practical purposes L will be expressed in magnitudes m according to the rule

$$\Delta m = -\tfrac{5}{2}\Delta \log_{10} L \quad \dots\dots\dots\dots\dots(100\cdot1).$$

In Table 14 the fixed value $\mu = 2\cdot11$ is used and corresponding values of M and $1 - \beta$ are tabulated by (84·6). Then by (100·1) and (99·2)

$$\Delta m = -\tfrac{7}{2}\Delta \log M - \tfrac{15}{4}\Delta \log (1 - \beta) - 2\Delta \log T_e \dots(100\cdot2),$$

and the column m in the table is computed from this formula, omitting the term containing T_e. We have adjusted the zero of m so that the observed mass and absolute bolometric magnitude of Capella correspond to one another, and the table should accordingly give the absolute bolometric magnitude for any other mass with the same effective temperature as Capella (about 5200°).

For a different effective temperature, we have by (100·2)

$$\Delta m = -2\Delta \log T_e \quad \dots\dots\dots\dots\dots(100\cdot3),$$

and this correction should be applied as indicated at the foot of the table. With the range of effective temperature commonly occurring in the stars this correction is comparatively small, and the bolometric magnitude of a star is mainly a function of its mass.

For the effect of small changes of μ see § 178. We need only note here that the result of a change of μ is not shown *explicitly* in (99·2), since there are consequential changes of $(1 - \beta)$ to be taken into account.

Table 14.

Mass M and Absolute Bolometric Magnitude m.

$(\mu = 2\cdot11, \qquad T_e = 5200°.)$

$1-\beta$	M	m	$1-\beta$	M	m	$1-\beta$	M	m
·001	·1284	14·143	·04	·879	5·211	·26	3·774	− 0·052
·0015	·1574	13·173	·05	1·004	4·645	·28	4·137	− 0·312
·002	·1820	12·484	·06	1·123	4·178	·30	4·529	− 0·562
·0025	·2036	11·950	·07	1·240	3·777	·35	5·675	− 1·156
·003	·2233	11·513	·08	1·354	3·426	·40	7·117	− 1·718
·004	·2583	10·823	·09	1·468	3·111	·45	8·984	− 2·264
·005	·2895	10·286	·10	1·582	2·825	·50	11·46	− 2·805
·006	·3176	9·848	·12	1·812	2·322	·55	14·84	− 3·354
·008	·3683	9·154	·14	2·050	1·884	·60	19·62	− 3·919
·010	·4135	8·615	·16	2·297	1·494	·65	26·66	− 4·516
·015	·5117	7·632	·18	2·557	1·138	·70	37·67	− 5·162
·02	·5968	6·929	·20	2·831	0·812	·75	56·15	− 5·882
·025	·6739	6·381	·22	3·124	0·507	·80	90·63	− 6·714
·03	·746	5·929	·24	3·437	0·220			

Add to m the temperature term, $-2\log_{10}(T_e/5200)$.

Heat Radiation and Luminosity.

101. It is now practicable to measure the heat received from a star by the use of a radiometer. Considerable sensitiveness in the method has been developed*. But the results attained are as yet very limited and in general we have to infer the total amount of heat emitted from the light emitted†. This involves a knowledge of the luminous efficiency of the energy emitted by stars of different types.

If the star is radiating as a black body of temperature T_e we know by Planck's Law the amount of radiation $I'(\lambda, T_e) d\lambda$ of wave-length λ to $\lambda + d\lambda$. Measurements have been made in the laboratory of the quantity of energy of different wave-lengths necessary to give the same amount of light as judged by eye; hence we know the factor $p(\lambda)$ by which the energy must be multiplied in order to give luminous intensity. The average factor for the whole radiation is then

$$p = \int p(\lambda) I'(\lambda, T_e) d\lambda \div \int I'(\lambda, T_e) d\lambda \ \ldots\ldots\ldots(101\cdot1).$$

The maximum of p is found to occur at about $T_e = 6500°$ so that stars of types F to G have the greatest luminous efficiency. Presumably that is because our visual sense has been developed with special reference to sunlight. It is convenient to take the maximum as standard, and to define the scale of bolometric magnitude so as to agree with visual magnitude at this effective temperature. At any other temperature p will be smaller and the star will be brighter bolometrically than visually.

Table 15.

Reduction of Bolometric to Visual Magnitude.

T_e	p	Δm (Vis.–Bol.)
		m
2540	·092	+ 2·59
3000	·206	+ 1·71
3600	·417	+ 0·95
4500	·723	+ 0·35
6000	1·000	0·00
7500	·985	+ 0·02
9000	·893	+ 0·12
10500	·749	+ 0·31
12000	·616	+ 0·53

* It is said that the equipment at Mount Wilson could detect the heat of a candle on the banks of the Mississippi.

† The deduction of bolometric magnitude from heat measurement is not really more direct than from light measurement, because large corrections must be applied on account of atmospheric absorption in the infra-red, and this involves assuming a spectral energy distribution just as the reduction of light measurements does.

Table 15 is calculated from Nutting's measures of the visual intensities of energy of different wave-lengths*. In the last column the intensity-ratio p, has been converted into magnitudes ($\Delta m = -\frac{5}{2} \log p$) so as to give the correction Δm reducing bolometric to visual magnitude.

Since the radiation per unit area is proportional to $T_e{}^4$ the surface brightness is proportional to $pT_e{}^4$; or, denoting by J the surface brightness expressed in magnitudes

$$J = \text{const.} - 10 \log T_e + \Delta m \quad \ldots\ldots\ldots\ldots(101\cdot2).$$

The following approximate formula for J was given by E. Hertzsprung in a rather inaccessible paper in 1906†

$$J = \text{const.} + 2\cdot3 \left(\frac{14300}{T_e}\right)^{0\cdot93} \quad \ldots\ldots\ldots\ldots(101\cdot3).$$

F. H. Seares‡ has pointed out that Table 15 (which was computed by me 10 years later) agrees entirely with this formula, the greatest difference being $0^{\text{m}}\cdot04$. As Δm and J are very frequently required in practical calculation we give a more extended table computed from Hertzsprung's formula. The values from $12{,}000°-20{,}000°$ are subject to some reserve, because Hertzsprung's formula was derived as an interpolation formula and it has not been ascertained how far his approximation remains satisfactory above $12{,}000°$.

Table 16.

Effective Temperature and Surface Brightness (Hertzsprung's Formula).

T_e	Δm	J	T_e	Δm	J	T_e	Δm	J
	m			m			m	
2500°	2·71	+ 6·27	6000°	0·02	− 0·22	11500°	0·50	− 2·56
2750	2·13	5·28	6500	0·00	0·58	12000	0·58	2·67
3000	1·67	4·44	7000	0·00	0·91	13000	0·73	2·86
3250	1·32	3·74	7500	0·02	1·19	14000	0·89	3·03
3500	1·03	3·13	8000	0·06	1·43	15000	1·04	3·18
3750	0·80	2·60	8500	0·10	1·65	16000	1·19	3·31
4000	0·62	2·14	9000	0·16	1·84	17000	1·34	3·42
4250	0·47	1·73	9500	0·22	2·01	18000	1·49	3·52
4500	0·35	1·36	10000	0·29	2·17	19000	1·63	3·61
5000	0·18	0·73	10500	0·36	2·31	20000	1·77	3·70
5500	0·08	+ 0·22	11000	0·43	2·44			

102. The correction Δm will not be accurate because the radiation of a star is not distributed exactly in accordance with the law of black-body radiation. The radiation comes from layers extending over an appreciable

* *Phil. Mag.* 1915, Feb. p. 304.

† *Zeits. für Wissenschaftliche Photographie*, 4, p. 43.

‡ *Astrophys. Journ.* 55, p. 197. Another independent computation has been made by W. Rabe, *Astr. Nach.* 225, p. 223.

range of temperature and the radiation of different wave-lengths suffers different amounts of absorption in passing outwards. The general effect is that the quality of the radiation corresponds to a rather higher effective temperature than the quantity.

In this book T_e stands for the effective temperature corresponding to the *quantity* of the radiant energy. A temperature T_e' corresponding to the quality is usually defined as follows. In a grating spectrum equal lengths of spectrum correspond to equal steps of wave-length $\delta\lambda$. Expressing Planck's Law (40·7) in terms of λ, we have

$$I'(\lambda, T)\, d\lambda = \frac{8\pi hc}{\lambda^5}\, \frac{d\lambda}{e^{hc/\lambda RT} - 1} \quad\ldots\ldots\ldots\ldots(102\cdot1).$$

The maximum intensity in the grating spectrum occurs at the value of λ which makes $I'(\lambda, T)$ a maximum, i.e. when

$$x^{-5}(e^x - 1)$$

is a minimum, where $x = hc/\lambda RT$. The minimum condition gives

$$x = 4\cdot965, \qquad \lambda T = 0\cdot288 \quad\ldots\ldots\ldots\ldots(102\cdot2).$$

Thus the temperature can be deduced by measuring the wave-length for maximum energy; and when the radiation is not black we define an effective temperature T_e' by the same formula

$$\lambda_{\max}.\ T_e' = 0\cdot288 \text{ cm. deg.} \quad\ldots\ldots\ldots\ldots(102\cdot3).$$

This is the basis of practical methods of determining the effective temperatures of stars by Wilsing and Scheiner, Rosenberg, Sampson, E. S. King and others*. Their results therefore refer to T_e' rather than the T_e of our theory. For the sun T_e' is about 4 per cent. higher than T_e (approximately 6000° against 5740) and the same ratio may be expected to hold for all stars, at any rate as a first approximation†.

It might therefore be appropriate to increase our effective temperatures by 4 per cent. before taking out the correction Δm in Tables 15 and 16. But study of the sun's spectral energy-curve indicates that the slight displacement of the maximum ordinate is not the significant feature of the sun's deviation from a black body, and it is doubtful whether the proposal would be an improvement (§ 228).

In the cooler stars further errors in Δm will arise from the absorption lines. Especially in types M, N and S the band spectra of chemical compounds occupy a considerable part of the spectrum. Of course, the radiation which is blocked by the bands must squeeze through the gaps, since L is determined by the internal conditions of the star and not by surface conditions; but unless the bands are uniformly spread over the

---

* As the range of observation does not always include the wave-length of maximum intensity, the procedure may be modified in detail.

† The increase of 4 per cent. for the sun is, however, purely empirical; so that it may be risky to generalise from it.

whole spectrum the radiation may become differently distributed in wavelength. Strong absorption in the yellow would divert the radiation into regions of less luminous efficiency. We can only hope that since the whole correction Δm is not unduly large the faults of Tables 15 and 16 will not be serious.

The temperature scale to correspond with spectral type is not as yet very certain. It is inferred partly from the measurements of T_e' above mentioned; but these sometimes differ rather widely from one another. It is also based partly on Saha's theory of stellar spectra (§ 240), which determines the temperature of a layer rather vaguely defined. We have also the fixed datum that T_e for the sun is 5740°. The following table given by Miss Payne* embodies the most recent evidence.

Table 16 A.

Temperature Scale.

Type	T_e	Type	T_e
Ma	3000°	$A\,5$	8,400°
$K\,5$	3000	$A\,3$	9,000
$K\,2$	3500	$A\,0$	10,000
$K\,0$	4000	$B\,8$	13,500
$G\,5$	5000	$B\,5$	15,000
$G\,0$	5600	$B\,3$	17,000
$F\,5$	7000	$B\,0$	20,000
$F\,0$	7500	O	25,000–35,000

This presumably refers to the stars of the "main series," the giants of types G–M being 400–800° lower for the same spectral type. On the whole, the temperature scale used in the calculations in this book accords very well with the above table†.

Energy of a Star.

103. The negative gravitational energy of a star, found by setting $n = 3$ in (60·4), is

$$\Omega = \frac{3}{2} \frac{GM^2}{R} \quad \dots\dots\dots\dots\dots\dots(103\cdot1).$$

The quantity of radiant energy enclosed in the star is

$$H = \int 3p_R \, 4\pi r^2 dr,$$

* *Stellar Atmospheres* (Harvard Observatory Monographs, 1925), p. 33.
† The calculations were made at various times; and, as no systematic temperature scale was adopted at the beginning, occasional deviations from uniformity may be noticed.

since the radiation pressure is $\frac{1}{3}$ of the energy-density. Hence by (83·3)

$$H = 3\,(1 - \beta) \int P\,4\pi r^2 dr$$
$$= (1 - \beta)\,\Omega \quad\dots\dots\dots\dots\dots\dots\dots\dots\dots(103\cdot2)$$

by (60·5).

The translatory energy of the molecules is

$$K_1 = \frac{3}{2} \int p_G\,4\pi r^2 dr,$$

since the pressure of a gas is $\frac{2}{3}$ of the translatory energy per unit volume. Hence by (83·3) and (60·5)

$$K_1 = \tfrac{1}{2}\beta\Omega \quad\dots\dots\dots\dots\dots\dots\dots\dots(103\cdot3).$$

If γ is the ratio of specific heats (averaged if necessary) the whole material energy K is eK_1, where

$$\gamma = 1 + 2/3e$$

by (28·4). Hence

$$K = \frac{\beta\Omega}{3\,(\gamma - 1)} \quad\dots\dots\dots\dots\dots\dots\dots(103\cdot4).$$

At high temperatures $K - K_1$ will consist solely of energy of ionisation*, i.e. energy expended in removing electrons from their orbits in the atom and setting them free.

The whole energy of the star is

$$-\,\Omega + K + H = -\,\frac{\beta\Omega\,(\gamma - \tfrac{4}{3})}{\gamma - 1} \quad\dots\dots\dots\dots(103\cdot5).$$

If the molecular weight varies as T^{-s} the value $n = (3 - s)/(1 + s)$ must be used in calculating Ω. Thus if $\mu \propto T^{-\frac{1}{3}}$, $\Omega = \frac{9}{8}GM^2/R$. Otherwise the investigation is unaltered, and in particular the result (103·5) holds good.

104. If $\gamma < \frac{4}{3}$ the whole energy is positive, that is to say, there is more energy than if the material were in a state of infinite diffusion at zero temperature. Quite apart from the loss by radiation during its past life, energy must have been supplied to the star to bring it to its present state. The contraction hypothesis which denies any extra supply (sub-atomic or other) accordingly requires that $\gamma > \frac{4}{3}$.

We now generally agree that there is some extra source of energy; but the condition

$$\gamma > \tfrac{4}{3}$$

is still necessary in order that the star may be stable. For suppose that a star with $\gamma < \frac{4}{3}$ undergoes a slight contraction so that Ω increases. By

---

* It is a matter of definition whether we state energy of excitation separately. A nucleus attended by a solitary electron in a 3-quantum orbit may be regarded (a) as having lost all electrons except one M electron, or (b) all except one K electron which has been excited into an M orbit.

(103·5) the whole energy must increase as Ω increases in order to maintain equilibrium. The star cannot obtain this extra energy at a moment's notice; hence $K + H$ is below the value required to maintain equilibrium. This means that there is too little heat and the pressures p_G and p_R are insufficient to support the weight of the material. Thus a further contraction ensues and the star deviates further and further from equilibrium.

We have said that the star cannot at a moment's notice secure the extra energy required to save it. If the star is being supplied with extraneous energy it is quite possible that the changing physical conditions may stimulate the supply; but this effort to prevent the collapse is too dilatory. In a star like the sun the heat stored up represents about 40 million years' supply of radiation and therefore (if the radiation is supplied by liberation of subatomic energy) is equal to the subatomic energy released in 40 million years. If the rate of release is doubled when the collapse starts, it will take a year to increase $H + K$ by 1 part in 40 million; whereas the threatened collapse due to withdrawal of pressure support is a matter of days or hours. It is important not to confuse this condition of stability with another condition to be investigated later. We shall find in § 211 that the supply of subatomic energy must satisfy certain conditions in order that the star may be stable; these conditions are independent of, and additional to, the condition here found that $\gamma > \frac{4}{3}$; also the threat to the star which violates them is a lingering fate and not the swift doom here contemplated.

It may perhaps be suggested that some extra source of energy could exist which is *immediately* releasable as heat when the temperature and density change. But immediately releasable heat is not "extra"; it is by definition part of the specific heat and must be taken account of in γ and, by (103·4), in K. Energy of ionisation is of this type. Energy which is very slowly released such as radio-active and other kinds of subatomic energy is, of course, not reckoned in the total heat $K + H$; it is treated as a non-realisable asset in the star's balance sheet which is neglected unless we are dealing with long periods of time.

There appears to be no objection to γ falling below $\frac{4}{3}$ in a limited region of the star provided that the general average is above $\frac{4}{3}$. Circulating convection currents will be set up in this region (§ 70), since the convection process produces mechanical energy when $\gamma < \frac{4}{3}$, instead of dissipating it. Presumably viscous forces will not allow the movement to increase indefinitely, and in any case the local instability can scarcely lead to consequences affecting the star as a whole.

The constant γ is least when the ratio of the energy of ionisation to the translatory energy is greatest. It is conceivable that in the course of evolution a star may reach a stage at which further contraction will involve a great deal of fresh ionisation, the stage being critical for the ionisation of some predominant element or group of elements. In that case γ could temporarily fall below $\frac{4}{3}$. There would be a sudden collapse of the star which would be arrested as soon as the contraction had provided enough energy to accomplish this critical ionisation; after that the star would resume orderly progress with $\gamma > \frac{4}{3}$, starting from the more condensed condition. Cepheid pulsations might possibly be started by a collapse of this kind, but I do not think the hypothesis has much to recommend it.

CHAPTER VII

THE MASS-LUMINOSITY RELATION

105. We give some examples showing how the formulae of Chapter VI are employed in actual calculations*.

(1) *Capella (brighter component)*.

Mass, $4\cdot18 \times \odot$; absolute visual magnitude, $- 0^m\cdot26$; type $G\ 0$, assumed to indicate effective temperature $5200°$.

The way in which the above data were obtained has been explained in § 13. Applying the correction $- \Delta m$ from Table 16, the absolute bolometric magnitude is $- 0^m\cdot40$. The sun's absolute visual magnitude is taken as $+ 4^m\cdot9$ which at $5740°$ corresponds to bolometric magnitude $+ 4^m\cdot85$. The difference of $5\cdot25$ bolometric magnitudes indicates a rate of radiation 126 times faster than the sun ($\log_{10} 126 = 5\cdot25 \times 0\cdot4$). Hence

$$L = 126 \times 3\cdot78.10^{33} = 4\cdot8.10^{35} \text{ ergs per second.}$$

From the relation $L = \pi a c R^2 T_e^4$ (equation (87·2))

$$R = 9\cdot55.10^{11} \text{ cm.}$$

We have also
$$M = 4\cdot18 \times 1\cdot985.10^{33} = 8\cdot30.10^{33} \text{ gm.}$$

Hence
$$\rho_m = M/\tfrac{4}{3}\pi R^3 = \cdot00227 \text{ gm./cm.}^3$$

By the formulae for the polytrope $n = 3$ we have (as already calculated in § 59)

$$\rho_c = \cdot1234 \text{ gm./cm.}^3,$$
$$P_c = 6\cdot11.10^{13} \text{ dynes per sq. cm.}$$

We assume that the average molecular weight can be taken as $\mu = 2\cdot11$. By interpolation in Table 14, or by direct solution of the fundamental quartic equation

$$1 - \beta = \cdot00309 \ (4\cdot18)^2 \ (2\cdot11)^4 \ \beta^4,$$
we find
$$1 - \beta = 0\cdot283.$$

The central temperature can now be calculated from

$$(1 - \beta)\ P_c = \tfrac{1}{3} a T_c^4,$$

or (without troubling to calculate P_c first) from (87·1)

$$T_c^3/\rho_c = 3\Re\ (1 - \beta)/a\mu\beta.$$

This gives
$$T_c = 9\cdot08.10^6 \text{ degrees.}$$

The differences from the figures given in Chapter I are due to our neglect here of variation of μ with temperature.

---

* The physical and astronomical constants required are given in Appendix I.

We have also
$$L/M = 57\cdot8 \text{ ergs per second per gram,}$$
and the coefficient of absorption is calculated from $(90\cdot1)$

$$\frac{L}{M} = \frac{4\pi cG\,(1-\beta)}{\alpha k_c} = \frac{25100\,(1-\beta)}{\alpha k_c},$$

which gives
$$\alpha k_c = 123.$$

It has been explained that α depends on the law of distribution of the source of energy. We adopt the value $2\cdot5$ which is a compromise between the most extreme suppositions and cannot in any case be very far out. The choice will not affect differential comparisons between the stars; it is only when we compare astronomical values of k with those calculated from atomic physics that attention need be paid to the uncertainty. Hence

$$k_c = 49\cdot1.$$

Since ρ_c and T_c have been found this fixes the constant k_1 in the absorption law
$$k = k_1\rho/T^{\frac{7}{2}}.$$
We find
$$k_1 = 8\cdot98\,.\,10^{26}.$$

This value will be used to predict the luminosity from the mass, or *vice versa*, in other stars.

(2) δ *Cephei*.

Cepheid variable. Mean absolute visual magnitude $- 2^{m}\cdot19$; mean type $F\,9$, assumed to indicate effective temperature $5200°$.

The absolute magnitude is taken from a discussion of the distances of the Cepheid variables by H. Shapley*. The mass is unknown except in so far as it can be deduced by the present theory.

Proceeding as before, we find absolute bolometric magnitude $- 2^{m}\cdot33$, and
$$L = 2\cdot81\,.\,10^{36} \text{ ergs per second,}$$
$$R = 2\cdot32\,.\,10^{12} \text{ cm.}$$

The mass can be easily deduced from the bolometric magnitude and effective temperature by interpolation in Table 14; but it will be instructive here to work out the result analytically. We have

$$L = \frac{4\pi cGM\,(1-\beta)}{\alpha k_c} = \frac{4\pi cGM\,(1-\beta)}{\alpha k_1}\frac{T^3}{\rho}\,T_c^{\frac{1}{2}}$$

$$= \frac{4\pi cGM\,(1-\beta)}{\alpha k_1}\frac{3\Re\,(1-\beta)}{a\mu\beta}\left(\frac{G}{4\Re}\frac{R'}{M'}\frac{\mu\beta M}{R}\right)^{\frac{1}{2}}$$

* *Astrophys. Journ.* **48**, p. 282.

by (87·1) and (58·4). Eliminating M by (84·4)

$$L = \frac{4\pi cG\,(1-\beta)}{ak_1} \frac{3\Re\,(1-\beta)}{a\mu\beta} \left(\frac{G}{4\Re}\frac{R'}{M'}\frac{\mu\beta}{R}\right)^{\frac{1}{2}} \left(\frac{48\Re^4 M'^2}{\pi G^3 a}\right)^{\frac{3}{4}} \frac{(1-\beta)^{\frac{3}{4}}}{\mu^3\beta^3}$$

$$= 1\cdot443\,.\,10^{71}\,\frac{(1-\beta)^{\frac{11}{4}}}{ak_1 R^{\frac{1}{2}}\mu^{\frac{7}{2}}\beta^{\frac{7}{2}}}.$$

Using the value of k_1 found from the discussion of Capella and adopting as before $\mu = 2\cdot11$, the only unknown in this equation is β. The equation gives

$$(1-\beta)^{\frac{11}{4}} = 0\cdot909\beta^{\frac{7}{2}}.$$

Hence $\qquad\qquad\qquad 1-\beta = 0\cdot451.$

Alternatively, $1-\beta$ may be found as follows. Since the same effective temperature and molecular weight have been assigned to Capella and δ Cephei, we have in a comparison between them

$$L \propto M^{\frac{7}{5}}\,(1-\beta)^{\frac{3}{2}}$$

by (99·2). Since $1-\beta \propto M^2\beta^4$, we obtain by eliminating M

$$L \propto (1-\beta)^{\frac{11}{5}}\,\beta^{-\frac{14}{5}}.$$

For δ Cephei L is greater by 1·93 magnitudes or in a ratio 5·92; hence $(1-\beta)^{\frac{11}{5}}\beta^{-\frac{14}{5}}$ has 5·92 times its value for Capella. This gives

$$(1-\beta)^{\frac{11}{5}} = 0\cdot935\beta^{\frac{14}{5}},$$

from which the same value of $1-\beta$ is obtained.

From $1-\beta$ the mass is obtained by interpolation in Table 14 or by direct calculation from (84·6), the result being

$$M = 9\cdot00 \times \odot = 1\cdot79.10^{34}\,\text{gm.}$$

Other details are now easily calculated—

$$\rho_m = \cdot000342,$$
$$\rho_c = \cdot0185,$$
$$T_c = 6\cdot16.10^6.$$

(3) V Puppis (brighter component).

Eclipsing variable. Mass $19\cdot2 \times \odot$; radius $5\cdot28.10^{11}$ cm.; type $B\,1$, assumed to indicate effective temperature 19,000°.

This star is beyond the reach of ordinary parallax measurement so that its absolute magnitude is not directly known; but we happen to be able to determine the radius from a study of the light-curve, etc., and the absolute magnitude can be calculated as below.

The spectroscopic orbits of both components have been determined*;

* Masses of both components are given in W. W. Campbell's *Stellar Motions*, p. 256; but in J. H. Moore's Catalogue of spectroscopic orbits, *Lick Bulletin*, No. 355, only the combined mass is given—no doubt with good reason. I am therefore doubtful whether the mass of V Puppis was obtained in the orthodox way described here; but the description would apply to nearly all other examples of eclipsing variables.

these supply $M \sin^3 i$ and $a \sin i$ as in the case of Capella (§ 11); but whereas for Capella i was found from the visual orbit, for V Puppis it is found by analysis of the light-curve. It can generally be inferred that i is near 90° for eclipsing variables since otherwise eclipses would not occur; but in V Puppis and some other systems the separation is not large in comparison with the radii of the components and a more trustworthy estimate is needed. The method of analysing the light-curve is due to H. N. Russell; it enables the quantities i and R/a to be found. Combining these with $M \sin^3 i$ and $a \sin i$, we obtain the values of M and R given above.

We have
$$L = \pi a c R^2 T_e^{4} = 2 \cdot 62 . 10^{37} \text{ ergs per second,}$$

which corresponds to bolometric magnitude $- 4^{\text{m}} \cdot 75$. Table 16 gives $\Delta m = 1 \cdot 63$, so that the visual magnitude is $- 3^{\text{m}} \cdot 12$.

For comparison with this we shall calculate the magnitude from M by the present theory. For $M = 19 \cdot 2$, we find $1 - \beta = \cdot 597$. Then L is conveniently found by comparison with Capella, using the relation
$$L \propto M^{\frac{7}{5}} (1 - \beta)^{\frac{3}{2}} T_e^{\frac{4}{5}},$$

so that
$$\frac{L \text{ for V Puppis}}{L \text{ for Capella}} = \left(\frac{19 \cdot 2}{4 \cdot 18}\right)^{\frac{7}{5}} \left(\frac{\cdot 597}{\cdot 283}\right)^{\frac{3}{2}} \left(\frac{19000}{5200}\right)^{\frac{4}{5}}$$
$$= 72 \cdot 9 = 4 \cdot 66 \text{ magnitudes.}$$

Hence the absolute bolometric magnitude of V Puppis determined from the observed M is
$$- 0^{\text{m}} \cdot 40 - 4^{\text{m}} \cdot 66 = - 5^{\text{m}} \cdot 06$$

in satisfactory agreement with the determination $- 4^{\text{m}} \cdot 75$ from the observed R.

Other details are—
$$\rho_m = \cdot 0618,$$
$$\rho_c = 3 \cdot 35,$$
$$T_c = 4 \cdot 24 . 10^7.$$

The comparison of theory and observation for V Puppis is of special interest because it takes us as far as is yet possible in the direction of high mass. It is known, however, that greater masses occur. J. S. Plaskett[*] has found for the spectroscopic binary B.D. 6° 1309
$$M_1 \sin^3 i = 75 \cdot 6 \odot, \qquad M_2 \sin^3 i = 63 \cdot 3 \odot.$$

Since i is unknown the masses cannot be determined, but they are necessarily greater than 75 and 63. In fact the masses are greater than 87 and 73 because i must be such that the two discs never overlap—otherwise eclipses would be observed.

---

[*] *Monthly Notices*, 82, p. 447. It is pointed out that 29 Canis Majoris also has a mass at least as great as that of V Puppis.

Still higher mass has with some plausibility been assigned to v Sagittarii ($M_1 \sin^3 i = 260$, $M_2 \sin^3 i = 54$), but the determination seems uncertain*.

(4) *The Sun.*

Mass $1\cdot985.10^{33}$ gm.; radius $6\cdot951.10^{10}$ cm.

Although we are no longer dealing with material of low density we suppose tentatively that the theory of a perfect gas applies. The methods of calculation have been shown by the previous examples. The results are—

$$1 - \beta = \cdot0499,$$
$$\rho_m = 1\cdot411,$$
$$\rho_c = 76\cdot5,$$
$$T_c = 3\cdot95.10^7,$$
$$k_c = 177\cdot0,$$
$$L = 5\cdot62.10^{33}.$$

The value of L found by direct measurement of the solar radiation is $3\cdot78.10^{33}$. The difference of calculated and observed values is equivalent to $0^{m}\cdot43$, the sun being fainter than predicted from its mass and radius. Although this is in the direction corresponding to the deviation of terrestrial gases from the perfect gas laws there is no reason to attribute it to such a cause, since it is within the margin of error. For example, it might be due to a slightly lower molecular weight in the sun than in Capella due to the very much higher temperature. Many other sources of small deviations can be suggested.

It may be remarked that by using in our calculations the radius of the sun and the effective temperature of Capella we have magnified any discrepancy. All our results are differential with respect to Capella which was used to determine k_1. A more direct method of comparison, using the spectral type instead of the radius of the sun, is as follows. Since Capella and the sun are of the same spectral type we neglect at first any difference of effective temperature. Then, using $L \propto M^{\frac{7}{6}}(1 - \beta)^{\frac{3}{2}}$ we find that the ratio of the L's is exactly 100 or $5\cdot00$ magnitudes. Hence the sun's bolometric magnitude is $-0\cdot40 + 5\cdot00 = +4\cdot60$. To allow for the more diffuse condition of Capella we have assigned it an effective temperature 9 per cent. lower†. The change in the factor $T_e^{\frac{4}{3}}$ gives a correction $0^{m}\cdot08$, raising the sun's bolometric brightness to $+4^{m}\cdot52$ as compared with the observed value $+4^{m}\cdot85$. The discrepancy is $0^{m}\cdot33$.

* H. Ludendorff, *Berlin Sitzungsberichte*, 1924, p. 67. [According to later information the determination must be rejected altogether. Another massive system (Boss 46) with masses 35 and 32 has been found by J. A. Pearce; this is the second largest mass known.]

† It is better not to refer to the actual effective temperatures here—to avoid suspicion of a vicious circle. The effective temperature of the sun is derived from the observed L which we are holding in reserve for the final test.

We perhaps naturally think that data for the sun must be more accurate than for any other star, but that is not true of its absolute magnitude which may be one or two tenths of a magnitude in error. Hertzsprung, for example, adopts as most probable $+ 4^{m}\cdot 67$ visual corresponding to $+ 4\cdot^{m}62$ bolometric. If he is right the discrepancy is only $0^{m}\cdot 10$.

I have considered the desirability of shifting our standard of reference from Capella to the sun; but it has seemed too daring a step whilst the notion of perfect gases of density 76 gm. per cu. cm. is still unfamiliar to us. It would perhaps be more accurate to determine k_1 from the sun; but the uncertainty of the sun's absolute magnitude would be a disadvantage for differential comparisons with other stars.

(5) *Krueger* 60.

Absolute visual magnitudes of components $11^{m}\cdot 25$ and $13^{m}\cdot 75$; combined
    mass of system $0\cdot 43 \times \odot$; both components of type Ma indicating
    effective temperature 3100°*.

Here the difficulty is that only the combined mass is known. It is true that several determinations of the ratio of the masses have been made but these range from 6 : 5 to 3 : 1, and we cannot place reliance on them. To avoid this difficulty we may predict the mass from the absolute magnitudes as we did for δ Cephei. The results are—

bright component: bol. mag. $9\cdot 82$, $\quad 1 - \beta = \cdot 00747$, $\quad M = \cdot 354$,

faint component: bol. mag. $12\cdot 32$, $\quad 1 - \beta = \cdot 00264$, $\quad M = \cdot 209$.

This gives a combined mass $0\cdot 563$ compared with the observed mass $0\cdot 43$. There is some reason to think that the discrepancy is real and that intrinsically faint stars deviate systematically in this direction, although the evidence in any particular case is not very strong. Assuming that the orbital elements of Krueger 60 are accurate, the mass $0\cdot 43$ corresponds to a parallax $0''\cdot 260$ and the mass $0\cdot 56$ to a parallax $0''\cdot 238$. The trigonometric measures of parallax are perhaps accurate enough to exclude the latter value.

If it is preferred to express the discrepancy in magnitudes (which is more convenient for comparison with other stars) we divide the mass $0\cdot 43$

* A later orbit by R. G. Aitken (*Lick Bulletin*, No. 365) was not available when this calculation was made, but the mass is only changed to $0\cdot 45 \odot$. Aitken gives the magnitudes as $11\cdot 3$, $12\cdot 8$ following most recent writers in ascribing a difference $1^{m}\cdot 5$. I think I am right in saying that in observing this star in company with Dr Aitken we both agreed that the difference was considerably greater. Burnham gives a difference 3^{m}. With an assumed magnitude difference $1^{m}\cdot 5$ the individual masses $0\cdot 25$, $0\cdot 18$ are obtained (*Monthly Notices*, **84**, p. 312) as compared with $0\cdot 27$ and $0\cdot 16$ here found.

between the two components in such proportions as will make the residual in magnitude the same for both. This is done by trial and error. We find

	Mass	$1 - \beta$	Bol. Mag. (calc.)	Bol. Mag. (obs.)	$O - C$
Bright component	0·27	·00439	11·07	9·82	− 1·25
Faint component	0·16	·00156	13·55	12·32	− 1·23

For the bright component additional results are—

$$\rho_m = 9\cdot06, \qquad \rho_c = 493, \qquad T_c = 3\cdot22 . 10^7.$$

Even at a density above 400 there is still no sign of failure of the gas laws, for the difference of observed and calculated brightness is actually in the *wrong* direction according to terrestrial analogy.

106. The last three examples indicate a substantial accordance between theory and observation for stars of mass 19·2, 1, 0·27 respectively, and bolometric magnitude − 4·7, + 4·9, + 9·8, the comparison being differential with respect to Capella (mass 4·2, mag. − 0·4). This covers the greater part of the known range of stellar mass and magnitude. It will, of course, be necessary to test whether the accordance is confirmed by a systematic survey of all the stars available for similar tests.

In passing it is interesting to note the central temperatures found for the five stars.

Capella ...	...	9·08 million degrees
δ Cephei ...	...	6·16
V Puppis	...	42·4
Sun	...	39·5
Krueger 60	...	32·2.

Allowing for the errors of the determinations there is a possibility that the last three temperatures are really the same. The three stars belong to what is now called the "main series" running from types O and B down the dwarf series to type M. The remaining two stars belong to the side series of giants whose relation to the main series has become obscure since we no longer accept the giant and dwarf theory of evolution. It certainly looks significant that along the main series the central temperature should be so steady through a seventy-fold range of mass and a million-fold range of radiation. We shall revert to this result in § 122.

The Mass-Luminosity Curve.

107. The values of m and M given in Table 14 are traced as a curve in Fig. 2, the ordinates being m and the abscissae log M.

It will be remembered that before comparison is made with the observed magnitude of a star of effective temperature T_e the small correction $\delta m = - 2 \log_{10} (T_e/5200)$ should be added to the value taken from the curve. For graphical comparison it is more convenient to leave the curve alone and apply the correction $- \delta m$ to the observed magnitudes. The observational points plotted in Fig. 2 represent bolometric magnitudes reduced to the standard temperature 5200° in this way.

We may notice that the curve (or Table) gives quite reasonable results beyond the range for which definite observational data can be found. Thus the predicted (uncorrected) bolometric magnitude of a star of mass 100 is $- 7^m$; allowing for the fact that the effective temperature of so massive a star would probably be very high the visual magnitude would be about $- 6^m$. This agrees with what is usually considered to be about the extreme limit of stellar luminosity—as indicated for example by the brightest stars observed in globular clusters. The faintest known star, Proxima Centauri, is about $+ 15^m$ visual or $+ 13^m$ bolometric; this should correspond to a mass $\frac{1}{6} \odot$—a fairly acceptable value. It is suspected, however, that the approximations of our theory begin to fail for these very small stars and I daresay that the actual mass is rather smaller.

The observational data plotted in Fig. 2 are set forth in Tables 17, 18, 19, 20. The necessary explanations are given in the following notes.

Tables 17 and 18. Ordinary binary stars.

The calculation of m is performed by straightforward use of Table 14; but where only one residual is given for two components the method described for Krueger 60 has been used, that is to say, the mass of the system has been divided between the two components in such proportions as will give the same residual for both.

Since an error of 10 per cent. in the parallax or semiaxis produces an error of 30 per cent. in the mass leading to residuals from $0^m \cdot 5$ to $1^m \cdot 3$ (according to the star's mass), only wide pairs with large parallaxes have been included with Capella and the sun as first-class determinations in Table 17. Procyon is reckoned second-class because the semiaxis of the orbit is not well determined; observations of this star are greatly to be desired and would form a most important check on the theory.

Except for ϵ Hydrae and δ Equulei the observational data have been taken from a table by E. Hertzsprung*. The parallax, combined mass and absolute visual magnitude are taken directly from his list; the only modifications are (1) the adopted absolute magnitude of the sun, changed for the sake of consistency with other parts of this book, and (2) the difference of magnitude of the components of Krueger 60, changed from $1^m \cdot 5$ to $2^m \cdot 5$ since the former estimate appeared to me incredible. The selection of the best possible observational material has thus been left in the main to an independent arbiter, who made his choice before the

* Bull. Astr. Inst. Netherlands, No. 43 (1923).

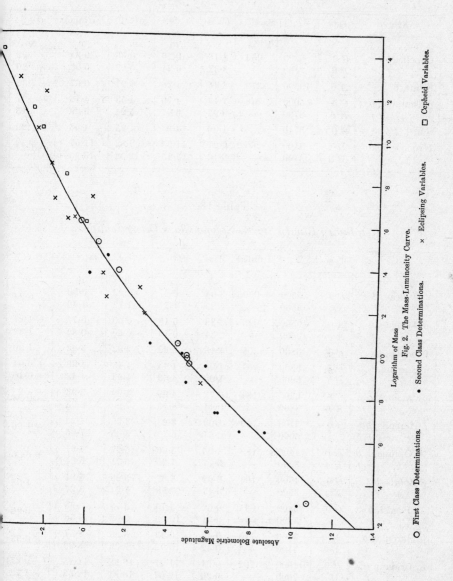

Logarithm of Mass

Fig. 2. The Mass-Luminosity Curve.

Absolute Bolometric Magnitude

○ First Class Determinations.   • Second Class Determinations.   × Eclipsing Variables.   □ Cepheid Variables.

Table 17.

Ordinary Binary Stars—First Class Determinations.

Star	Type	T_e	Parallax	Mass	m (vis.)	m (bol.)	m (calc.)	$O - C$
			″	.	m	m	m	m
Capella, b	$G\ 0$	5200	·063	4·18	− 0·26	− 0·36	− 0·34	− ·02
,, f	$F\ 0$	7400	—	3·32	0·24	0·22	0·02	+ ·20
Sirius, b	$A\ 0$	10500	·373	2·45	1·28	0·97	0·67	+ ·30
a Centauri, b	$G\ 5$	5000	·748	1·14	4·70	4·53	4·16	+ ·37
,, f	$K\ 5$	3700	—	0·97	6·07	5·24	5·09	+ ·15
Sun	$G\ 0$	5740	...	1·00	4·9	4·85	4·56	+ ·29
Krueger 60, b	$M\ a$	3100	·260	0·27	11·35	9·82	11·07 ⎫	− 1·24
,, f	$M\ a$	3100	—	0·16	13·85	12·32	13·55 ⎭	

Table 18.

Ordinary Binary Stars—Second Class Determinations.

Star	Type	T_e	Parallax	Mass	m (vis.)	m (bol.)	m (calc.)	$O - C$
			″	.	m	m	m	m
ϵ Hydrae, b	$F\ 9$	5500	·0206	3·64	0·27	0·22	0·00 ⎫	+ 0·24
,, f	...	5500	—	2·29	1·77	1·72	1·46 ⎭	
β Aurigae, b	$A\ 0p$	10500	·025	2·38	− 0·19	− 0·50	0·77	− 1·27
,, f	$A\ 0p$	10500	—	2·34	− 0·19	− 0·50	0·82	− 1·32
Procyon, b	$F\ 5$	6800	·308	1·13	2·92	2·92	3·92	− 1·00
δ Equulei, b	$F\ 5$	6800	·067	1·01	4·43	4·43	4·39	+ 0·04
,, f	$F\ 5$	6800	—	1·00	4·53	4·53	4·43	+ 0·10
η Cassiop., b	$F\ 8$	6200	·184	0·72	4·99	4·99	5·93 ⎫	− 0·94
,, f	$K\ 5$	3800	—	0·41	8·73	7·99	8·93 ⎭	
ζ Herculis, b	$G\ 0$	5700	·109	1·09	3·23	3·20	4·22 ⎫	− 1·06
,, f	...	5000	—	0·51	6·73	6·56	7·65 ⎭	
70 Ophiuchi, b	$K\ 0$	4400	·189	1·05	5·66	5·27	4·61 ⎫	+ 0·66
,, f	$K\ 4$	3900	—	0·77	7·36	6·71	6·04 ⎭	
ξ Bootis, b	$G\ 6$	4900	·164	0·62	5·87	5·69	6·81 ⎫	− 1·08
,, f	$K\ 4$	3900	—	0·47	7·89	7·24	8·27 ⎭	
85 Pegasi, b	$G\ 0$	5800	·095	0·62	5·75	5·73	6·66 ⎫	− 0·90
,, f	...	3200	—	0·31	10·95	9·52	10·38 ⎭	
μ Herculis, b	$M\ b$	3100	·110	0·46	10·42	8·86	8·57 ⎫	+ 0·33
,, f	$M\ b$	3100	—	0·42	10·92	9·36	8·99 ⎭	
o_2 Eridani, b	$B\ 9$	11000	·202	0·21	11·27	10·88	11·15	(− 0·27)
,, f	$M\ d$	2900	—	0·20	12·67	10·81	12·53	− 1·72

theory to be tested was put forward. Only two stars in Hertzsprung's list are omitted, viz. the companions of Sirius and Procyon, the former because it is a "white dwarf" to which our theory does not apply and the latter because the spectrum is unknown and it is impossible to guess what corrections may be involved. The bright component of o_2 Eridani which is also a white dwarf is for that reason not represented in Fig. 2, although (presumably by a cancelling of errors) it happens to agree with the curve.

Table 19.

Eclipsing Variables.

Star	Gr.	Type	T_e	$\cos i$	Mass	R/a	$R(\odot=1)$	m (bol.)	m (calc.)	$O-C$
								m	m	m
V Puppis	1	$B\ 1$	19000	·274	19·2	·417	7·60	− 4·61	− 5·00	+ 0·4
Y Cygni	3	$B\ 2$	18000	·088	16·6	·166	4·60	− 3·29	− 4·66	+ 1·4
β Lyrae	2	$B\ 8$	12500	·467	13·9	·219	12·09	− 3·80	− 3·98	+ 0·2
u Herculis	1	$B\ 3$	17000	·268	7·6	·290	4·29	− 2·89	− 2·90	0·0
U Ophiuchi	1	$B\ 9$	11500	·105	5·36	·240	3·07	− 0·47	− 1·69	+ 1·2
Z Vulpec.	2	$B\ 3$	17000	·013	5·24	·262	3·94	− 2·70	− 1·98	− 0·7
RS Vulpec.	4	$A\ 0$	10500	·000	4·34	·252	5·16	− 1·20	− 1·05	− 0·2
U Coronae	2	$B\ 3$	17000	·148	4·27	·167	2·90	− 2·04	− 1·43	− 0·6
β Aurigae	1	$A\ 0p$	10500	·228	2·38	·158	2·80	0·13	0·77	− 0·6
TX Herculis	3	$A\ 2$	9800	·065	2·04	·125	1·33	2·04	1·35	+ 0·7
TV Cassiop.	4	$A\ 0$	10500	·176	1·83	·272	2·45	0·34	1·68	− 1·3
Z Herculis	2	$F\ 2$	7600	·139	1·56	·117	1·77	2·53	2·55	0·0
W Ursae Maj.	1	$F\ 8p$	6200	·244	0·74	·323	0·70	5·42	5·81	− 0·4

Table 20.

Cepheid Variables.

Star	Type	T_e	Period	Mass	m (vis.)	m (bol.)	m (calc.)	$O-C$
			d		m	m	m	m
Y Ophiuchi	$G\ 2$	4800	17·113	26·2	− 4·0	− 4·21	− 4·43	+ 0·22
η Aquilae	$G\ 0$	5100	7·176	13·9	− 2·62	− 2·76	− 3·19	+ 0·43
δ Cephei	$F\ 9$	5200	5·366	11·3	− 2·19	− 2·30	− 2·77	+ 0·47
SU Cassiop.	$F\ 5$	6000	1·950	6·82	− 1·2	− 1·20	− 1·74	+ 0·54
RR Lyrae	$A\ 9$	7300	0·567	4·14	− 0·35	− 0·36	− 0·61	+ 0·25

The star 80 Tauri omitted here is included in the fuller discussion of the Hyades which follows. The parallax given by Hertzsprung for β Aurigae depends on the probable assumption that it is a member of the Ursa Major stream, but since it is near the stream apex the probable error is rather large.

The stars δ Equulei and ϵ Hydrae have been added*. Their parallaxes are obtained by a comparison of the visual and spectroscopic orbits—

* Aitken, *The Binary Stars*, p. 209.

the method used for Capella. For ϵ Hydrae the spectroscopic orbit of the bright component has to be combined with the relative orbit of the two components measured visually; thus a knowledge of the mass ratio is required at an early stage. There being no direct measurement of mass ratio worth considering, I have used the magnitude difference of the two components to determine the mass ratio—an extension of the principle adopted for Krueger 60 and other stars.

Spectral types of most of these stars were taken from *Lick Bulletin*, No. 343; the effective temperatures assigned to the types are still unfortunately a matter of judgment. Above 6000° an error in the assigned temperature does not make much difference to the comparisons since the temperature correction δm is set off against the reduction to bolometric magnitude Δm. In the redder stars the two corrections add up, and in the neighbourhood of 3000° where Δm is changing rapidly an error is more serious.

When only one residual for two components is determined, it is represented in Fig. 2 at an abscissa corresponding to the mean of the two masses.

Table 19. *Eclipsing Variables.*

The method of finding the mass and bolometric magnitude has been explained in § 105 for V Puppis. In the headings of the Table, R is the radius of the star, and a the semiaxis of the relative orbit. The column m (bol.) gives the absolute magnitude derived from the formula

$$L = \pi a c R^2 T_e{}^4,$$

and the column m (calc.) is derived from the mass by Table 14.

The results in all cases refer to the bright component which has been identified with the more massive component except in β Lyrae. The inevitable uncertainties would probably be magnified if the method were applied to the faint components. The photometric results R/a and $\cos i$ are from H. Shapley's discussion, the "darkened" solution being preferred*. The second column gives the grade of the orbit as classified by Shapley, Grade 1 being the most trustworthy. The spectroscopic data are chiefly due to J. S. Plaskett†.

In this series of comparisons the effect of an error in the assigned effective temperature would be considerable, and it is the more unfortunate that many of the stars are of B type where the temperature scale is most uncertain. We can show that

$$\delta\,(O - C) = -\,8\delta\,(\log_{10} T_e),$$

* *Princeton Contributions*, No. 3 (1915). For a few stars better data are now available; but it was considered best to use one standard source of data (as in Tables 17 and 18) in order to avoid bias in selection.

† *Publications of the Dominion Astrophysical Observatory*, Vols. 1 and 2.

so that by assigning to V Puppis the temperatures 15,000°, 19,000°, 23,000° we should obtain residuals $+ 1^{m}\cdot2$, $+ 0^{m}\cdot4$, $- 0^{m}\cdot3$ respectively. But in any case considerable errors in the results are inevitable, and the test can only be approximate *.

Table 20. *Cepheid Variables.*

This test is very indirect and depends on the theory of Cepheid variation developed in Chapter VIII. If the pulsation theory of Cepheids is not accepted the test falls to the ground. The procedure is as follows—

The effective temperature having been assigned according to the type (allowance being made for the fact that these are very diffuse stars), we adopt for trial an arbitrary value of M. From M and T_e we find L by Table 14. From L and T_e we find R. Hence ρ_m and $1 - \beta$ are found. The pulsatory theory gives an equation determining the period from ρ_m and $1 - \beta$. By trial and error we vary the value of M until the predicted period agrees with the observed period. This then fixes the mass and m (calc.) given in the Table.

The observed absolute visual magnitude is taken from H. Shapley's discussion† and reduced to bolometric magnitude by applying the usual correction Δm.

In predicting the period a value of Γ (the ratio of specific heats of the material) must be assumed. The value $\Gamma = \frac{5}{3}$ corresponding to a monatomic gas has here been used. Owing to the energy of ionisation the actual Γ must be less; but as it is difficult to estimate how much less, we have preferred to leave out this correction rather than arbitrarily guess the amount. A discussion of the likely values of Γ will be found in § 189. The following examples show the effect of changing Γ—

Star	Γ	Mass	m (bol.)	m (calc.)	$O - C$
			m	m	m
Y Ophiuchi	1·666	26·23	− 4·21	− 4·43	+ 0·22
,,	1·555	21·67	− 4·21	− 4·22	+ 0·01
,,	1·444	18·21	− 4·21	− 3·77	− 0·44
η Aquilae	1·666	13·86	− 2·76	− 3·19	+ 0·43
,,	1·555	12·53	− 2·76	− 2·98	+ 0·22
,,	1·444	10·17	− 2·76	− 2·53	− 0·23

The correction would thus have brought the observed points still closer to the curve, or possibly have shifted them across the curve so as to stand out by about the same amount on the other side.

Many more Cepheids could have been used for the comparison, but their

---

* Some of the unsatisfactory features are pointed out in *Monthly Notices*, **84**, p. 318.

† *Astrophysical Journ.* **48**, p. 282.

relations are so regular that the same kind of agreement must necessarily be reproduced. In assessing the evidence it is undesirable to over-represent this one kind of check because there are sources of systematic error which would affect all the Cepheids to about the same extent. The "observed" magnitudes all depend on a common zero point which may be rather uncertain; and we have already seen that there is another small systematic correction on account of Γ.

The Hyades.

There are six double stars of known period in the Hyades all of much the same brightness*. Their mean parallax is known with considerable accuracy from the geometry of the moving cluster, viz. $0''\cdot027$. The orbital data are rough, but a mean result for the 6 stars should be accurate enough for us to use. We deduce first the masses from the absolute magnitudes by means of our theory as follows—

Burnham G.C.	M_1	M_2	$M_1 + M_2$
2134	1·08	0·72	1·80
2154	1·03	0·66	1·69
2187	0·83	0·73	1·56
2230	1·48	0·81	2·29
2381	0·93	0·93	1·85
2383	1·16	0·58	1·75

The predicted mean of $M_1 + M_2$ is thus 1·82.

Hertzsprung found the mean dynamical parallax† (for mass 2) to be $0''\cdot026$. Since the mass deduced from a double-star orbit varies as the inverse cube of the parallax an assumed mass 1·79 would have given the correct mean parallax $0''\cdot027$. Another mode of averaging (averaging the masses instead of the dynamical parallaxes) gives the mean mass 1·93. Either 1·79 or 1·93 is in excellent agreement with our predicted value 1·82.

This has been represented in Fig. 2 as a first-class determination at a point corresponding to the mean mass of the 12 components.

108. It will be seen from Fig. 2 that there is good agreement between all classes of observational data and the theoretical mass-luminosity curve. For the 37 points representing observed data the average discordance is $\pm 0^{m}\cdot57$ and this may well be attributed to errors of observation.

The agreement is the more noteworthy when we recall that the equation

* E. Hertzsprung, *Bull. Astr. Inst. Netherlands*, No. 16.

† The parallax of a visual double star can be calculated from the combined mass, period and semiaxis (in arc). The parallax calculated on the assumption that the combined mass is 2 is called the "dynamical parallax"—formerly the "hypothetical parallax."

of the curve contains only two constants, viz. the average molecular weight μ and the constant k_1 in the law of absorption. Apart from these the equation contains only fundamental constants of nature.

If k_1 and μ are regarded as adjustable constants the curve can be shifted to any extent vertically and laterally but is not otherwise deformable. A slight improvement in the general agreement would be produced by shifting the curve downwards and towards the left, more or less along its own slope; this would correspond to increasing the molecular weight. But when attention is paid more particularly to the first-class data, and when account is taken of certain corrections which are needed in the theory for stars of small mass, it appears that there would be no real gain. If we had no theoretical knowledge of the molecular weight in the interior of a star, we could determine it observationally by this method, and we should obtain a value quite near to 2·1. This constitutes a very satisfactory observational check on the theory of ionisation in the stellar interior.

Naturally a formula covering the widest variety of stellar conditions with only two constants can only be a first approximation and certain refinements must be introduced before a definitive theoretical curve is obtained. The further developments needed for a second approximation will be considered in due course in Chapters IX and X. The observations seem to suggest that the curve is a little too high on the right, but we do not think the evidence is of much weight. The points denoting Cepheid variables must certainly be raised a little on account of the neglected energy of ionisation and the best estimate we can make of this correction would just about bring them on to the curve; the results for eclipsing variables are not very trustworthy. On the left the curve seems to be about a magnitude too low; we believe that this divergence is real, and that in a second approximation the theory will follow more closely the line of the observations*.

There seems to be no doubt that (subject to the last-mentioned correction) the theoretical curve is statistically confirmed. Whether all individual stars will keep to the curve or whether there is room for exceptional behaviour is more doubtful. It is possible that when more and better observational material is available individual deviations will be more apparent. I am conscious of weak points in the present evidence and do not consider that the full agreement of all ordinary stars with the curve is as yet strongly established. But on the theoretical side it is very difficult to see how a star without unusual spectral features can possess individual character sensibly different from other stars of the same mass and density unless the divergences of chemical composition are much

---

* It is probably worth while to allow for this in making practical applications of Table 14. A correction varying linearly with the mass from $0^m\cdot 0$ at mass 0·75 to $1^m\cdot 0$ at mass 0·25 would about meet requirements.

greater than commonly supposed. Rotation can have little effect on the brightness unless it is very rapid. Provisionally, we shall assume that the mass-luminosity relation is true not only statistically but individually.

109. We have preferred in most cases not to trust mass ratios of components of double stars deduced from discussions of the absolute orbits. It may, however, be of interest to compare these measured mass ratios with the ratios deduced by the theory from the luminosities. The following table is due to G. Shajn*—

Table 21.

Mass Ratios of Double Stars.

Star	M_2/M_1 theory	M_2/M_1 observed	Star	M_2/M_1 theory	M_2/M_1 observed
η Cassiop.	0·55	0·76	ζ Herculis	0·41	0·43
ϵ Hydrae	0·64	0·9	Krueger 60	0·59	0·56
η Cancri	0·95	1·00	70 Ophiuchi	0·79	0·82
ξ Urs. Maj.	0·90	1·00	Capella	0·86	0·79
γ Virginis	0·99	1·00	β Aurigae	0·98	1·00
α Centauri	0·92	0·85	80 Tauri	0·31	0·39
ξ Bootis	0·81	0·87	μ Herculis	0·89	1·00

Apart from the first two stars the agreement is surprisingly good. The two apparent discordances fade away on scrutiny. For η Cassiopeiae the observed M_2/M_1 is a weighted mean between the results 0·4 and 1·6 derived from declinations and right ascensions respectively; it need not be taken seriously. For ϵ Hydrae the separation of the components is only $0''\cdot8$; the astronomer who attempted to measure the mass ratio was an optimist.

H. N. Russell has called my attention to the star 85 Pegasi (apparent magnitudes 5·8, 11·0). It has been alleged that the faint component is heavier than the bright star. This may be doubted; but there is certainly an indication that the faint star has more than its proper share of the mass†. Possibly the explanation may be that it is a white dwarf and therefore in a condition outside the scope of this theory.

110. Besides the foregoing data for individual stars there is a certain amount of statistical data as to masses and luminosities which can be compared with the theoretical curve. The material is contained in a paper by Russell, Adams and Joy‡ in which the mean dynamical parallax and the mean spectroscope parallax for groups of double stars are compared.

* *Monthly Notices*, **85**, p. 247. A revised value for Krueger 60 has been substituted.

† L. Boss, *Preliminary General Catalogue*, p. 278.

‡ *Pub. Astr. Soc. Pacific*, **35**, p. 189 (1923).

The dynamical parallax is obtained on the assumption that the mass of the system is 2; if the mass is actually $2M$, the linear dimensions of the orbit will be $M^{\frac{1}{3}}$ times greater than supposed, and the true distance $M^{\frac{1}{3}}$ times greater than the inferred distance. By comparing the dynamical parallax with a true parallax (trigonometrical or spectroscopic) the mass factor $M^{\frac{1}{3}}$ is determined. The accidental error is reduced by taking the mean for a number of stars, but the investigation can only be expected to give very rough results.

In Table 22 we give (1) the spectral type according to which the stars were grouped (giants and dwarfs being grouped separately), (2) the effective temperature adopted to correspond, (3) the mean mass of a component, (4) the mean absolute magnitude of a component, (5) the corresponding bolometric magnitude, (6) the bolometric magnitude calculated from M and T_e, (7) the residual, and (8) the number of systems in the group.

Table 22.

Statistics of Double Stars.

Type	T_e	Mass	m (vis.)	m (bol.)	m (calc.)	$O-C$	No.
			m	m	m		
$O\,5-B\,2$	20000	3·1	− 1·76	− 3·53	− 0·64	− 2·9	10
$B\,3-B\,8$	15000	2·8	+ 0·01	− 1·03	− 0·08	− 1·0	8
$B\,9-A\,1$	10500	1·2	+ 1·34	+ 0·98	+ 3·29	− 2·3	35
$G\,9-M\,6$	3500	1·25	+ 1·28	+ 0·25	+ 4·08	− 3·8	28
$F\,6-G\,8$	5000	1·9	+ 1·39	+ 1·21	+ 2·19	− 1·0	31
$A\,2-A\,4$	9500	1·05	+ 2·20	+ 1·98	+ 3·95	− 2·0	29
$A\,5-A\,9$	8500	1·0	+ 2·75	+ 2·65	+ 4·23	− 1·6	35
$F\,0-F\,3$	7500	1·3	+ 3·26	+ 3·24	+ 3·28	0·0	17
$F\,4-F\,5$	7000	0·85	+ 3·65	+ 3·65	+ 5·13	− 1·5	24
$F\,6-F\,8$	6500	1·25	+ 4·47	+ 4·47	+ 3·55	+ 0·9	28
$F\,9-G\,0$	6000	0·85	+ 4·66	+ 4·64	+ 5·27	− 0·6	25
$G\,1-G\,5$	5000	1·2	+ 5·32	+ 5·14	+ 3·95	+ 1·2	24
$G\,6-K\,1$	4500	1·1	+ 5·79	+ 5·44	+ 4·39	+ 1·0	25
$K\,2-K\,6$	4000	0·7	+ 7·00	+ 6·38	+ 6·45	− 0·1	21
$K\,7-M\,6$	3500	0·5	+ 9·94	+ 8·91	+ 8·09	+ 0·8	7

This comparison does little more than demonstrate a general slope of the mass-luminosity curve roughly accordant with that given by our theory. But the paper is of historic interest because it gave evidence of a mass-luminosity relation persisting from the giant to the dwarf stars without break of continuity.

About the same time as Russell, Adams and Joy's investigation, E. Hertzsprung also indicated the continuous mass-luminosity relation in the paper already quoted as supplying much of our observational material.

These two researches carried an implication of serious import for the giant and dwarf theory of evolution; for that theory required a bifurcated and not a continuous mass-luminosity curve. We shall see presently that this unexpected result involves the abandonment of what had been regarded as a cardinal point in the giant and dwarf theory. It is interesting to record that the authors of that theory were concerned in the two investigations which foreshadowed its overthrow.

111. Another line of inquiry may be mentioned which may ultimately help to confirm or disprove our conclusions. A possible method of determining the mean masses of groups of stars from their distribution in star clusters has been developed by H. von Zeipel*. On certain assumptions the density of distribution of the stars may be expected to depend on the gravitation potential ϕ according to the Boltzmann formula $\rho \propto e^{2hM\phi}$. Writing $\alpha = e^{2h\phi}$, we have $\rho \propto \alpha^M$, where α is a function of the position in the cluster, diminishing as we go away from the centre. Hence if the distribution density of stars of mass M_1 at the centre and at various distances from it is proportional to

$$1, \qquad \alpha_1^{M_1}, \qquad \alpha_2^{M_1}, \qquad \alpha_3^{M_1} \dots,$$

the distribution density for stars of mass M_2 will be proportional to

$$1, \qquad \alpha_1^{M_2}, \qquad \alpha_2^{M_2}, \qquad \alpha_3^{M_2} \dots.$$

Hence the mass for any group can be determined in terms of an unknown unit from a study of its distribution.

Von Zeipel has examined in this way the cluster Messier 37, which is of a kind to which the theory may be expected to apply, and has found that the formulae fit excellently. The research, however, related to the mean masses of different spectral types, whereas we should have preferred for our purpose a grouping according to bolometric magnitude.

Von Zeipel's results for his four groups are—

	M	No. of stars
G giants	$2 \cdot 15 \pm 0 \cdot 12$	57
B and A	$1 \cdot 00$	795
F dwarfs	$0 \cdot 67 \pm 0 \cdot 02$	682
G dwarfs	$0 \cdot 36 \pm 0 \cdot 02$	1203

If the G dwarfs may be considered to have a mean mass equal to the sun, the unit of M is about $3 \times \odot$. If (as happens in the globular clusters) the G giants are brighter than the B and A stars, their mass $6 \cdot 5$ is in general accordance with our expectation. A discussion of the same data with special reference to the mass-luminosity relation would seem likely to yield useful results.

* *Astronomische Nachrichten*, Jubilee No., p. 33 (1921).

The Gas Laws in Dense Stars.

112. At the beginning of 1924 the giant and dwarf theory of Hertz-sprung and Russell was almost universally accepted. A brief outline of this theory has been given in § 7. Hertzsprung and Russell revealed a remarkable division of the stars into two series of high and low luminosity respectively, and brought the relations of luminosity to spectral type into a simple system. Their results have been fully confirmed by subsequent researches and have had far-reaching effects on the development of stellar astronomy. A noteworthy advance was the recognition that many of the stars are diffuse, with densities equal to that of our atmosphere or lower, and yet show a spectrum nearly indistinguishable from the dense stars. This challenged the spectroscopists to find discriminating differences and an important new field of spectroscopy was opened up. The method, now commonplace, of calculating the radius of a star from its absolute magnitude and spectral type originated with Hertzsprung and Russell. The deter-mination of densities of eclipsing binaries and a general appreciation of the usefulness of dynamical parallaxes were incidents in the development of the theory. Whatever may be the explanation of the division into giants and dwarfs, their separation has become essential in all statistical researches and has been fertile of results. Needless to say the chief in-vestigations in this book would not have been started without Hertzsprung and Russell's advance.

In speaking of the "overthrow" of the giant and dwarf theory, we do not intend to imply that there is to be any retrogression with regard to these results. They are mostly the ascertained facts, some of which the authors discovered at the same time that they theorised on them; others followed by natural development. In any reconstruction of theory these facts must be attended to. But the facts were welded by an attractive theory of evolution on the lines of Lane's and Lockyer's earlier proposals into a remarkably coherent scheme. I do not think it is too blunt an expression to say that this is now overthrown; at least it has been gutted, and it remains to be seen whether the empty shell is still standing.

The theory was that the transition from the giant or highly luminous series to the dwarf or faint series occurred when the star in contracting reached a density at which the laws of a perfect gas ceased to apply. The transition density $0\cdot1$–$0\cdot5$ was about the value anticipated from the be-haviour of terrestrial gases. The rapid fall of luminosity down the dwarf series was ascribed to increasing deviation from the gas laws—the dwarf star in fact behaved like a gradually cooling liquid or solid. On account of these views early researches on the mass-luminosity law were limited to giant stars; in the dwarfs the main factor controlling luminosity should no longer be the mass but rather the density which determined the deviation from a perfect gas.

If giants and dwarfs are treated together the absolute magnitude should be a double-valued function of the mass, the effective temperature being fixed. Any given mass passes through the same effective temperature twice, once rising in temperature as a giant and once falling as a dwarf, with a different luminosity in the two stages owing to the contraction of surface. We have mentioned that two investigations in 1923 ought to have aroused misgiving as to the tenability of this view. There was no sign of two branches of the mass-luminosity curve one above the other. This might conceivably have been an accident of the data; but at least the part of the curve relating to the dwarfs should have fitted disjointedly to the part relating to the giants instead of being continuous with it. I am aware from conversation with Hertzsprung in the autumn of 1923 that he considered this difficulty to be serious; his objections made little impression on me at the time*.

113. The theoretical mass-luminosity law for a perfectly gaseous star was obtained in February 1924 and the comparison with observation, embodied in Fig. 2, followed. The agreement of the observations with the curve was a complete surprise for it was not at all the result that was being looked for. Nearly all the accurate data relate to dwarf stars; Capella had been used to fix one of the constants of the curve; and it was regretfully decided that no other truly gaseous stars were available to test the curve. (The use of Cepheid and eclipsing variables was an afterthought.)

Accepting the curve on theoretical grounds, it seemed possible to make an interesting comparison of the dwarf stars with it so as to measure how large a drop of luminosity resulted from the deviation from the gas laws. For example, the curve gives a certain absolute magnitude corresponding to mass 1 and $T_e = 5740°$. According to the giant and dwarf theory this would not be the sun's present magnitude but its magnitude at the time when it passed through the same temperature as a diffuse star rising in temperature. Since that time the sun has contracted to its present high density and its luminosity has decreased proportionately to the decrease of its surface. The present magnitude should be well below the curve—about 3^m to 4^m according to the usual estimates. Similarly, Krueger 60 was expected to be 9^m to 10^m below the curve, that being the general difference between giants and dwarfs of type M. Exact measure-

---

* A minor difficulty raised by him was the scarcity of ordinary (non-Cepheid) giants of types A and F. This makes almost a breach in the linking of the G, K, M giants to the dwarf series, and the suggestion of continuous transition from the giants to the main series is weaker than is often supposed (see Fig. 3, p. 175).

ment of these differences would have been very helpful in investigations on the lines explained in § 95.

Nothing of the kind was found. All the stars in the left half of Fig. 2 have high densities not ordinarily associated with a perfect gas. Yet they lie on, or even a little above, the theoretical curve for a perfect gas.

We must conclude either that we have been misled altogether in the theory of the mass-luminosity relation or that in dense stars like the sun the material behaves as a perfect gas. We have therefore to consider whether it is physically possible for matter of the density of platinum or even higher to have the compressibility of a perfect gas. On examining the question we shall see that there is no earthly reason why it should not be a perfect gas—or it would be more accurate to say that the reason why it should not *is earthly* and does not extend to the stars.

114. We have to examine the suggestion that matter of very high density may in stellar conditions have the compressibility of a perfect gas. Our first impulse is to dismiss the idea as incredible and to assume that some fallacy must have crept into the investigation of stellar luminosity. But closer inquiry shows that this behaviour of matter at high temperatures is not only possible but might have been foretold. We have reached by a roundabout route a conclusion which had really become obvious from modern advances in physics and was waiting to be recognised.

The ordinary failure of Boyle's law when a terrestrial gas is compressed to high density is due to the finite size of the atoms or molecules. If the molecules were rigid the gas could not be compressed beyond a certain maximum density at which they became jammed in contact. This maximum density is roughly that of the substance in the liquid or solid state. It is shown in the theory of gases that the effect of the finite size of the molecules is to change the law from $pv = \Re T$ to $p(v - b) = \Re T$, where b is 4 times the aggregate volume of the molecules; in other words, it is not the whole volume but the waste space which is inversely proportional to the pressure*.

For example, a gram of nitrogen at standard temperature and pressure occupies 800 cu. cm.; of this 0·51 cu. cm. is the aggregate volume of the molecules, the rest being empty space. There are $2·15.10^{22}$ nitrogen molecules in a gram and the volume of each is equivalent to that of a sphere of radius $1·8.10^{-8}$ cm.

The reason why an atom behaves like a rigid body of definite size is imperfectly understood; but the size agrees roughly with that of the system of electrons circulating round the nucleus. The only element for which we can make a direct comparison is helium, since it is difficult to make

---

* Strictly b is half the volume so occupied that the *centre* of another molecule cannot enter it. As the packing becomes close b diminishes from four times to twice the aggregate volume of the molecules.

any theoretical estimate of the size of the electron system in other mon-atomic gases. The radius of the helium atom derived from the theory of gases is about three times the radius of its electron orbits. The behaviour is as though there were a rigid envelope enclosing with a reasonable margin all the electron orbits and so preventing the electrons of two colliding atoms from becoming entangled.

If the size of the atom depends on the size of its electron system the atoms in the interior of a star will be very small; for most of the electrons are broken away by ionisation and those which remain describe small inner orbits. In a typical star the light elements such as nitrogen are stripped bare to the nucleus, and presumably the nitrogen atom has no "size" other than that of the nucleus which is of the order 10^{-12} cm. in radius. Iron will retain only the two K electrons and the corresponding radius is about 2.10^{-10} cm. Thus the stellar atoms have in general not more than $\frac{1}{100}$ of the radius or $\frac{1}{1,000,000}$ of the volume of terrestrial atoms. The constant b is accordingly divided by a million; and equal deviations from the gas laws should occur in the stars at densities a million-fold greater than on the earth. If a perfect gas is one in which the molecules are geometrical points, the stellar gas composed of electrons and tiny ions approaches perfection far more closely than the bulky terrestrial molecules.

It might perhaps be argued that the rigid envelope of the atom is determined by the position of the quantum orbits independently of whether these orbits are occupied by electrons or not—that the electrons are boundary stones not boundaries, and their removal does not mean a reduction of size. This is unlikely for several reasons. Firstly, it is at variance with the views generally held by physicists as to the origin and nature of the forces which keep the atoms from penetrating one another. Secondly, when a helium atom is stripped of its electrons, as in an α particle, it can penetrate other atoms; all trace of its former size is lost and it preserves no memory of a radius other than that of the nucleus to which it is now reduced. Thirdly, the size of a normal atom corresponds to the lowest quantum orbits, i.e. the orbits which are actually occupied; higher quantum orbits extending to much greater distances exist, but being unoccupied they have no relevance to the size.

The ground for our expectation that the stars will deviate from the gas laws when their density approaches that of ordinary liquids and solids has been cut away entirely. It was based on an analogy with the behaviour of terrestrial substances—an analogy which is now seen to be baseless. There is no longer any reason to mistrust the observational evidence that the dense stars are still in the state of a practically perfect gas, for this false analogy was the original reason for our mistrust.

In order to examine this important conclusion from as many stand-points as possible, we shall treat it also on more conservative assumptions.

Suppose that after all an atom, when its electron system is dismantled, retains its original property of behaving as a rigid sphere of 10^{-8} cm. radius. The law $p\,(v - b) = \Re T$ then applies as in a terrestrial gas, *but only to about 5 per cent. of the pressure.* About 95 per cent. of the gas pressure is contributed by free electrons which permeate freely through the atoms and are not affected by the b term. The full gas pressure is therefore given by

$$p_G = \tfrac{1}{20}\Re T \left(\frac{1}{v - b} + \frac{19}{v} \right).$$

The result is that there is very little deviation from the gas laws until the maximum density is nearly attained; the deviation then sets in rapidly and a small increase of density gives infinite pressure. A dense star will therefore consist approximately of a central core of incompressible fluid surrounded by a perfect gas, the density of the core being about that of terrestrial solids. Some calculations were made by the author on this stellar model in 1923, as a revision of the investigation of § 95; but they were suspended in order that problems of the stellar absorption law might first be settled. It was clear, however, that the luminosity would be much less affected by the finite size of atoms on this theory than on the Van der Waals model. Had the work been completed it would have formed a kind of half-way stage between the old treatment of dense stars on the full analogy of terrestrial gases and the present view that the b term is to be abandoned altogether; and even if doubt should arise as to this latter view the half-way modification seems essential.

115. The stellar gas differs from terrestrial gases in two important respects. Firstly, its molecules are much smaller. Secondly, they carry electric charges so that there are very large inter-molecular forces. Owing to the first condition the deviations from the perfect gas law prominent in terrestrial gases do not occur in the stars. May not the second condition introduce new deviations peculiar to the stellar gas?

Inter-molecular forces are not entirely absent in terrestrial gases and it is recognised that they produce deviations from the gas laws which become prominent at low temperatures. But these forces of cohesion are all of the same type—all attractive or all repulsive. They are not very closely comparable with the electrostatic forces in the stellar gas which on the whole give a balance of attractive and repulsive forces. In the stars we are concerned with the deviations from perfect balance of comparatively large forces, instead of the full first-order effects of small forces, and the ordinary gas theory is not of much help.

We shall show that even if the effect of these electrostatic forces is considerable it is easily distinguishable from an effect due to finite size of the molecules; and in particular *it cannot play the part ascribed in the giant and dwarf theory to finite size of the molecules.* For a star of constant mass and molecular weight the effect is independent of the star's density. It therefore affects the luminosity throughout the evolution of the star— in the diffuse stages as much as in the dense stages. It cannot be invoked to explain the turning-point from the giant to the dwarf series at a critical density.

The electrical attractions and repulsions contribute a pressure which should be taken into account in forming the equations of equilibrium of a star. Naturally this pressure increases as the star condenses and the charges are squeezed closer together; but it increases at just the same rate as all the other forces in the star, so that relatively it is no more important in dense stars than in diffuse stars of the same mass.

It has often been pointed out in the theory of the atom that if inverse-square forces alone are acting no definite scale of size can be fixed. This is illustrated by our results for a perfectly gaseous star, where, under the inverse-square force of gravitation, no scale of volume for the star is fixed—a giant star of given mass is equally comfortable with any radius. By varying the radius we have a perfectly homologous series. Thus if A is a star in equilibrium and B a replica of it—a precise copy of the instantaneous distribution of molecules—but with all lengths altered in the ratio l and all speeds in the ratio $l^{-\frac{1}{2}}$, then B will also be in equilibrium. For then ρ is altered in the ratio l^{-3} and T in the ratio l^{-1} so that the relation $\rho \propto T^3$ for stars of the same mass is satisfied. Looking into the details of the balance, we see that any potential energy arising from inverse-square forces is altered in the ratio l^{-1}—the same as the ratio of alteration of kinetic energy of all the molecules; moreover, radiant energy per unit volume is altered in the ratio T^4 or l^{-4}, and therefore radiant energy per unit mass is altered in the ratio l^{-1}.

To upset the homology we must have other than inverse-square forces, such as those which act during a collision between molecules; the potential energy from these forces is not altered in the ratio l^{-1}, so that its importance will be relatively greater or less according to the radius of the star. When the molecule is for most of the time free from collision this energy is negligible, but it becomes important when the molecules are kept jammed in contact. According to the older theory this happened at a density approaching that of water, and the homologous series of giant stars stopped at about that point; but our present theory is that these contact forces do not attain the corresponding importance until enormously higher densities are reached. We admit that there are large forces between the molecules when still far apart; but these are inverse-square forces with potential energy varying as l^{-1}, so that the homology is not disturbed.

Therefore although the electrostatic forces will change the equilibrium of the stars A and B to new models A_0 and B_0, B_0 is derived from A_0

by the same transformation as used in deriving B from A. The pressures will be transformed in the ratio l^{-4} and therefore in the same ratio as ρT. The perfect gas law is obeyed, except that the constant of proportionality between p_G and ρT is modified by the electrostatic forces, so that we have

$$p_G = a\Re\rho T/\mu \quad \dots\dots\dots\dots\dots\dots(115\cdot1),$$

where a is the same throughout the homologous series and depends only on the mass of the star. Since μ only appears in the astronomical formulae through this equation for p_G, the effect of electrostatic forces is very simply taken into account by substituting a fictitious molecular weight μ/a instead of μ in our formulae.

It is true that the star B could not actually be a precise copy of A because at the different temperature and density the ionisation would be slightly altered. The ionisation depends on other than inverse-square forces and is therefore not purely a function of ρ/T^3. Thus B_0 would not be strictly homologous to A_0; but no more is B (without electrostatic forces) strictly homologous to A. The differences are no greater than those that have previously been neglected.

116. The investigation of the magnitude of the electrostatic forces is taken up in Chapter x. We shall find that they are comparatively small and have little effect on the mass-luminosity curve, except that they appear to be responsible for about half of the difference between the line of the observations and the theoretical curve on the left of Fig. 2. They make the gas superperfect; that is to say, the pressure is less than in a perfect gas, whereas the deviations familiar in terrestrial gases make the pressure greater.

At first sight it seems absurd that we should secure greater compressibility—render the atoms less able to ward off one another—by stripping them of their electrons and thereby exposing the large repulsive forces of their nuclei which were previously shielded. But the electrons set free by ionisation are not removed; they wander among the ions and shield their repulsions very much as they did when they were bound. The mystery really lies in the origin of the forces corresponding to the rigidity of the atoms, which seem to be much greater than any electrostatic repulsions in the small region in which they act.

The following calculation is intended solely to allay the idea that the electrostatic forces will, by creating around an ion a large region impenetrable to other ions, give it an effective volume sufficient to produce large effects. In order to take the most favourable case, consider a small star like Krueger 60, which at a more or less average point has a temperature $2\cdot5.10^7$ and a density 360. If the material is iron there will be $3\cdot9.10^{24}$ ions per cu. cm. giving an average separation of $0\cdot64.10^{-8}$ cm. The charge of an ion retaining 3 electrons is $23e$ and two such ions at average separation have a mutual potential energy nearly equal to the average kinetic energy of 4 free molecules. At the average separation this mutual energy merely cancels that due to the free electrons in the neighbourhood since the average potential is zero. Now let the two ions approach to a distance $0.42 \cdot 10^{-8}$ cm. Their mutual energy being proportional to r^{-1} increases by 50 per cent.; and there is no corresponding increase in the cancelling term, since the negative charge being divided between 23 free electrons has a comparatively non-fluctuating distribution. The increase is thus equal to the average kinetic energy of 2 free molecules, and the 2 ions can just make the approach at the expense of all their kinetic energy if they were originally endowed with the average amount. Hence on the average two ions cannot approach nearer than $\frac{2}{3}$ of their mean distance, which means that effectively an ion is barred out from $\frac{1}{3}$ of the whole volume.

When a molecule is barred from a third of the volume by finite size of other molecules the constant b in the gas equation is $\frac{1}{6}v$, so that the pressure equation becomes $\frac{5}{6}pv = RT$. Accordingly, the pressure is increased 20 per cent. But in the present case only $\frac{1}{24}$ of the gas pressure comes from the ions; the rest is from the free electrons which are not barred from any appreciable volume. Thus the increase in the pressure would be less than 1 per cent.

We repeat, however, that this is not a calculation of the true electrostatic effect. It deals with a particular objection which arises in most minds, viz. that ions will act as though they had large volumes. A rather difficult mathematical investigation will show that the objection is a phantasm (§ 184); meanwhile, we take the easier course of showing that, phantasm or not, it is at any rate not of large order of magnitude. The barring out of ions from close approach to one another has actually an effect which would scarcely have been anticipated. It means that in very small stars the ions are constrained to keep at the greatest possible distance from one another, whilst the electrons can wander as they like. The repulsive forces are thus kept down to a minimum, whilst the attractive forces have a good chance of exceeding the minimum. The result is that attractive forces predominate and assist the compression of the material.

White Dwarfs.

117. If stellar matter at the density of platinum has still the compressibility of a perfect gas, the limiting density must be much higher. It is therefore possible that matter in the stars may attain densities unparalleled in terrestrial experience. Conversely, if we can discover in the universe matter of transcendently high density, it will be the strongest possible confirmation of our conclusion that in the ordinary dwarf stars

matter is still a long way from the maximum density and therefore behaves as a perfect gas.

We realise at once where the search should begin, for it happens that the *white dwarf* stars have raised this very question. "Strange objects, which persist in showing a type of spectrum entirely out of keeping with their luminosity, may ultimately teach us more than a host which radiate according to rule."* The most famous of these stars is the Companion of Sirius.

The mass of Sirius *comes* is found from the double star orbit and is quite trustworthy. The determinations range from $0.75 \odot$ to $0.95 \odot$; we adopt 0.85. The absolute magnitude is $11^{m}.3$ corresponding to a luminosity $\frac{1}{360}$ of that of the sun. The faintness would occasion no surprise if this were a red star; but in 1914 W. S. Adams† made the surprising discovery that the spectrum is that of a white star not very different from Sirius itself. The spectrum is $F\,0$, or, if anything, a little earlier (towards A). Assuming that type F corresponds to an effective temperature 8000°— it can scarcely be less in so dense a star—and using the absolute magnitude $11^{m}.3$ we find by (87·2) the radius 18,800 km. Apparently then we have a star of mass about equal to the sun and of radius much less than Uranus. The calculated density is 61,000 gm. per cu. cm.—just about a ton to the cubic inch.

This argument has been known for some years. I think it has generally been considered proper to add the conclusion "which is absurd."

Apart from the incredibility of the result, there was no particular reason to view the calculation with suspicion. The mass is well established and the radius is found by the method used in predicting the radii of α Orionis, Antares, etc.—predictions afterwards confirmed by direct measures with the interferometer. It has been suggested that the light is reflected from Sirius, the companion being of low density and having little light of its own. Apart from any intrinsic difficulties in this suggestion, nothing is gained by explaining the companion of Sirius in a way which will not apply to the other white dwarfs that have been discovered. The bright component of o_2 Eridani is a white dwarf and it has no bright and hot star in its neighbourhood.

It seems that Sirius *comes* either has the enormous density above stated, or else at some low effective temperature probably below 3000° it is able by unexplained means to produce an imitation of the leading features of the F spectrum sufficiently close to deceive the expert observer. I suppose that until recently the first alternative was considered incredible. It seemed that the radiation of the white dwarfs must be set down as one of those paradoxes which arise from time to time when imperfect theoretical

---

* Centenary Address, *Monthly Notices*, **82**, p. 436 (1922).

† *Pub. Astr. Soc. Pac.* **27**, p. 236 (1915).

knowledge is brought to bear on observation. But we have now reached the conclusion that the density is not incredible, and have some inclination to accept the straightforward calculation. Some difficulties remain— sufficiently impressive to deter us from accepting the high density as proved without further confirmation.

I do not see how a star which has once got into this compressed condition is ever going to get out of it. So far as we know, the close packing of matter is only possible so long as the temperature is great enough to ionise the material. When the star cools down and regains the normal density ordinarily associated with solids, it must expand and do work against gravity. *The star will need energy in order to cool.* Sirius *comes* on solidifying will have to expand its radius at least tenfold, which means that 90 per cent. of its lost gravitational energy Ω must be replaced. We have seen (§§ 103, 104) that the heat energy including energy of ionisation is necessarily less than Ω so that there is likely to be a deficit. We can scarcely credit the star with sufficient foresight to retain more than 90 per cent. in reserve for the difficulty awaiting it. It would seem that the star will be in an awkward predicament when its supply of sub-atomic energy ultimately fails. Imagine a body continually losing heat but with insufficient energy to grow cold!

It is a curious problem and one may make many fanciful suggestions as to what actually will happen. We here leave aside the difficulty as not necessarily fatal.

118. The density of the companion of Sirius can be submitted to a crucial observational test, viz. the third Einstein effect or shift of spectral lines to the red. If the high density is right this effect will be very large since it is proportional to M/R which is 31 times as great for the star as for the sun. The predicted shift is equivalent to a Doppler displacement of 20 km. per sec., and there is no fear of confusing it with miscellaneous sources of spectral shift (the K term) which can scarcely exceed 3 or 4 km. per second. In an isolated star there would be no means of separating the Einstein shift from a genuine Doppler displacement due to line-of-sight velocity; but for this star we know the line-of-sight velocity by observation of Sirius itself. The observation in fact consists in differential measures of the spectra of Sirius and its companion; the small difference of orbital motion between them is known and can be allowed for.

This test has been carried out by W. S. Adams at the Mount Wilson Observatory*. Difficulty arises from the faintness of the object and its nearness to Sirius. The spectrum of the companion is overlaid by a scattered spectrum of Sirius. Scattering increases rapidly with diminishing wavelength so that the long wave-length end of the spectrum is the purest.

* *Proc. Nat. Acad. Sci.* **11**, p. 382 (July, 1925); erratum, *Observatory*, **49**, p. 88.

At $H\beta$ there is practically no interference, the scattered light of Sirius being weak. The displacements of $H\beta$ measured on 4 different photographs (different methods of measurement giving 8 determinations in all) were found to be

$$+ 31,\ 23,\ 24,\ 17,\ 31,\ 27,\ 28,\ 25\ \text{km. per sec. Mean} + 26.$$

At $H\gamma$ it was found that the scattered light was just about equal in intensity to the true light of the companion; thus the line is presumably a blend in equal proportions of $H\gamma$ for the companion and for Sirius. The measures should therefore be multiplied by a factor nearly equal to 2. The measured displacements of $H\gamma$ were

$+ 13,\ 17,\ 2,\ 4,\ 8,\ 14,\ 12$ km. per sec. Mean (corrected for blend) $+ 21$ km. per sec.

Fainter lines which could be measured gave, after multiplying by the factor for blend, the mean result $+ 22$ km. per sec. We have then

General mean, Companion *minus* Sirius $+ 23$
True Doppler Effect (orbital motion) $\underline{+ \ 4\cdot3}$
                          Einstein Shift $+ 19$ km. per sec.

The device that was resorted to for $H\gamma$ and the faint lines is, of course, unsatisfactory; but the evidence from $H\beta$ alone seems decisive.

This observation is so important that I do not like to accept it too hastily until the spectroscopic experts have had full time to criticise or challenge it; but so far as I know it seems entirely dependable. If so, Prof. Adams has killed two birds with one stone; he has carried out a new test of Einstein's general theory of relativity and he has confirmed our suspicion that matter 2000 times denser than platinum is not only possible, but is actually present in the universe.

119. White dwarfs are probably very abundant. Only three are definitely known, but they are all within a small distance of the sun. It is only in rare conditions that we are likely to suspect, much less to establish, this condition of a star. In this book the phrase "ordinary stars" is to be understood to exclude white dwarfs; but if we say little about them it is because we know little and not because we regard them as a negligible minority.

The bright component of o_2 Eridani suggests itself for an additional test. It is fainter than Sirius *comes*, but there is no bright star to interfere with its spectral measurement. The Einstein effect is, however, smaller. The companion of o Ceti has been suspected of being a white dwarf, but its spectrum seems to be peculiar and its nature is rather obscure.

The conditions in the white dwarfs are outside the limits to which our theoretical investigations apply. In particular, our formula for k ceases to be a valid approximation and we have as yet no determination of the probable degree of ionisation. It seems likely that the ordinary failure of the gas laws due to finite size of molecules will occur at these high densities, and I do not suppose that the white dwarfs behave like perfect gas. The companion of Sirius would fall well below the theoretical mass-luminosity curve; this may be an indication that the gas laws have at last failed, but it might also be explained by an increase of the absorption coefficient arising from the close packing of the ions and electrons.

If the gas laws were obeyed the companion of Sirius would have a central density of about 3,000,000 gm./cm.³ and a central temperature 1,000,000,000°. The temperature is of the order required to affect the rate of radio-active processes and bring about nuclear changes, so that a new series of phenomena unknown in ordinary stars may be occurring. If the white dwarfs could be placed at the beginning instead of at the end of evolution the origin of the chemical elements would be less mysterious.

Evolution.

120. We have been considering the *luminosity-mass* relation indicated both by theory and observation, and the consequences arising from it. We now turn to the *luminosity-type* relation which at present is a purely empirical one.

Fig. 3, due to F. H. Seares, contains the known statistics of absolute magnitude and spectral type of the stars. Impressions formed from the diagram may be misleading unless attention is paid to the great influence of selection of data. Naturally bright stars are represented in numbers out of all proportion to their abundance in space. Absolute magnitudes found by the spectroscopic method have been more fully studied for the redder than for the whiter types. Nevertheless, the diagram is extremely instructive.

The feature of the distribution which is generally accepted as indubitable is represented schematically in Fig. 4. The statistics cluster strongly to a pair of lines PQR. The slope of PQ is small, and it is not certain that it is in the direction shown; but the reduction of Seares's visual magnitudes to bolometric magnitude increases the slope in this direction*. In the globular clusters the slope of PQ is definitely in this direction and seems to be larger than in our local system.

We may either suppose that PQR is the track of evolution of an average star, or we may suppose that stars born with different masses develop rapidly until they reach a point on PQR and then stick there almost indefinitely. The line is either a track of evolution or a locus of equilibrium points or a mixture of both.

* Ordinary giants of types A and F which would lie on the direct line of PQ are scarce, and the stars shown on Seares's diagram are chiefly Cepheids or pseudo-Cepheids.

According to the present theory a star remains of practically constant bolometric magnitude so long as its mass does not alter. More accurately the track of evolution of a star of constant mass has a slight upward slope

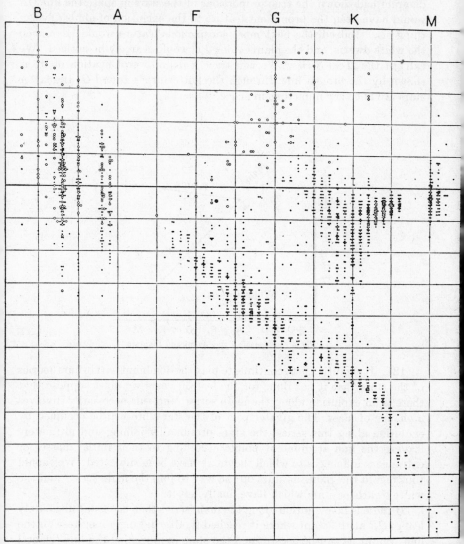

Fig. 3. Statistics of Absolute Magnitude and Spectral Type.

to the left; such a track is shown by the dotted line SS'. Any considerable vertical displacement in Fig. 4 involves a change of mass. In particular, there can be no evolution of a star along QR unless the star is changing mass—and changing it considerably. Evolution along PQ involves at the most minor changes of mass.

The dwarf stars enormously outnumber the giants, and if Seares's diagram had shown the true proportions of the stars in space the line QR would have been the prominent feature to the exclusion of almost everything else. Indeed, the next most conspicuous feature would have been the white dwarfs, and the giants along PQ would scarcely be noticed. We call QR the *Main Series*. We can trace a definite prolongation of it, as shown by the broken line, through the hotter types B and O; the latter stars are not very numerous in space.

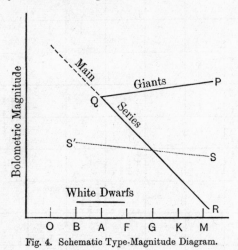

Fig. 4. Schematic Type-Magnitude Diagram.

121. If evolution is to continue to play the dominant part in our theories of the stars that it has done for the last 50 years we must suppose that there is an evolution along the main series; and this necessarily involves a change of mass. The greater part of the star's life will be occupied by evolution along this series, the stars presumably joining and ultimately leaving the line at different points according to their initial masses or extraneous influences to which they may have been subjected. We should thus regard the giants as stars on the way to join the main series, and the white dwarfs as stars which have finally left it.

If there is no evolution along the main series then each star ultimately leaves QR at the point where it reached it, after taking a long rest on the line. So far as can be ascertained the stars approaching the line (giants) are mostly of considerably larger mass than the stars leaving the line (white dwarfs), so that evolution down the line is strongly suggested.

It will be seen that any modern theory of evolution is bound up with the question of the possibility of change of mass of a star.

122. The motion (if any) of a star along QR must be due to changing mass and not to any lack of balance of supply and demand of energy. It is important to remember this because it has usually been supposed that the impulse for a star to move on to a new condition comes from a failure of energy supply. But here a failure of supply would cause the star to move away from QR along a line parallel to SS'; it cannot reach any other point on QR without changing its mass.

It appears then that along QR there is a semipermanent balance of supply of sub-atomic energy and loss by radiation, the radiation being determined by Table 14. For different masses the corresponding point on this line gives the right internal conditions for a liberation of sub-atomic energy at a rate which balances the fixed rate of radiation. This will be true for the greater part of the star's life, but the composition of the material is gradually being transformed and the time ultimately arrives when the star must leave the line.

It is therefore of interest to study the internal conditions of stars on the line of the main series. I do not think we should expect to find any common characteristic, because, for example, V Puppis has to liberate 8500 times as much energy per gram as Krueger 60 in order to keep the balance. But whether by accident or by some significant law of physics there is a common characteristic; *the stars on the main series possess nearly the same internal temperature distribution.*

Attention has been called to this curious result by H. N. Russell[*]. Examples of it were given in § 106. Perhaps the best way of discovering how closely the stars conform to it is to assume a common central temperature of 40 million degrees for all stars of the main series, and calculate the resulting relation between absolute magnitude (or mass) and effective temperature (or type).

In Table 23 the first two columns are taken directly from Table 14. Then by (99·3) the radius R of the star is given by

$$R = 0{\cdot}856\,\frac{G\mu\beta M}{\Re T_c} \qquad\dots\dots\dots\dots\dots\dots(122{\cdot}1).$$

Hence R corresponding to the assumed central temperature can be found.

If m is the absolute bolometric magnitude, and m_0 the magnitude taken directly from Table 14,

$$m_0 - 2\log\,(T_e/5200) = m = -\tfrac{5}{2}\log L + \text{const.}$$
$$= -5\log R - 10\log T_e + \text{const.}$$

so that $\qquad 8\log T_e = -m_0 - 5\log R + \text{const.} \qquad\dots\dots\dots(122{\cdot}2).$

Thus T_e is found and is given in the fifth column of the Table. We can now determine m $(= m_0 - 2\log\,(T_e/5200))$ and reduce it to visual magnitude.

[*] *Nature*, **116**, p. 209 (1925).

Finally, the type corresponding to T_e according to the usual temperature scale is added in the sixth column.

It should be mentioned that we have in these calculations applied to m_0 the correction suggested in the footnote on p. 159; that is to say, we have followed the line of the observational data rather than the theoretical curve at the left of Fig. 2, because we think that the correction is genuine*.

Table 23.

Results for assumed Central Temperature 40,000,000°.

$1-\beta$	Mass	Bol. Mag.	Vis. Mag.	Eff. Temp.	Type
		m	m	°	
·002	·182	11·94	14·5	2550	$< M\,d$
·004	·258	10·25	11·6	3210	$K\,9$
·015	·512	7·26	7·6	4540	$K\,0$
·03	·746	5·93	6·1	5160	$G\,4$
·05	1·00	4·47	4·5	6290	$F\,8$
·10	1·58	2·43	2·5	8250	$A\,8$
·18	2·56	0·52	0·9	10520	$A\,0$
·30	4·53	$-1·38$	$-0·6$	13260	$B\,7$
·50	11·46	$-3·86$	$-2·4$	17460	$B\,2$
·70	37·67	$-6·44$	$-4·3$	22500	$O\,e$
·80	90·63	$-8·12$	-6	26200	O

If these magnitudes and types are plotted on a diagram similar to that of Seares we obtain a line which agrees as nearly as we can judge with the central line of the main series. The observational evidence is thus consistent with the assumption of a uniform central temperature of 40 million degrees throughout the whole length. At any rate, the deviation from uniformity must be small.

The question arises whether the main series is strictly a line in the diagram or a rather narrow band. This can scarcely be determined from the statistics, because the spread is largely caused by observational error. It is risky to appeal to particular individuals since we cannot be certain that these have reached the stable point; thus the fainter component of α Centauri is considered by Russell to be a giant of unusually small mass which is approaching the main series but has not reached it. I think that a certain amount of spread must be admitted more particularly at the hot

* Whether the correction if genuine ought to be applied depends on its origin. If it is due to a decreased absorption coefficient rendering the stars more luminous than the law $k \propto \rho/\mu T^{\frac{1}{2}}$ predicts, our procedure is justified. If it is due to an increase of molecular weight (whether actual or used as a fictitious equivalent of the electrostatic forces as in § 115) μ should be increased in determining R from (122·1). This would make R larger and the effective temperature smaller and to a large extent compensate the decrease of m_0 in (122·2). If, for this or other reasons, it is inappropriate to apply the correction, T_c must increase a little for the smaller stars.

end of the series; for example, Alcyone although the brightest of the Pleiades is by no means the hottest. Exceptions of this kind become rarer as we go down the series and apparently the band narrows. Perhaps the effect of diverse initial conditions of the stars wears out after they have been a long time on the main series. The luminosity-spectrum relation is primarily an empirical one, whereas the luminosity-mass relation is based on a definite theory; there is no reason to anticipate that the former will be as exact as the latter for individual stars.

It is difficult to know what to make of this constancy of central temperature. It may be an accidental relation due to the exhaustion of the sources of sub-atomic energy balancing the decrease in demand as the mass diminishes; but this seems an unlikely adjustment. Taken at face value it suggests that whether a supply of 680 ergs per gram is needed (V Puppis) or whether a supply of 0·08 ergs per gram (Krueger 60) the star has to rise to 40,000,000° to get it. At this temperature it taps an unlimited supply.

The obvious difficulty is that temperature is a statistical attribute, and if we turn to the individual processes, anything characteristic of 40 million degrees is still moderately abundant at 20 million degrees. It is true that at low temperatures we have experience of critical transitions, but the analogy seems inapplicable. Does energy issue freely from matter at 40,000,000° as steam issues from water at 100°?

CHAPTER VIII

VARIABLE STARS

CEPHEID VARIABLES

123. Although variable stars of the Cepheid type show a periodic change of radial velocity it is improbable that they are binary systems. The theory which now seems most plausible attributes their variation to the pulsation of a single star; and accordingly the varying radial velocity measures the approach and recession of the surface presented towards the observer as the star swells and contracts. If this explanation is correct we have an opportunity of extending the study of the internal state of a star from static to disturbed conditions.

The leading facts about these variables ascertained by observational study are as follows—

About 170 galactic Cepheids are known with periods ranging from a few hours to about 50 days; so-called "orbits" have been determined for 20 of these from measurements of radial velocity. In addition large numbers of Cepheids have been found in some globular clusters; among these periods less than 12 hours are especially prevalent. Cepheids have also been found in the Andromeda nebula.

Relatively few periods are between 0·7 and 3 days, so that the Cepheids may be subdivided into two groups with periods above and below this gap.

The light-range rarely exceeds 1^{m}·2 visual; the photographic range is greater than the visual. The spectral type changes during the period, corresponding to a higher temperature at maximum than at minimum.

The light-curve and the velocity-curve are closely similar*; the correspondence is the more marked because both curves are usually unsymmetrical. The light-variation is marked by a rapid rise to maximum and a comparatively slow decline often arrested by a definite hump in the downward course of the curve†. This asymmetry is reproduced in the velocity-curve; if interpreted as orbital motion it indicates that the orbit is eccentric with periastron at the point farthest from the observer. There are occasional exceptions to this rule.

The relation of phase between light and velocity is very definite, maximum light occurring simultaneously with—or perhaps slightly before

---

* When plotted according to the usual conventions the one is a mirror image of the other.

† A progressive relation between the period and the form of the light-curve has been found by E. Hertzsprung. For periods 2–3 days and again for periods 10–12 days the curve is fairly symmetrical (*Bull. Astr. Inst. Netherlands*, No. 96).

—maximum velocity of approach. This fact rules out any interpretation of the variation as an occultation effect.

The absolute magnitude is a definite function of the period. This was first shown by Miss Leavitt from a study of the variables in the Lesser Magellanic Cloud. A full confirmation was obtained by H. Shapley from the variables in globular clusters. In the same cluster the absolute magnitude differs from the apparent magnitude by a *constant* (depending on the unknown distance of the cluster) so that the period-luminosity relation is given directly without the intervention of parallax. It is found that the period determines the absolute magnitude to within a probable error of $\pm$ $0^{m\cdot}25$. Having thus found the period-magnitude curve applicable to all Cepheids except for the unknown constant, we proceed to anchor the curve by combining our knowledge of the mean luminosity of the nearer Cepheids (derived from their parallactic and cross motions) into a single mean determination of the constant.

There is a progression of spectral type in the direction from A towards M as the period (and luminosity) increases.

The Cepheids are more luminous than ordinary giant stars of the same spectral class, although some giant stars of high luminosity, called pseudo-Cepheids, are found which seem to resemble them very closely without showing any light-variation. Cepheids and pseudo-Cepheids are sometimes described as "super-giants."

124. Tables 24 and 25 contain results for those Cepheids which have been sufficiently investigated. The observational data have been taken from a compilation by Margarete Güssow*.

In Table 24, column 3 gives for most stars the *range* of spectral type since the type changes during the light-period. In column 4 an effective temperature is assigned to correspond to the median spectral type. The basis adopted in this assignment is 4900° for type G 0 with an increase of $\log_{10} T_e$ by 0·0140 for each tenth of a type between M and A, so that A 0 = 9300°, M 0 = 2600°. The temperatures are taken rather low, partly because these stars are super-giants of low density, and partly because the types here used (mostly due to Shapley†) are systematically $\frac{3}{10}$ or $\frac{4}{10}$ of a type bluer than those assigned by Adams and Joy. The absolute visual magnitude in column 6 is derived from the period by Shapley's period-luminosity curve‡. Differentially these magnitudes should be correct to within $0^{m\cdot}25$, but the zero point of the period-luminosity curve is not so well determined, and there may be a constant correction applicable to the whole series. I suspect also that there may be a progressive error (originat-

---

* "Kritische Zusammenstellung sämtlicher Beobachtungsergebnisse der Veränderlichen vom δ Cephei-Typus und Kritik der Eddingtonschen Pulsationstheorie" (lithographed, Berlin, 1924).

† *Astrophys. Journ.* **44**, p. 274.   ‡ *Ibid.* **48**, pp. 114, 232.

Table 24.

Cepheid Variables—Observational Data.

No.	Star	Type	T_e	Period (II)	Magnitude		Light-Range		e	ω	δ? $(10^6$
					Vis.	Bol.	Vis.	Photog.			
			°	d	m	m	m	m		°	
1	l Car.	F 8–G 9	4400	35·523	− 5·13	− 5·53	1·5	...	0·36	99	8·5
2	Y Oph.	F 5–G 3	5050	17·121	− 4·00	− 4·17	0·61	...	0·16	202	1·7
3	X Cyg.	F 5	5750	16·385	− 3·92	− 3·97	0·69	1·16	0·25	101	6·1
4	ζ Gem.	G 0	4900	10·155	− 3·16	− 3·37	0·42	1·00	0·20	338	1·8
5	S Sge.	F 4–G 3	5150	8·382	− 2·87	− 3·02	0·50	0·86	0·60	75	1·4
6	W Sgr.	A 8–G 2	5750	7·594	− 2·72	− 2·77	0·85	...	0·36	43	1·9
7	η Aql.	A 8–G 5	5500	7·176	− 2·62	− 2·70	0·51	1·09	0·47	66	1·7
8	X Sgr.	F 1–G 5	5250	7·012	− 2·60	− 2·73	0·67	...	0·40	94	1·3
9	Y Sgr.	F 4–G 4	5050	5·773	− 2·30	− 2·47	0·74	1·13	0·42	74	1·3
10	δ Cep.	F 0–G 2	5550	5·366	− 2·19	− 2·27	0·61	1·08	0·48	85	1·2
11	T Vul.	A 9–G 1	5750	4·435	− 1·95	− 2·00	0·71	1·13	0·44	104	0·9
12	SU Cyg.	A 6–F 7	6450	3·845	− 1·78	− 1·78	0·74	1·15	0·31	108	0·7
13	RT Aur.	A 7–G 1	5950	3·728	− 1·74	− 1·76	0·80	...	0·37	95	0·8
14	SZ Tau.	A 9–G 0	5850	3·148	− 1·58	− 1·62	...	0·58	0·24	77	0·4
15	SU Cas.	A 9–F 5	6350	1·950	− 1·15	− 1·15	0·33	0·47	0·0	...	0·2
16	RR Lyr.	B 9–F 2	7800	0·567	− 0·35	− 0·39	0·85	1·06	0·25	111	0·1
17	Polaris	F 8	5250	3·968	− 1·81	− 1·94	0·08	0·17	0·13	80	0·1
18	β Cep.	B 1	19000	0·190	− 0·37	− 2·00	0·05	...	0·0	...	0·0

Table 25.

Cepheid Variables—Theoretical Results.

No.	Star	M (Sun=1)	$1-\beta$	R $(10^6$ km.)	ρ_c	$\Pi \sqrt{\rho_c}$	T_c $(10^6$ degrees)	a' $(10^6$ km.)	$\dfrac{\delta R}{R}$
1	l Car.	50·3	·74	145	·000433	0·74	2·61	117	·059
2	Y Oph.	22·6	·62	58·6	·00288	0·92	4·24	54·9	·031
3	X Cyg.	19·2	·60	41·1	·00713	1·38	5·39	50·5	·148
4	ζ Gem.	15·4	·56	43·0	·00496	0·71	4·56	34·1	·042
5	S Sge.	12·8	·52	33·3	·00894	0·79	5·34	28·2	·044
6	W Sgr.	10·9	·49	23·7	·0209	1·10	6·78	25·0	·081
7	η Aql.	10·7	·49	25·3	·0170	0·94	6·23	24·0	·070
8	X Sgr.	11·1	·49	27·9	·0131	0·80	5·87	23·9	·048
9	Y Sgr.	10·0	·47	26·8	·0134	0·67	5·72	20·3	·050
10	δ Cep.	8·8	·45	20·2	·0273	0·89	6·93	18·5	·063
11	T Vul.	7·7	·42	16·7	·0427	0·92	7·74	15·6	·058
12	SU Cyg.	6·8	·39	12·0	·102	1·23	10·00	13·6	·059
13	RT Aur.	6·9	·39	13·9	·0656	0·95	8·76	13·4	·062
14	SZ Tau.	6·6	·38	13·5	·0691	0·83	8·76	11·8	·034
15	SU Cas.	5·3	·33	9·2	·175	0·82	11·2	8·0	·032
16	RR Lyr.	3·7	·26	4·32	1·18	0·62	18·3	3·1	·039
17	Polaris	7·8	·42	19·6	·0267	0·65	6·66	14·5	·008
18	β Cep.	5·1	·33	1·52	37·3	1·16	65·5	1·7	·030

ing in a faulty reduction from photographic to visual magnitude) which makes the first three or four stars too bright and their calculated masses too large. The bolometric magnitude is derived from the visual magnitude by Table 16. The light-range in columns 8 and 9 often differs considerably from the value given in a former Table of this kind* owing to more recent photometric work. The last three columns contain elements of the spectrographic "orbits." The quantity e is not to be interpreted literally as an eccentricity, but it serves to measure the deviation from a simple harmonic oscillation. The element ω indicates the position of periastron according to the orbital interpretation; if $\omega = 90°$, periastron is at the point of the orbit farthest from us, so that the drop from greatest receding velocity to least receding velocity is sharper than the ascent of the velocity-curve. This is generally a characteristic feature. The quantity δR is the element $a \sin i$ of the spectrographic orbit, but is here considered to be the semiamplitude of the pulsation. Strictly speaking, if ω is not 90° or 270° so that the major axis is not in the line of sight, a correction for eccentricity should be applied, but in all these stars the correction is trivial.

In Table 25 columns 3 and 4 give the mass and $1 - \beta$, deduced by our theory from the absolute magnitude and T_e. In column 5 the radius is obtained as usual from the absolute magnitude and T_e. The central density and central temperature in columns 6 and 8 are then found by (99·3). In column 9 we calculate the radius a' of the orbit of a hypothetical satellite revolving round the star of mass M in the period Π. In column 11 δT_e is the semiamplitude of a variation of T_e which would account for the visual light range given in Table 24. Due allowance is made for the change in luminous efficiency when T_e varies, so that $\delta T_e / T_e$ is not exactly proportional to the range of magnitude. The relation of phase of the light-curve and velocity-curve is such that the radius has approximately its mean value both at maximum and minimum light. Accordingly it is legitimate to ascribe the light-range to a change of effective temperature and not to a change of radius; but we may perhaps be in error in assuming that the relation of visual light to heat intensity is the same as in a static star.

The stars Polaris and β Cephei are given for reference at the end of the Tables. The light-range is very small, but they are believed to be genuine Cepheids. In discussing the Tables we shall, however, confine attention to the typical Cepheids with large variation.

125. We shall first explain why the binary hypothesis for these stars has been abandoned.

If there are two stars, the secondary must be relatively faint because

* *Monthly Notices*, **79**, p. 4.

its spectral lines are never detected. The explanation often given for the light variation is that there is a resisting medium surrounding the whole system, and as the principal star moves through the medium its front surface becomes heated by the resistance. Consequently the star goes through phases like the moon according as the cooler hemisphere or the heated hemisphere is presented towards us; in particular the brightest phase is presented when the star has its maximum velocity towards us—in agreement with the observed relation of brightness and velocity. To generate so considerable an increase of heat the resistance must be great enough to alter the period fairly rapidly; to meet this objection it has sometimes been suggested that the resistance does not actually generate the heat, but it brushes aside the outer layers of the star exposing a hotter substratum. The suggestion does not seem to us very intelligible; one would think that there must be an accumulation rather than a deficiency of absorbing matter on the front side of a star pushing its way through a medium.

First suspicions of the orbital interpretation of the observed radial velocities were aroused by the general tendency of the element ω to fall near $90°$. It is absurd to suppose that the orbits can have a systematic orientation with respect to the line of vision from the sun. But the tendency is too well marked to be a matter of chance; the conspicuous exceptions Y Ophiuchi and ζ Geminorum both have small eccentricities so that the value of ω for them has not so much significance.

The regular relation between period and density which makes $\Pi\sqrt{\rho_c}$ practically constant (Table 25) also tells against a binary theory. We shall see later that such a relation would naturally be expected if the period is intrinsic in a single star.

But the most convincing disproof of the binary theory is afforded by a consideration of the dimensions of the system, which shows that there is no room for the supposed orbits and the binary model is a geometrical impossibility. The column $\delta R/R$ (i.e. $a_1 \sin i/R_1$ on the binary interpretation) shows that $a_1 \sin i$ is on the average $\cdot054R_1$. Now the distance $a_1 + a_2$ between the two components cannot be less than the radius R_1 of the principal star. Hence the ratio of the masses is

$$\frac{M_2}{M_1} = \frac{a_1}{a_2} < \frac{\cdot054 \operatorname{cosec} i}{1 - \cdot054 \operatorname{cosec} i}.$$

Cosec i will not in general be much greater than 1, and it certainly will not be large for all the stars in our Table; hence in general M_2 is not more than, say, $\frac{1}{12}M_1$. Practically we can consider M_1 (i.e. M in Table 25) to be the whole mass of the system. That being so, the semiaxis of the relative orbit is the quantity tabulated as a'. But in most cases a' is a little less than R; that is to say, we have to place the secondary *inside* the principal star. Allowing for the large eccentricities the secondary must dip deeply into the principal star at periastron. The orbital interpretation has to be discarded because there is not enough room for the hypothetical orbits*.

A disproof of the binary hypothesis does not necessarily compel us to adopt the pulsation hypothesis. We are, however, reduced to the consideration of a single star, and the period of light variation must therefore be a period intrinsic in that star. If the period is not that of some form of pulsation, the only alternative seems to be that it is the period of the star's rotation. We do not know of any theory connecting the variations with the star's rotation, sufficiently plausible to be discussed here. No doubt there are other kinds of pulsation which might claim some attention besides the symmetrical mechanical pulsations which we consider and advocate in this Chapter†.

126. Accepting the pulsation theory the relative amplitude $\delta R/R$ has the kind of value which would be anticipated. It is large enough to produce important changes of internal temperature and density and so cause the rate of radiation to fluctuate. There is some indication that $\delta R/R$ is proportional to the temperature amplitude $\delta T_e/T_e$; the fact that the correspondence is not very exact can be attributed to errors of the observational data. For the 15 stars (omitting X Cygni) the mean values are

$$\delta R/R = \cdot 052, \qquad \delta T_e/T_e = \cdot 066.$$

But $\delta R/R$ must certainly be increased a bit because the spectroscopic measures of δR refer to the integrated light of the hemisphere and do not give the true rate of expansion of R. If the law of darkening of the disc is the same as for the sun the values of $\delta R/R$ have to be multiplied by $\frac{24}{17}$, giving a mean value $\cdot073$. But I think that the pulsation may cause the light at maximum to rush out more in a normal direction than in a static star and the correction is probably not so large. It seems then that $\delta R/R$

* The chief arguments against the binary theory and in favour of the pulsation theory were put forward by H. Shapley (*Astrophys. Journ.* **40**, p. 448 (1914)). The pulsation theory was previously advocated by H. C. Plummer, chiefly because deviations from elliptic motion were detected of a kind impossible to ascribe to gravitational perturbations by a third body (*Monthly Notices*, **73**, p. 665; **74**, p. 662).

† [Recently there has been a recrudescence of criticism of the pulsation theory, and rival theories have been advocated. A summary of these discussions will be found in *Monthly Notices*, **86**, p. 251. I have never regarded the hypothesis of symmetrical pulsations as conclusively established but I am not persuaded that anything has transpired in the recent discussions to weaken the case for it as here set forth. Those theories which identify the light period with the period of the star's rotation seem to be ruled out by the following consideration. For δ Cephei the radius 2.10^7 km. and period 5·4 days give an equatorial velocity 270 km. per sec., so that between different portions of the stellar disc there would be a differential velocity of 540 km. per sec. in the line of sight. The spectral lines would be extremely diffuse with total width 8 Å and effective width (not counting faint margins) at least 3 Å.]

and $\delta T_e / T_e$ are nearly the same. The theoretical relation between them has not been worked out and there is no reason to expect exact equality.

We might expect that the "eccentricity," i.e. the deviation from simple harmonic oscillation, would increase with the relative amplitude; but there is no evidence of this in the Table. If there is such a tendency it is probably masked by the more prominent relation of eccentricity to period noticed by Hertzsprung (p. 180, footnote).

The amplitude δT_e of the temperature oscillation should also correspond to the observed change of spectral type. The mean value $\pm \cdot 066 T_e$ corresponds to a relative range $\cdot 934$ to $1\cdot 066$ which represents an increase of about four-tenths of a type. The range given in our Table is generally greater than this. But a great deal depends on the characteristics chosen in assigning the type. For the types given in the Table the intensities of the hydrogen lines were used as the principal criterion. Adams and Joy* have shown that the hydrogen lines behave anomalously in the Cepheids, and the more general spectral features indicate a smaller change of type. For the mean of nine stars they found a range of six-tenths of a type from the hydrogen lines, and one-tenth from the general features of the spectrum.

Adiabatic Oscillations of a Star.

127. We shall now investigate the theory of the pulsation of a gaseous star. The exact theory of the changes of temperature and density, taking into account the flow of heat, involves differential equations of the fourth order which at present seem unmanageable. But the problem is simplified by noticing that owing to the high opacity of stellar material the oscillations through the greater part of the interior are approximately adiabatic. We therefore start by considering adiabatic oscillations of a sphere of gas; we can afterwards calculate the flow of heat which would result, and determine whereabouts in the star it becomes so great as to render the adiabatic approximation invalid.

Let P, ρ, T be the pressure, density, and temperature at a point distant ξ from the centre and let g be the value of gravity there. We fix attention on a particular piece of matter so that ξ oscillates with the pulsation. Let ξ_0, P_0, ρ_0, etc. denote the undisturbed values, and let

$$\xi - \xi_0 = \delta \xi = \xi_0 \xi_1, \qquad P - P_0 = \delta P = P_0 P_1 \quad\ldots\ldots(127\cdot1),$$

and similarly for all the other variables. If the period of pulsation is $2\pi/n, \xi_1, P_1$, etc., will contain a factor $\cos nt$. We consider small oscillations and neglect the square of the amplitude.

For adiabatic changes the pressure and density of a particular piece of matter are connected by

$$P \propto \rho^\gamma,$$

* *Proc. Nat. Acad. Sci.* **4**, p. 131.

where γ is the effective ratio of specific heats (regarding the matter and enclosed radiation as one system, since P is the total pressure). Hence

$$\frac{\delta P}{P_0} = \gamma \frac{\delta \rho}{\rho_0},$$

or
$$P_1 = \gamma \rho_1 \quad \dots\dots\dots\dots\dots\dots(127\cdot21).$$

The matter in the spherical shell ξ to $\xi + d\xi$ occupies in the undisturbed state the shell ξ_0 to $\xi_0 + d\xi_0$; hence, equating the mass

$$\rho \xi^2 d\xi = \rho_0 \xi_0^2 d\xi_0 \quad \dots\dots\dots\dots\dots(127\cdot22).$$

Hence, differentiating logarithmically,

$$\frac{\delta \rho}{\rho_0} + 2\frac{\delta \xi}{\xi_0} + \frac{d\delta\xi}{d\xi_0} = 0,$$

so that
$$\rho_1 = -2\xi_1 - \frac{d}{d\xi_0}(\xi_0 \xi_1) = -3\xi_1 - \xi_0 \frac{d\xi_1}{d\xi_0}\dots\dots\dots(127\cdot23).$$

The ordinary equation of motion is

$$\frac{1}{\rho}\frac{dP}{d\xi} = -g - \frac{d^2\xi}{dt^2}$$
$$= -g + n^2 \xi_0 \xi_1.$$

Hence, using $(127\cdot22)$

$$\frac{1}{\rho_0 \xi_0^2}\frac{dP}{d\xi_0} = -\frac{g}{\xi^2} + \frac{n^2 \xi_0 \xi_1}{\xi^2} \quad \dots\dots\dots\dots(127\cdot3).$$

Now $g/\xi^2 = GM/\xi^4$, where M is the mass interior to ξ which remains constant as the star pulsates; hence

$$\delta(g/\xi^2) = -4GM\delta\xi/\xi_0^5 = -4g_0\xi_1/\xi_0^2.$$

Hence $(127\cdot3)$ becomes

$$\frac{1}{\rho_0 \xi_0^2}\frac{d}{d\xi_0}(P_0 + P_0 P_1) = -\frac{g_0}{\xi_0^2} + \left(\frac{4g_0}{\xi_0^2} + \frac{n^2}{\xi_0}\right)\xi_1,$$

which breaks up into the equilibrium formula

$$\frac{dP_0}{d\xi_0} = -g_0\rho_0 \quad \dots\dots\dots\dots\dots\dots(127\cdot41),$$

and the equation for the deviation from equilibrium values

$$\frac{d(P_0 P_1)}{d\xi_0} = \rho_0(4g_0 + n^2\xi_0)\xi_1 \quad \dots\dots\dots\dots(127\cdot42),$$

which reduces by $(127\cdot41)$ to

$$P_0 \frac{dP_1}{d\xi_0} - g_0\rho_0 P_1 = \rho_0(4g_0 + n^2\xi_0)\xi_1 \quad \dots\dots(127\cdot51).$$

From $(127\cdot21)$ and $(127\cdot23)$

$$P_1 = -\gamma\left(3\xi_1 + \xi_0 \frac{d\xi_1}{d\xi_0}\right) \quad \dots\dots\dots\dots(127\cdot52).$$

Eliminating P_1 from (127·51) and (127·52) we have

$$\frac{d^2\xi_1}{d\xi_0{}^2} + \frac{4-\mu}{\xi_0}\frac{d\xi_1}{d\xi_0} + \left\{\frac{n^2\rho_0}{\gamma P_0} - \left(3 - \frac{4}{\gamma}\right)\frac{\mu}{\xi_0{}^2}\right\}\xi_1 = 0\ldots\ldots(127\cdot6),$$

where $\qquad\qquad\qquad \mu = g_0\rho_0\xi_0/P_0.$

The equilibrium values which appear as coefficients in equation (127·6) can be tabulated with the help of Table 6*. It is easily shown that μ (which is of the dimensions of a pure number) is given by

$$\mu = -\,4\,\frac{z}{u}\frac{du}{dz},$$

also $\qquad\qquad\qquad \frac{\rho_0}{P_0} = \frac{1}{u}\left(\frac{\rho_0}{P_0}\right)_c,$

where the suffix c denotes the values at the centre of the star.

Let $\qquad\qquad\qquad \omega^2 = \frac{n^2}{\gamma}\left(\frac{\rho_0}{P_0}\right)_c \qquad\ldots\ldots\ldots\ldots\ldots\ldots(127\cdot71),$

$$\alpha = 3 - 4/\gamma \qquad\ldots\ldots\ldots\ldots\ldots\ldots(127\cdot72).$$

Then (127·6) can be written

$$\xi_1'' + \frac{4-\mu}{\xi_0}\xi_1' + \left(\frac{\omega^2}{u} - \frac{\alpha\mu}{\xi_0{}^2}\right)\xi_1 = 0\ldots\ldots\ldots\ldots(127\cdot8),$$

the accents denoting differentiation with respect to ξ_0.

128. The equation (127·8) has to be solved numerically. We must first decide on a value of α, which depends on the effective ratio of specific heats. The maximum value of α is 0·6, corresponding to the maximum value $\gamma = \frac{5}{3}$ for a monatomic gas; the minimum value of α is 0, corresponding to $\gamma = \frac{4}{3}$, since a star is unstable for smaller values (§ 104).

As an example we shall consider $\alpha = 0\cdot2$. It is then necessary to try various values of ω^2, i.e. try various periods, until we find a solution which satisfies the boundary conditions and so represents a possible free oscillation. For the fundamental oscillation the first node (place of constant pressure) must fall at the boundary of the star.

We start from the centre with an arbitrary value of ξ_1 (according to the amplitude of the pulsation) which is here taken as unity. Evidently ξ_1' must be taken zero. Proceeding first by a solution in series, and changing to quadratures when the series becomes inconvenient, we calculate ξ_1, ξ_1', ξ_1'' at successive points. Table 26 contains the results of the calculation for three values of ω^2, viz. ·055, ·060, ·065. The unit of length here used is 1/6·9 of the radius of the star, so that the first column ξ_0 corresponds to z in Table 6.

Consider the solution for $\omega^2 = \cdot060$. At $\xi_0 = 5$, ξ_1'' has become negative and is decreasing very rapidly, so that ξ_1' is diminishing and will probably become negative before the boundary is reached. The node is given by

* An auxiliary table giving values of μ will be found in *Monthly Notices*, **79**, p. 10.

$3\xi_1 + \xi_0\xi_1' = 0$ and will probably fall within the boundary; the wave is thus a little too short to fit the star. We lengthen it by diminishing ω^2. On trying $\omega^2 = \cdot055$ we see that we have greatly overshot the mark; ξ_1'' is (as far as we trace it) increasing more and more rapidly and the wave is quite out of control. Taking $\omega^2 = \cdot065$ we find that the wave is much too short and there will be a node well within the star. The results show that the solution is very sensitive to small changes of ω^2 so that the true solution cannot be far from $\omega^2 = \cdot060$.

Table 26.

Trial Solutions for a Pulsating Star ($\alpha = 0\cdot2$).

ξ_0	$\omega^2 = \cdot055$			$\omega^2 = \cdot060$			$\omega^2 = \cdot065$		
	ξ_1	ξ_1'	ξ_1''	ξ_1	ξ_1'	ξ_1''	ξ_1	ξ_1'	ξ_1''
0	1	0	$\cdot0423$	1	0	$\cdot0413$	1	0	$\cdot0403$
1	1$\cdot$0218	$\cdot0443$	$\cdot0504$	1$\cdot$0212	$\cdot0431$	$\cdot0476$	1$\cdot$0206	$\cdot0420$	$\cdot0448$
1$\frac{1}{4}$	1$\cdot$0345	$\cdot0573$	$\cdot0538$	1$\cdot$0335	$\cdot0554$	$\cdot0506$	1$\cdot$0325	$\cdot0535$	$\cdot0474$
1$\frac{1}{2}$	1$\cdot$0505	$\cdot0713$	$\cdot0585$	1$\cdot$0489	$\cdot0685$	$\cdot0541$	1$\cdot$0474	$\cdot0657$	$\cdot0497$
1$\frac{3}{4}$	1$\cdot$0702	$\cdot0867$	$\cdot0644$	1$\cdot$0678	$\cdot0825$	$\cdot0584$	1$\cdot$0654	$\cdot0784$	$\cdot0524$
2	1$\cdot$0940	$\cdot1037$	$\cdot0718$	1$\cdot$0903	$\cdot0977$	$\cdot0634$	1$\cdot$0867	$\cdot0919$	$\cdot0550$
2$\frac{1}{4}$	1$\cdot$1223	$\cdot1227$	$\cdot0806$	1$\cdot$1168	$\cdot1142$	$\cdot0688$	1$\cdot$1114	$\cdot1059$	$\cdot0570$
2$\frac{1}{2}$	1$\cdot$1556	$\cdot1441$	$\cdot0912$	1$\cdot$1475	$\cdot1320$	$\cdot0744$	1$\cdot$1396	$\cdot1202$	$\cdot0577$
2$\frac{3}{4}$	1$\cdot$1946	$\cdot1685$	$\cdot1041$	1$\cdot$1829	$\cdot1514$	$\cdot0804$	1$\cdot$1715	$\cdot1346$	$\cdot0568$
3	1$\cdot$2401	$\cdot1965$	$\cdot1203$	1$\cdot$2234	$\cdot1723$	$\cdot0862$	1$\cdot$2069	$\cdot1484$	$\cdot0529$
3$\frac{1}{4}$	1$\cdot$2932	$\cdot2290$	$\cdot1407$	1$\cdot$2692	$\cdot1945$	$\cdot0917$	1$\cdot$2456	$\cdot1606$	$\cdot0440$
3$\frac{1}{2}$	1$\cdot$3551	$\cdot2672$	$\cdot1676$	1$\cdot$3208	$\cdot2181$	$\cdot0968$	1$\cdot$2870	$\cdot1697$	$\cdot0276$
3$\frac{3}{4}$	1$\cdot$4272	$\cdot3135$	$\cdot2045$	1$\cdot$3784	$\cdot2427$	$\cdot0999$	1$\cdot$3300	$\cdot1735$	$-\cdot0014$
4	1$\cdot$5122	$\cdot3707$	$\cdot2571$	1$\cdot$4422	$\cdot2678$	$\cdot0994$	—	—	—
4$\frac{1}{4}$	1$\cdot$6131	$\cdot4442$	$\cdot3361$	1$\cdot$5122	$\cdot2919$	$\cdot0927$	—	—	—
4$\frac{1}{2}$	1$\cdot$7349	$\cdot5427$	$\cdot4621$	1$\cdot$5879	$\cdot3130$	$\cdot0735$	—	—	—
4$\frac{3}{4}$	—	—	—	1$\cdot$6680	$\cdot3266$	$\cdot0289$	—	—	—
5	—	—	—	1$\cdot$7497	$\cdot3233$	$-\cdot0680$	—	—	—

It will be shown later that the adiabatic approximation breaks down near the boundary so that it would not be possible to introduce exact boundary conditions. But this does not much matter. So long as the node falls well inside the star (where the approximation is valid) we have to go on lengthening the wave; and when we have lengthened it a little too much the solution changes in such a way that no node can possibly occur.

It is found that the value of ω^2 for the fundamental oscillation is roughly proportional to α. The following results have been found:—

$$\alpha = 0\cdot1, \qquad \omega^2 = \cdot0315,$$
$$\alpha = 0\cdot2, \qquad \omega^2 = \cdot060,$$
$$\alpha = 0\cdot6, \qquad \omega^2 = \cdot156.$$

We may adopt as sufficiently accurate

$$\omega^2 = \tfrac{3}{10}\alpha \quad\dots\dots\dots\dots\dots\dots\dots(128\cdot1).$$

The full solution for $\alpha = 0\cdot1$ (calculated by H. E. Green) is given in Table 27, which also contains the corresponding values of ρ_1 from (127·23).

Table 27.

Solution for a Pulsating Star.

$$\alpha = 0\cdot1, \qquad \omega^2 = \cdot0315.$$

ξ_0	ξ_1	ξ_1'	ξ_1''	$-\rho_1$
1	1·0104	·0211	·0225	3·0523
$1\tfrac{1}{4}$	1·0163	·0268	·0237	3·0824
$1\tfrac{1}{2}$	1·0238	·0329	·0249	3·1208
$1\tfrac{3}{4}$	1·0328	·0393	·0263	3·1671
2	1·0434	·0461	·0278	3·2224
$2\tfrac{1}{4}$	1·0558	·0532	·0293	3·2871
$2\tfrac{1}{2}$	1·0701	·0607	·0309	3·3621
$2\tfrac{3}{4}$	1·0862	·0686	·0324	3·4473
3	1·1044	·0769	·0337	3·5439
$3\tfrac{1}{4}$	1·1247	·0855	·0348	3·6520
$3\tfrac{1}{2}$	1·1472	·0943	·0353	3·7716
$3\tfrac{3}{4}$	1·1719	·1031	·0351	3·9024
4	1·1988	·1117	·0333	4·0432
$4\tfrac{1}{4}$	1·2278	·1197	·0291	4·1921
$4\tfrac{1}{2}$	1·2587	·1260	·0201	4·3431
$4\tfrac{3}{4}$	1·2908	·1289	·0017	4·4846
5	1·3231	·1251	$-\cdot0367$	4·5948

Effective Ratio of Specific Heats.

129. Let Γ be the ratio of specific heats of the material. Radiation behaves as though it had a ratio of specific heats $\tfrac{4}{3}$. Hence we may expect that the appropriate value of γ in the foregoing work, which refers to matter and radiation jointly, will be intermediate between Γ and $\tfrac{4}{3}$. We shall investigate the precise value.

Writing the whole pressure as

$$P = N\rho T + \tfrac{1}{3}aT^4, \qquad (N = \Re/\mu) \quad\dots\dots\dots(129\cdot11),$$

the energy per unit volume is

$$E = \frac{N}{\Gamma - 1}\rho T + aT^4 \dots\dots\dots\dots\dots(129\cdot12),$$

since the specific heat of the matter c_v is equal to $N/(\Gamma - 1)$.

For adiabatic changes of volume V the condition is

$$\delta(EV) + P\delta V = 0,$$

so that $\quad \delta E = -(E + P)\,\delta V/V = (E + P)\,\delta\rho/\rho = (E + P)\,\rho_1 \quad (129\cdot2).$

Using (129·11) and (129·12) this becomes

$$\frac{N}{\Gamma - 1} \rho_0 T_0 (\rho_1 + T_1) + 4aT_0{}^4 T_1 = \left(\frac{\Gamma N}{\Gamma - 1} \rho_0 T_0 + \tfrac{4}{3} aT_0{}^4 \right) \rho_1 \quad (129\cdot3).$$

Or since $\qquad N\rho_0 T_0 = \beta P_0, \qquad \tfrac{1}{3} aT_0{}^4 = (1 - \beta) P_0,$

$$\left\{ \frac{\beta}{\Gamma - 1} + 12(1 - \beta) \right\} T_1 = \{\beta + 4(1 - \beta)\} \rho_1 \quad\ldots\ldots(129\cdot4).$$

Also by (129·11)

$$P_1 = \beta (\rho_1 + T_1) + 4(1 - \beta) T_1$$
$$= \beta\rho_1 + (4 - 3\beta) T_1.$$

Hence by (129·4) $\qquad P_1 = \gamma\rho_1 \quad\ldots\ldots\ldots\ldots\ldots\ldots\ldots\ldots\ldots\ldots\ldots\ldots(129\cdot51),$

where $\qquad \gamma = \beta + \dfrac{(4 - 3\beta)^2 (\Gamma - 1)}{\beta + 12(\Gamma - 1)(1 - \beta)} \quad\ldots\ldots\ldots\ldots(129\cdot52).$

This can be reduced to

$$\frac{\gamma - \tfrac{4}{3}}{\Gamma - \tfrac{4}{3}} = \frac{4 - 3\beta}{1 + 12(\Gamma - 1)(1 - \beta)/\beta} \quad\ldots\ldots\ldots\ldots(129\cdot6).$$

We have also $\qquad T_1 = \dfrac{\gamma - \beta}{4 - 3\beta} \rho_1 \quad\ldots\ldots\ldots\ldots\ldots\ldots(129\cdot7).$

If we write by analogy with the usual equation for matter without radiation

$$T_1 = (\gamma' - 1) \rho_1 \quad\ldots\ldots\ldots\ldots\ldots\ldots(129\cdot75),$$

we have $\qquad \gamma' - \tfrac{4}{3} = (\gamma - \tfrac{4}{3})/(4 - 3\beta) \quad\ldots\ldots\ldots\ldots(129\cdot8).$

Here γ is the effective ratio of specific heats for the pressure-density relation and γ' for the temperature-density relation. As the mass of the star increases and β diminishes, γ' approaches $\tfrac{4}{3}$ more rapidly than γ.

In considering a star compressed by pulsation our first impulse is to compare it with a star which has undergone slow contraction in the course of evolution; but in the latter case T varies as $\rho^{\frac{1}{3}}$, whereas in the former

Table 28.

Effective Ratio of Specific Heats.

$1 - \beta$	Values of γ			Values of $(\gamma a)^{\frac{1}{2}}$		
	$\Gamma = 1\tfrac{4}{9}$	$\Gamma = 1\tfrac{5}{9}$	$\Gamma = 1\tfrac{2}{3}$	$\Gamma = 1\tfrac{4}{9}$	$\Gamma = 1\tfrac{5}{9}$	$\Gamma = 1\tfrac{2}{3}$
·20	1·410	1·467	1·511	·478	·632	·730
·30	1·398	1·443	1·476	·439	·573	·655
·35	1·392	1·433	1·462	·421	·546	·621
·40	1·387	1·423	1·449	·401	·519	·589
·45	1·382	1·414	1·437	·382	·493	·558
·50	1·377	1·406	1·426	·363	·466	·527
·60	1·368	1·390	1·405	·321	·412	·464
·70	1·359	1·375	1·386	·277	·353	·397
·80	1·350	1·361	1·368	·225	·286	·321

it varies more rapidly. In the more massive stars the excess of temperature is not so great as we might expect from the value of γ (which for
general purposes is regarded as the effective ratio of specific heats) because
the change of temperature depends on γ' which is smaller.

Table 28 shows the values of γ for different values of Γ and $(1 - \beta)$
calculated by (129·6). It also contains calculations of $(\gamma\alpha)^{\frac{1}{2}} = (3\gamma - 4)^{\frac{1}{2}}$
which will be useful subsequently.

Period of the Pulsation.

130. In equation (127·71) the unit of length is R/R', where R is the
radius of the star and $R' = 6·901$. In order to make the equation independent of the unit of length we write it in the form

$$\omega^2 = \frac{n^2}{\gamma} \left(\frac{\rho}{P}\right)_c \left(\frac{R}{R'}\right)^2 \quad \dots\dots\dots\dots\dots(130·1),$$

which makes the dimensions consistent, ω being a pure number.

By (55·41) and (55·42) with $n = 3$, we have

$$\frac{\rho_c^2}{P_c} = \frac{\phi_c^2}{16\kappa^3}.$$

But by (57·3) $\qquad \phi_c^2 = \left(\frac{GM}{M'}\frac{R'}{R}\right)^2, \qquad 16\kappa^3 = \pi G \left(\frac{GM}{M'}\right)^2.$

Hence $\qquad\qquad \dfrac{\rho_c^2}{P_c} \left(\dfrac{R}{R'}\right)^2 = \dfrac{1}{\pi G} \quad \dots\dots\dots\dots\dots(130·2).$

Thus (130·1) can be written

$$\omega^2 = n^2/\pi G \gamma \rho_c.$$

Since the period Π is $2\pi/n$ and $\omega^2 = \frac{3}{10}\alpha$, we obtain

$$\Pi^2 \rho_c = \frac{10}{3} \cdot \frac{4\pi}{G\gamma\alpha} \quad \dots\dots\dots\dots\dots(130·3),$$

whence $\qquad\qquad\qquad \Pi \sqrt{\rho_c} = 25080 \, (\gamma\alpha)^{-\frac{1}{2}}.$

Or if Π is expressed in days

$$\Pi \sqrt{\rho_c} = 0·290 \, (\gamma\alpha)^{-\frac{1}{2}} \quad \dots\dots\dots\dots(130·4).$$

The factor $(\gamma\alpha)^{-\frac{1}{2}}$ should vary a little from one Cepheid to another since
it depends on $(1 - \beta)$ and hence on the mass; but we see from Table 28
that the change is fairly small. Hence $\Pi \sqrt{\rho_c}$ should be approximately
constant. The values of $\Pi \sqrt{\rho_c}$ for the eighteen Cepheids are calculated in
Table 25 and it will be seen that they are in very satisfactory agreement.
The values ought to increase a little with increasing mass; this is not
confirmed by the Table, but we could scarcely expect the observational
results to be accurate enough to show this effect. There are several possible
sources of systematic error which may affect one end of the Table as compared with the other. It seems likely that Shapley's period-luminosity

relation ascribes too high a luminosity to the long-period Cepheids*. Moreover, we have no reason to suppose that Γ is exactly the same throughout the Table.

The value of γ or Γ has been calculated from physical data by Fowler and Guggenheim for several representative Cepheids (§ 189). Unfortunately, it depends considerably on the assumed chemical composition. It is not so much a question whether the elements are mainly light or heavy, but whether a particular group of, say, 10 consecutive elements for which the conditions of the star are critical, is abundant. We infer from these calculations that unless there is some peculiar accident of composition the value of Γ will not be greatly less than its value for a monatomic gas, and we may perhaps take 1·55 as probable for an average star.

For δ Cephei $1 - \beta = 0\cdot45$, so that with $\Gamma = 1\frac{5}{9}$

$$(\gamma a)^{\frac{1}{2}} = \cdot493.$$

Since $\sqrt{\rho_c} = \cdot165$ (Table 25) we have by (130·4)

$$\Pi = 3\cdot57 \text{ days}$$

compared with the observed period 5·37 days. Considering the uncertainties both of the absolute magnitude and the effective temperature the agreement is very satisfactory.

Moreover, without using any actual estimate of the value of Γ we can predict the period as accurately as the other data warrant. For the values $\Gamma = 1\frac{2}{3}$, $1\frac{5}{9}$, $1\frac{4}{9}$, $1\frac{1}{3}$, we have $(\gamma a)^{\frac{1}{2}} = \cdot558$, $\cdot493$, $\cdot382$, $\cdot000$; whence

$$\Pi = 3\cdot15, \ 3\cdot57, \ 4\cdot60, \ \infty \text{ days}$$

respectively. The value 3·15 days is definitely a lower limit; there is no upper limit but a period substantially greater than 4·6 days could only occur as the result of an improbably close coincidence of Γ with the value $\frac{4}{3}$. There is no special likelihood that the ratio of specific heats of a sample of stellar matter will be in the neighbourhood of $\frac{4}{3}$; in fact, we infer from Fowler's calculations that for any likely mixture it is well above that value. If it is considered that there is a one-tenth chance of $\Gamma - \frac{4}{3}$ lying between 0 and $\frac{1}{30}$ (the whole possible range being 0 to $\frac{1}{3}$), then it results that the chances are 9 to 1 that the period of δ Cephei will be between 3·15 and 7·78 days.

To find the value of Γ which best fits the observations, the mean of stars Nos. 5–9 gives $1 - \beta = \cdot49$, $\Pi \sqrt{\rho_c} = \cdot85$. Hence $(\gamma a)^{\frac{1}{2}} = \cdot342$, $\Gamma = 1\cdot43$. The mean of Nos. 10–14 gives $1 - \beta = \cdot41$, $\Pi \sqrt{\rho_c} = \cdot96$. Hence $(\gamma a)^{\frac{1}{2}} = \cdot302$, $\Gamma = 1\cdot39$. We may accordingly adopt $\Gamma = 1\cdot40$. According to the theory of § 28 this value signifies that the internal energy of the matter (energy of ionisation) is $\frac{2}{3}$ of the translatory energy (chiefly energy

* *Monthly Notices*, **79**, pp. 21–22.

of the free electrons)—or rather that the internal and translatory energies are changing with temperature in this proportion. This result is given only for illustration of the principles, since the observational data are not accurate enough to justify such emphasis on the determination of Γ.

In § 138 it is suggested that a low value of Γ favours the setting up of Cepheid pulsation. If so, the conditions in a Cepheid are necessarily critical for the ionisation of some abundant element or group of elements; and it is right that we should find a value $\Gamma = 1\cdot40$ lower than the value we suppose likely for the stars in general.

R. H. Fowler has pointed out that in the light of modern knowledge of conditions at high temperatures Γ has become a fiction—but perhaps a useful fiction. In the elementary theory of the internal heat of a gas (§ 28) it is assumed that the molecular weight is constant; but when the internal heat consists of energy of ionisation this assumption is self-contradictory and the elementary theory has no application. Any addition to the internal heat is due to the liberation of an extra molecule, and so involves a diminishing molecular weight. Fowler, in his investigations, proceeds straight to the determination of γ—defined as the exponent in the law $P \propto \rho^\gamma$. But there may be some advantage in retaining the general conceptions of § 129, viz. that the material factor $(\Gamma - \frac{4}{3})$ is watered down by the admixture of more and more radiation in the larger stars—the oscillating power of the matter being diluted with the neutrality of the radiation. Thus Γ, which may now be *defined* by (129·6), retains an interesting approximate interpretation.

Limit to the Pulsation.

131. The condition for a node or region of steady pressure is

$$\delta P = P_0 P_1 = 0.$$

In § 128 we have used this in the form $P_1 = 0$, which is correct so long as the region is within the star. But for a node at the boundary where $P_0 = 0$ it is sufficient that P_1 should be finite; and as a matter of fact P_1 does not tend to zero at the boundary in a free oscillation. By (127·41) and (127·42)

$$\frac{d\,(P_0 P_1)}{dP_0} = - \left(4 + \frac{n^2 \xi_0}{g_0}\right) \xi_1 \dots\dots\dots\dots\dots(131\cdot1).$$

Since $P_0 P_1$ and P_0 are zero at the boundary it follows that at a point a short distance within the boundary

$$\frac{P_0 P_1}{P_0} = P_1 = - \left(4 + \frac{n^2 R}{g_0}\right) \xi_1 \dots\dots\dots\dots(131\cdot2).$$

Now $$\frac{n^2R}{g_0} = \frac{n^2R^3}{GM} = \frac{4\pi^2}{\Pi^2}\frac{3}{4\pi G\rho_m} = \frac{3\pi}{\Pi^2 G\rho_c}\frac{\rho_c}{\rho_m}$$

$$= 12\cdot2\gamma\alpha \dots\dots\dots\dots\dots\dots\dots\dots\dots(131\cdot3),$$

by (130·3) introducing the value $\rho_c/\rho_m = 54\cdot36$.

For the two groups of Cepheids Nos. 5–9 and 10–14 we found

$$(\gamma\alpha)^{\frac{1}{2}} = \cdot342, \cdot302.$$

Hence $$\frac{n^2R}{g_0} = 1\cdot4, 1\cdot1.$$

Substituting in (131·2), we see that at the boundary ξ_1 is between $-\frac{1}{5}P_1$ and $-\frac{1}{6}P_1$. Since the pressure cannot become negative P_1 must not exceed unity. Hence there is an upper limit to ξ_1 or $\delta R/R$ between $\frac{1}{5}$ and $\frac{1}{6}$.

Although the observed values of $\delta R/R$ in Table 25 do not reach so high a limit, it seems possible that the vanishing of the pressure is effective in setting the limit to the amplitude attained in Cepheid pulsation and that the more typical Cepheids reach this limit. It has been explained that the values of $\delta R/R$ are probably systematically too low since the spectroscopic determination of δR refers to the integrated light of a hemisphere. Allowing for this the amplitude generally attained seems to be about half the theoretical limit. The discrepancy may well be due to certain imperfections in the theory. When $P_1 = 1$ it is clearly illegitimate to neglect the squares of the amplitudes as we have done; a correction on account of this is necessary, but I do not think this is the whole cause of the difference. It is not sufficient that the total pressure P should remain positive; both p_G and p_R must be positive. In the outermost part of the star p_R and p_G become out of phase with one another. This phase-difference is not shown in our theoretical equations because it is a result of the failure of the adiabatic approximation in this region; but we supply the gap by our observational knowledge. The critical time is when the star is at its greatest expansion. At that time we know from observation that the star is near its mean luminosity. Since the outflowing stream of radiation has its mean intensity it seems permissible to assume that p_R has its mean value which for an average Cepheid is about $\frac{1}{2}P_0$. Then since p_G is not negative we must have $P_0 + \delta P > \frac{1}{2}P_0$ which requires that the amplitude of P_1 shall not exceed $\frac{1}{2}$. By (131·2) the corresponding limit of ξ_1 is $\frac{1}{10}$ to $\frac{1}{12}$ in good agreement with observation. This argument depends on a patched-up treatment of the non-adiabatic region which may be fallacious, and it is put forward only as a suggestion*.

---

* I believe that some years ago, when closely engaged with this branch of the subject, I came to the conclusion that the whole argument given in this section was fallacious; but I cannot remember the reasons, and do not now see the flaw, if any. In *Monthly Notices*, **79**, p. 22 (1918) I stated that the discussion would appear in Part II of the paper, but for reasons now forgotten withheld it when Part II was published.

Dissipation of Energy.

132. The outward flow of radiation across a sphere of radius ξ is

$$F = 4\pi\xi^2 H = -\frac{4\pi ac\xi^2}{3k\rho}\frac{dT^4}{d\xi}$$

$$= -\frac{4\pi ac\xi^4}{3k\rho_0\xi_0^2}\frac{dT^4}{d\xi_0} \text{ by (127·22).}$$

Hence differentiating logarithmically and writing $F = F_0 + F_0F_1$, etc.

$$F_1 = -k_1 + 4\xi_1 + \frac{4d\,(T_0{}^4 T_1)}{dT_0{}^4} \quad\text{...............(132·1).}$$

By (127·21) and (129·75)

$$P_1 = \eta T_1 \quad\text{...............................(132·21),}$$

where

$$\eta = \gamma/(\gamma' - 1) \quad\text{.........................(132·22).}$$

Then

$$\frac{d\,(T_0{}^4 T_1)}{dT_0{}^4} = \frac{d\,(P_0 T_1)}{dP_0} = \frac{1}{\eta}\frac{d\,(P_0 P_1)}{dP_0} = -\frac{1}{\eta}\left(4 + \frac{n^2\xi_0}{g_0}\right)\xi_1$$

by (131·1). Hence

$$F_1 = -k_1 + 4\xi_1\left\{1 - \frac{1}{\eta}\left(4 + \frac{n^2\xi_0}{g_0}\right)\right\} \quad\text{............(132·3).}$$

Also with the absorption law $k \propto \rho/T^{\frac{7}{2}}$,

$$k_1 = \rho_1 - \tfrac{7}{2}T_1 = -\theta\rho_1 \quad\text{..................(132·41),}$$

where

$$\theta = \tfrac{7}{2}(\gamma' - 1) - 1 \quad\text{.....................(132·42).}$$

Note that θ is positive and greater than $\frac{1}{6}$.

Let dQ/dt be the rate of gain of heat per unit mass in the shell between ξ and $\xi + d\xi$ owing to the transfer by radiation. Then

$$\frac{dQ}{dt} = -\frac{d\,(F_0 + F_0 F_1)}{4\pi\rho_0\xi_0^2 d\xi_0}$$

$$= -\frac{1}{4\pi\rho_0\xi_0^2}(1 + F_1)\frac{dF_0}{d\xi_0} - \frac{F_0}{4\pi\rho_0\xi_0^2}\frac{dF_1}{d\xi_0}.$$

The steady part on the right-hand side must be balanced by the rate of liberation of sub-atomic energy ϵ in the shell. Hence

$$\frac{dQ}{dt} = -\epsilon(1 + F_1) - \tfrac{1}{3}\epsilon_m\frac{\rho_m}{\rho_0}\xi_0\frac{dF_1}{d\xi_0} \quad\text{............(132·5),}$$

where ϵ_m and ρ_m are mean values interior to ξ, so that $\epsilon_m = F_0/\tfrac{4}{3}\pi\rho_m\xi_0^3$.

133. For numerical discussion of (132·5) we shall use the calculations of Table 27, which correspond to $\alpha = 0\cdot1, \gamma = 1\cdot380$. We take $1 - \beta = \cdot385$ corresponding to a Cepheid of period about 4 days. Then

$$\gamma' = 1\cdot355, \qquad \eta = 3\cdot90, \qquad \theta = 0\cdot24, \qquad \Gamma = 1\cdot43.$$

By (131·3) $n^2\xi_0/g_0$ is 1·71 at the boundary and at other points its value is easily found from Table 6 since it is inversely proportional to the mean density interior to ξ_0. If σ is the ratio of the mean density of the star to the mean density interior to ξ_0, (132·3) becomes

$$F_1 = 0·24\rho_1 - (0·10 + 1·75\sigma)\,\xi_1 \quad \ldots\ldots\ldots\ldots(133·1).$$

With the aid of Table 27 the following values are found—

ξ_0	F_1	$\dfrac{1}{3}\dfrac{\rho_m}{\rho_0}\xi_0\dfrac{dF_1}{d\xi_0}$	Sum
0	− ·85	·00	− ·85
1	− ·87	− ·02	− ·89
2	− ·96	− ·14	− 1·10
3	− 1·16	− 1·05	− 2·21
4	− 1·52	− 6·28	− 7·80
5	− 2·12	− 46	− 48

Here the unit of amplitude is that of ξ_1 at the centre, which is roughly 0·7 times that of ξ_1 at the boundary, or $0·7\,\delta R/R$.

If we ignore the variation of ϵ within the star so that $\epsilon_m = \epsilon$, the last column gives $- dQ/\epsilon dt$ by (132·5). For example, at $\xi_0 = 3$

$$\frac{dQ}{dt} = 2·21\epsilon \times 0·7\,\frac{\delta R}{R} + \text{const.} \quad \ldots\ldots\ldots\ldots(133·2).$$

The adiabatic approximation neglects this periodic gain and loss of heat and we can now show that the approximation is justified. For half the period, say 2 days, the region at $\xi_0 = 3$ is gaining heat at an average rate about $\frac{1}{20}\epsilon$ (taking $\delta R/R$ about ·05), equivalent to $\frac{1}{10}$ day at the rate ϵ. The total heat inside the Cepheid represents about 100,000 years' supply of radiation. Hence the heat gained in the half-period is to the heat already present in the ratio of $\frac{1}{10}$ day to 100,000 years. This heat is lost in the next half-period. The result is a temperature variation with amplitude of the order $0°·01$. This is, of course, superposed on the main temperature oscillation, due to the adiabatic compression and expansion, which has an amplitude of some half-million degrees and differs $90°$ in phase. Clearly we were justified in assuming that in the main part of the star the leakage effect is trivial. It appears that the adiabatic approximation is much more accurate for a Cepheid than for ordinary sound waves.

The negative sign of F_1 shows that the flow of heat is greatest when ξ_1 is least, i.e. at the moment of greatest compression. The positive sign of dQ/dt shows that a region gains most heat at the time of greatest expansion, i.e. when it is coolest. It is important to notice that the negative sign of F_1 arises from *both* terms in (133·1); the increased flow at greatest compression is partly due to diminished opacity but there would be some increase even if the opacity were constant.

There will be a region near the boundary of the star where the adiabatic approximation ceases to be valid; the heat content there is small and the leakage becomes relatively important.

Towards the boundary the second term in (132·5) becomes predominant so that

$$\frac{dQ}{dt} = -\frac{F_0}{4\pi\rho_0\xi_0{}^2}\frac{dF_1}{d\xi_0} = -\frac{H_0}{\rho_0}\frac{dF_1}{d\xi_0}.$$

We have tabulated F_1 up to $\xi_0 = 5$. It is difficult to trace it beyond; but remembering that there has to be a node at the boundary, we need not fear any abnormal increase. Probably the maximum value of $-dF_1/d\xi_0$ is about 1 in terms of the central value of ξ_1, or about ·05 in absolute amplitude.

Hence the gain of heat per unit volume per second may amount to

$$\rho_0\frac{dQ}{dt} = \tfrac{1}{20}H_0\cos nt$$
$$= \tfrac{1}{80}acT_e{}^4\,(R'/R)\cos nt,$$

the factor R'/R being inserted in order to change the unit of length to 1 cm. Since R/cR' is about 10 seconds

$$\rho_0\frac{dQ}{dt} = \tfrac{1}{800}aT_e{}^4\cos nt.$$

The heat accumulated per cu. cm. in the half-period (2 days) is then about $200aT_e{}^4$. The normal heat content of a cu. cm. is somewhat larger than aT^4, say $2aT^4$. The amplitude T_1 is about ·08. It follows that the temperature oscillation due to heat leakage is about equal to the oscillation due to adiabatic pulsation when $T = 5T_e$. In the region of the star for which $T < 5T_e$ the adiabatic approximation fails utterly.

134. The small leakage of heat found in the last section will gradually dissipate the energy of pulsation if there is no countervailing agency. We shall estimate roughly the rate of decay.

Suppose that the pulsation of the region is kept steady by supplying mechanical work W, so that by the conservation of energy

$$W + \int dQ = 0 \quad\ldots\ldots\ldots\ldots\ldots\ldots(134\text{·}1),$$

for any number of complete cycles. If we substitute in this our expressions for dQ/dt such as (133·2) we merely obtain $W = 0$ to the first order of small quantities. We must obtain an expression which will enable us to calculate W to the second order. Since the state is steady, the change of entropy of the material must be zero for complete cycles, so that

$$\int \frac{dQ}{T} = 0,$$

or since

$$\frac{1}{T} = \frac{1}{T_0} - \frac{\delta T}{T_0{}^2} = \frac{1}{T_0} - \frac{T_1}{T_0},$$

$$\int dQ\,(1 - T_1) = 0.$$

Hence

$$W + \int T_1\,dQ = 0 \quad\ldots\ldots\ldots\ldots\ldots(134\text{·}2).$$

Since T_1 and dQ are known correct to the first power of the amplitude, we can now find W correct to the square of the amplitude.

We shall take the values at $\xi_0 = 3$ as representative of the average conditions in a star. Less than 20 per cent. of the mass is outside $\xi_0 = 3$; but in view of the rapidly increasing dissipation per unit mass in the outer parts, this seems a fair representation. Denoting by $[\xi_1]_c$ the central amplitude of ξ_1, so that roughly

$$[\xi_1]_c = 0.7\delta R/R,$$

we have by (133·2) at $\xi_0 = 3$

$$\frac{dQ}{dt} = 2.2\epsilon\,[\xi_1]_c \cos nt \quad\dotfill(134.25),$$

$$T_1 = (\gamma' - 1)\rho_1 = -0.355 \times 3.54\,[\xi_1]_c \cos nt,$$

so that $\quad T_1 \dfrac{dQ}{dt} = -1.38\epsilon\,[\xi_1]_c^2\,(1 + \cos 2nt).$

Hence W (per gram per sec.) is

$$W = 1.38\epsilon\,[\xi_1]_c^2 \quad\dotfill(134.3),$$

and the rate of dissipation of energy by the whole star is

$$1.38\,[\xi_1]_c^2\,L \quad\dotfill(134.4).$$

The kinetic energy of the pulsation per gram is

$$\tfrac{1}{2}\,(n\xi_0\xi_1)^2.$$

By a rough quadrature the mean value of this at time of greatest velocity is found to be about

$$\tfrac{1}{14}n^2R^2\,[\xi_1]_c^2,$$

so that the whole mechanical energy of pulsation of the star is

$$\tfrac{1}{14}n^2R^2M\,[\xi_1]_c^2 \quad\dotfill(134.5).$$

By (134·4) and (134·5) the time of decay is

$$\tfrac{1}{20}n^2R^2\,\frac{M}{L} \quad\dotfill(134.6).$$

The following numerical results are obtained for δ Cephei*. We have

$$[\xi_1]_c = .05.$$

$$M = 1.75 . 10^{34} \text{ gm.}$$

$$L = 2.80 . 10^{36} \text{ ergs per sec.}$$

$$\epsilon = L/M = 160 \text{ ergs per gm. per sec.}$$

Negative potential energy, $\Omega = 8.65 . 10^{14}$ ergs per gm.

---

* The values of α and β on which (134·3) depends only roughly fit δ Cephei; but the formula is only intended to give the order of magnitude; probably the most serious inaccuracy is the use of a mean value for ϵ.

Heat content, $K + H$ ($\Gamma = 1{\cdot}55$)* $= 6{\cdot}75 . 10^{14}$ ergs per gm.

$\qquad\qquad\qquad\qquad\qquad\qquad\quad = 134{,}000$ years' supply of radiation.

Mechanical energy of pulsation $\quad = 1{\cdot}3 . 10^{11}$ ergs per gm.

Dissipation of mechanical energy $= 0{\cdot}5$ ergs per gm. per sec.

Time of decay $\qquad\qquad\qquad\quad = 8000$ years.

Maintenance of the Pulsation.

135. It has sometimes been supposed that the pulsation is started by some accident—possibly the near approach of another star. The frequent occurrence of Cepheids in star clusters where the stars are closer together might be held to favour this view. But we see that a pulsation so originated would decay in about 8000 years. According to present views this is so small a fraction of the life of the star, that we should rarely observe a star in this condition. It would scarcely be possible to account for the observed abundance of Cepheids on this hypothesis.

The alternative hypothesis is that there are causes at work within the star tending to increase and maintain a pulsation. If these are stronger than the dissipative causes discussed above, any infinitesimal pulsation will grow until either it reaches the natural limit explained in § 131, or it reaches an amplitude for which the dissipative forces balance the assisting forces. If we are right in believing that for many of the observed Cepheids the amplitude reaches the natural limit this view is supported. Since it is only at a certain stage of the evolution of a star that Cepheid pulsation occurs, we must suppose that at this stage the maintaining cause is especially strong, but that during most of the life of a star (and in stars of small mass) it is too weak to overcome the dissipation.

The heat that is continually being liberated in the star is an abundant source from which the energy required to keep up the pulsation might be derived. Thus in δ Cephei 160 ergs per gm. is liberated, and only 0·5 ergs per gm. is required to maintain the pulsation. But this heat can only be made available as mechanical work if the star behaves as a thermodynamic engine; that is to say, excess heat must be added to matter when at a high temperature and withdrawn at a low temperature. We require, in fact, something corresponding to the valve-mechanism of a heat engine.

136. We first consider the obvious position for placing the "valve," viz. at the point of entrance of the subatomic energy into the engine. On the steady supply ϵ_0 there must then be superposed a periodic supply $\epsilon_0 \epsilon_1$, representing positive supply at high temperature and negative supply or withdrawal of heat at low temperature. Since the liberation of subatomic energy is likely to be stimulated by increased temperature, and

---

* A comparatively high Γ is adopted here because the low value used for the pulsations refers only to *differential* changes of heat content at the temperature of the Cepheids.

perhaps also by increased density, the requirement that ϵ_1 shall have the same phase with T_1 is naturally fulfilled.

The mode of operation is easily realised. At the time of greatest compression heat is being generated in a star at more than the average rate needed to replace loss; this strengthens the ensuing expansion. At the time of greatest expansion there is a net loss of heat which diminishes the opposition to the ensuing compression.

The condition for an exact balance just maintaining the pulsation is*

$$\epsilon_0\epsilon_1 + \frac{dQ}{dt} = 0 \quad \ldots\ldots\ldots\ldots\ldots\ldots(136\cdot1).$$

Thus for a mean region we have by (134·25)

$$\epsilon_1 = -\ 2\cdot2\ [\xi_1]_c \cos nt \quad \ldots\ldots\ldots\ldots\ldots(136\cdot2),$$

which may be compared with

$$\rho_1 = -\ 3\cdot5\ [\xi_1]_c \cos nt, \qquad T_1 = -\ 1\cdot2\ [\xi_1]_c \cos nt.$$

The rate of liberation of subatomic energy must increase nearly proportionately to the square of the temperature or to the two-thirds power of the density in order to keep the pulsations going.

There seems to be no possible cause for decay of a mechanical pulsation other than the leakage of heat. There are practically no viscous forces operating in a symmetrical pulsation. It would seem that if ϵ increases faster than T^2 pulsation must occur. This condition of the star may be described as one of "over-stability." In the usual kinds of *instability* a slight displacement provokes forces tending away from equilibrium; in *over-stability* it provokes restoring forces so strong as to overshoot the corresponding position on the other side of equilibrium and set up an increasing oscillation.

The limiting condition $\epsilon_1 = 2T_1$ is slightly modified according to the values chosen for β and Γ, but no very substantial alteration is possible except in stars of small mass. I think we can safely say that if ϵ increases as fast as ρ or as T^3 every star of mass greater than Sirius will be set pulsating.

The application of this condition to non-pulsating stars is quite as interesting as its application to pulsating stars. It gives an upper limit to the rate of variation of ϵ with ρ and T in ordinary non-Cepheid stars, and limits the kind of method by which subatomic energy may be liberated. For example, if the liberation depends on encounters of two agents (electrons and atomic nuclei) the number of such encounters per unit mass will be proportional to the density and presumably the simultaneous increase of temperature will also stimulate the liberation of energy. But we see that this increase with density and temperature is too rapid to be admissible. Our result seems to favour the view that the energy is liberated by spontaneous disintegration of single atoms and is not dependent on

* More strictly the condition is that the integral of $T_1\,(\epsilon_0\epsilon_1 + dQ/dt)$ over the whole star is zero; but it is sufficient for our purpose to consider an average region.

the density; but in that case it is difficult to see how such emission could be stimulated by temperature unless the temperature were very much higher than it is in the Cepheids. We are on the horns of a dilemma; any plausible theory that makes ϵ dependent on the compression of a star makes it vary so rapidly as to set every star pulsating.

I think that there are other grounds that compel us to admit that ϵ does depend on ρ or T, and it is difficult to suppose that the variation is slow enough to avoid over-stability. A suggestion which would meet the immediate difficulty is that the change of ϵ is delayed—that increase of ρ and T accelerates the formation of a source of energy which only yields up its energy after months or perhaps many years. Then long continued changes would affect ϵ, but for short-period pulsations ϵ would be constant. In that case we have to seek another source of maintenance of Cepheid pulsations.

137. We now consider another position of the "valve"—fantastic in an ordinary engine but not necessarily so in the star. Suppose that the cylinder of the engine leaks heat and that the leakage is made good by a steady supply of heat. The ordinary method of setting the engine going is to vary the *supply* of heat, increasing it during compression and diminishing it during expansion. That is the first alternative we considered. But it would come to the same thing if we varied the *leak*, stopping the leak during compression and increasing it during expansion. To apply this method we must make the star more heat-tight when compressed than when expanded; in other words, the opacity must increase with compression.

The obvious objection arises that according to our formula (132·41)

$$k_1 = - \{\tfrac{7}{2} (\gamma' - 1) - 1\} \rho_1,$$

the opacity decreases with compression and the engine will not work. But this is not altogether unsatisfactory; in most stars the engine does *not* work, and it is right that our standard formulae should show this. Suppose it possible that in the exceptional conditions occurring in the Cepheids the law of absorption is modified to

$$k \propto \rho/T^{\frac{5}{2}}.$$

Taking as before $\gamma' = 1\cdot355$, $(1 - \beta) = \cdot385$, we obtain $k_1 = + \cdot114\rho_1$ and the values run—

ξ_0	F_1	$\dfrac{1}{3}\dfrac{\rho_m}{\rho_0}\xi_0\dfrac{dF_1}{d\xi_0}$	Sum
0	+ ·21	·00	+ ·21
1	+ ·20	− ·01	+ ·19
2	+ ·18	− ·08	+ ·10
3	+ ·10	− ·56	− ·46
4	− ·09	− 4·0	− 4·1
5	− ·50	− 33	− 33

Here the dissipation $- T_1 dQ$ is negative for the inner part of the star up to about $\xi_0 = 2 \cdot 5$ and positive beyond, and it is touch and go whether the integrated dissipation is positive or negative. I think that, if allowance were made for the increase of ϵ towards the centre, an actual integration for this example would show the dissipation to be negative, so that the pulsations would increase up to the natural limit.

This method of accounting for Cepheid variation seems hopeful because it at the same time accounts for its rarity. It definitely requires a deviation, but not a very extravagant deviation, from the state of things found in the more typical stars.

A point of some importance has been urged by S. Shinjo and by J. H. Jeans in criticism of the pulsation-theory of Cepheids. We have considered only the fundamental vibration of the gas sphere; but harmonics, with one or more nodes in the interior are also possible. If these are excited the light-curves and velocity-curves of the Cepheids will contain a number of incommensurable periods superposed. No such harmonics have been observed. To meet this criticism we ought to show that for reasonable values of the constants the fundamental pulsation is maintained and the harmonic pulsations are dissipated. The lengthy calculations necessary to investigate this have not been tackled*.

138. Up to a certain point the suggestion made in the last section can be supported. The necessary reversal of phase of the opacity-variation is brought about by reduction of the exponent in the absorption law from $\frac{7}{2}$ to below 3 combined with a low value of γ'; low γ' results either from low Γ or high $(1 - \beta)$.

A high value of $1 - \beta$ corresponds to large mass. Cepheid variation is not found in stars of low mass and the typical Cepheids of types F and G are super-giants. This is in favour of the theory.

But in addition we must find some cause for the reduced exponent in the absorption law. Even for high mass it must be brought down to a value not much above $\frac{5}{2}$. Lowering of Γ is comparatively unimportant, though as a matter of fact any cause tending to reduce the exponent of the absorption law abnormally would be likely at the same time to reduce Γ.

Consider a star say of mass 10. There is only one stage of its evolution at which it can be a Cepheid owing to the empirical luminosity-period relation (§ 123). Since the luminosity depends mainly on the mass, and

* [Dr J. Woltjer has shown me some interesting calculations relating to the first overtone, which correspond to those in Table 26 for the fundamental. It appears that the amplitude remains relatively small between the centre and the first node and becomes very large between the first and second nodes. Whether we follow the theory of § 136 or § 137 the motor part of the star is near the centre and the dissipating part towards the outside. It seems therefore that the dissipation is relatively greater for the overtones, so that their absence is accounted for.]

the period depends mainly on the density, there is a particular density at which this star becomes a Cepheid; at higher or lower densities it is static. The close agreement of all stars with the period-luminosity curve (checked especially in the star clusters) shows that the range of density is a rather narrow one, but I daresay the density may change in the ratio 1 to 3 or 4 and the internal temperature by 50 per cent. between the beginning and end of the Cepheid stage.

This suggests that the lowering of the exponent is a transitory feature in the development of the star synchronising with some important change in the internal condition. The only kind of change that we have been able to think of is a step in the ionisation of some element predominating in the constitution of the star. If this is the explanation the step must almost certainly be the loss of the L electrons reducing the element from a neon-like to a helium-like ion. This ionisation is rather sudden, and the temperature range required for its completion corresponds roughly to the probable duration of the Cepheid stage.

Undoubtedly there would be an abnormal change of absorption with temperature during this ionisation—that is to say, the reduction with temperature would be less than normal. But so far as we can see it would not be great enough for our purpose. There are extra electrons to be captured and captures occur at the deeper levels now vacant so that emission is increased and absorption must keep pace with it. But not much of this increase is reflected in the opacity coefficient, when account is taken of Rosseland's correction. The increased absorption is chiefly of high-frequency radiation forming an inconsiderable part of the whole.

It is evidently necessary that the predominant element should be in a critical stage of ionisation for all the Cepheids, or at least all those which seem to fall into continuous series. Since temperature is the main factor in determining ionisation the Cepheids should have nearly the same internal temperature. There would be a slight increase of central temperature (to counteract the increased density) as we pass down the list in Table 25, but not nearly so much as is shown in that Table. Various sources of systematic error may render the progression of T_c with temperature in Table 25 rather unreliable and probably as there shown it is a little exaggerated. But we do not feel able to make such changes in the data as would give the practically constant central temperature that the theory demands.

If the central temperature were strictly constant we should have by (99·2)

$$T_e^{\frac{3}{5}} \propto M^{\frac{1}{5}} (1 - \beta)^{\frac{1}{2}},$$

so that

$$T_e \propto M^{\frac{1}{3}} (1 - \beta)^{\frac{5}{6}}.$$

Accordingly, the effective temperature should increase slightly with the mass. The observed progression of spectral type with mass is in the opposite direction.

Our conclusion is that the suggestions in § 136 and § 137 both lead to serious difficulties. On the whole, the difficulties of the former seem to be of the more fundamental kind; whereas the difficulties of the latter may perhaps be set down as numerical misfits natural to an early stage in the development of a complex theory.

Miscellaneous Problems.

139. In the investigation of § 127 the square of the amplitude has been neglected. In typical Cepheids ξ_1 may amount to $\frac{1}{12}$ and P_1 to nearly $\frac{1}{2}$, so that the second order terms are quite considerable; these will give rise to terms containing $\cos 2nt$.

For a treatment of the theory with retention of terms of the second order, reference may be made to *Monthly Notices*, **79**, p. 183. The computations are there carried far enough to show that the complete formula for ξ_1 will be of the form

$$\xi_1 = a_1 \cos nt - a_2 \cos 2nt,$$

where a_1 and a_2 are both positive. Hence the velocity of recession has the form

$$V = b_1 \sin nt - b_2 \sin 2nt$$

with b_1 and b_2 positive. This represents a velocity-curve having the general characteristics of the observed velocity-curves of Cepheids, viz. a sharp decrease from maximum to minimum receding velocity and a slower return to maximum with indications of a hump in the curve. The equivalent elliptic orbit has its periastron at $\omega = 90°$.

The close similarity of the light-curve and velocity-curve and the relation of phase between them has not as yet received adequate theoretical explanation. It is not that any opposition of theory and observation has been found; but the difficulty of the mathematics has hitherto proved too great an obstacle. We have found that in the adiabatic region of the star the outward flow of radiation is greatest at the time of maximum compression; this is true for the whole region (§ 133) or, at any rate, for the outer part of it (§ 137). But the greatest outward flow from the surface is observed to occur simultaneously with maximum velocity of approach, that is to say, a quarter-period later. Presumably the retardation occurs in the non-adiabatic region near the surface. The leakage wave discussed in § 133 is 90° behind the adiabatic wave in phase, and it grows in importance as we approach the surface. It would, however, be too crude a deduction to attribute the 90° retardation of flux to the leakage wave supplanting the adiabatic wave. Undoubtedly there will be some retardation in the non-adiabatic region, but no definite prediction of the amount of retardation can yet be made.

If the pulsation theory is correct there should be a broadening of the spectral lines by the Doppler effect as well as an average displacement of them at times of maximum and minimum velocity, since different points of the surface have different velocities in the line of sight. Owing to the "darkening at the limb" of a star the broadening of the lines is considerably less than would be predicted for a disc of uniform brightness and perhaps we can scarcely expect the effect to be observable. It has escaped detection hitherto*.

LONG-PERIOD VARIABLES

140. Variables of this class have, with few exceptions, periods ranging from 100 to 500 days with a strong preference for periods near 300 days. The light-range is comparatively large, averaging about 4·8 magnitudes; it is seldom, if ever, less than 3 magnitudes. The stars are all of type M or of the closely allied rare types S (zirconium type) and N (carbon type). Great changes in the spectrum occur between minimum and maximum, and bright emission lines of hydrogen and other elements appear. The periodicity is imperfect and the star may be some weeks behind or ahead of the predicted phase; the amplitude of the variation is not always the same in successive periods†.

There is growing evidence that long-period variation and Cepheid variation are essentially the same phenomenon. The very low density and temperature of the long-period variables exaggerates and renders more erratic the effects of the same kind of pulsation as in the Cepheids. This is still a very speculative conclusion, but we shall consider the evidence pointing in this direction.

It has been shown by Pettit and Nicholson‡ that the range of variation in heat is very much less than the light-range. For example, χ Cygni gives 1300 times as much light at maximum as at minimum, but only 1·7 times as much heat. The following results were obtained from direct measurements of the heat received from o Ceti§—

Near minimum, visual magnitude 8·9, bolometric magnitude 1·5.
Near maximum, visual magnitude 4·5, bolometric magnitude 0·2.

The heat range is generally about 1 magnitude, so that in this respect the variation is quite similar to that of the Cepheids.

---

* For a detailed discussion see Shapley and Nicholson, *Proc. Nat. Acad. Sci.* **5**, p. 417 (1919). A curious feature of the observations is that the lines at minimum light are much broader than at maximum although the Doppler broadening should be the same at both times.

† Collected data are given by T. E. R. Phillips, *Journal B.A.A.* **27**, p. 2.

‡ *Mount Wilson Report*, 1924, p. 101.

§ *Mount Wilson Report*, 1922, p. 238; we have applied a correction of $- 0^{m}\cdot3$ to reduce to the standard of bolometric magnitude used in this book.

The unpunctuality of the variation is strongly suggestive of an intrinsic period rather than a forced oscillation caused by external agency. For an extraneous cause could scarcely fail to be strictly periodic; and although the response of the star might be irregular there would be no *cumulative* deviation from a periodic ephemeris. But the long-period variables show little or no tendency to recover in phase after an irregularity, and the deviations pile up in the manner to be expected of an uncontrolled accumulation of accidental delays and accelerations.

It has been suggested that at the low surface temperature (indicated by the great difference between visual and bolometric magnitude) the material cannot remain gaseous and that condensations will occur. These might obstruct the regular flow of energy from the interior, which would be dammed back until it had sufficient strength to volatilise or to blow away the obstacle. After this relief the clouds would form again, and the whole process would be roughly periodic like the spirts from a kettle boiling over. It is likely that something of this kind occurs and is a feature of the variation absent in ordinary Cepheids, but it is doubtful whether it would in itself impose a periodicity. It seems more likely that if no other cause of variation were present a balance would be reached between the amount of cloud formed and the power of the obstructed radiation to disperse it. The alternative is that the period is primarily determined by the pulsation of the star as a whole and the above-mentioned skin effect is a consequence of this pulsation. The catastrophic skin effect reacts on the internal conditions and causes irregularity in the period; that is to say, in these extreme conditions of pulsation "the tail wags the dog" to some extent. We may test the pulsation hypothesis by examining whether the mean period is consistent with what we know of the internal condition of these stars. It is first necessary to estimate the mass.

141. From mean parallactic motions and mean cross motions the average absolute magnitude is found to range from $- 0^{m} \cdot 6$ to $+ 0^{m} \cdot 6$ according to the division of type from $M 1$ 'to $M 8$*. Confirmation is obtained from the star X Ophiuchi which has a non-variable companion of type $K 0$. Using the spectroscopic parallax of the companion, the absolute magnitude of X Ophiuchi is $+ 0^{m} \cdot 3$ as compared with the average for its class ($M 6$) of $+ 0^{m} \cdot 5$. The heat measurements show that even at maximum the reduction to bolometric magnitude is large, the effective temperature being well below 3000°. The absolute bolometric magnitude is about $- 3^{m}$. This refers to maximum and the mean rate of radiation may be taken to correspond to $- 2^{m} \cdot 5$. Assuming an effective temperature

* P. W. Merrill and G. Strömberg, *Astrophys. Journ.* **59**, p. 105. W. Gyllenberg finds the average absolute magnitude $- 0^{m} \cdot 7$, *Arkiv för Math., Astr. och Fysik*, **14**, No. 5; his result refers to the extreme maxima whereas that of Merrill and Strömberg refers to the mean maxima of the stars.

2200° the mass by Table 14 is 14 ⊙. But the conditions in such a star are so far from typical that there is risk in applying our theory; at any rate, the molecular weight in the interior may be greater than 2·1 owing to the low temperature, and $1 - \beta$ will be increased. Probably 10 ⊙ is a fair estimate of the mass of a typical long-period variable.

Let us now consider what must be the radius of the star for a pulsation period of 300 days. We may take $(\gamma\alpha)^{\frac{1}{2}} = 0\cdot4$; then by (130·4) the mean density is $1\cdot1.10^{-7}$. From the mass and mean density the required radius is

$$350,000,000 \text{ km.} = 2\cdot3 \text{ astronomical units.}$$

Direct measurements of the angular diameter of o Ceti made by F. G. Pease with the interferometer give a diameter $0''\cdot06$, or somewhat larger if allowance is made for darkening at the limb. The probable parallax according to the foregoing discussion of absolute magnitude is $0''\cdot020$. This gives a radius of at least 1·5 astronomical units. Alternatively from the bolometric magnitude at maximum combined with an effective temperature 2200° (estimated from the heat-index) we obtain a radius of 1·3 astronomical units. For such a rough calculation the agreement is as close as could be expected; and the dimensions are accordingly consistent with the hypothesis that the period of about 300 days is that of the natural pulsations of the star.

As regards spectral type the long-period variables fit on to the Cepheids in natural sequence. In the Cepheids the type reddens as the period increases, so that a very red type is anticipated for a 300-day period.

Eclipsing Variables

142. The adaptation of our theory of the mass-luminosity relation to calculations for eclipsing variables has been illustrated by the example of V Puppis, and eclipsing variables which have known orbits for both components have been used to check the theory. Some further applications may be noted here.

Theoretically it is possible to check the theory by stars with only one component observed spectroscopically; but it is difficult to find an example with data accurate enough to hold out any hope of success.

The light-curve furnishes amongst other data the ratio J_2/J_1 of the surface luminosities of the components. Hence if the spectral type or effective temperature of the primary is observed the effective temperature of the secondary can be found from Table 16. The light-curve gives also the ratio of the luminosities and this will suggest an approximation to the mass ratio M_2/M_1.

Assume for trial an arbitrary value of M_2/M_1; then we can work out L for each component in the manner explained for V Puppis (§ 105), firstly, from the calculated radius of each star, and secondly from the calculated mass—thus obtaining a residual for each star. If the theory is correct it should be possible to find a mass ratio which makes both residuals vanish simultaneously. If not, we vary the mass ratio until the two residuals become equal, and their common value measures the discrepancy between theory and observation.

It is, I think, an accident that no suitable example for discussion presents itself*. We desire to illustrate the method but have to use an unsuitable star β Persei (Algol). The photometric orbit of Algol was obtained by J. Stebbins† by selenium photometry but we shall (unjustifiably) treat the results as though they were visual observations.

The ratio of surface brightness of the primary to the faint hemisphere of the secondary is $J_1/J_2 = 20$, or a difference of $3^m\cdot25$. Adopting $T_1 = 13,000°$ for the effective temperature of the primary (observed type $B\ 8$) we find $T_2 = 5350°$ by Table 16.

From Stebbins's results the ratio of the radii is $R_2/R_1 = 1\cdot14$. Hence the difference of bolometric magnitude (reduced to standard T_e for direct comparison with Table 14) is

$$m_2 - m_1 = -5 \log 1\cdot14 + 8 \log (13000/5350) = 2^m\cdot80.$$

We expect a star of type $B\ 8$ to have a mass about 4. Examples of pairs of masses in Table 14 with magnitude difference $2^m\cdot80$ are $5\cdot67, 2\cdot20$ and $3\cdot44, 1\cdot50$, the mass ratios being $0\cdot39, 0\cdot43$ respectively. Hence we adopt provisionally $M_2/M_1 = 0\cdot41$.

The observational data give

$$a_1 = 1,700,000 \text{ km}.$$

hence the above ratio gives

$$a = a_1 + a_2 = 5,850,000 \text{ km}.$$

Combining this with the period $2\cdot867$ days we find the mass of the system

$$M_1 + M_2 = 0\cdot97,$$

so that $\qquad\qquad M_1 = 0\cdot69, \qquad M_2 = 0\cdot28.$

The photometric data also give $R_1 = 0\cdot21a$, $R_2 = 0\cdot24a$, so that

$$R_1 = 1,230,000, \qquad R_2 = 1,400,000.$$

We can now calculate the bolometric magnitude from the M's and R's respectively; but it is clear that there will be a hopeless discordance since the masses are much too small. We cannot therefore pursue the calculation further.

Since much interest has been taken in the dimensions of the system of β Persei on account of its celebrated history, we may give the conclusions

---

* Excellent photometric orbits are known for a number of eclipsing variables (enumerated in Table 28 A below); but only two besides β Persei have spectrographic orbits and for them the orbits of both components have been measured.

† *Astrophys. Journ.* 32, p. 185.

of the radiative theory on this point. The dimensions that have usually been given are very improbable on general grounds. We now abandon the hopeless task of utilising the light measurements of the faint component, and without *testing* the theory apply it to the bright component alone. After some trials a mass ratio $M_1 = 5M_2$ is found to fit satisfactorily. This gives

$$a = 6a_1 = 10,200,000 \text{ km.},$$

whence
$$M_1 = 4 \cdot 30, \qquad M_2 = 0 \cdot 86,$$
$$R_1 = 2,140,000 \text{ km.}, \qquad R_2 = 2,450,000 \text{ km.}$$

The absolute magnitude of the bright star predicted from the mass is then $- 1^{\text{m}} \cdot 21$ and from the radius and effective temperature is $- 1^{\text{m}} \cdot 14$. The absolute visual magnitude would be $- 0^{\text{m}} \cdot 45$, and the parallax $0'' \cdot 028$.

Referring to Table 23 we notice that the mass $4 \cdot 3$ is just right for a $B\,8$ star on the main series—a fact which increases our confidence in the result. The faint component is a giant as in most eclipsing variables*.

Reflection Effects.

143. In a number of eclipsing variables the components are so close that the reflection by the faint component of the light of the bright component is conspicuous in the light-curve; superposed on the eclipse effects there is a brightening of the star as the faint component changes from "new" to "full." Another cause of continuous variation is the spheroidal form of the stars; but this can be disentangled from the reflection effect by the difference of phase. It is usual to investigate and allow

* [When this was sent to press I was unaware that a trustworthy determination of the dimensions of the Algol system had been made by an interesting new observational method (D. B. McLaughlin, *Astrophys. Journ.* **60**, p. 22) which gives the radius $R_1 = 2,180,000$ km. During the progress of the eclipse different portions of the disc remain unobscured so that differential radial velocities between portions of the disc can be measured; hence the equatorial speed of rotation is found. Multiplying by the rotation period (which can be assumed to be the same as the revolution period when the components are so close together) we obtain the circumference of the star, and hence R_1 is found. As the differential velocity amounted to 35 km. per sec. the determination is presumably satisfactory; indeed it is probable that the radius of Algol is now more accurately known than that of any other star except the sun. McLaughlin determined from this the mass ratio $M_1/M_2 = 5 \cdot 0$ in agreement with our result above.

It has also transpired that our failure to determine the correct mass ratio from the light of the faint star is not the fault either of the photometric data or of the mass-luminosity relation. The Algol system contains a third distant component with period 1·885 years. Light is coming from this at the time of deepest eclipse, and this has been *falsely* attributed to the faint hemisphere of the secondary. The mass ratio 0·41 determined above is presumably the ratio of the *tertiary* to the primary; and the secondary may well be extremely faint as the value $M_1/M_2 = 5$ would require.

This is a rather striking confirmation of the theory by a star which at first seemed unfavourable to it.]

for both effects when the light-curve is analysed and interpreted by the method of Russell and Shapley.

For the moment we pass over the difficulty of translating a light-curve into a heat-curve, and suppose that the reflection effect can be determined in energy units. The theory is then very simple. *A star necessarily re-emits the radiation incident on it.*

The solution for the interior of a star is determined by the differential equations together with a boundary condition; and we have seen (§ 93) that the latter is expressed with sufficient accuracy in the form "p_G and p_R both become less than 10^8 dynes per sq. cm." The incident light from the companion star may contribute a radiation pressure of about 1 dyne per sq. cm. at the boundary. This gentle pat on the surface does not alter the boundary condition within the limits of accuracy required. Consequently the solution for the interior is unaltered; in particular, the ordinary radiation L streams out from the interior unmodified.

Accordingly, if we draw a sphere surrounding the star, there must be a *net* flow L outwards across the sphere. If a quantity L_r from another star is flowing into the sphere, the gross outward flow must be $L + L_r$. Thus the radiation from the star is increased by precisely the amount of the radiation incident on it. It is convenient to speak of the extra radiation as *reflected*, although the actual process is absorption with re-emission. In this sense a star is a perfect reflector of heat.

It is probable that in these close binaries the components keep the same hemispheres turned towards each other. The state is then steady and the re-emission occurs from the hemisphere that is receiving the radiation. A relative rotation would introduce a lag between the incidence and the re-emission, time being needed for the newly-exposed surface to be heated up to the temperature required for the extra emission; but I do not think that the lag would be appreciable, since the changed conditions affect only a thin outer shell which has small heat capacity.

144. The foregoing conclusion may be stated in the form that the heat-albedo of a star is 1. It is interesting to examine whether the observed reflection coefficients are in agreement with this result*.

Let L_1, L_2 be the ordinary heat emissions of the two stars S_1, S_2; and let L_r be the additional emission of the second star due to reflection. Let R_1, R_2 be the radii and a the distance between the centres. The radiation of S_1 intercepted by S_2 is approximately

$$\pi R_2{}^2 . L_1/4\pi a^2 \qquad \text{......................(144·1)}$$

if R_2/a is not too large. Since this falls on one hemisphere only it has sometimes been assumed that (for albedo 1) S_2 is brightened at full phase

---

* It would be inappropriate here to give a full discussion of the geometrical problem. Details will be found in *Monthly Notices*, **86**, p. 320.

in the ratio $L_2 + \frac{1}{2}L_1R_2{}^2/a^2 : L_2$. This, however, is not true. A globe illuminated from without does not present a uniformly bright disc, and the formula (144·1) tells us nothing about the brightness as seen in a specified direction. Allowing for this, the simple geometrical theory gives the ratio

$$L_2 + \tfrac{2}{3}L_1R_2{}^2/a^2 : L_2 \quad \text{.....................(144·2).}$$

In addition, there is a small effect due to "darkening at the limb" which affects both the ordinary emission and the re-emission (§ 227). At full phase the reflected radiation has an advantage, since it comes mainly from the centre of the disc and avoids the darkening. This is found to increase the albedo in the ratio $\frac{17}{16}$, the increased brightness for the observer who sees the full phase being at the expense of reduced brightness in other directions.

Since R_2/a is often rather large it is well to retain higher powers. A more accurate expression for the increase is then

$$\tfrac{17}{24}L_1 \{\sin^2\phi + (2 + \cos^3\phi - 3\cos\phi)/\sin\phi\} \quad \text{......(144·3),}$$

where $\sin\phi = R_2/a$.

It may be added that the variation of this added brightness with phase is proportional to $\dfrac{1}{\pi}(\sin\psi - \psi\cos\psi)$, the phase-angle ψ being reckoned from zero at "new." The observed reflection coefficients have been calculated on the assumption that the variation is proportional to $\frac{1}{2}(1 - \cos\psi)$. It so happens that this introduces no error in the reflection coefficient, but it makes an appreciable difference in the calculation of the ellipsoidal elongation of the stars. Determinations of the elongation of the stars under each other's attraction must ultimately yield important information for the development of our theory; but at present the treatment is too crude for our purposes.

145. Results for those variables in which the reflection effect has been thoroughly studied are collected in Table 28 A.

The type given is that of the brighter component; the type of the fainter can be estimated from the ratio of the surface luminosities J_1/J_2 by reference to Table 16 (where J is measured in magnitudes). The unit of heat intensity used for L_1 and L_r is the maximum for the system, i.e. $L_1 + L_2 + L_r = 1$. The calculated value of L_r is found from (144·3), and the observed value is taken directly from the published discussions of the photometric data; the probable error assigned by the investigator is given in the last column. (The L's in the table refer to the light or heat in the direction towards the observer, and seen by him except in so far as the eclipse interferes.) No. 9 depends on selenium photometry; the others depend on visual observations.

For 6 stars the agreement of L_r is excellent; 4 give large positive residuals and 1 a negative residual. It is difficult to base any conclusion on the table without examining the strength of the determination for each star in detail. The probable errors refer only to L_r (obs.); but L_r (calc.) is also subject to uncertainty arising in the determination of R_2/a. In some cases the circumstances of the eclipse are more favourable for a determination of the elements than in others. We discuss below the question whether the calculated and observed values ought to agree without further correction; tentatively we are inclined to think that they should agree nearly, and we must hope that the 5 outstanding residuals will be reduced when improved data are obtained.

Table 28 A.
Reflection Effect in Eclipsing Variables.

No.	Star	Type	J_1/J_2	R_1/a	R_2/a	L_1	L_r (calc.)	L_r (obs.)	$C-O$	P.E.
1	SZ Her.	—	4·3	·318	·331	·800	·078	·030	+ ·048	—
2	U Cep.	A	13·5	·191	·308	·838	·069	·043	+ ·026	± ·009
3	TV Cas.	$B\,9$	6·9	·275	·302	·849	·068	·074	− ·006	± ·008
4	RZ Cas.	A	12·2	·253	·288	·902	·064	·063	+ ·001	± ·008
5	RT Per.	—	4·8	·309	·269	·863	·053	·022	+ ·031	± ·009
6	Z Dra.	—	12·8	·238	·263	·911	·053	·040	+ ·013	± ·006
7	RS Vul.	$B\,8$	7·0	·201	·262	·804	·048	·078	− ·030	—
8	R CMa.	F	13·2	·245	·236	·934	·046	·015	+ ·031	—
9	β Per.	$B\,8$	11·6	·210	·239	·895	·043	·045	− ·002	—
10	Y Cam.	$A–F$	20·0	·236	·225	·955	·041	·041	·000	—
11	RV Oph.	A	12·2	·125	·200	·825	·027	·018	+ ·009	± ·006

In this comparison we have made no discrimination between heat reflection and light reflection. If a residual such as that in No. 5 is not due to observational error, it signifies that the secondary in reflecting the heat of the primary reduces its luminous efficiency to less than 50 per cent. But in typical eclipsing variables we expect an increase rather than a decrease of luminous efficiency. The primary is usually of type B or A so that the original efficiency corresponds to a temperature above 10,000°; it is reflected from a star of lower surface brightness corresponding (as judged from J_1/J_2) to a temperature near 6000°. Not unless the temperature of re-emission is below 4500° is there a *loss* of luminous efficiency. Moreover, even if the temperature is below 4500° there is a compensating gain, since the original radiation L_2 is now emitted at a higher temperature. We should expect the residuals $C-O$ to be in general negative as in No. 7; the puzzling thing about No. 7 is that it is the solitary exception and not the general rule.

I think the fact that we have only one important negative residual must be taken to indicate that the incident light is re-emitted without much change of quality—that it never really mixes with the ordinary radiation L_2. Take as a typical case $T_1 = 12,000°$, $T_2 = 6,000°$. The high frequency radiation of S_1 will be able to do things in the atmosphere of S_2 which the latter's own radiation cannot do; and it will do them vigorously because it finds virgin material. It is for this reason absorbed rapidly in the upper atmosphere of S_2—more rapidly than in the atmosphere of S_1 because the conditions are further from thermodynamical equilibrium. By keeping its mechanism of absorption and emission distinct from that of the general radiation of S_2 and by the great departure from conditions of thermodynamical equilibrium it seems likely that the reflected radiation will, to a large extent, preserve its original constitution.

This seems to be confirmed by spectroscopic observations. In many cases the spectrum of the faint component is measured for radial velocity. Sometimes it is explicitly stated that the two spectra are nearly the same; more often no remark is made—a silence which is equally significant, since a difference of type corresponding to the known values of J_1/J_2 would scarcely pass without comment.

We may suggest further that the spectrum of the hemisphere of S_2 turned towards a component S_1 at higher temperature is likely to approximate to the spectrum of S_1 even when the reflected radiation is relatively weak. The reflected radiation has the strategic advantage of attacking the material of S_2 from the outside, so that the conditions caused by it imprint their spectrum last of all on the radiation flowing out from S_2, and the lines cannot be blurred out by subsequent experiences of the radiation.

These suggestions however require a more detailed consideration than I have been able to give, and I am by no means confident that they will be found tenable.

The star TV Cassiopeiae is among those treated in Table 19. It appears from Table 28 A that it is well behaved as regards reflection effect and the circumstances seem to be favourable for a more intensive treatment. Using the most recent data, viz. Plaskett's orbits (*Pub. Dom. Obs. Victoria*, 2, p. 141) and McDiarmid's photometric solution (*Princeton Pub.* No. 7) we have

$$M_1 = 1·74, \qquad M_2 = 1·02, \qquad R_1/a = ·279, \qquad R_2/a = ·306,$$
$$R_1 = 2·45 \times R_{\odot}, \qquad R_2 = 2·68 \times R_{\odot}, \qquad J_1/J_2 = 13·6,$$
$$T_1 = 10,500, \qquad T_2 = 5,200,$$

the former temperature being estimated from the observed type B 9 and the latter from J_1/J_2. The results are—

	Bol. Mag. (from R)	Bol. Mag. (from M)	Residual
S_1	+ 0·34	+ 1·86	+ 1·52
S_2	+ 3·18	+ 4·58	+ 1·40

The agreement is not good, but there seems to be a simple explanation of this. The illuminated hemisphere is twice as bright as the dark hemisphere so that the spectroscopic measurements of the secondary do not refer to the centre of the disc. Plaskett does not note any difference of type, so that the lines which he measured could presumably only be produced in the illuminated hemisphere. Since $R_2 = \cdot 306a$ the displacement may well amount to $\cdot 08a$ and the radius of the relative orbit is to be increased in the ratio 100 to 92. This gives

	M	Bol. Mag. (from R)	Bol. Mag. (from M)	Residual
S_1	2·35	+ 0·16	+ 0·81	+ 0·65
S_2	1·20	+ 3·00	+ 3·91	+ 0·91

and the accordance is now tolerable. The faults which remain are probably due to the roughness of the data (photometric and spectrographic) for the secondary. To reduce the residual for S_1 to zero we must further increase M_1/M_2 and the revised value of M_1 will then be about 3·0. The primary then falls on the central line of the main series, and the secondary is a giant star as in β Persei.

We have had two instances where, by expurgating the less reliable data and trusting to the radiative theory, the primary has been brought on to the line of the main series; and I believe that other examples confirm this, though less definitely. We might perhaps take the risk of assuming in the treatment of eclipsing variables that one of the conditions to be fulfilled is that the central temperature of the primary is 40,000,000°. If it is true that eclipsing binaries (i.e. very close binaries) are only formed by stars of this class, the fact must have some fundamental significance which we cannot yet understand.

CHAPTER IX

THE COEFFICIENT OF OPACITY

146. Results reached in the present Chapter have been used in anticipation from § 89 onwards. We must therefore return and take up the problem of the absorption coefficient as it presented itself in § 88. At that stage we were occupied with our first astronomical result of importance, viz. that for the series of giant stars from type M to type A the opacity is nearly constant although the internal temperature increases twelvefold between the beginning and end of the series. This suggested (but, as we now see, wrongly) that the opacity might tend to a constant value at high temperatures and so be the same for all stars. Actually, however, the constancy of the opacity was a statistical result applying to groups of stars presumed to be of the same average mass, and there was no test whether the constancy continued for stars of a different mass.

The radiation in the main interior of a star consists of X rays, and comparison is invited with measurements of absorption of X rays made in the laboratory. In § 105 we have found the absorption coefficient at the centre of Capella to be 49 c.g.s. units. This is of the general order of magnitude of the measured coefficients of most elements for hard X rays; for example, it agrees with the coefficient for iron for wave-length about 0.8 Å. It must, however, be noted that the radiation at the centre of Capella is of much greater wave-length, the maximum intensity being at 3.2 Å.

According to laboratory determinations k increases very rapidly with the wave-length. Subject to certain discontinuities it varies as λ^3. This brings about a double discrepancy with astronomical observation; firstly, it makes the laboratory coefficients much greater than the astronomical coefficient for the same wave-length*; secondly, it is at variance with the astronomical result that stars differing widely in temperature show little change of k.

It is clear that there is something which invalidates the direct comparison of astronomical and terrestrial determinations. That which stands in the way of the comparison is *ionisation*, strong in the stars, but almost absent in terrestrial experiments.

---

* The difference is even wider than would at first appear; for the comparison would more fairly be made at an average temperature of Capella (to which the astronomical coefficient must be supposed to refer) instead of with values extrapolated for the central temperature.

147. There can be little doubt that the principal process of absorption in the stars is the photoelectric effect. A quantum of radiation is absorbed and its energy is employed in removing an electron from the atom and endowing it with kinetic energy. Other processes of absorption are known, but these contribute relatively little to the stellar opacity. Ionisation reduces the absorption because it leaves fewer electrons capable of performing the photoelectric process. The decrease may also be described—but perhaps less accurately—as a saturation effect; the atoms cannot deal efficiently with a very large quantity of radiation which removes their electrons faster than they can be replaced. The ionisation is the sign of overwork. We said *less accurately* because ionisation can also be caused by collisions of atoms and electrons, so that in certain circumstances the decrease of the coefficient might occur without implying great intensity of the radiation; but, on the other hand, the principle of detailed balancing in thermodynamical equilibrium permits us to deal with the photoelectric effect and its converse as if these were the only processes occurring in the stellar interior, so that the small absorption coefficient in the stars is directly attributable to the intensity of the radiation.

The practical effect of ionisation on the absorption coefficient will be seen from the following numerical results which have been calculated for iron at the temperature and density of the centre of Capella*. If X rays of similar wave-length but of ordinary laboratory intensity were directed on iron in a terrestrial experiment they would be very strongly absorbed. The absorption is mainly performed by the L group of 8 electrons. As each quantum is absorbed, an L electron is expelled; but in terrestrial experiments the L group is completed again by the falling in of an outer electron or by capture of a wandering electron before the atom's turn for another absorption. The coefficient of absorption by the L electrons alone is found experimentally to be 2950 C.G.S. units. Now let the intensity of the X rays be raised to the actual strength in Capella. The L electrons will be wrenched away almost immediately they take their places so that they are not usually present in the atom. At any moment only 1 out of 1200 places for L electrons is filled; that is to say, instead of each atom having eight L electrons, only 1 atom in 150 has even a solitary L electron. The L absorption coefficient has therefore only $\frac{1}{1200}$ of its laboratory value and is reduced to 2·5. Actually more absorption in Capella is performed by the two K electrons. In the laboratory these do relatively little work, because most of the radiation has a frequency too low to operate the K mechanism; the laboratory absorption coefficient is 8·3. But in Capella about 70 per cent. of the K electrons are in their places at any

* *Monthly Notices*, **84**, p. 113. Corresponding results for other elements are also given.

moment so that this coefficient is reduced to 5·9. Thus we obtain the comparison

	Laboratory	Capella
Absorption coefficient due to L electrons	2950	2·5
„ „ K „	8·3	5·9
Total	2958	8·4

148. In the stars the absorption is equal to the emission of radiation, so that we may, if we prefer, proceed by calculating the emission. The converse process to the expulsion of an electron is the capture of an electron, and the capture accordingly gives the emission corresponding to the absorption which we have been discussing. This cannot be studied directly by laboratory experiment because it is not possible in terrestrial conditions to obtain ions with vacant places for capture in the K and L groups; but the problem can be studied theoretically. Here again we shall have two coefficients to consider: first, the ideal coefficient of emission when all the ions have their full capturing power; second, the coefficient as reduced by *lack of ionisation*. In proportion as the places for electrons are filled up so the chance of capture is diminished.

The ideal (or laboratory) absorption coefficient and the ideal emission coefficient (not realised in the laboratory or the stars) are each reduced, the one by ionisation and the other by lack of ionisation. The ionisation, in fact, reaches the value required to bring them to a balance; and the ionisation formula (47·1) was obtained from this balance as expressed by Einstein's equation.

The *ideal* absorption coefficient is independent of the density. Each complete atom is an absorbing mechanism which works independently of other atoms, and it makes no difference whether a given mass of material occupies a large thickness or a small.

The *ideal* emission coefficient is approximately proportional to the density, or more nearly to ρ/μ. A stripped ion emits by capturing electrons, and, other things being equal, the number of captures by it will be proportional to the number of free electrons in given volume. The total number of particles per cu. cm. is equal to ρ/μ (μ being here measured in grams). In stellar conditions the number of ions is small compared to the number of free electrons so that the number of free electrons per cu. cm. is nearly equal to ρ/μ.

Thus we approach the problem of stellar opacity with the idea that it is likely to be (*a*) independent of density, (*b*) proportional to density, according as we begin with absorption or emission. Whichever line we follow there will be a modification when account is taken of the effect of density on ionisation. It is a question of expediency and not of principle which end we should begin from, depending on which of the two ideal coefficients undergoes least modification.

149. Preliminary calculations show that, whereas in all cases the ideal absorption coefficient is enormously modified, the modification of the emission coefficient is small in most stars, and in any case it can be left to be attended to in a second approximation. At first sight it seems that the figures given for iron in § 147 are in contradiction to this since it appears that 70 per cent. of the K electrons are in their places and only 30 per cent. of the ideal K emission for iron is operative. But the calculation of § 147 referred to the true absorption coefficient and we now have in mind the astronomical opacity (§ 77), which is less dependent on the K processes*. However, we do not insist here that the modification of the emission coefficient is negligible but that it is small in comparison with the modification of the absorption coefficient by a factor $\frac{1}{1200}$. Accordingly, the stellar opacity will approximate to the law $k \propto \rho/\mu$, and not to k independent of ρ.

Now consider the effect of temperature. The number of electrons which in given time encounter a particular ion, besides being proportional to the electron-density will be proportional to their mean velocity V and therefore to $T^{\frac{1}{2}}$. Further, granting an encounter, the chance of capture will depend on the speed of the electron. Presumably fast electrons will be more elusive than slow ones; we therefore set the chance of capture proportional to

$$V^{-x},$$

or to $T^{-\frac{1}{2}x}$. We can only determine x by following up some special theory of capture, so for the present we leave it indefinite. When a capture occurs the emission of energy is equal to the difference between the energy of the free electron and the negative energy of the level which it will occupy in the atom. The free energy is proportional to T and the energy of the level is presumably roughly proportional to T†. Combining these temperature factors, the emission per ion will be proportional to

$$\frac{\rho}{\mu} T^{\frac{3}{2} - \frac{1}{2}x},$$

and the absorption per ion is the same. To obtain k we must divide the absorbed energy by the total energy traversing the material, which is proportional to T^4. Hence

$$k \propto \rho/\mu T^{\frac{5}{2} + \frac{1}{2}x} \quad \dots\dots\dots\dots\dots\dots(149\cdot1).$$

The astronomical result that k is nearly constant for a series of stars of constant mass requires that approximately k must be a function of

---

* In § 79 we showed that it was not important to consider frequencies greater than $7RT/h$. Hence in a star in which the atoms are ionised down to an energy-level $-7RT$ there will be no appreciable modification of the ideal emission coefficient.

† Alternatively, the captures chiefly contributing to the opacity are those yielding radiation of frequency $2\cdot5RT/h$ to $7RT/h$ (§ 79). The corresponding quantum is therefore proportional to T.

$\rho/\mu T^3$, since this combination of density and temperature depends only on the mass. Comparing with (149·1) we obtain $x = 1$ and

$$k \propto \rho/\mu T^3.$$

We decided that owing to the uncertainties of observation an additional factor $T^{\frac{1}{2}}$ or $T^{-\frac{1}{2}}$ was admissible, so that the variation of k is between $\rho/\mu T^{\frac{5}{2}}$ and $\rho/\mu T^{\frac{7}{2}}$. This corresponds to (149·1) with values of x between 0 and 2.

Experiments by E. Rutherford on the capture of electrons by α particles have been shown by him to correspond to a probability of capture varying as the inverse fifth power of the velocity. The law $x = 5$ is far outside the above limits and could not be reconciled with the uniformity of magnitude of giant stars. We must infer that Rutherford's experiments relate to a different process of capture. It has been shown by Fowler that they are radiationless captures analogous to the capture of comets by the combined efforts of the sun and a planet. Captures of this kind no doubt occur in the stars; but by the principle of detailed balancing they do not affect our study of the absorption problem, since they are not accompanied by radiation.

150. It is interesting that we should be able to get so far with the determination of the law of opacity without having come to grips with the problem of the mechanism of capture or expulsion of electrons. We might perhaps narrow the limits a little more because it is scarcely conceivable that x should be less than 1. The choice between exponents 3 and $\frac{7}{2}$, or even between $\frac{5}{2}$ and $\frac{7}{2}$, does not make a great difference in practical calculations of the luminosities of the stars. But there are certain theoretical considerations which make it important to decide on which side of 3 the exponent really falls. One illustration of this has already arisen in considering Cepheid pulsations; the pulsations can maintain themselves automatically when the exponent is a little less than 3 (§ 137). This is in itself an argument against an exponent as low as 2·5 for ordinary (non-pulsating) stars; but if the normal exponent were, say, 3 there would be less difficulty in admitting the slightly lower value required in the Cepheids. Another problem for which the value 3 is critical will arise in § 211.

Since the value $x = 2$ is given by what is now considered to be the best physical theory of electron-capture we have adopted $k \propto \rho/\mu T^{\frac{7}{2}}$. But the theory is scarcely an adequate guide and it is desirable to see whether there is observational support for the odd half-power of T. We obtained good agreement between theory and observation by using it in Fig. 2; but it is necessary to consider how far this agreement depends on the power of T. Most of the stars represented belong to the main series, which is characterised by constant internal temperature (§ 122); these afford no scope for testing a variation of k with T. There remain Capella and the Cepheids which are not on the main series. Capella has an internal temperature $\frac{1}{4}$ of that of the main series. If the exponent is 3 instead of $3\frac{1}{2}$ we have assigned to the main series half its proper opacity compared with Capella and have therefore predicted a magnitude $0^{m.}75$ too bright. The sun, Sirius and α Centauri are actually $0^{m.}3$ fainter than the original prediction, so that they lie about half-way between the results for the two assumptions.

It seems then scarcely possible to decide from the observations whether $\rho/\mu T^{\frac{7}{2}}$ or $\rho/\mu T^3$ is nearer to the true law; but $\rho/\mu T^{\frac{5}{2}}$ seems to be definitely ruled out, and there is considerable probability that the exponent is above rather than below 3.

The Target for Electron-Capture.

151. We first make some numerical calculations as to the number of captures and expulsions concerned in the stellar absorption and emission. Consider the conditions at the centre of Capella as given in § 13.

$$T = 7 \cdot 2 \cdot 10^6, \qquad \rho = 0 \cdot 0547, \qquad \mu = 2 \cdot 1.$$

The value of αk_c found from the mass and absolute magnitude is 133, which for $\alpha = 2 \cdot 5$ gives
$$k = 53.$$

This is strictly the opacity coefficient and not the absorption coefficient, but we shall not here trouble about the difference. The emission per gm. per second is (74·5)
$$kacT^4 = 3 \cdot 25 \cdot 10^{25} \text{ ergs} \dots\dots\dots\dots\dots\dots(151 \cdot 1).$$

By (40·93) the average energy of a quantum of radiation at temperature T is $2 \cdot 70RT$, where R is Boltzmann's constant. The average quantum is thus
$$2 \cdot 67 \cdot 10^{-9} \text{ ergs} \dots\dots\dots\dots\dots\dots(151 \cdot 2).$$

Hence by division the number of quanta emitted per gm. per sec. is
$$1 \cdot 22 \cdot 10^{34} \dots\dots\dots\dots\dots\dots(151 \cdot 3).$$

A correcting factor may be necessary since the average quantum concerned in k may not be equal to the average quantum present in the radiation, but this will not affect the order of magnitude.

The number of hydrogen atoms in a gram is $6 \cdot 02 \cdot 10^{23}$; hence the number of particles of average weight $2 \cdot 1_H$ is
$$2 \cdot 87 \cdot 10^{23}.$$

Allowing about 1 ion to every 20 free electrons, this makes the number of free electrons per gm.
$$2 \cdot 74 \cdot 10^{23} \dots\dots\dots\dots\dots\dots(151 \cdot 4).$$

By (151·3) and (151·4) each free electron is responsible for the emission of
$$4 \cdot 45 \cdot 10^{10} \text{ quanta per second} \dots\dots\dots\dots(151 \cdot 5).$$

Each emission results from a capture, so that each free electron is captured $4.45 \cdot 10^{10}$ times per second. The reciprocal of this gives the time of free path*

$$2.25 \cdot 10^{-11} \text{ secs.} \quad \dots\dots\dots\dots\dots\dots(151 \cdot 6).$$

The average speed of an electron at the temperature $7.2 \cdot 10^6$ is

$$V = 1.67 \cdot 10^9 \text{ cm. per sec.} \dots\dots\dots\dots\dots(151 \cdot 7).$$

Multiplying by the time of free path, the length of free path is

$$\lambda = \cdot 0375 \text{ cm.} \quad \dots\dots\dots\dots\dots\dots(151 \cdot 8).$$

Here again an averaging factor will slightly modify the result since the slower moving electrons are likely to be the more easily captured.

The "free path" in the sense of the theory of gases, i.e. from collision to collision, is much less than ·0375 cm. The electron hits a large number of atoms before it meets one in such a way as to be captured—or at least it hits *what would have been the atom* if the atom had not been reduced to small dimensions by ionisation. We introduce the idea of a target in the atom, i.e. a sphere of size such that the probability of capture is equal to the probability of hitting the sphere. This representation is primarily intended to be statistical and leaves open the question whether capture is actually determined by hitting such a target. If σ is the radius of the target and N the number of targets per cu. cm. it is shown in the theory of gases that

$$\lambda = \frac{1}{\pi N \sigma^2} \quad \dots\dots\dots\dots\dots\dots(151 \cdot 91),$$

the paths being treated as rectilinear.

We have $\qquad N = \rho / A_H \dots\dots\dots\dots\dots\dots(151 \cdot 92),$

where A is the atomic weight and H the mass of a hydrogen atom. For iron ($A = 56$) at the density of the centre of Capella, this gives

$$N = 5.88 \cdot 10^{20} \quad \dots\dots\dots\dots\dots\dots(151 \cdot 93),$$

so that by (151·91) and (151·8)

$$\sigma = 1.20 \cdot 10^{-10} \text{ cm.} \quad \dots\dots\dots\dots\dots(151 \cdot 94).$$

This is a little less than the radius of the K ring in iron, which at the centre of Capella is all that is left of the system of satellite electrons. But there is no special importance to be attached to this coincidence. In (151·91) the paths are treated as rectilinear so that the target is the *apparent target* aimed at by the electrons. Owing to the attraction of the nucleus, the *true target*, or target actually hit, may be much smaller.

---

* At first sight this makes no allowance for the time spent in the captured state; but this is compensated, because if each electron spent one-tenth of its time in a captured state the number of electrons concerned in the emission would be ten-ninths of the number (151·4) free at a given moment.

152. It seems natural to assume that the target is an actual sphere round the centre of the atom which the electron track must intersect as the condition for capture. This idea is the basis of the theory of nuclear capture investigated in § 170. But there are certain considerations which weigh strongly against this assumption. The frequency of the X ray emitted when an electron changes its velocity is presumably dependent on the abruptness of the stoppage. Electrons aimed to pass within a distance σ of the nucleus suffer an extremely rapid change of velocity as they swing round at pericentron. It appears that the corresponding X rays would have a frequency much greater than the range $2 \cdot 5RT/h$ to $7RT/h$ to which the stellar opacity corresponds. It is now generally believed that radiation from these close penetrating electrons is inhibited; but it is not very important for us to decide here whether that is so or not. If we are right in concluding that they would yield radiation of frequency considerably above $7RT/h$, then clearly these are not the captures calculated in the last section as responsible for the astronomical opacity. To give radiation in the required frequency range the stoppage of the electron must be not too abrupt and not too slow. This points to *a target of annular section.*

The theory of emission and absorption, which seems to be in close accordance with laboratory experiment and expresses the most modern ideas on the subject, is due to H. A. Kramers*. We regard this as likely to be correct, at least in its main essentials. There are some subtleties in Kramers' theory, vital for its application to terrestrial experiments but only of subsidiary importance in the determination of stellar opacity. As simplified for stellar applications, Kramers' theory really amounts to this: *we may calculate the stellar opacity just as if all electrons radiated according to the laws of the classical electromagnetic theory.*

For this reason we take as our first problem the determination of stellar opacity according to classical theory. This is not a preliminary exercise; it is the quickest route to the formulae which we accept as definitive. Afterwards Kramers' theory will be invoked to explain why so antiquated a procedure is justified notwithstanding the advent of the quantum theory, and to introduce those subtleties which are needed in order to check the theory by laboratory experiment.

Classical Theory of Emission.

153. According to the electromagnetic theory an accelerated electron radiates energy. If Γ is the acceleration, the energy radiated in time dt is

$$\frac{2}{3} \frac{e^2}{c^3} \Gamma^2 dt \dots\dots\dots\dots\dots\dots(153 \cdot 1).$$

* *Phil. Mag.* **46**, p. 836 (1923).

Consider an electron with initial velocity V which would, if undisturbed, pass at a distance σ from a nucleus of atomic number Z. Under the attraction of the nucleus it will describe an orbit which will be a hyperbola—unless the approach is so close as to make it necessary to allow for change of mass with velocity.

The acceleration will be

$$\Gamma = \mu/r^2, \qquad \mu = Ze^2/m \quad \dots \dots \dots (153 \cdot 2).$$

Let the equation of the hyperbola be

$$\frac{l}{r} = 1 + \epsilon \cos \theta \quad \dots \dots \dots \dots (153 \cdot 3).$$

If h is the constant of areas

$$r^2 \frac{d\theta}{dt} = h = \sigma V \quad \dots \dots \dots \dots (153 \cdot 4),$$

and by the usual astronomical equation

$$\sigma^2 V^2 = h^2 = \mu l \quad \dots \dots \dots \dots (153 \cdot 5).$$

Also by the well-known property that σ (the perpendicular from the focus on the asymptote) is equal to the minor axis of the hyperbola

$$\epsilon^2 - 1 = l^2/\sigma^2 = \sigma^2 V^4/\mu^2 \quad \dots \dots \dots (153 \cdot 6),$$

and if 2ϕ is the angle between the asymptotes

$$\tan \phi = \surd(\epsilon^2 - 1) = \sigma V^2/\mu \quad \dots \dots \dots (153 \cdot 7).$$

By $(153 \cdot 3)$ and $(153 \cdot 4)$

$$\frac{2}{3} \frac{e^2}{c^3} \Gamma^2 dt = \frac{2}{3} \frac{e^2 \mu^2}{c^3} \frac{dt}{r^4}$$

$$= \frac{2}{3} \frac{e^2 \mu^2}{c^3 l^2 h} (1 + \epsilon \cos \theta)^2 \, d\theta \quad \dots \dots (153 \cdot 75).$$

Hence the total radiation during the encounter is

$$Q = \frac{2}{3} \frac{e^2 \mu^2}{c^3 l^2 h} \int_{-(\pi - \phi)}^{\pi - \phi} (1 + \epsilon \cos \theta)^2 \, d\theta$$

$$= \frac{2}{3} \frac{e^2 \mu^2}{c^3 l^2 h} \{(\pi - \phi) (\sec^2 \phi + 2) + 3 \tan \phi\} \quad \dots (153 \cdot 8),$$

where ϵ has been replaced by its value $\sec \phi$.

For not too large values of σV^2, ϕ is a small angle; that is to say, the orbits are practically parabolas. The result then reduces to

$$Q = \frac{2\pi e^2 \mu^2}{c^3 l^2 h} = \frac{2\pi e^2 \mu^4}{c^3 h^5} = \frac{2\pi Z^4 e^{10}}{c^3 m^4 \sigma^5 V^5} \dots \dots \dots \dots (153 \cdot 9).$$

154. As a slight digression we may notice that if Q is greater than $\frac{1}{2} m V^2$ the electron loses more than its free energy and must be captured. Thus there is an apparent target for capture with radius σ given by

$$\frac{1}{2} m V^2 = \frac{2\pi Z^4 e^{10}}{c^3 m^4 \sigma^5 V^5}.$$

Or, writing $b = e^2/mc^2 = 2 \cdot 81 . 10^{-13}$ cm., this reduces to

$$\sigma = b \,(4\pi)^{\frac{1}{5}} \, Z^{\frac{4}{5}} \,(c/V)^{\frac{7}{5}} \quad \dots\dots\dots\dots\dots(154 \cdot 1).$$

For iron at the centre of Capella this gives

$$\sigma = 3 \cdot 6 . 10^{-10} \text{ cm.}$$

about three times the target radius and nine times the target area found from the observations $(151 \cdot 94)$. Thus the crude classical theory gives an emission coefficient nine times too high—to say nothing of the additional emission by electrons which are not captured.

155. It turns out that much of the classical radiation is of high frequency beyond the range chiefly concerned in the astronomical opacity. It is therefore not sufficient to determine the total amount of emission; we must find its distribution in frequency—in fact we must apply a spectroscope to it.

For this purpose Γ is first resolved into two rectangular components Γ_x, Γ_y along the major and minor axes of the orbit. Each component is expressed as a Fourier integral, viz.

$$\Gamma_x = \int_0^\infty A_x \cos (2\pi\nu t)\,d\nu, \qquad \Gamma_y = \int_0^\infty A_y \sin (2\pi\nu t)\,d\nu,$$

where A_x and A_y are functions of ν. The energy of the radiated wave being proportional to Γ^2 $(153 \cdot 1)$ its amplitude is proportional to Γ; the Fourier analysis accordingly separates out the amplitude corresponding to periodic components of Γ of frequency ν to $\nu + d\nu$. The energy radiated between ν and $\nu + d\nu$ will be proportional to $(A_x{}^2 + A_y{}^2)\,d\nu$.

The analysis is difficult, but it has been carried out by Kramers[*] with the following result:—the classical radiation of frequency between ν and $\nu + d\nu$ emitted during an encounter is[†]

$$Q_\nu d\nu = \frac{4\pi^2 Z^2 e^6}{c^3 m^2 \sigma^2 V^2} \, P(\gamma)\,d\nu \quad \dots\dots\dots\dots(155 \cdot 1),$$

where

$$\gamma = 2\pi\nu\sigma^3 V^3 m^2 / Z^2 e^4 \quad \dots\dots\dots\dots\dots(155 \cdot 2),$$

and P is a certain function possessing the properties

$$\int_0^\infty P\,(\gamma)\,d\gamma = 1 \quad \dots\dots\dots\dots\dots(155 \cdot 31),$$

$$\int_0^\infty P\,(\gamma)\,\frac{d\gamma}{\gamma} = \frac{4}{\pi\sqrt{3}} \quad \dots\dots\dots\dots(155 \cdot 32).$$

The function P, of which a rough graph is given in Kramers' paper, is zero at $\gamma = 0$, rises to a maximum of about $0 \cdot 23$ near $\gamma = 1 \cdot 5$, and then falls more slowly, reaching $0 \cdot 05$ near $\gamma = 6$.

---

[*] *Phil. Mag.* **46**, p. 845.

[†] This is the result for parabolic orbits which is the important practical case. Kramers also gives a result for rectangular hyperbolas.

By (155·31) we find

$$Q = \int_0^\infty Q_\nu d\nu = \frac{2\pi Z^4 e^{10}}{c^3 m^4 \sigma^5 V^5},$$

in agreement with (153·9).

Suppose that n electrons encounter normally a thin sheet of material containing s nuclei per sq. cm. To pass at a distance between σ and $\sigma + d\sigma$ from a nucleus an electron must strike one of s annuli covering a total area $s \cdot 2\pi\sigma d\sigma$ per sq. cm. Thus the number of encounters made within these limits is $ns \cdot 2\pi\sigma d\sigma$ and the total radiation from them in the frequency range $d\nu$ is by (155·1)

$$nsd\nu \frac{8\pi^3 Z^2 e^6}{c^3 m^2 V^2} P(\gamma) \frac{d\sigma}{\sigma}.$$

This must now be integrated for all values of σ. By (155·2)

$$\frac{d\gamma}{\gamma} = 3 \frac{d\sigma}{\sigma}.$$

Hence the radiation of frequency ν to $\nu + d\nu$ is

$$nsd\nu \frac{8\pi^3 Z^2 e^6}{3c^3 m^2 V^2} \int_0^\infty P(\gamma) \frac{d\gamma}{\gamma} \quad\dots\dots\dots\dots\dots(155\cdot41)$$

$$= nsd\nu \frac{32\pi^2}{3\sqrt{3}} \frac{Z^2 e^6}{c^3 m^2 V^2} \quad\dots\dots\dots\dots\dots(155\cdot42)$$

by (155·32).

The striking feature of this result is that it is independent of ν. If we used a spectroscope which spread out the spectrum proportionately to ν the spectrum of the radiation would be of uniform intensity.

The result (155·1) refers to orbits which can be treated as parabolic. Orbits of higher eccentricity have also been investigated by Kramers, and the correcting factor to (155·42) can be approximately determined when it is necessary to take account of the hyperbolic eccentricity. Using (153·6) we can write (155·2) in the form

$$\gamma = 2\pi\nu (\epsilon^2 - 1)^{\frac{3}{2}} \frac{Ze^2}{mV^3} \quad\dots\dots\dots\dots\dots(155\cdot51).$$

For material at temperature T the mean value of mV^2 is $3RT$, so that

$$\gamma = \tfrac{2}{3}\pi \frac{e^2}{hc} Z \left(\frac{c}{V}\right) \frac{h\nu}{RT} (\epsilon^2 - 1)^{\frac{3}{2}}$$

$$= \frac{Z}{411} \left(\frac{c}{V}\right) \frac{h\nu}{RT} (\epsilon^2 - 1)^{\frac{3}{2}} \quad\dots\dots\dots\dots\dots(155\cdot52).$$

For a temperature of 20 million degrees $c/V = 11$. The values of $h\nu/RT$ which are concerned in the stellar opacity are in the neighbourhood of 4. We may take $Z = 20$ for average material. With these values

$$\gamma = 2 (\epsilon^2 - 1)^{\frac{3}{2}}.$$

The range of γ which contributes chiefly to the integral in (155·41) is in the neighbourhood of $\gamma = 1$ and the corresponding eccentricity is $\epsilon = 1·27$.

It thus appears that in astronomical applications we shall be concerned with orbits which are beginning to be appreciably hyperbolic, but not to such an extent as to require any large correcting factor.

156. In the material of a star the direction of motion of an electron makes no difference to the probability of an encounter; we may therefore simplify the calculation by considering them to be all moving in the same direction normal to a certain surface. A column of electrons of height V cm. will pass through each sq. cm. per second and the number n of electrons in a volume V cu. cm. is

$$n = V \frac{\rho}{\mu_H (1 + f)} \quad\dots\dots\dots\dots\dots\dots(156·1),$$

where f is the ratio of the number of ions to the number of electrons. (We can usually neglect f.) The number of ions in a thickness dx will be per sq. cm.

$$s = dx \frac{\rho}{A_H} \quad\dots\dots\dots\dots\dots\dots(156·2),$$

where A is the atomic weight. Inserting these values of n and s in (155·42) we obtain the emission per second from a volume dx. Setting $dx = 1/\rho$, the emission per gram per second is

$$\frac{\rho}{H^2 \mu A (1 + f)} \frac{32\pi^2}{3\sqrt{3}} \frac{Z^2 e^6}{c^3 m^2 V} d\nu \dots\dots\dots\dots\dots(156·3).$$

The contributions of electrons with different speeds V are additive; hence in (156·3) we must use the mean value of $1/V$. By Maxwell's law if V_0 is the arithmetic mean speed, the harmonic mean speed is $\frac{1}{4}\pi V_0$. Hence in a star the emission per gram per second of radiation between ν and $\nu + d\nu$ is $Q d\nu$, where

$$Q = \frac{\rho}{H^2 \mu A (1 + f)} \frac{128\pi}{3\sqrt{3}} \frac{Z^2 e^6}{c^3 m^2 V_0} \quad\dots\dots\dots\dots(156·4).$$

So far as the chemical constitution is concerned this is proportional to Z^2/A which is roughly proportional to Z.

157. We can now calculate the opacity. In equation (77·15) the emission there represented by dj is now equal to $Q d\nu$. Hence (77·15) becomes

$$Q d\nu = c k_\nu I (\nu) d\nu,$$

so that

$$k_\nu = \frac{Q}{c I (\nu)} \quad\dots\dots\dots\dots\dots\dots(157·1).$$

By (77·4) the coefficient of opacity k_2 is given by

$$\frac{1}{k_2} = \frac{c}{Q} \int I (\nu) \frac{\partial I (\nu)}{\partial T} d\nu \div \int \frac{\partial I (\nu)}{\partial T} d\nu \quad\dots\dots\dots(157·15)$$

$$= \frac{c}{2Q} \frac{d}{dT} \int \{I (\nu)\}^2 d\nu \div \frac{d}{dT} \int I (\nu) d\nu \quad\dots\dots\dots(157·2).$$

By Planck's Law

$$I(\nu)\,d\nu = \frac{C\nu^3 d\nu}{e^{h\nu/RT} - 1} = \frac{CR^4T^4}{h^4}\frac{x^3 dx}{e^x - 1},$$

$$\{I(\nu)\}^2\,d\nu = \frac{C^2R^7T^7}{h^7}\frac{x^6 dx}{(e^x - 1)^2},$$

where $x = h\nu/RT$. Hence (157·2) becomes

$$\frac{1}{k_2} = \frac{c}{2Q}\frac{7}{4}\frac{CR^3T^3}{h^3}\int_0^\infty \frac{x^6 dx}{(e^x - 1)^2} \div \int_0^\infty \frac{x^3 dx}{e^x - 1} \quad\ldots\ldots(157\cdot3).$$

We have
$$\int_0^\infty \frac{x^3 dx}{e^x - 1} = \int_0^\infty (x^3 e^{-x} + x^3 e^{-2x} + x^3 e^{-3x} + \ldots)\,dx$$
$$= 6\alpha,$$

where
$$\alpha = 1^{-4} + 2^{-4} + 3^{-4} + \ldots = 1\cdot0823,$$

$$\int_0^\infty \frac{x^6 dx}{(e^x - 1)^2} = \int_0^\infty (x^6 e^{-2x} + 2x^6 e^{-3x} + 3x^6 e^{-4x} + \ldots)\,dx$$
$$= \frac{6!}{2^7}\beta,$$

where
$$\beta = 2^7(2^{-7} + 2\cdot3^{-7} + 3\cdot4^{-7} + \ldots) = 1\cdot151.$$

Also by Stefan's Law

$$aT^4 = \int I(\nu)\,d\nu = 6\alpha CR^4T^4/h^4,$$

so that
$$C = \frac{ah^4}{6\alpha R^4} \quad\ldots\ldots\ldots\ldots\ldots\ldots(157\cdot4).$$

Hence (157·3) gives
$$\frac{1}{k_2} = \frac{35}{256}\frac{\beta}{\alpha^2}\frac{h}{RQ}acT^3,$$

so that
$$k_2 acT^4 = (7\cdot44RT/h)\,Q \quad\ldots\ldots\ldots\ldots(157\cdot5).$$

By comparing this with the simple formula (74·5)

$$\text{emission} = kacT^4,$$

which takes no account of the variation of k with frequency, we can see the effect of Rosseland's correction. It is as though the spectrum of uniform intensity Q were limited to a frequency range

$$\delta\nu = 7\cdot44RT/h \quad\ldots\ldots\ldots\ldots\ldots(157\cdot6).$$

The emission and absorption in a range of this extent gives us a *partial absorption coefficient* which is equal to the *full opacity coefficient*.

158. Inserting the value of Q from (156·4) in (157·5) we now have

$$\frac{\mu k_2 T^4(1 + f)}{\rho} = 7\cdot44\frac{128\pi}{3\sqrt{3}}\frac{Z^2}{A}\frac{e^6}{H^2 am^2 c^4 h}\frac{RT}{V_0}.$$

If $u_0\ (= (8R/\pi m)^{\frac{1}{2}})$ is the arithmetic mean speed of an electron at 1° absolute

$$V_0 = u_0 T^{\frac{1}{2}}.$$

Hence
$$\frac{\mu k_2 T^{\frac{7}{2}}(1+f)}{\rho} = 7\cdot44\,\frac{128\pi}{3\sqrt{3}}\,\frac{Z^2}{A}\,\frac{Re^6}{H^2am^2c^4hu_0} \quad\ldots\ldots\ldots(158\cdot1)$$

$$= 7\cdot44\,\frac{128\pi}{3\sqrt{3}}\,\frac{Z^2}{A}\,\frac{Rb^2c}{H^2au_0}\,\frac{e^2}{hc},$$

where $b = e^2/mc^2 = \frac{3}{2} \times$ conventional radius of electron

$$= 0\cdot668\,\frac{Rb^2c}{H^2au_0}\,\frac{Z^2}{A} \quad\ldots\ldots\ldots\ldots\ldots\ldots(158\cdot2),$$

since hc/e^2 is 861 (a pure number).

Neglecting possible variations in the small correction f and assuming uniform chemical composition (Z^2/A) we obtain the law

$$\mu k_2 T^{\frac{7}{2}}/\rho = \text{const.}$$

which is the law of opacity adopted in our investigations. The constant, however, is not in good agreement with the value derived from Capella. For iron at the centre of Capella

$$Z = 26, \quad A = 56, \quad \mu = 2\cdot1, \quad \rho = \cdot0547, \quad T = 7\cdot20\,.\,10^6, \quad f = \cdot05,$$

we find by $(158\cdot2)$ $\qquad k_2 = 4\cdot95,$

as compared with the astronomical result $k = 53$.

At a later stage we shall have to discuss this discrepancy which amounts to a factor 10.

Kramers' Theory of Emission.

159. It must now be explained why the results obtained according to the classical theory of emission are expected to be valid although the theory itself is not accepted.

According to the quantum theory any transfer of energy between matter and radiation must occur in quanta. An electron accelerated under the attraction of the nucleus must, if it radiates at all, radiate a quantum.

Consider electrons with initial velocity V and let ν_0 be a frequency such that
$$h\nu_0 = \tfrac{1}{2}mV^2 \quad\ldots\ldots\ldots\ldots\ldots\ldots(159\cdot1).$$

A quantum of frequency less than ν_0 contains less than the free energy of an electron; hence the electron radiating it will remain free. But an electron radiating a quantum of frequency greater than ν_0 will be left with negative energy, that is to say, it is captured. Hence the spectrum of the radiation is divided into two stretches—

(α) Frequencies from 0 to ν_0 due to electrons which are not captured, but are switched into new hyperbolic orbits of less energy.

(β) Frequencies greater than ν_0 due to capture of electrons.

We discuss first the spectrum (α). Out of a large number of electrons encountering ions some will radiate quanta of one frequency, some of

another, and some perhaps will escape without radiating. It is in accordance with the general idea of the Correspondence Principle that the
statistical average of these quantum radiations will amount to the radiation
given by the classical theory. To put it another way, the Fourier terms in
the classical radiation are interpreted, not as representing actual radiation
of that frequency from an accelerated electron, but as probabilities of
radiation of that frequency. With a large number of electrons it makes
no difference whether each electron radiates $\frac{1}{1000}$ of a quantum or has a
$\frac{1}{1000}$ chance of radiating a whole quantum; so the classical theory should
give the total radiation of a large number of electrons correctly.

Turning to the spectrum (β), the new point arises that the electron
after capture must be in one of the quantised orbits within the atom, so
that its final negative energy must have one of a discrete series of values.
Thus the electrons can emit only frequencies forming a discrete series,
$\nu_K, \nu_L, \ldots$, given by

$$h\nu_K = \tfrac{1}{2}mV^2 + \psi_K, \quad h\nu_L = \tfrac{1}{2}mV^2 + \psi_L, \quad h\nu_M = \tfrac{1}{2}mV^2 + \psi_M, \ldots\ldots(159\cdot2),$$

where $-\psi_K, -\psi_L, -\psi_M, \ldots$, are the energies of the $K, L, M, \ldots$, orbits
in which it can find a resting-place.

Thus the quantum theory predicts a line spectrum whilst the classical
theory predicts a continuous spectrum.

In discussing the theory of "weights of states" in § 48 we have seen
that as the periodicity becomes more perfect the weight of each unit cell
becomes more and more strongly concentrated into the single quantised
orbit contained in that cell. We are scarcely going beyond this principle
if we suppose that the captured electrons which in the absence of periodicity
would have been distributed over the cell, are, when periodicity is present,
to be found concentrated on the quantised orbit which has drained the
weight of the cell. If the electron had been captured by a very complicated
system in which the orbits had little or no periodicity so that no quantisation occurred, we should have had no reason to anticipate a breakdown of,
the treatment adopted for spectrum α. It is therefore likely that we may
apply the same principle to spectrum β, but with the addition that the
classical radiation corresponding to each cell is heaped up into a single line
corresponding to the quantised orbit in that cell.

If it is a question of capture of an electron by an isolated nucleus, the
dividing lines of the cells are presumably as follows. If $\chi_1 (= -\psi_1)$ is the
energy in a one-quantum orbit the energy in an n-quantum orbit is
χ_1/n^2. Hence

the K line corresponds to the stretch $\chi_1/(\tfrac{1}{2})^2$ to $\chi_1/(\tfrac{3}{2})^2$
,, L ,,   ,, $\chi_1/(\tfrac{3}{2})^2$,, $\chi_1/(\tfrac{5}{2})^2$ $(159\cdot3)$,
,, M ,,   ,, $\chi_1/(\tfrac{5}{2})^2$,, $\chi_1/(\tfrac{7}{2})^2$

and so on. We have no great confidence that the proper limits are precisely at the half-way mark—more especially as regards the first limit for the K line; but fortunately this uncertainty does not matter much in astronomical applications.

If this view is right the classical radiation will cease altogether at a frequency ν_1 given by

$$h\nu_1 = \tfrac{1}{2}mV^2 + \psi_1/(\tfrac{1}{2})^2,$$

since beyond this it is not heaped up into any line. If, however, the two K orbits are already occupied captures at the K level are impossible, and the K line cannot be emitted. The guillotine then falls at

$$h\nu_1 = \tfrac{1}{2}mV^2 + \psi_1/(\tfrac{3}{2})^2,$$

or rather (since the simple theory of the hydrogen atom no longer applies strictly) at some point about half-way between the K and L lines which cannot be very definitely specified. If the eight L orbits are occupied the limit ν_1 is between the L and M lines. Presumably if *some* of the L orbits are occupied the stretch of spectrum corresponding to L is emitted but with proportionately reduced intensity.

Having duly placed the guillotine-frequency ν_1 according to the ionisation, Kramers' theory asserts that the total emission is equal to the classical radiation up to frequency ν_1, but between ν_0 and ν_1 it is emitted in line spectrum instead of continuous spectrum.

When we are dealing with electrons having a Maxwellian distribution of velocities the varying value of the initial energy $\tfrac{1}{2}mV^2$ spreads the lines into bands. Thus the Maxwellian spread of the initial energies to a large extent undoes the quantum concentration of the final energies. When, moreover, we have to do with a mixture of elements having their spectral lines in different places there can be very little trace left of concentration to particular values of ν. It appears then that in the end the classical continuous spectrum is re-established practically unchanged; all that remains of Kramers' modifications is the "guillotine" cutting off the radiation beyond a frequency ν_1 determined by the state of ionisation of the atoms—or determined by a half-quantum orbit if they are completely ionised.

Even the guillotine will not concern us in astronomy if it is placed beyond the range of frequencies contributing sensibly to the opacity. If it is not placed so high it will reduce the opacity and consequently increase the discordance between theory and observation reached in § 158. It will be found that for Capella ν_1 is so high that there is very little correction required; but there are other stars (including the sun) which should suffer a considerable reduction of opacity.

Apart from the guillotine effect the astronomical results obtained from the classical theory in § 158 equally represent Kramers' theory.

160. We shall now try to calculate the reduction of the coefficient of opacity when the guillotine is placed at too low a frequency to be neglected.

We have agreed that the emission consists of the classical spectrum $Q\,d\nu$ extending from $h\nu = 0$ to

$$h\nu = \tfrac{1}{2}mV^2 + \psi \qquad\qquad\qquad (160\cdot1),$$

where in an ordinary mixture of elements ψ may generally be taken to represent the average energy-level down to which the atoms are ionised*. We could substitute RT for $\tfrac{1}{2}mV^2$ since this is its mean value allowing for the greater frequency of capture of the slower electrons. This approximation gives the emission and absorption quantitatively; qualitatively there is a certain amount of shifting of the frequencies, but in a mixture of elements this cancels out to a large extent and for most purposes it is a fair approximation qualitatively. But if we use this representation to calculate the opacity, its qualitative defect becomes conspicuous. It leaves a region of the spectrum perfectly transparent; and if any region is transparent the mean opacity of the whole is zero. There is, of course, no danger in actual stars of very high transparency for any frequency; even if Kramers' absorption left a window, electron-scattering would prevent the transparency exceeding a moderate limit. However, by treating Kramers' absorption a little more carefully we can avoid introducing this spurious high transparency.

If $\chi = \tfrac{1}{2}mV^2$, the number of free electrons with energy between χ and $\chi + d\chi$ is proportional to $e^{-\chi/RT}V\,d\chi$. Remembering that the emission per electron in a range $d\nu$ is proportional to $1/V$, the emission from electrons between χ and $\chi + d\chi$ is proportional to $e^{-\chi/RT}d\chi$. This gives the relative intensity of the partial spectrum contributed by electrons of energy χ, and in accordance with the previous discussion we take it to extend with this uniform intensity up to frequency $(\chi + \psi)/h$ and there terminate. The total intensity at $(\chi + \psi)/h$ is obtained by integrating over those partial spectra which extend up to or beyond this frequency; the result is proportional to

$$\int_{\chi}^{\infty} e^{-\chi/RT}\,d\chi$$

or to $e^{-\chi/RT}$. Hence, instead of taking the spectrum to continue with uniform intensity Q to $RT + \psi$ and there terminate abruptly, we must take it to have uniform intensity Q up to ψ and afterwards to have intensity $Qe^{-\chi/RT}$ at $\psi + \chi$. This gives the same total intensity.

It is easily seen that all Kramers' lines give rise to bands starting

---

* This may be modified when there is ionisation of the K electrons; but in the chief stellar applications a low position of the guillotine accompanies low ionisation, so that the modification does not arise.

abruptly and shaded off according to this law on the high-frequency side. It cannot be pretended that the continuous representation now proposed gives a very accurate summation of these effects for individual lines. But it serves the main purpose of avoiding a failure of the representation at very high frequencies which would have led to our integrals diverging.

Introducing this modification into the investigation of § 157 we have in place of (157·15)

$$\frac{1}{k_2} = \frac{c}{Q} \left[\int_0^{\nu_1} I(\nu) \frac{\partial I(\nu)}{\partial T} d\nu + \int_{\nu_1}^{\infty} e^{h(\nu - \nu_1)/RT} I(\nu) \frac{\partial I(\nu)}{\partial T} d\nu \right] \div \int_0^{\infty} \frac{\partial I(\nu)}{\partial T} d\nu$$

$$\ldots(160\cdot2),$$

where ν_1 is the frequency corresponding to ψ. From this it is deduced that the opacity is decreased in the ratio

$$\int_0^{x_1} x^7 e^{-2x} (1 - e^{-x})^{-3} dx + e^{-x_1} \int_{x_1}^{\infty} x^7 e^{-x} (1 - e^{-x})^{-3} dx : \int_0^{\infty} x^7 e^{-2x} (1 - e^{-x})^{-3} dx$$

$$\ldots(160\cdot3),$$

where $x_1 = \psi/RT$.

The reducing factors calculated from (160·3) are—

Table 29.

Guillotine-Factors.

ψ/RT	Factor
8	1·025
6	1·33
4	4·51
2	30·8

When $\psi < 6RT$ the guillotine begins to have a serious effect on the opacity and the luminosity of the star should be multiplied by the factor here given.

An alternative (but very crude) way of allowing for the guillotine is to suppose that the opacity is cut down so as to be proportional to the weight of the region of the spectrum which survives, i.e. a spectrum occupying a domain of only half the total weight is considered equivalent to a spectrum of half the intensity occupying the whole domain. By Table 8 the factors for the above 4 values of ψ/RT are then 1·10, 1·36, 2·42, 11·9. This procedure involves an incongruous mixture of harmonic and arithmetic means; but it confirms the rapidly increasing factor found by the other method which is possibly more accurate.

It may be stated at once that the observational evidence does not support these factors (§ 179). Stars for which ψ/RT is small appear to agree with the uncorrected law $k \propto \rho/T^{\frac{7}{2}}$. There is perhaps a small reduction of opacity, but it is not at all comparable with the large reductions here predicted. This is not altogether surprising. Whilst Kramers' theory undoubtedly contains a great deal of truth, the details are as yet somewhat tentative, and, moreover, in its present form, it accounts for only a small part of the stellar opacity.

Comparison with Laboratory Experiments.

161. If Kramers' theory were merely a speculation as to the manner in which classical laws pass over into quantum laws, it would not greatly disturb us to find astronomical results partly discordant with it. But the theory has been compared with laboratory experiments and found satisfactory, so that astronomical conflict with Kramers' theory is virtually a conflict with laboratory experiment.

In an X ray tube a stream of electrons, all with the same velocity V acquired under a known fall of potential, falls on the material of the anti-cathode. In this case the atoms have their full complement of electrons so that there is no opportunity for capture, and only spectrum a can be emitted. Within the anticathode the electrons gradually lose their energy chiefly by other dissipative causes and only to a small extent by the radiation of spectrum a. The total spectrum is therefore due to electrons with all velocities from 0 to V. We can measure the radiation $J_\nu d\nu$ corresponding to an initial velocity V, and $(J_\nu + \Delta J_\nu)\, d\nu$ corresponding to an initial velocity $V + \Delta V$; then $(\Delta J_\nu)\, d\nu$ represents the spectrum emitted by the electrons whilst their velocity falls from $V + \Delta V$ to V—after which fall they are in a position to radiate J_ν just as if they were first entering the anticathode*. Hence the spectrum due to electrons of the same velocity V is of intensity $Q_\nu d\nu$, where

$$Q_\nu = \Delta J_\nu = \frac{dJ_\nu}{dV} \Delta V \dots\dots\dots\dots\dots\dots(161\cdot1),$$

and Q_ν should be given by $(155\cdot42)$ provided that s represents the number of atoms per sq. cm. in a thickness of anticathode such that the average electron velocity diminishes by ΔV in traversing it.

The best experimental determinations of J_ν appear to be those of H. Kulenkampff†. Due correction has been made for the absorption by the anticathode of the radiation emitted within it. Deriving Q_ν by $(161\cdot1)$, these experiments show that the spectrum Q_ν is of uniform intensity up to ν_0 and ceases abruptly at ν_0. Further, $dJ_\nu/d\nu_0$ is proportional to Z and independent of ν_0, so that dJ_ν/dV is proportional to ZV. According to the Thomson-Whiddington law the decrease of velocity ΔV in a sheet containing a constant number of atoms s, is proportional to Z/V^3; hence by

---

* This is only true because the proportion of electrons concerned in radiating spectrum a is small; the electrons radiating ΔJ_ν have their velocities suddenly reduced by a large amount and can take little part in the further radiation J_ν.

† *Ann. d. Physik*, **69**, p. 548 (1922).

(161·1) Q_ν is proportional to $(ZV) \times (Z/V^3) = Z^2/V^2$ in agreement with (155·42). Kramers' result is thus confirmed in every detail.

It remains to test the absolute value of Q. This is more difficult since it depends on absolute instead of differential experiments. According to a direct comparison the experiments give about twice as much radiation as the theory; but as Kramers points out they are not strictly comparable and the actual agreement is probably closer. In any case the experimental confirmation of this part of Kramers' theory is so close as to constitute a remarkable triumph for the theory.

162. One doubtful point remains which may conceivably have astronomical importance. In addition to the radiation here described Kulenkampff found a considerable emission at or very near to the limiting frequency ν_0; that is to say, J_ν does not rise uniformly from zero value at ν_0 but starts almost abruptly at a finite value. This radiation, which he calls spectrum B, must be emitted by electrons which just lose their whole energy. Presumably they may be considered as captured in high quantum orbits; if so, the atoms capturing them become negatively charged*. But there is no provision for the corresponding radiation in either spectrum α or spectrum β of the classical theory†. It may be that capture in ordinary orbits being blocked, the spectrum β heaps itself up at the limit ν_0; but this is not in accordance with Kramers' ideas. The slight reference to spectrum B in Kramers' paper (*loc. cit.* p. 870) does not seem to elucidate the phenomenon. We cannot foresee what will happen to this radiation when we are dealing with ions instead of complete atoms, so it is impossible to say what part (if any) it will play in stellar opacity.

163. The spectrum between ν_0 and ν_1 is not emitted under laboratory conditions; and the theoretical predictions cannot be tested directly. But since coefficients of emission and absorption are connected by Einstein's relation (38·4) we may make equivalent tests on the corresponding absorption spectrum. Consider the emission and absorption of a line which replaces a stretch of continuous spectrum of extent $f\psi_1$ in energy units or $f\psi_1/h$ in frequency units (cf. (159·3)). Here $\psi_1 = -\chi_1$ is the negative energy of a 1-quantum orbit. To calculate the emission for this line $d\nu$ must be replaced by $f\psi_1/h$ in (155·42). Consider a cubic centimetre of material containing s fully-ionised atoms and n' free electrons of velocity V to $V + dV$. In unit time $n'V$ electrons will traverse the cubic centimetre so that the emission per cu. cm. per second is by (155·42)

$$\frac{sn'Vf\psi_1}{h} \frac{32\pi^2}{3\sqrt{3}} \frac{Z^2e^6}{c^3m^2V^2}.$$

* It is known from positive ray experiments that atoms can become negatively charged.

† The part of spectrum β assignable to the high quantum orbits is extremely small.

Dividing this by the energy of a quantum $h\nu$ we obtain the number of captures per second

$$sn' \frac{64\pi^4}{3\sqrt{3}} \frac{Z^4 e^{10} f}{c^3 h^4 m V\nu} \qquad\qquad (163\cdot1),$$

where we have inserted the value $\psi_1 = 2\pi^2 m Z^2 e^4 / h^2$ from (42·62).

An ionised atom and a free electron will be regarded as a system in state 2 in the argument of § 36. The total number of such systems in the cubic centimetre is sn', i.e. there are sn' combinations each having a certain chance of transformation to a system in state 1. Hence the coefficient b_{21} giving the probability of a single system returning to state 1 in unit time by the capture process is

$$b_{21} = \frac{64\pi^4}{3\sqrt{3}} \frac{Z^4 e^{10} f}{c^3 h^4 m V\nu} \qquad\qquad (163\cdot2).$$

By (40·63) the atomic absorption coefficient is

$$\alpha = \frac{q_2}{q_1} \frac{c^2}{8\pi\nu^2} \frac{b_{21}}{d\nu}.$$

Also by (45·6) $q_2 = \dfrac{m^3}{h^3} 4\pi V^2 dV,$

since $dx\,dy\,dz$ is here 1 cu. cm. Again, for a change of V

$$h\,d\nu = mV\,dV.$$

Hence $\alpha = \dfrac{m^2 c^2 V}{2 q_1 h^2 \nu^2} b_{21}$

$$= \frac{32\pi^4}{3\sqrt{3}} \frac{e^{10} mf}{q_1 c^4 h^6} Z^4 \lambda^3 \qquad\qquad (163\cdot3),$$

where $\lambda = c/\nu = $ the wave-length of the radiation absorbed.

Inserting numerical values we have

$$\alpha = \cdot0052 \frac{f}{q_1} Z^4 \lambda^3 \qquad\qquad (163\cdot4).$$

The proportionality of α to $Z^4 \lambda^3$ agrees with a well-known experimental law so that this prediction is confirmed in a highly satisfactory manner.

To evaluate further the numerical coefficient, consider, for example, the ionisation of a K electron. Since the system in state 2 consists of a fully-ionised atom and a free electron, our calculation of α applies to an atom in state 1 containing just 1 electron in a K orbit. As an approximation we shall neglect the interference of the electrons with one another and suppose that each K electron in a complete atom gives the absorption coefficient (163·4). We have $q_1 = 2$ and by (159·3) $f = (\frac{1}{2})^{-2} - (\frac{3}{2})^{-2} = \frac{32}{9}$; including a factor 2 to allow for the two K electrons in each atom the result is

$$\alpha_K = 0\cdot0185 Z^4 \lambda^3 \qquad\qquad (163\cdot5).$$

Similarly for the L absorption, $q_1 = 6$, $f = (\frac{3}{2})^{-2} - (\frac{5}{2})^{-2} = \frac{64}{225}$; except in very light elements the result must be multiplïed by 8 on account of the 8 L electrons in each atom. Hence

$$\alpha_L = 0 \cdot 0020 Z^4 \lambda^3 \quad \dots\dots\dots\dots\dots\dots (163 \cdot 6).$$

These formulae apply to wave-lengths short enough to effect the K and L ionisations respectively; there are abrupt absorption edges at the limits where the K and L ionisations suddenly cease.

The experimental value of the constant for α_K is about $0 \cdot 020$, and for α_L about $0 \cdot 003$, so that the agreement of the theory is entirely satisfactory.

It will be seen that the stellar opacity can be predicted from laboratory data without appeal to Kramers' theory or any other theory of absorption. The laws $\alpha_K = \cdot 020 Z^4 \lambda^3$, $\alpha_L = \cdot 003 Z^4 \lambda^3$ were discovered empirically before any theory was suggested. To apply them to stellar absorption we have to discover first what proportion of the K and L electrons are retained—how much of the absorption indicated by these laws is still in working order in the stellar conditions; but that is found by the ionisation formula which rests on general thermodynamics and has no reference to Kramers' or any other theory of the absorption processes. The small additional absorption corresponding to spectrum α can also be calculated from laboratory measurements of the continuous X ray spectrum.

Evidently these experimental laws will give practically the same value of the stellar opacity as the theoretical laws with which they approximately agree. They will lead to the result $k \propto \rho / \mu T^{\frac{7}{2}}$ but with values of k approximately $\frac{1}{10}$ of those found in the stars.

164. The question may be raised whether the material of a star may not have a refractive index for the radiation traversing it, which should be taken into account in the calculations. As the crude macroscopic conceptions of refractive index and dielectric constant are liable to be misleading, it may be well first to insist on two points: (1) the speed of propagation of radiant energy is c whatever the refractive index of the material; (2) the density of the radiant energy in thermodynamic equilibrium is given by Stefan's and Planck's Laws whatever the dielectric constant of the material. The macroscopic formulae appear to contradict these statements, because (by a fiction which is sometimes convenient) they include energy of polarisation of the atoms and molecules in the radiant energy.

Clearly we must not combine a macroscopic theory of wave propagation with a microscopic theory of absorption; and the investigation is more or less at a deadlock because the quantum theory of refraction, polarisation, etc. is scarcely far enough advanced to help us.

It is unlikely that there can be much effect on the absorption coefficient from this cause. In any case, the change of refractive index will *ceteris paribus* be proportional to the density, so that it will give rise to differences between dense and rarefied stars; hence the discrepant factor 10 which affects dense and diffuse stars alike cannot be accounted for in this way.

Other sources of Opacity.

165. The success of the correspondence principle as applied in Kramers' theory seems to be greater than we could have expected. The general idea of the principle is that the results of the classical and the quantum theory will *converge*; but, for example, in dealing with K absorption from a 1-quantum orbit we are as far as possible from the convergence point and it is fortunate that the difference is no greater. The discussion has shown that the use of Kramers' theory (or of the classical theory) to calculate astronomical opacity is practically equivalent to using the laws ascertained by terrestrial experiment. Consequently, the discordance found in § 158 is a matter of very serious concern.

It is not as though any wide extrapolation were required in applying experimental results to the interior of a star. The approximate treatment of the electron orbits as parabolic is as satisfactory in the stars as in laboratory conditions*. The main point of difference is that in the stars the outer part of the electron system is missing and this may conceivably make some difference to the ease of expelling an inner electron by radiation. We should also like to know more about Kulenkampff's spectrum B. Does it remain at frequency ν_0 when the atoms are ionised, or does it move on to correspond with the last occupied level?

166. We must consider whether there are any further sources of absorption responsible for an appreciable part of the stellar opacity. This brings us to the question of line absorption due to excitation of the atoms. Rosseland, in pointing out the distinction between opacity and absorption, suggested that this could be disregarded since fine absorption lines can have no appreciable effect on opacity. We dare not trust to this because, as J. Woltjer† has urged, the lines may be broadened in the stellar interior and effectively screen the whole spectrum. As before, we attack this problem by calculating emission rather than absorption.

If we are dealing with a large number of excited electrons, a certain proportion will relapse and emit quanta within a given time, so that there will be an average rate of emission of energy per excited electron. Not very much is known about this emission for deep-lying electrons, since experimental values have only been obtained for the outermost electrons. But according to the general principles of the quantum theory the emission

---

* Some further discussion of the applicability of Kramers' formulae to stellar conditions will be found in *Monthly Notices*, **84**, p. 115.

† *Bull. Astr. Inst. Netherlands*, No. 82.

should not exceed that given by the classical theory. Presumably the classical emission is guillotined at a frequency determined by the occupied orbits below the excited electron or by the half-quantum limit just as the classical radiation from a free electron is guillotined. There should be no discontinuity in behaviour between electrons in high quantum orbits and free electrons. Indeed, Kramers' theory of radiation from electrons in hyperbolic orbits seems to have been a generalisation of the ideas originally developed in connection with elliptic orbits.

Consider first circular orbits and let the energy of the orbit be $-\psi$; then the acceleration is

$$\Gamma = 4\psi^2/Ze^2m,$$

and by (153·1) the classical radiation per second is

$$\frac{32\psi^4}{3Z^2e^2m^2c^3} \quad\dots\dots\dots\dots\dots\dots\dots\dots(166\cdot1).$$

Consider electrons normally in an n_1-quantum orbit excited into an n-quantum orbit; the energies of the orbits will be $-(n/n_1)^2\,\psi$, $-\psi$ respectively, and by Boltzmann's Law the proportion of excited electrons will be

$$e^{-\theta\psi/RT},$$

where $\qquad\qquad\qquad\qquad \theta = n^2/n_1{}^2 - 1.$

Let x measure the ionisation of the n_1 electrons so that $(1 - x)$ is the proportion retained. Then the number of n_1 electrons excited into n-orbits per gm. is

$$\frac{p\,(1-x)}{A_H}\, e^{-\theta\psi/RT} \quad\dots\dots\dots\dots\dots\dots(166\cdot2),$$

where $p = 2$ for K electrons, 8 for L electrons, etc. We have neglected weight-factors.

The emission per gm. per sec. is obtained by multiplying (166·1) and (166·2). Equating this to the absorption $kacT^4$, we have

$$kacT^4 = \frac{p\,(1-x)}{A_H}\frac{32}{3Z^2e^2m^2c^3}\frac{R^4T^4}{\theta^4}\,y^4e^{-y} \quad\dots\dots\dots(166\cdot3),$$

where $y = \theta\psi/RT$. The function y^4e^{-y} has a maximum value 4·69 at $y = 4$. (If the energy emission is in the midst of the range of frequency which contributes most to the opacity y will be near 4.) Hence

$$k < 4\cdot69\,\frac{32R^4}{3_Hm^2c^4e^2a}\frac{p\,(1-x)}{\theta^4Z^2A} \quad\dots\dots\dots\dots\dots(166\cdot4)$$

$$< 9340000\,\frac{p\,(1-x)}{\theta^4Z^2A}.$$

For K electrons excited into 2-quantum orbits, $p = 2$, $\theta = 3$, and hence

$$k < 230{,}000\,(1-x)/Z^2A.$$

When the atomic number is below 20 the K ionisation is nearly complete (in Capella and stars of the main series) and $(1 - x)$ is small. For elements above 20, Z^2A is greater than 16,000, so that k is less than 14. Remembering that we are dealing with an extreme upper limit, that some at least of the classical radiation is likely to be guillotined, and that not all the matter will be of the atomic number giving greatest efficiency, the actual value of k will probably be considerably smaller. Moreover, this limit 14 applies to all stars; and is therefore to be compared not only with the astronomical opacity 53 at the centre of Capella but with much higher opacities in the sun and Krueger 60.

If we took account of weight factors the limit would be increased a little but not so much as we might be inclined to suppose. The selection principle gives only a small number of n-orbits from which a direct transition can be made to a particular n_1-orbit, and we need not take account of excited electrons unable to make the required transition.

The classical radiation in an elliptic orbit is greater than in the corresponding circular orbit, being proportional (cf. (153·75)) to

$$(1 - \epsilon^2)^{-\frac{5}{2}} \int_0^{2\pi} (1 - \epsilon \cos \theta)^2 \, d\theta = 2\pi (1 + \tfrac{1}{2}\epsilon^2)/(1 - \epsilon^2)^{\frac{5}{2}}.$$

Thus the classical radiation in a 2_1 orbit is 40 times that in a 2_2 orbit. But there is no need to multiply our upper limit for k by this factor, because we know that the *actual* emission from these elliptic orbits is not faster than from circular orbits. The evidence for this has been given in § 51. The fact is that the enhanced classical emission in the elliptic orbit occurs during the quick passage round pericentron, and is of too high frequency to be connected with any possible transition of the electron.

For heavier elements there may be line absorption due to L electrons excited into 3-quantum orbits. Then $p = 8$, $\theta = \tfrac{5}{4}$, so that the limit of k is 133 times higher. This, however, must be whittled down for several reasons. If all the 8 L electrons are to be present Z must be at least 50, so that the divisor Z^2A is increased in the ratio 16. Also the greater part of the classical radiation is now associated with a fall to the K level, and does not concern the transition under consideration. Moreover, it seems unlikely that elements above $Z = 50$ will be abundant. Thus, so far as we can judge, line absorption by L electrons is likely to be weaker if anything than that by K electrons.

It has been pointed out to me by J. Woltjer that the foregoing argument is insufficient to exclude the possibility of large emission from electrons excited into orbits of high quantum number. By the selection principle transitions to a $(1, 1)$ orbit can be made from $(4, 2)$, $(5, 2)$, $(6, 2)$, ... orbits. Since these are highly eccentric their classical emission is large; and although we anticipate that most of this emission will be irrelevant to the transitions concerned, we cannot deal with it by the foregoing calculation of upper limits. We shall therefore attempt to calculate more closely the line emission from electrons in high quantum orbits.

By the correspondence principle there is continuity between free electrons and electrons in high quantum orbits; Kramers' theory of emission from free electrons can therefore be pushed beyond the zero mark so as to include electrons of small negative energy. The investigation of § 155 refers strictly to parabolic orbits, but we may use it for eccentricities rather less than 1 as we have already used it for eccentricities rather greater than 1. By (155·1) and (155·2) Q_ν is given as a function of the angular momentum $m\sigma V$. In quantised orbits the angular momentum is given by the second quantum number n', so that we have the equivalence

$$m\sigma V = n'h/2\pi \quad\text{......................}(166\cdot5).$$

Consider a particular orbit (n, n', n''). The number of electrons per atom in this state is

$$Be^{K/n^2RT},$$

where $-K/n^2$ is the energy and B is expressed in terms of the density σ_0 of the free electrons by (46·2), viz.

$$B\frac{m^3}{h^3} = \left(\frac{m}{2\pi RT}\right)^{\frac{3}{2}}\sigma_0.$$

The period of the orbit is $n^3h/2K$. Hence the number of pericentron passages per atom per second is

$$\frac{2K}{n^3h}\left(\frac{h^2}{2\pi mRT}\right)^{\frac{3}{2}}\sigma_0 e^{K/n^2RT} \quad\text{.................}(166\cdot6).$$

Keeping n' fixed we sum this for the values of n belonging to the high quantum orbits under consideration, say from n_0 to ∞, where $n_0 \geqslant n'$. Replacing the summation by integration, the number of "encounters" (i.e. perihelion passages) becomes

$$\frac{RT}{h}\left(\frac{h^2}{2\pi mRT}\right)^{\frac{3}{2}}\sigma_0(e^{K/n_0^2RT} - 1).$$

To each value of n' there correspond $(n' + 1)$ values of n''. We replace $(n' + 1)$ by n' (thereby introducing an error not greater than a factor 2) and write the number of encounters per atom per second for all orbits in a range n' to $n' + dn'$ equal to

$$\frac{RT}{h}\left(\frac{h^2}{2\pi mRT}\right)^{\frac{3}{2}}\sigma_0(e^{K/n_0^2RT} - 1)\,n'dn'.$$

By (155·1) and (166·5) the corresponding emission per atom is

$$dQ_\nu = \frac{16\pi^4 Z^2 e^6}{c^3 n'^2 h^2}\cdot\frac{RT}{h}\left(\frac{h^2}{2\pi mRT}\right)^{\frac{3}{2}}\sigma_0(e^{K/n_0^2RT} - 1)\,n'dn'P(\gamma)\,...(166\cdot7).$$

By (155·2) and (166·5) $\dfrac{dn'}{n'} = \dfrac{d\sigma}{\sigma} = \dfrac{1}{3}\dfrac{d\gamma}{\gamma}$,

so that treating $e^{K/n_0{}^2RT}$ as constant and integrating from $n' = 0$ to ∞, we obtain by (155·32)

$$Q_\nu = \frac{32\pi^2}{3\sqrt{3}}\left(\frac{m}{2\pi RT}\right)^{\frac{1}{2}}\frac{Z^2e^6\sigma_0}{c^3m^2}\left(e^{K/n_0{}^2RT} - 1\right).$$

The harmonic mean velocity V of the free electrons is $(\frac{1}{2}\pi RT/m)^{\frac{1}{2}}$, so that this becomes

$$Q_\nu = \frac{16\pi^2}{3\sqrt{3}}\frac{Z^2e^6\sigma_0}{c^3m^2V}\left(e^{K/n_0{}^2RT} - 1\right) \quad\ldots\ldots\ldots\ldots(166\cdot8).$$

Comparing with (155·42), where $n = \sigma_0 V$, we find the ratio of the emission from the bound electrons to the emission from the free electrons is

$$\tfrac{1}{2}\left(e^{K/n_0{}^2RT} - 1\right) = \tfrac{1}{2}\left(e^{\psi_0/RT} - 1\right) \quad\ldots\ldots\ldots\ldots(166\cdot9)$$

where $-\psi_0$ is the energy of an n_0 quantum orbit.

We apply this to the electrons in orbits of quantum number 4 or greater. Then throughout the integration n_0 is 4 or greater, and ψ_0 corresponds to the energy of the N group or higher groups of electrons. At 10,000,000° RT corresponds to 14·3 Å, and by Table 30 the factor $e^{\psi_0/RT}$ must be practically unity even for the heaviest elements. Hence it appears that Kramers' absorption is increased by a very small fraction when we take into account the line absorption due to excitation into orbits beyond $n = 3$. It is true that we have rather diminished the result by substituting n' for $n' + 1$, but on the other hand, we have probably exaggerated it considerably by integrating from $n' = 0$ and by neglecting the shielding of the nucleus for the distant orbits.

For the lighter elements up to about $Z = 30$ the 3-quantum orbits can be included without altering the conclusion. For heavier elements the 3-quantum orbits should be examined separately, but I think it is not difficult to convince oneself that these do not add very much to the emission.

It appears therefore that line absorption cannot be responsible for any large part of the observed stellar opacity.

It is instructive to look at the problem from another point of view also. We found (151·5) that in Capella each free electron was responsible for the emission of $4\cdot5.10^{10}$ quanta per second. If now we propose to transfer the duty to bound electrons, we must recall that whereas about 20 free electrons are allowed to each ion an allowance of 1 excited electron per ion is excessive. So that each excited electron must emit 10^{12} quanta per second, or rather must emit its quantum in 10^{-12} sec. and make room for another to take its place in the steady average. This is between 1000 and 10,000 times shorter life than that of electrons excited in optical orbits, and I believe it is contrary to the views generally held by physicists to admit anything like so great a speeding up at X ray levels.

167. I have considered elsewhere* the emission and absorption of radiation at encounters of free electrons with one another. For Capella the absorption coefficient due to this process was found to be $k = \cdot038$, so that the contribution is negligible. My investigation, however, did not take account of the interference of the waves from the two accelerated electrons. Rosseland has pointed out that this interference reduces the emission almost to zero. The algebraic sum of the accelerations of the two charges is zero, and it is well known in classical theory that this is the condition for the absence of radiation.

Scattering of radiation by the free electrons must be included in the opacity. It is shown in (53·5) that the contribution from this source is only 0·2.

Complex processes such as the simultaneous encounter of three bodies (ions or electrons) could be considered; but these would give an absorption varying as the square of the density, and cannot constitute an important part of the astronomical absorption which is found to be proportional to the first power of the density.

The possible radiation from ions encountering one another will not be important. The velocities of the ions are comparatively small, their high charges ward off collisions, and they can scarcely come close enough to disturb the remnants of their electron systems.

It seems that we cannot discover any other important source of absorption to supplement that of which Kramers' theory claims to be a full treatment.

Effect of Chemical Constitution.

168. Denote the opacity calculated from the observed mass and luminosity by k_a and the opacity calculated by Kramers' theory by k_t. As the comparison stands at present $k_a = 10k_t$. By combining (158·2), (87·1) and (90·1) we obtain

$$\frac{k_t}{k_a} = 0 \cdot 0443 \frac{b^2}{G_H u_0} \frac{Z^2}{A} \frac{L}{M} \frac{\beta}{(1-\beta)^2} \frac{1}{(1+f) T_c^{\frac{1}{2}}} \quad \ldots\ldots\ldots(168 \cdot 1),$$

where α has been taken as 2·5 in the numerical factor.

By taking an element heavier than iron the factor Z^2/A is increased. It might seem that the discrepancy between k_t and k_a could be partly accounted for by supposing that the stars are composed mainly of the heaviest elements. This hypothesis turns out to be useless because the assumption of heavier elements involves consequential changes in β which neutralise the improvement.

For example, if Capella were made of gold Z^2/A would be 2·6 times greater than for iron. But the molecular weight for completely ionised

* *Monthly Notices*, **84**, p. 117.

gold is 2·46. In Capella gold would retain at least the 10 inner electrons and perhaps some of the M electrons as well; this raises μ to at least 2·8. Changing μ from 2·1 to 2·8 increases $1 - \beta$ from 0·28 to 0·41 and reduces $\beta/(1 - \beta)^2$ from 9·2 to 3·5. This precisely cancels the increase in $Z^2/A*$.

169. There is one way in which k_t and k_a can be reconciled by an assumed chemical composition of the star, namely, by mixing a considerable proportion of hydrogen with a heavier element, say, iron. Hydrogen alone would be comparatively transparent to stellar radiation, since its K line is of comparatively low frequency. The actual k_t would be much less than the value given by (158·2), since the guillotine cuts off most of the classical radiation capable of affecting the opacity. But a mixture of hydrogen and iron may be more opaque than either element separately.

Suppose that we have a mixture containing 15 hydrogen atoms ($A = 1$, $Z = 1$) to 1 iron atom ($A = 56$, $Z = 26$). The hydrogen atoms will be ionised, and the iron atom (in Capella) will have lost 24 electrons; hence the weight 71 corresponds to 16 ions and 39 electrons. We have

$$\mu = \tfrac{71}{55} = 1\cdot29, \qquad f = \tfrac{16}{39} = 0\cdot41.$$

In applying (158·2) A should be taken as 71 instead of 56, since the number of iron ions per gram is now $1/71_H$, and the hydrogen ions are ineffective. We must also recalculate T with the new value of μ. We find that $(1 - \beta)$ is now 0·100 and the central temperature of Capella is reduced in the ratio 1·30.

By these changes in (158·2) the absorption of the iron is increased in the ratio 2·38 so that
$$k_t = 11\cdot8.$$

The absorption by the hydrogen ions is negligible. The chief function of the hydrogen is to lower the molecular weight; but in addition it nearly pays for its own inactivity by providing more numerous electrons for the iron to capture.

The astronomical coefficient is reduced in proportion to $1 - \beta$, and now becomes
$$k_a = 18\cdot7$$

which is in good enough agreement with k_t.

For any star of small mass such as the sun the above mixture would increase k_t/k_a 37 times, so that the original discordance would be very much over-corrected. About half the quantity of hydrogen (7 atoms to 1 iron atom) is needed in order to obtain the same agreement as for Capella. It may be urged that this would be in keeping with the view that the stars

---

* The adopted molecular weight 2·1 was not intended to correspond strictly to iron but to allow for some admixture of lighter elements; so that by taking Z^2/A for iron we have rather minimised the discrepancy.

of small mass are older stars, and the hydrogen has been gradually used to form heavier elements.

Hydrogen is the only element which can make these changes; admixture of helium would give very little increase of k_t/k_a.

Some writers have thought that hydrogen is unable to remain in the interior of a star and necessarily rises to the surface. This would be fatal to the foregoing suggestion. It seems, however, that there is no such separation of the hydrogen (§ 195).

I was formerly attracted to the view that stars, especially in the giant stage, contain a large proportion of hydrogen—the idea being that the stars are the main, if not the only, seat of the manufacture of the higher elements from protons and electrons, the star's heat being incidentally provided by the process. But the low molecular weight involved is out of keeping with the general trend of astronomical evidence. It upsets altogether the relation which we have found between the masses of the stars and the critical values of $1 - \beta$. And it leaves room for haphazard fluctuations depending on how much hydrogen is left which seems contrary to the general uniformity of the mass-luminosity diagram. I would much prefer to find some other explanation of the discordance between k_t and k_a.

The Theory of Nuclear Capture.

170. Before Kramers' theory of electron capture was put forward I had proposed a theory of nuclear capture. The interest of this theory is that it gives full agreement with astronomical observation. That almost automatically brings it into conflict with laboratory experiment, since we have seen that the discordance really lies between the two classes of observation. A brief account of this theory may be given here, although I do not think it can be accepted.

We return to the apparent target for iron at the centre of Capella (151·94)
$$\sigma = 1\cdot20.10^{-10} \text{ cm.,}$$

and follow up the first idea that this is an actual sphere at the centre of the atom. The electron tracks which if undisturbed would have just grazed the apparent target will curve towards the nucleus and envelope a much smaller true target.

Since these tracks approach close to the nucleus it is necessary to take account of change of mass with velocity. Let an electron of initial mass m and velocity V be aimed at the edge of the apparent target so that its angular momentum is $mV\sigma$. Let the pericentron distance be σ' and the mass and velocity there be m', V'. Then σ' will be the radius of the true target.

Conservation of angular momentum gives

$$m\sigma V = m'\sigma' V' \quad\text{............................(170·11)}.$$

Conservation of energy gives

$$m'c^2 = mc^2 + Ze^2/\sigma' \quad\text{..................(170·12)},$$

since Ze^2/σ' is the loss of potential energy. The law of change of mass with velocity gives

$$m^2\left(1 - V^2/c^2\right) = m'^2\left(1 - V'^2/c^2\right) \quad\text{.........(170·13)}.$$

Eliminating m' and V' between these three equations we obtain

$$\sigma^2 = \sigma'^2 + Zb\left(Zb + 2\sigma'\right)c^2/V^2 \quad\text{...............(170·2)},$$

where $b = e^2/mc^2$. Preliminary trials show that σ' is very small compared with σ so that σ'^2 can be neglected. Hence

$$1 + \frac{2\sigma'}{Zb} = \left(\frac{V}{c}\frac{\sigma}{Zb}\right)^2 \quad\text{..........................(170·3)}.$$

Inserting numerical values this gives

$$1 + \frac{2\sigma'}{Zb} = 0\cdot84.$$

Formally this makes σ' negative, but allowing a reasonable margin for the errors of the data the actual conclusion is that $2\sigma'/Zb$ is, say, less than 1, or σ' is less than 3.10^{-12} cm. Thus it suggests itself that the true target is the nucleus which has a radius of the order 10^{-12} cm., or perhaps a fairly full hit on the nucleus may be necessary corresponding to $\sigma' = 0$.

The precise value of σ' (if of nuclear dimensions) makes little difference to σ, so we shall take $\sigma' = 0$. Then by (170·3)

$$\sigma = \frac{Zbc}{V} \quad\text{...............................(170·4)}.$$

Hence by (151·91) $\qquad \lambda = \frac{1}{\pi N \sigma^2} = \frac{1}{\pi}\frac{A_H}{\rho}\frac{V^2}{Z^2 b^2 c^2}.$

The total distance travelled by all the free electrons per gram per second is

$$\frac{V}{\mu_H\left(1 + f\right)}.$$

Hence dividing by λ, the number of captures is

$$\frac{\pi Z^2 b^2 c^2 \rho}{A\mu_H^2 V\left(1 + f\right)} \quad\text{..........................(170·5)}.$$

Multiplying (170·5) by the average energy of a quantum $2\cdot7RT$ we obtain the total emission, which is equal to the absorption $kacT^4$ per gm. per sec. Also V must be replaced by its harmonic mean value $\frac{1}{4}\pi V_0 = \frac{1}{4}\pi u_0 T^{\frac{1}{2}}$. The result is

$$\frac{\mu k T^{\frac{7}{2}}\left(1 + f\right)}{\rho} = 10\cdot8\,\frac{Rb^2 c}{H^2 a u_0}\frac{Z^2}{A} \quad\text{..................(170·6)}.$$

which agrees precisely with the result of Kramers' theory (158·2) except
that the numerical coefficient is 10·8 instead of 0·668. Thus the nuclear
theory of capture gives an absorption 16·2 times greater. For example, at
the centre of Capella the result is $k = 80$ which is satisfactorily close to
the astronomical value 53. The nuclear theory predicts the absolute
brightness of Capella to within half a magnitude; and since it also gives
the recognised law $k \propto \rho/T^{\frac{7}{2}}$ the agreement for other stars will be equally
good.

As already stated it appears to be impossible to accept the nuclear
theory in spite of this agreement. It is, however, instructive to find an
entirely different theory leading to the same formula for stellar absorption as Kramers' theory, except for a purely numerical factor. It serves
to emphasize the very general basis of an absorption law approximating
to $\rho/T^{\frac{7}{2}}$.

171. The case for the hypothesis of nuclear capture is that, although
Kramers' theory is presumed to be right so far as it goes, it apparently
needs supplementing, since it leaves $\frac{9}{10}$ of the absorption unaccounted
for—if our figures are correct. Now Kramers never refers to those electron
tracks which are interrupted by a collision with the nucleus. His target
is an annulus; as we go inwards from the annulus and the orbits become
sharper and sharper the frequency of capture becomes rarer; his theory
gives good reason for this decline. But it is possible that there might be
a recrudescence of capture when the tracks strike the nucleus and so
introduce a state of things not discussed by him. According to mechanical
ideas an electron would not rebound with perfect elasticity from a cushion
composed of 86 protons and electrons (the iron nucleus). The kinetic
energy at the impact is so enormous that the loss of $\frac{1}{1000}$ part of it would
leave the electron with negative total energy and so unable to escape.
Unfortunately for the theory, mechanical ideas are not to be trusted, and
according to quantum ideas capture is less probable. Our impression is
that the impact would be of such brief duration that there would not be
enough *low frequency* radiation to effect capture; the classical radiation
would be on the wrong side of the guillotine.

We have assumed in the calculation that the energy emitted on capture
is the mean quantum of the stellar radiation $2·7RT$. This will not be exact;
but we are bound to assume that the emission is in this region, for otherwise Rosseland's argument (§ 77) shows that the corresponding absorption
would not be equivalent to opacity. This means that the captures are
required at the K level in light elements and at the L level in heavy
elements. We at once encounter the difficulty that owing to the thermodynamical relation between absorption and emission coefficients there
would have to be a corresponding K and L absorption in un-ionised

atoms. Laboratory experiments show no such additional absorption beyond that given by Kramers' theory.

This last difficulty could be met by supposing that the loss of energy at the nuclear collision is slight and the electron is first captured in a high quantum orbit. Then (if it is not at once ionised away) it will drop to the lowest vacant level, this second step giving the main emission of energy. By this device laboratory tests are eluded, because in the emission and in the converse absorption the electron requires an intermediate resting-place which is not afforded in the un-ionised atoms of laboratory experiment. But whilst this suggestion seems not unreasonable when we think only of the emission, it becomes, I think, entirely incredible when we consider the reverse steps in the absorption.

The last remark reveals the essentially weak point in the idea of capture by collision with the nucleus—that its plausibility does not survive reversal. To suppose that when absorbing the electron retraces its steps—descends to the nucleus and then bounds off into a hyperbolic orbit—is not particularly plausible. Again, the exact formula for emission on a nuclear capture theory must involve the radius of the nucleus; but it seems impossible that this can play any part in the corresponding absorption.

172. A summary of the position reached with regard to the coefficient of absorption divides itself into two parts, (1) the law $k \propto \rho/\mu T^{\frac{7}{2}}$, and (2) the absolute value of k.

(1) The law $k \propto \rho/\mu T^{\frac{7}{2}}$ or something sufficiently near to it for most stellar applications is given by—

(a) The most general theoretical considerations of absorption and emission coupled with the observed approximate constancy of brightness from type M to type A in the giant series.

(b) Kramers' theory, or equivalently the classical theory of emission.

(c) Laboratory data as to absorption of X rays coupled with the thermodynamic theory of ionisation.

(d) The theory of nuclear capture.

(e) The observed agreement of the luminosities of stars with the mass-luminosity curve based on this law.

We do not lay overmuch stress on the half-power of T, nor exclude corrections varying with the level of ionisation of the atoms; but the "guillotine corrections" suggested by Kramers' theory seem to be definitely too large.

(2) The predicted opacity from (b) or (c) is only $\frac{1}{10}$ of the observed opacity of the stars; and no satisfactory explanation of the discordance

can be given. Other sources of opacity have been examined without success. The field of inquiry is narrowed down to sources of emission of frequency between $2 \cdot 5RT/h$ and $7RT/h$. By assuming that the stars contain a large proportion of hydrogen the discrepancy would be removed; but this hypothesis would be in disagreement with earlier conclusions as to the intensity of radiation pressure. Other changes of chemical constitution make no important difference.

At present the only suggestion of a possible reconciliation lies in the mysterious emission of Kulenkampff's spectrum B, which is not accounted for by Kramers' theory. We may also await developments of the new quantum mechanics of Heisenberg.

CHAPTER X

IONISATION, DIFFUSION, ROTATION

Ionisation.

173. The determination of the degree of ionisation of the atoms under the conditions of temperature and density found in the stars is important in connection with the following applications—

(*a*) We derive from it the molecular weight μ which is required for nearly all numerical calculations. Accuracy is important since μ is often raised to a rather high power in the formulae. We have to find—

(1) What is the most probable value of μ for the stars in general? (The standard value adopted by us is 2·1.)

(2) What is the magnitude of the differential effects (more particularly as affecting the mass-luminosity relation) caused by differences of μ between different stars?

(3) What is the change of μ between the centre and the outer parts of a star?

(*b*) A knowledge of the ionisation is required in connection with theories of absorption, since each ionisation destroys an absorbing mechanism; in particular, it determines the "guillotine" correction to the opacity on Kramers' theory.

(*c*) It determines the energy of ionisation of a star and hence the ratio of specific heats γ, which is important in the study of the pulsations of Cepheids.

Another subject appropriately treated in connection with ionisation is the determination of the deviation of stellar material from the laws of a perfect gas.

The results generally depend appreciably on the chemical constitution of a star. The dependence on the chemical element is of two kinds, viz. a progressive change from the light to the heavy elements, and exceptional phenomena for a small group of consecutive elements which are in a critical stage of their K or L ionisation at the temperature and density chosen. It may be expected that the latter effects will be largely smoothed out in any reasonable mixture of elements.

In discussing numerical results we have in mind as the most likely constitution of the material a predominance of elements in the neighbourhood of iron with some admixture of lighter non-metallic elements; we do not think it necessary to allow for more than ten per cent. of elements above $Z = 50$. Of course, we give some attention to the changes required if this assumed composition is considerably in error.

174. The fundamental formula for determining the degree of ionisation of an element at given temperature and density is (47·1). Since a large number of possible stages of ionisation and degrees of excitation may have to be considered simultaneously the application of the formula may become very complicated in practice. We give first a simplified discussion which may, or may not, be accurate enough for actual computation, but will in any case exhibit some of the more essential features of the problem.

The series of terms on the right-hand side of (47·1) corresponds to atoms with successive degrees of excitation. We shall here suppose that excitation is rare and that only the first term corresponding to unexcited atoms need be considered. Further, we drop the weight factors q. Consider the pth ionisation and let $\psi\,(= -\chi)$ be the energy required to remove the pth electron. Then the ratio of the number of atoms with $p - 1$ electrons missing to the number with p electrons missing is by (47·1)

$$\frac{1 - x}{x} = \sigma \left(\frac{h^2}{2\pi mRT}\right)^{\frac{3}{2}} e^{\psi/RT} \quad \ldots\ldots\ldots\ldots\ldots(174\cdot1),$$

where σ is the number of free electrons per unit volume, so that

$$\sigma = \frac{\rho}{\mu H\,(1 + f)}.$$

Neglecting as usual the small correction f, we have

$$\frac{1 - x}{x} = \frac{h^3}{(2\pi mR)^{\frac{3}{2}} H} \frac{\rho}{\mu T^{\frac{3}{2}}} e^{\psi/RT},$$

or

$$\log \frac{1 - x}{x} = \frac{0\cdot4343\psi}{RT} + \log \frac{\rho}{\mu T^{\frac{3}{2}}} + 8\cdot3925 \quad \ldots\ldots(174\cdot2),$$

the logarithms being to the base 10.

For example, if $T = 10^7$, $\rho = \cdot02$, $\mu = 2$,

conditions corresponding roughly to the centre of Capella, we have by (174·2)

$$x = 0\cdot1, \qquad\qquad 0\cdot5, \qquad\qquad 0\cdot9,$$

for

$$\psi = 11\cdot7RT, \qquad 9\cdot5RT, \qquad 7\cdot3RT,$$

and

$$\lambda = 1\cdot22\ \text{Å}, \qquad 1\cdot51\ \text{Å}, \qquad 1\cdot96\ \text{Å},$$

where the wave-length λ corresponds to the energy ψ according to the quantum relation

$$\psi = hc/\lambda \quad \ldots\ldots\ldots\ldots\ldots\ldots\ldots\ldots(174\cdot3).$$

For brevity we often speak of an energy λ, i.e. describe the quantity of energy by the wave-length of the radiation having a quantum of this amount.

This is an example of conditions giving a rather clean ionisation since the ionisations in progress are mostly confined to a narrow range of energy $\lambda = 1\cdot2$ to $1\cdot9$ Å. The removal of electrons from deeper energy levels has scarcely begun and removal from higher levels is nearly complete. Only those electrons, if any, at an energy level within these limits require detailed consideration. How this affects the atoms of different elements will be seen from Table 30. For titanium ($Z = 22$) the last K electron is detached at $\lambda = 1\cdot9$, so that for titanium and lighter elements the final ionisation is very far advanced and the ions are mostly bare nuclei. After titanium there will be a short sequence of elements in critical condition as regards K ionisation and retaining mostly 1 or 2 K electrons; the sequence ends at zinc ($Z = 30$) for which the first K ionisation requires $1\cdot3$ Å so that x is not much more than $\frac{1}{10}$. Then follows a much longer sequence $Z = 31$–45 for which the range $\lambda = 1\cdot2$–$1\cdot9$ falls in the gap between the K and L ionisations; these will be practically all helium-like ions retaining two K but no L electrons. For rhodium ($Z = 45$) the last L ionisation is $\frac{9}{10}$ complete. Elements from 45 to 73 are in various stages of L ionisation; for tantalum ($Z = 73$) the first L ionisation is only $\frac{1}{10}$ complete. Here we reach the gap between L and M ionisation and the ions are neon-like retaining 10 electrons. The heaviest elements may retain two or three M electrons*.

Table 30.
Energy Levels. Wave-lengths in Ångströms.

Z	Elem.	K	K′	L_1	L′	M_1	M′	N_1	Z + 1, 2, 3		
13	Al	7·95	5·39	175	30	—	—	—	Si	P	S
17	Cl	4·38	3·15	62·0	16·2	—	—	—	A	K	Ca
21	Sc	2·75	2·07	30·4	10·1	—	—	—	Ti	V	Cr
25	Mn	1·89	1·46	19·05	6·89	—	—	—	Fe	Co	Ni
29	Cu	1·38	1·08	13·05	5·00	—	—	—	Zn	Ga	Ge
33	As	1·04	·84	—	3·79	—	—	—	Se	Br	Kr
37	Rb	·814	·666	—	2·97	—	—	—	Sr	Y	Zr
41	Nb	·650	·542	5·22	2·40	61·1	8·5	—	Mo	—	Ru
45	Rh	·533	·450	4·13	1·97	41·0	—	—	Pd	Ag	Cd
49	In	·443	—	3·30	1·65	—	—	—	Sn	Sb	Te
53	I	·373	—	2·71	1·40	21·5	4·44	—	X	Cs	Ba
57	La	·319	—	2·25	1·20	14·8	3·71	—	Ce	Pr	Nd
61	—	·274	—	1·91	1·04	11·9	3·15	—	Sm	Eu	Gd
65	Tb	·238	—	1·64	·92	9·96	2·71	—	Ds	Ho	Er
69	Tm	·208	—	1·43	—	8·40	2·35	—	Yb	Lu	Hf
73	Ta	·184	—	1·25	—	7·14	2·07	415	W	—	Os
77	Ir	·163	—	1·10	—	6·08	1·83	—	Pt	Au	Hg
81	Tl	·143	—	·98	—	5·16	1·63	95	Pb	—	—
83	Bi	·136	—	·92	—	4·76	1·54	70·0	Po	—	Nt
92	U	·107	·107	·72	·45	3·49	1·22	33·0	—	—	—

* These conclusions being based on a first approximation are subject to revision.

Table 30 gives the energy levels, as far as possible, for every fourth element. The columns K, L_1, M_1, N_1* are observed values obtained either from measurements of the absorption edges or from the terms of the spectral series; in a few cases where the element itself has not been measured the value given is an interpolation between the elements next before and after. These values are considered to give the energy of removal of the *first* electron of the group, though there may be an appreciable difference between the energy of removal from a complete atom and from an ion with the outer groups missing. The columns K', L', M' are the theoretical energies of removal of the *last* electron of the group calculated from (42·62). For calculation of L' the two K electrons are considered to coincide with the nucleus; and for calculating M' the ten inner electrons are considered to coincide with the nucleus. For reference the intermediate elements are named in the last column; and values for them can readily be interpolated.

175. We denote the values of ψ and λ which correspond to $x = 0·5$ by ψ_1 and λ_1. When there is not too much overlapping of the different stages of ionisation we may take the atoms to be all ionised down to the energy level ψ_1. Even if there is overlapping this is generally the best average level to adopt. But it is quite possible for ψ_1 to be negative, that is to say, no ionisation is as much as half completed; nevertheless if T is large a great number of successive ionisations may be partially accomplished so that there is on the whole a fair amount of ionisation.

The cleanness of the ionisation depends on ψ_1/RT. If this is large a small percentage change of ψ will make a big change in x. It is when the conditions are such that ψ_1/RT is less than 2 or 3 that we may expect most trouble from overlapping. Moreover, when ψ_1/RT is large, excited atoms are rare and our neglect of them in this discussion is justifiable. To excite a K or L electron to a higher orbit more than half the energy of ionisation is required, so that by Boltzmann's Law the proportion of excited systems is of the order $e^{-\frac{1}{2}\psi/RT}$. If $\psi < \psi_1$ the excitation is forestalled by ionisation; and if $\psi > \psi_1$ the proportion of excited atoms is small provided that ψ_1/RT is large.

176. We now examine what value of the molecular weight corresponds to the ionisation found at the centre of Capella. Roughly, the elements up to $Z = 22$ retain no electrons, from 30–50 they retain 2 electrons and from 50–70 from 2 to 10 electrons. This gives the following results for typical elements—

Element	C	O	Al	Ti	Fe	As	Zr	Ag	Ba	Sm	Ta	Pb
Z	6	8	13	22	26	33	40	47	56	62	73	82
μ	1·7	1·8	1·9	2·1	2·2	2·3	2·3	2·3	2·6	2·7	2·9	2·9

* The suffix 1 indicates the uppermost level of a group—corresponding to greatest λ.

The adoption of a mean value must necessarily be a matter of judgment. Having regard to the rarity of the elements heavier than Ag and the cosmical abundance of Fe and some lighter elements we have adopted 2·1. We do not think this is likely to be in error by as much as 0·2.

177. We next seek to obtain an idea of the variation of ψ_1 in stars of different mass and spectral type. Since

$$\frac{\mu T^3}{\rho} = \frac{3\Re\,(1-\beta)}{a\beta},$$

we have from (174·2)

$$0\cdot4343\psi_1/RT = 14\cdot1182 - \log \beta/(1-\beta) - \tfrac{3}{2}\log T.$$

For stars of the main series the central temperature is approximately 40 million degrees. We shall calculate the ionisation conditions at a point where the temperature is 26 million degrees in accordance with § 94. Making use of Table 23 the results are—

Table 31 A.

Ionisation in Stars of the Main Series.

$1-\beta$	Mass	T_e	ψ_1/RT	λ_1	Examples
·002	·182	2600	0·69	8·0	Faintest red dwarfs
·004	·258	3200	1·40	3·9	Krueger 60
·015	·512	4600	2·72	2·0	
·05	1·00	6300	3·96	1·4	Sun
·10	1·58	8200	4·71	1·2	Procyon
·18	2·56	10500	5·40	1·0	Sirius
·30	4·53	13300	6·07	0·9	}
·50	11·46	17500	6·92	0·8	} Eclipsing variables
·80	90·6	26000	8·31	0·7	Plaskett's star

Table 31 B contains some examples of giant stars also calculated for a point where the temperature is $\tfrac{2}{3}$ of the central temperature.

Table 31 B.

Ionisation in Giant Stars.

$1-\beta$	Mass	T_e	$10^{-6}T$	ψ_1/RT	λ_1	Examples
·283	4·18	5200	6·06	8·17	2·9	Capella
·283	4·18	3000	2·51	9·49	6·0	
·50	11·46	5200	3·73	9·84	3·9	Cepheids
·50	11·46	3000	1·55	11·16	8·3	
·75	56·15	3000	0·92	13·03	11·9	Betelgeuse

The stars given under the heading "Examples" do not accurately correspond to the data of mass and T_e but will call to mind the kind of star to which the tabulated results relate.

178. With these results before us we can consider two questions which have been reserved from our earlier work for discussion here.

(1) How far are we justified in adopting a constant molecular weight for all stars?

(2) Is the opacity appreciably reduced by the "guillotine" (§ 160) so as to fall below that given by the approximate law $k \propto \rho/T^{\frac{7}{2}}$ used in our discussions?

The molecular weight depends on the degree of ionisation and therefore mainly on λ_1, although some attention should be paid to ψ_1/RT which determines the cleanness of the ionisation. We are chiefly interested in those stars for which a comparison of theory and observation has been made in Fig. 2, so that the more extreme values of λ_1 in Table 31 do not concern us. For all comparison stars λ_1 falls within the range 0·8–4·0 Å, whilst the most accurate comparisons are covered by the range 1–3 Å.

For elements of atomic number about 50–60 the L ionisation falls in this range and, for example, iodine ($Z = 53$, $A = 127$) might perhaps lose the eight L electrons in passing from Capella to Sirius, thereby reducing its molecular weight from 2·89 to 2·44. A long series of elements below 50 will be unaffected, and then we come to a few elements in the neighbourhood of titanium ($Z = 22$, $A = 48$) which lose their two K electrons; the molecular weight for titanium will change from 2·28 to 2·08 between Capella and Sirius. The lighter elements will be fully ionised in both stars. Since the change amounts to 0·2–0·4 for a few of the elements only, and is much smaller for the majority, it seems clear that the difference of molecular weight between the various stars used in our comparisons is unlikely to exceed 0·1.

The effect of a change $\Delta\mu$ in the adopted molecular weight on the predicted bolometric magnitude m of a star can be calculated from (84·4) and (99·2). We find

$$- \Delta m = \frac{9\beta + 8}{4 - 3\beta} \log_{10} e \, \frac{\Delta\mu}{\mu}.$$

Table 32 gives the increase of brightness ($- \Delta m$) for an increase of 0·1 in the molecular weight—

Table 32.

Effect of Increase of 0·1 in the Molecular Weight.

$1 - \beta$	Mass	$- \Delta m$	$1 - \beta$	Mass	$- \Delta m$
		m			m
0·0	0·0	0·35	0·3	4·5	0·16
0·05	1·0	0·30	0·4	7·1	0·13
0·1	1·6	0·25	0·6	19·6	0·09
0·2	2·8	0·20	0·8	90·6	0·06

We conclude that the effect on the brightness of the stars of the difference of molecular weight arising from differences of internal condition is inconsiderable, amounting at the outside to $\frac{1}{10}$ or $\frac{2}{10}$ of a magnitude*.

We can also find from Table 32 the effect of an error of 0·1 in the adopted average molecular weight for all stars. Since the comparisons are differential with respect to Capella we have in that case to subtract $0^m \cdot 16$ from the column $-\Delta m$.

179. The reduction of opacity caused by the "guillotine" (according to Kramers' theory) depends on ψ_1/RT; the corresponding reduction factors have been found in § 160. For Capella $\psi_1/RT = 8$ and there is no appreciable effect. But for the sun $\psi_1/RT = 4$ and the opacity is reduced in the ratio 4·5; this would make it $1^m \cdot 6$ brighter. The guillotine correction would accordingly upset the good accordance between theory and observation. For Krueger 60 the brightness would be increased by 4 or 5 magnitudes; it is true that this star is somewhat brighter than the original prediction, but this may be accounted for in another way and the guillotine correction is much too large.

If the guillotine correction had been applied in Fig. 2 the accordance of theory and observation would have been far from satisfactory.

The values of ψ_1/RT in Tables 31 A and 31 B have been calculated in a very provisional way and it may perhaps be suggested that more accurate computation would remove this difficulty. I do not think this is so; the more obvious corrections needed for a second approximation tend to reduce the values of ψ_1/RT.

This seems to affect very seriously the position of Kramers' theory of absorption as applied to the stars. An absorption law approximating to $\rho/T^{\frac{7}{2}}$ is suggested (as we have seen) by extremely general considerations, and the fact that the stars seem to obey it cannot be regarded as favouring Kramers' theory in particular. When we turn to the features more especially characteristic of his theory we meet with failure; the absolute constant in the formula is considerably too small, and the peculiar modification caused by the cutting off of high frequency radiation seems to be decisively contradicted.

180. The foregoing discussion aimed at a general survey of the problem without attempting high accuracy. It may be supplemented by the numerical results of Fowler and Guggenheim† who have made extensive calculations for typical stars and typical elements taking into account many refinements of the theory of ionisation.

---

* Some reservation should be made in the case of stars of mass less than half that of the sun owing to the low value of ψ_1/RT.

† *Monthly Notices*, **85**, p. 939 (1925).

The chief points in which they improve on our crude discussion are as follows—

(a) The weight factor q in the ionisation formula has been attended to; and the formulae have been adapted to treat symmetrical groups of electrons. The reason for the latter modification is that at the pth ionisation it is usually not one particular electron which is marked down as the next to be detached but one of a symmetrical group.

(b) A so-called "electrostatic correction" is introduced. In (174·1) ψ represents the energy required to detach the electron in the actual circumstances of the atom in the star. But we usually prefer to regard ψ as a constant of the atom determined by experiment and theory. In that case an electrostatic correction must be applied on account of the disturbance of the ion by the ions and electrons around it; the ion tends to surround itself with negative charge since it repels other positive charges from its vicinity. This shields the outer part of the field of the nucleus and therefore less work is done in removing a bound electron to infinity.

(c) Attention is paid to the careful calculation of successive ionisation potentials, following the method of D. R. Hartree. By X ray experiments we can only find the ionisation potentials for removing an electron from an orbit in a complete atom; this must be supplemented by theory to obtain the ionisation potential of an ion from which the outer electrons have already been removed. The following table for iron* giving the energy of removal of the pth electron in volts and in Ångströms will show the nature of the results—

Table 33.

Successive Ionisation Potentials for Iron.

p	Volts	λ	p	Volts	λ	p	Volts	λ
26	9150	1·35	19	1350	9·16	12	300	41·1
25	8650	1·43	18	1250	9·89	11	280	44·1
24	2010	6·15	17	1150	10·72	10	250	49·5
23	1880	6·57	16	480	25·8	9	220	56·1
22	1730	7·15	15	435	28·4	8	150	82
21	1590	7·77	14	390	31·7	7–2	(80)	(150)
20	1490	8·29	13	350	35·3	1	8·15	1520

(d) Due account is taken of overlapping of successive ionisations.

(e) The terms representing excited states of the atom are included†.

---

* Hartree, *Proc. Camb. Phil. Soc.* 22, p. 473 (1924). Similar tables for oxygen and silver are there given. Tables for zinc and bromine are given in Fowler and Guggenheim's paper.

† Mr Fowler informs me that the treatment of excitation is incomplete and he hopes to improve it. When account is taken of atoms with more than one excited electron the molecular weight in stars of small mass will probably be increased.

Table 34 contains Fowler and Guggenheim's results for a typical star at various distances from the centre. The star chosen is of mass 2·13 and mean density ·002, that is to say, a rather faint giant star of about type G. The first column gives the distance from the centre in terms of Emden's unit $R/6\cdot9$.

Table 34.

Variation of Molecular Weight in a Star.

z	$T \times 10^{-6}$	ρ	Molecular weight for		
			Oxygen	Iron	Silver
0	6·59	·1085	1·95	2·33	2·87
1	5·64	·0678	—	2·33	—
2	3·84	·0215	1·93	2·34	2·94
3	2·37	·0050	1·92	2·53	3·37
4	1·38	·0010	1·95	3·16	4·0
Main series	26·4	6·95	1·97	2·18	2·40

It will be noticed that μ is rather higher than appeared from the crude calculation. Iron even at the centre of the star retains 3 electrons, whereas we have previously allowed it $1\frac{1}{2}$ electrons; this is a rather large difference since there is a big gap in ionisation potential between the second and third electrons. Oxygen retains $\frac{3}{4}$ of an electron against nil on the crude theory. These changes are mainly due to the corrections (*a*) to (*e*) and not to the difference in the temperature and density.

Judging from these figures the formula $\mu \propto T^{-\frac{1}{2}}$ used in § 13 (see also § 94) will, if anything, overcorrect the variation of molecular weight within a star.

In the last line of the table we give the mean molecular weight (i.e. at a place where T is $\frac{2}{3}$ the central temperature) for a star of the same mass which has reached the main series. It happens that both Ag and Fe are critical elements for this change, and most elements would have shown a much smaller difference. There appears to be no reason to amend our former conclusion that the range of mean molecular weight between Capella and Sirius-Sun conditions is not likely to exceed 0·1.

Table 35 extends the comparison to stars of different mass on the main series. Of particular interest are the results for stars of small mass. We felt some hesitation in applying the crude theory to these owing to the lack of cleanness in the ionisation.

The increasing overlapping of the ionisation is exhibited in the last columns of the table, which shows the percentages of iron atoms retaining respectively 1, 2, 3, 4 electrons. The change of μ is remarkably small; but that is partly because the elements chosen are not in a critical state in this range. (They had just completed their critical range in passing from Capella to the first star of the Table.)

Fowler and Guggenheim comment on the very small effect of change of density on the ionisation, and give other examples of this. For Fe at $5\cdot6\,.\,10^6$ degrees a change of density from $0\cdot5$ to $0\cdot0004$ alters μ only 2 per cent. This is an extreme case. The other extreme is represented by Br which undergoes L ionisation in this range, and μ increases 25 per cent. The slightness of dependence on density (i.e. electron density) justifies us in calculating the molecular weight for any element independently of other elements which may be present; for the degree of ionisation of the other elements affects the electron density by a factor which is evidently unimportant.

Table 35.

Average molecular weight in stars of the Main Series
$$T = 26\cdot36\,.\,10^6$$

M	ρ	Molecular weight for			Electrons retained by Iron (percentages)			
		Oxygen	Iron	Silver	1	2	3	4
2·13	6·95	1·97	2·18	2·40	57	37	—	—
1·27	15·2	1·98	2·21	2·40	40	48	10	—
0·75	38·4	2·00	2·24	2·40	23	53	22	—
0·54	71·6	—	2·25	2·40	15	50	31	—
0·36	156	2·06	2·26	2·40	10	44	38	6
0·22	392	2·14	2·28	2·40	9	41	41	7·5

181. Before leaving the subject of molecular weight reference should be made to "the correction for excluded volumes." This is treated by Fowler and Guggenheim as a deviation from the laws of a perfect gas and discussed in that connection in their paper; but it is convenient here to amalgamate it with the molecular weight. Whilst the electrons and unexcited ions can be treated as of infinitesimal volume in all stars except white dwarfs, the volume of the excited ions should be taken into account. Finite size of the atoms has the effect of increasing P for given ρ and T (in accordance with Van der Waals' equation); this is equivalent to a decrease of the molecular weight or to an addition to the number of independent molecules. It is found that the volumes of the excited atoms have an effect on the pressure equivalent to the addition of phantom molecules in the proportion of $\frac{2}{3}$ of a molecule per atom (or according to another, perhaps better, theory $\frac{1}{2}$ a molecule per atom). This constant limit is practically reached in all stars. Since it does not vary from star to star it can conveniently be taken account of in the molecular weight.

This treatment is specially appropriate in the present discussion because Fowler and Guggenheim have slightly increased the molecular weights found in our crude theory, and we can now reduce them again. Under sufficiently similar conditions they make the oxygen atom retain $\frac{3}{4}$ of an electron against 0 according to us. We lose $\frac{3}{4}$ of a free electron but gain $\frac{2}{3}$ of a phantom molecule; so there is not much change. Iron retains 3 electrons against $1\frac{1}{2}$; the loss of $1\frac{1}{2}$ free electrons is partly balanced by the $\frac{2}{3}$ of a molecule gained.

We have thus the satisfaction of taking account of this subtle correction, whilst altering our original estimate of molecular weight less than at first seemed necessary.

This correction for "excluded volume" has a theoretical interest, because it amends our first judgment that the volumes of stellar atoms are roughly one millionth of those of terrestrial atoms. This is true of the normal atoms; but a considerable proportion contain excited electrons and the total volume of these brings up the average, although not to an extent sufficient to affect stellar problems appreciably. But since the excitation is highly variable with temperature and density, this temporary volume does not behave like the constant b in Van der Waals' equation. It is always on the verge of importance but eludes any attempt to enhance its importance by itself diminishing. It varies in such a way that the perfect gas law $p \propto \rho T$ is obeyed.

Deviations from a Perfect Gas.

182. Before investigating deviations from the gas laws in stellar material we shall review the theory of these deviations in terrestrial gases.

If X, Y, Z are the components of force acting on a molecule of mass m the equations of motion are

$$m \frac{d^2x}{dt^2} = X, \text{ etc.}$$

Hence

$$m \left(\frac{dx}{dt} \right)^2 = \frac{1}{2} m \frac{d^2}{dt^2} x^2 - mx \frac{d^2x}{dt^2}$$

$$= \frac{1}{2} m \frac{d^2}{dt^2} x^2 - xX,$$

so that

$$\tfrac{1}{2} m V^2 = \tfrac{1}{4} m \frac{d^2}{dt^2} (x^2 + y^2 + z^2) - \tfrac{1}{2} (xX + yY + zZ).$$

Summing over all the molecules in unit volume

$$\Sigma \tfrac{1}{2} m V^2 = \frac{1}{4} \frac{d^2 I}{dt^2} - \tfrac{1}{2} \Sigma (xX + yY + zZ) \quad \ldots\ldots\ldots(182 \cdot 1),$$

where I is the moment of inertia of the molecules about the origin, and $-\tfrac{1}{2} \Sigma (xX + yY + zZ)$ is called the *virial*.

If the volume is enclosed by actual walls I remains constant on the average, so that
$$\Sigma \tfrac{1}{2} m V^2 = - \tfrac{1}{2} \Sigma \, (xX + yY + zZ) \quad \ldots\ldots\ldots\ldots(182\cdot2),$$
but we must include in (X, Y, Z) the forces on the molecules when they are reflected from the walls, viz. the external pressure. If the walls are fictitious, we replace each escaping molecule by a molecule entering at the same spot so that I is kept constant; the transfer of momentum involved in these replacements is still represented by the pressure at the boundary.

The pressures on the 6 faces of a centimetre cube give a contribution $- 3p$ to $\Sigma \, (xX + yY + zZ)$. The remaining part of the expression is easily shown to amount to $\Sigma\Sigma r R_1$, where R_1* is the force (positive if repulsive) between two molecules at a distance r and the summation extends over each pair of molecules (counted once). Hence (182·2) becomes
$$p = \tfrac{2}{3} \Sigma \tfrac{1}{2} m V^2 + \tfrac{1}{3} \Sigma\Sigma r R_1 \quad \ldots\ldots\ldots\ldots\ldots(182\cdot3).$$

Consider molecules which repel one another, and let ϕ be the potential of the field of force so that $m\phi$ is the potential energy of a molecule. If σ_0 is the number of molecules per cu. cm. in regions where ϕ is zero, the number at any other point is (46·1)
$$\sigma = \int_0^\infty \left(\frac{m}{2\pi R T} \right)^{\frac{3}{2}} \sigma_0 e^{-(\frac{1}{2} m V^2 + m\phi)/RT} \, 4\pi V^2 dV \quad \ldots\ldots(182\cdot41)$$
$$= \sigma_0 e^{-m\phi/RT} \quad \ldots\ldots\ldots\ldots\ldots\ldots\ldots\ldots\ldots\ldots\ldots\ldots\ldots\ldots\ldots\ldots\ldots(182\cdot42).$$
From (182·41) we also see that the mean value of $\tfrac{1}{2} m V^2$ is independent of ϕ and equal to $\tfrac{3}{2} R T$. Hence by (182·3)
$$p = \sigma' R T + \tfrac{1}{3} \Sigma\Sigma r R_1 \quad \ldots\ldots\ldots\ldots\ldots(182\cdot43),$$
where σ' is the actual number of molecules per cu. cm.

Suppose that the molecules are rigid and of diameter d so that the centres of two molecules cannot approach within distance d. We may regard them as kept apart by a repulsive force of enormous intensity at distance d, with ϕ increasing from 0 to ∞ in an infinitesimal range at the value $r = d$.

Let us calculate the contribution of one rigid molecule to the virial. The average number of other molecules within a distance r to $r + dr$ is $\sigma . 4\pi r^2 dr$; and for these $R_1 r = (- m \, d\phi/dr) \, r$. Hence, using (182·42), the contribution to $\Sigma\Sigma R_1 r$ is
$$- 4\pi r^2 dr \, \sigma_0 e^{-m\phi/RT} \, mr \, \frac{d\phi}{dr} \quad \ldots\ldots\ldots\ldots(182\cdot44),$$
so that the first summation of $R_1 r$ gives
$$- 4\pi\sigma_0 m \int_0^\infty r^3 e^{-m\phi/RT} \, d\phi$$
$$= 4\pi\sigma_0 d^3 R T,$$
since $d\phi$ only differs from zero at $r = d$.

* The suffix is used to distinguish it from Boltzmann's constant.

Multiplying by the whole number of molecules σ' and dividing by 2, since each pair of molecules has then been counted twice over, we have

$$\Sigma\Sigma r R_1 = 2\pi\sigma'\sigma_0 d^3 RT,$$

and by (182·43) $\qquad p = \sigma' RT\,(1 + \tfrac{2}{3}\pi d^3\sigma_0)$ ....(182·45).

Now $\tfrac{2}{3}\pi d^3\sigma'$ is the constant b of Van der Waals' equation and is equal to $\tfrac{1}{2}$ the volume effectively occupied by the molecules, i.e. such that the centre of no other molecule can lie within it.

Since ϕ is infinite in a volume $2b$ and zero elsewhere, $\sigma = 0$ in a volume $2b$ and $\sigma = \sigma_0$ elsewhere by (182·42); hence it would appear that

$$\sigma' = \sigma_0\,(1 - 2b).$$

But this is not a fair way of using the equation. The formula (182·42) rejects every molecule which would come within distance d of another molecule, and since every molecule is tested in this way in turn *both* the interfering molecules are rejected instead of only one. The correct result is thus
$$\sigma' = \sigma_0\,(1 - b).$$
Hence (182·45) becomes

$$p = \sigma' RT\,(1 + b\sigma_0/\sigma') = \sigma' RT\,(1 + b/(1 - b)),$$

or $\qquad\qquad\qquad p\,(1 - b) = \sigma' RT$ ....(182·5),

which is the usual formula for excluded volume. It breaks down when the square of b is not negligible, so that interferences of more than 2 molecules have to be considered.

For extended fields of repulsive force we have to return to equation (182·44). A repulsion always increases the pressure for given temperature and density just as the finite volume of the molecules does; and this deviation is the ordinary characteristic of an imperfect gas.

183. We might hastily suppose that the foregoing treatment would also apply to molecules attracting instead of repelling one another, the necessary changes of sign being made. But attractive forces introduce a new consideration. We have to replace (182·41) by

$$\sigma = \int_{V_0}^{\infty}\left(\frac{m}{2\pi RT}\right)^{\frac{3}{2}}\sigma_0 e^{-(\frac{1}{2}mV^2+m\phi)/RT}\,4\pi V^2 dV$$ ....(183·1),

where V_0 is given by $\qquad \tfrac{1}{2}mV_0^2 = -\,m\phi,$

ϕ now being negative*. The reason for the lower limit is that when $V < V_0$ the total energy of the molecule is negative; it is bound to other molecules and the combined system has to be regarded as a single molecule according to the theory of gases.

---

* The convention as to the sign of the potential here followed is that the sign is positive for a field of repulsive force—as in electrostatics. It will be remembered that gravitation potential follows the opposite convention.

Owing to the limit of the integral it is no longer true that

$$\sigma = \sigma_0 e^{-m\phi/RT}.$$

This amendment is especially important when we consider free electrons under attractive forces due to an ion. If ψ is the electric potential the potential energy $- e\psi$ replaces $m\phi$ in (183·1). Writing

$$x^2 = e\psi/RT \qquad \dots\dots\dots\dots\dots\dots(183\cdot2),$$
$$t^2 = \tfrac{1}{2}mV^2/RT,$$

(183·1) reduces to
$$\sigma = \frac{4}{\sqrt{\pi}}\,\sigma_0 e^{x^2}\int_x^\infty e^{-t^2} t^2 dt$$
$$= \frac{2}{\sqrt{\pi}}\,\sigma_0\left(x + e^{x^2}\int_x^\infty e^{-t^2}dt\right) \quad\dots\dots\dots(183\cdot3).$$

Table 36 shows the course of σ/σ_0 according to this formula compared with the uncorrected Boltzmann formula $\sigma/\sigma_0 = e^{e\psi/RT}$.

Table 36.

Distribution Density of Free Electrons.

$e\psi/RT$	σ/σ_0	$e^{e\psi/RT}$
0	1·00	1·00
$\tfrac{1}{2}$	1·32	1·65
1	1·56	2·72
2	1·93	7·39
3	2·24	20·09
4	2·51	54·60

For large values of x (183·3) approximates to $\sigma/\sigma_0 = 2x/\sqrt{\pi}$, so that near a nucleus σ becomes infinite like $\psi^{\frac{1}{2}}$ or $r^{-\frac{1}{2}}$; but the number of electrons near the nucleus will be finite. The concentration of free electrons round a nucleus is remarkably small compared with expectations based on Boltzmann's formula.

By continuing the integral below its lower limit V_0 we should obtain the captured electrons according to the classical theory; and it might be suggested that Boltzmann's formula will give the density of free and captured electrons together. Up to a certain point this is true (by the Correspondence Principle); but the quantum theory and classical theory afterwards part company, and the enormous concentration at the nucleus given by Boltzmann's formula is wholly fictitious.

184. We turn now to the ionised gas in a star. Here the forces between the molecules are the electrostatic attractions and repulsions of their charges. These are inverse-square forces, and for them $\Sigma\Sigma r R_1$ is equal to the potential energy. Hence by (182·43)

$$p = NRT + \tfrac{1}{3}U \quad\dots\dots\dots\dots(184\cdot1)$$

where N is the number of ions and free electrons per cu. cm. and U is the electrostatic energy per cu. cm.

The problem of determining U when it is sufficiently small compared with p has been treated by S. Rosseland[*] following the theory developed by Debye and Hückel[†] for ionised solutions. Consider material consisting of positive ions of charge Ze with the requisite number of free electrons to make it neutral. Let s_0 be the number of ions and σ_0 the number of electrons per cu. cm. at regions where the potential is zero; then at a place where the potential is ψ Boltzmann's formula gives the respective densities

$$s_0 e^{-Ze\psi/RT}, \qquad \sigma_0 e^{e\psi/RT}.$$

If ψ is positive the first expression is correct, but the second needs amendment as explained in § 183. However, for the present we leave it uncorrected. The average charge density is accordingly

$$\rho = Ze\, s_0 e^{-Ze\psi/RT} - e\, \sigma_0 e^{e\psi/RT} \quad \ldots\ldots\ldots\ldots(184\cdot21).$$

We set $\sigma_0 = Zs_0$; the correct equation for neutrality of the material is $\sigma' = Zs'$, but the two equations are the same to a fairly high approximation. Expanding the exponentials in (184·21) and neglecting the square of $Ze\psi/RT$, we have

$$\rho = Zes_0 (1 - Ze\psi/RT) - Zes_0 (1 + e\psi/RT) \quad \ldots(184\cdot22)$$
$$= - Z (Z + 1)\, e^2 s_0 \psi/RT \quad \ldots\ldots\ldots\ldots\ldots\ldots(184\cdot23).$$

Hence by Poisson's equation

$$\nabla^2 \psi = \frac{4\pi Z (Z + 1)\, e^2 s_0}{RT}\, \psi \quad \ldots\ldots\ldots\ldots(184\cdot3).$$

It is to be remarked that (184·3) is only true of a time average since the Boltzmann formula refers to probabilities or time averages. Further, it is obtained from two relations between ρ and ψ, one of which is exponential and the other linear, so that an averaging factor will be introduced. The effect of the fluctuations requires fuller investigation but it seems probable that the averaging factor is not important.

Let us apply (184·3) to the time average of the field around a particular ion. The average field will be symmetrical about the ion, so we must take the well-known symmetrical solution of (184·3)

$$\psi = \frac{Ce^{-yr}}{r} \quad \ldots\ldots\ldots\ldots\ldots\ldots\ldots\ldots(184\cdot41),$$

where

$$y^2 = \frac{4\pi e^2 Z (Z + 1)\, s_0}{RT} \quad \ldots\ldots\ldots\ldots\ldots(184\cdot42).$$

The charge within a sphere of radius r is then

$$e' = - r^2 \frac{d\psi}{dr} = C (1 + yr)\, e^{-yr} \ldots\ldots\ldots\ldots(184\cdot43).$$

[*] *Monthly Notices*, **84**, p. 720.   [†] *Phys. Zeits.* **24**, p. 1 (1923).

This is itself responsible for a potential at r

$$\psi' = \frac{C(1 + yr)e^{-yr}}{r} \quad \text{......................(184·44)}.$$

Hence the material outside r produces a potential

$$\psi - \psi' = -Cye^{-yr} \quad \text{......................(184·45)},$$

at r, and therefore at all points within r. By (184·43)

$$\psi - \psi' = -e'y/(1 + yr) \quad \text{..................(184·46)},$$

and the mutual potential energy of the charges inside and outside r is accordingly

$$-e'^2y/(1 + yr) \quad \text{........................(184·47)}.$$

185. If we take r very small e' becomes the charge Ze of the positive ion. Then by (184·47) the potential energy of the ion due to the matter around it becomes in the limit

$$-Z^2e^2y \quad \text{..............................(185·1)}.$$

Similarly the energy of an electron in the field around it is

$$-e^2y.$$

Hence (neglecting the difference between s_0 and s')

$$2U = s_0(-Z^2e^2y) + \sigma_0(-e^2y)$$
$$= -s_0Z(Z+1)e^2y \quad \text{........................(185·2)},$$

the factor 2 being required because the mutual energy of two charges is ascribed to both charges in turn. Inserting the value of y

$$U = -\left(\frac{\pi Z^3(Z+1)^3 e^6 s_0^3}{RT}\right)^{\frac{1}{2}} \quad \text{...............(185·3)}.$$

We shall presently criticise the inconsistency of taking r very small although a previous approximation (neglecting the square of $Ze\psi/RT$) required that r should be moderately large. Meanwhile we can consider the results of using this value of U in (184·1).

Since $\qquad\qquad\qquad s_0 \propto \rho,$

$$U \propto \rho^{\frac{3}{2}}/T^{\frac{1}{2}} \propto \rho T(\rho/T^3)^{\frac{1}{2}}.$$

Since $\frac{1}{3}U$ is the increment of pressure Δp due to electrostatic forces, we have

$$\frac{\Delta p}{p_G} \propto \left(\frac{\rho}{T^3}\right)^{\frac{1}{2}} \quad \text{............................(185·4)},$$

and therefore depends on the mass of the star only and not on the density; moreover, it is constant throughout the star. This property of the electrostatic forces was noted in § 115.

This change of p_G in a constant ratio is equivalent to multiplying the molecular weight by a factor constant in any one star and for all stars of the same mass. We adopt a fictitious molecular weight μ' such that

$$p_G + \Delta p = \frac{\Re}{\mu'}\,\rho T,$$

so that
$$\frac{\mu'}{\mu} = \frac{p_G}{p_G + \Delta p} \quad\dots\dots\dots\dots\dots(185\cdot5).$$

We can then perform all astronomical calculations according to the usual theory using this fictitious value of the molecular weight*.

186. Table 37 contains numerical results calculated by Fowler and Guggenheim on the basis of equation (185·3). The results, although calculated primarily for stars of the main series (chosen as in Table 35), are applicable to all stars of the same mass, and to all parts of the interior of these stars. For reasons which we shall presently develop we do not accept Table 37 as definitive.

Table 37.

Electrostatic Correction to the Pressure (first theory).

Mass	Percentage decrease of p_G			Iron		Silver	
	O	Fe	Ag	$M + \Delta M$	$- \Delta m$	$M + \Delta M$	$- \Delta m$
					m		m
2·13	0·8	5·0	11·4	1·99	0·20	—	—
1·27	1·3	7·2	17·4	1·143	0·36	0·974	0·93
0·75	1·9	11·2	27·4	0·627	0·72	—	—
0·54	—	14·9	34·4	0·421	0·95	0·288	2·52
0·36	3·5	21·9	55·0	0·248	1·51	—	—
0·22	5·2	34·4	87·5	0·120	2·61	—	—

The last four columns are obtained from Fowler and Guggenheim's figures as follows. In conjunction with (185·5) the last line shows that for a certain value of T^3/ρ (corresponding to a perfect gas of mass 0·22 and given explicitly in Table 35) the molecular weight in an Fe star is effectively increased from 2·11 to $2\cdot11/0\cdot656 = 3\cdot22$. With the new value of μ we find $1 - \beta$ by (87·1) and a corrected mass $M + \Delta M$ by (84·6). The value of $1 - \beta$ corresponding to $M + \Delta M$ and to $\mu = 2\cdot11$ is also found by (84·6). The increase of brightness $- \Delta m$ of a star of mass $M + \Delta M$ due to change from the perfect gas ($\mu = 2\cdot11$) to the actual state ($\mu = 3\cdot22$) is then found, since $L \propto (1 - \beta)^{\frac{3}{2}}\,\mu^{\frac{4}{5}}$ by (99·2). The correction indicated in the footnote changes this to $L \propto (1 - \beta)^{\frac{3}{2}}\,\mu^{-\frac{1}{5}}$.

* An exception should be made for the absorption coefficient, the true value of μ still occurring in the law $k \propto \rho/\mu T^{\frac{7}{2}}$. This could be set right by multiplying the final luminosities by μ/μ'. I have attended to this correction in Tables 37 and 38.

Note that there is an *increase* of brightness, the material being a super-perfect gas.

187. In (184·22) the density of the ions has been set equal to

$$s_0 (1 - Ze\psi/RT),$$

which becomes negative for large values of ψ. When we come to examine the figures we find that this nonsensical minus quantity of ions is responsible for a great part of the electrostatic energy calculated in (185·3). Clearly it will be a better approximation (though still imperfect) if we sweep away this absurd negative density and adopt zero density when

$$Ze\psi/RT > 1.$$

Let r_0 be the value of r for which the potential ψ_0 is given by

$$Ze\psi_0/RT = 1 \quad \ldots\ldots\ldots\ldots\ldots\ldots(187\cdot1).$$

Outside r_0 we leave the previous approximation undisturbed. Inside r_0 we set the density of the ions zero—as an improvement on the previous approximation which makes it negative. We further suppose the negative electrons to have uniform density $\sigma_0 = Zs_0$. The justification for neglecting the concentration of the negative electrons about the ions is that in the previous approximation when the concentration $1 + e\psi/RT$ was adopted, this merely changed Z to $Z + 1$ in (184·23) so that the contribution to U was quite unimportant. Reference to Table 36 shows that the actual concentration of the electrons is less than $1 + e\psi/RT$, and the contribution to U is even smaller.

Accordingly the charge within r_0 is

$$Ze - \tfrac{4}{3}\pi r_0^3 s_0 Ze = e_0'$$
$$= C (1 + yr_0) e^{-yr_0} \text{ by } (184\cdot43)$$
$$= \psi_0 r_0 (1 + yr_0) \text{ by } (184\cdot41)$$
$$= \frac{RTr_0}{Ze} (1 + yr_0) \text{ by } (187\cdot1).$$

We use the results of the previous discussion which are valid for $r \geq r_0$. Let

$$z = yr_0, \qquad a = Z^2 e^2 y/RT, \qquad b = y^3/\tfrac{4}{3}\pi s_0 \quad \ldots\ldots(187\cdot2).$$

Then we have the following cubic for z

$$\frac{z^3}{b} + \frac{z^2 + z}{a} = 1 \quad \ldots\ldots\ldots\ldots\ldots\ldots(187\cdot3).$$

After solving for z, we find the charge of the negative electrons inside r_0

$$- \tfrac{4}{3}\pi r^3 s_0 Ze = - Zez^3/b \quad \ldots\ldots\ldots\ldots(187\cdot4).$$

These form a uniform spherical distribution and the potential at their centre is

$$- \tfrac{3}{2} Zez^3/br_0 = - \tfrac{3}{2} Zez^2 y/b \quad \ldots\ldots\ldots\ldots(187\cdot5).$$

To this must be added the potential within r_0 due to charges outside r_0 which by (184·46) is

$$- e_0'y/(1 + yr_0) = - RTz/Ze = - Zeyz/a \quad \text{......}(187·6).$$

Hence the potential energy of the ion is

$$- Z^2e^2y \left(\frac{3}{2} \frac{z^2}{b} + \frac{z}{a} \right) \text{.........................}(187·7),$$

instead of the value $- Z^2e^2y$ in the previous approximation (185·1).

188. For an example, take the star in the fifth line of Table 37 which corresponds to the values (Table 35)

$$\rho = 156, \qquad T = 26·36.10^6.$$

We have for iron $\qquad s_0 = \rho/AH = 1·68.10^{24}.$

For $Z = 24$ (iron retaining its two K electrons) we find from (184·42)

$$y = 8·93.10^8,$$

and by (187·2) $\qquad a = 32·4, \qquad b = 101·3.$

The solution of $\qquad \dfrac{z^3}{101·3} + \dfrac{z^2 + z}{32·4} = 1$

is $z = 3·65$. By (187·4) the charge of the negative electrons inside r_0 is

$$- 0·480Ze.$$

The number of electrons inside r_0 is $11\frac{1}{2}$. The potential at the centre is then found from (187·5) and (187·6) to be

$$- 0·198Zey \text{ from the electrons inside } r_0$$

$$- 0·112Zey \text{ from the matter outside } r_0.$$

The total $- 0·31Zey$ gives a potential energy of the ion

$$- 0·31Z^2e^2y,$$

or less than one-third of the result of the previous approximation. Accordingly the 21·9 per cent. reduction of pressure given in Fowler and Guggenheim's table now becomes 6·8 per cent.; and we must proceed to calculate the new values of $M + \Delta M$ and the luminosity of the star with this value.

We notice that $\qquad r_0 = z/y = 4·1.10^{-9}$ cm.

This is about 20 times the radius of the Fe ion with two electrons, so that the finite size of the ion is not a complicating consideration.

In Table 38 we give the results for this and three other masses.

Improvement of the approximation may still further reduce these corrections, because the formulae still exaggerate the power of the ion to keep away other ions from its neighbourhood; but we think that the most glaring faults have been removed. The corrections are already reduced to the verge of observability. If the corrections in Table 38 are applied to the mass-luminosity curve they improve the accordance of theory and observation for the faint stars to an appreciable extent; but the main conclusion is that deviations from the laws of a perfect gas are not sufficient even in the smallest stars to affect the luminosity by more than about half a magnitude.

Table 38.

Electrostatic Correction to the Pressure (improved theory).
(Iron stars.)

$M + \Delta M$	$-\Delta m$	$-\Delta p_G$ (per cent.)
	m	
1·04	0·17	3·3
0·70	0·24	4·3
0·32	0·42	6·8
0·205	0·58	8·9

Energy of Ionisation.

189. From a table of ionisation potentials such as that given for iron in Table 33 we can obtain the energy of ionisation of an atom stripped to a given level. Summing over the atoms in different stages of ionisation the total ionisation energy I per cu. cm. at given T and ρ can be calculated.

Knowledge of I is chiefly important in connection with the theory of the pulsations of Cepheid variables. Fortunately in these stars the ionisation is very clean, ψ_1/RT being about 10 (Table 31 B). There will generally be not more than one degree of ionisation in progress and excitation will be rare, so that the calculation is simplified. Energy of excitation if appreciable should be estimated and added to I which is intended to denote the whole internal energy of the matter. As the Cepheids are very massive stars the electrostatic energy (considered in §§ 184–188) is insignificant.

The total energy per unit volume is

$$E = \frac{3}{2}\frac{\Re}{\mu}\rho T + aT^4 + I \quad\dots\dots\dots\dots\dots(189\cdot11),$$

and the total pressure $P = \frac{\Re}{\mu}\rho T + \tfrac{1}{3}aT^4 \quad\dots\dots\dots\dots\dots(189\cdot12).$

Hence when we have sufficiently tabulated I and μ as functions of ρ and T we can find dE and dP in the forms

$$dE = c_1 dT + c_2 d\rho, \qquad dP = c_\circ dT + c_4 d\rho\dots\dots\dots(189\cdot2).$$

It was pointed out by Fowler that we must take account of the variation of μ as well as of I, because the change of I is due almost entirely to liberation of additional free electrons and these take up kinetic energy of amount comparable to their energy of ionisation besides exercising additional pressure.

The adiabatic condition is

$$d\,(EV) + P\,dV = 0,$$

or

$$d\,(E/\rho) + Pd\,(1/\rho) = 0 \quad \ldots\ldots\ldots\ldots\ldots(189\cdot3).$$

By eliminating dE and dT between (189·2) and (189·3) we find dP in terms of $d\rho$ and hence determine the coefficient γ in the equation

$$\frac{dP}{P} = \gamma\,\frac{d\rho}{\rho} \quad \ldots\ldots\ldots\ldots\ldots\ldots\ldots(189\cdot4).$$

The calculation is numerical and the resulting value of γ applies only to small variations from the particular values of ρ and T under discussion.

A valuable series of calculations of γ has been made by Fowler and Guggenheim. We give a selection from their results; but for convenience of comparison with the theory of Cepheids in Chapter VIII we have converted their γ into corresponding values of Γ by (129·6). A star composed of ideal undissociating material with a ratio of specific heats Γ (together with the necessary radiant energy) would pulsate in the same way as the actual star.

Table 39.

Values of Γ.

Star		$10^{-6}T$	ρ	O (8)	Fe (26)	Zn (30)	Br (35)	Ag (47)
Y Oph.	Centre	4·24	·0029	1·75	1·61	—	—	1·51
,,	Mean	2·82	·0009	1·69	1·61	1·30	1·28	1·49
η Aqu.	Centre	6·00	·015	1·75	1·68	—	—	1·405
,,	Mean	4·00	·0047	1·83	1·68	1·62	1·255	1·57
RT Aur.	Centre	8·76	·0657	1·71	1·475	—	—	1·335
,,	Mean	5·85	·0208	1·71	1·66	—	—	1·41
RR Lyr.	Centre	18·3	1·18	1·72	1·55	—	—	1·65
,,	Mean	12·2	·372	1·70	1·50	—	—	1·58
Giant	Centre	6·59	·1085	1·70	1·68	1·64	1·57	1·50
,,	$z = 1$	5·64	·0678	—	1·65	—	—	—
,,	$z = 2$	3·84	·0215	1·68	1·49	1·38	1·33	1·54
,,	$z = 3$	2·37	·0050	1·70	1·31	1·35	1·50	1·39
,,	$z = 4$	1·38	·0010	1·66	1·295	1·50	—	< 1·33

190. It will be seen that some values of Γ, particularly those for oxygen, are slightly above $\tfrac{5}{3}$. This has no physical significance. It arises because Fowler and Guggenheim's results were calculated for a star composed wholly of oxygen and therefore with molecular weight rather below 2, which we have replaced by undissociating material of standard molecular weight 2·11*.

It will be remembered that it is the excess of Γ above $\frac{4}{3}$ that is of chief significance. At first sight the results appear entirely irregular. Under ordinary circumstances Γ is not much different from $\frac{5}{3}$; but for any element the value drops when T and ρ are such that the atoms are in the midst of their L ionisation and it may even fall below $\frac{4}{3}$. Another dip occurs at the K ionisation but it is not so deep. The low value for silver in the last example corresponds to the M ionisation.

If either of the first two stars in the table were composed wholly of bromine they would probably be unstable, since $\Gamma < \frac{4}{3}$ in a mean region at least. Ordinarily, if a star is suddenly compressed its temperature and pressure rise so much as to provide a restoring force; but in the bromine star the rise of temperature is insufficient because most of the energy of contraction is used in tearing the L electrons from the atom and there is not much energy left over. The bromine star would collapse still further until the L electrons were finally got rid of; after that it would become stable at a much higher density.

The first example shows that zinc and bromine can be in this critical state simultaneously. Fowler and Guggenheim estimate that not more than 8 consecutive elements can be in the critical condition of L ionisation simultaneously; further, the critical condition will not extend throughout the whole star.

Naturally the examples in the table have to some extent been selected to show the more peculiar features, so that a simple mean of all the values of Γ there given would not necessarily be a suitable estimate of the likely average value. So far as we can judge, a reasonable mixture of elements would, in general, give a value well over 1·5. It is conceivable, however, that a range of eight consecutive elements might include the greater part of the mass of stellar material; in that case we might obtain low resultant values of Γ in stars of appropriate temperature and density.

The stars for which we particularly wish to know Γ—the Cepheids—are not necessarily unselected average stars. The theory of the maintenance of pulsations has rather suggested that the Cepheid phenomenon may be a symptom of unusually low Γ. But if so, we ought to obtain the series of Cepheids by keeping one preponderant element or group of elements in a critical stage of ionisation. Table 39 is scarcely extensive enough to test this; but it gives no sign of persistence of low values of Γ for any element in all four Cepheids. The question can be settled by reference to the general ionisation formulae. The middle of the L ionisation of an element will occur at a temperature which is nearly constant but increases a little

---

* This was done because our primary purpose is to obtain the most likely value of Γ for use in investigations in which $\mu = 2\cdot11$ has already been adopted.

with increasing density; the actual change of temperature shown in Table 25 is much too rapid.

If it is considered that this sufficiently disproves the association of exceptional values of Γ with the Cepheids we may presumably adopt for them a value about $1\cdot55$. This brings the Cepheids as nearly as possible on to the theoretical mass-luminosity curve (p. 153). We do not, however, attach importance to the lucky agreement.

Electric Charge in the Interior.

191. In a gas maintained at uniform temperature in a gravitational field the molecules sort themselves out to some extent, the lighter molecules preponderating at the top and the heavier at the bottom. This is an immediate consequence of the Maxwell-Boltzmann distribution law $(46\cdot1)$. If there are two sorts of molecules of masses m_1, m_2 the numbers in a velocity range $du\,dv\,dw$ and volume $dx\,dy\,dz$ are

$$\left.\begin{array}{l} A_1 e^{-m_1\{\frac{1}{2}(u^2+v^2+w^2)-\phi\}/RT}\ du\,dv\,dw\,dx\,dy\,dz \\ A_2 e^{-m_2\{\frac{1}{2}(u^2+v^2+w^2)-\phi\}/RT}\ du\,dv\,dw\,dx\,dy\,dz \end{array}\right\} \quad \dots\dots(191\cdot1),$$

where ϕ is the gravitation potential. Integrating for all velocities the densities are

$$s_1 = (2\pi RT/m_1)^{\frac{3}{2}}\,A_1 e^{m_1\phi/RT}, \qquad s_2 = (2\pi RT/m_2)^{\frac{3}{2}}\,A_2 e^{m_2\phi/RT} \quad (191\cdot2),$$

so that s_1/s_2 changes with ϕ according to the law

$$s_1/s_2 \propto\ e^{(m_1-m_2)\,\phi/RT} \quad\dots\dots\dots\dots\dots\dots(191\cdot3).$$

If $m_1 > m_2$ this diminishes as we go upwards to smaller values of ϕ.

In ionised material the electrons are far lighter than the ions and tend to rise to the top in accordance with $(191\cdot3)$. But this separation is stopped almost before it has begun, because the minutest inequality creates a large electrostatic field which stops any further diffusion.

Let ψ be the potential of the field set up to prevent the separation; m, $-e$, the mass and charge of the electron; A, Ze the mass and charge of the ion. Then the potential energies (gravitational and electrical) are*

$$-m\phi - e\psi, \qquad -A\phi + Ze\psi,$$

and as in $(191\cdot2)$ the densities vary proportionately to

$$e^{(m\phi+e\psi)/RT}, \qquad e^{(A\phi-Ze\psi)/RT}.$$

The ratio of these densities must remain sensibly constant since not more than the minutest separation of the charges can occur. Hence

$$m\phi + e\psi = A\phi - Ze\psi,$$

so that

$$e\psi = \frac{A-m}{Z+1}\,\phi \quad\dots\dots\dots\dots\dots(191\cdot4).$$

---

* The convention as to sign is opposite for gravitational and electrical potentials.

The average molecular weight μ (in grams) is

$$\mu = (A + Zm)/(Z + 1).$$

Hence

$$\psi = \frac{\mu - m}{e}\, \phi \quad \dots\dots\dots\dots\dots\dots\dots(191\cdot5),$$

or very nearly $\psi = \mu\phi/e$.

The density σ of the volume charge can now be found since

$$4\pi\sigma = -\, \nabla^2\psi = -\, \frac{\mu}{e}\, \nabla^2\phi = \frac{4\pi\rho G\mu}{e},$$

so that

$$\sigma = G\rho\mu/e \quad \dots\dots\dots\dots\dots\dots(191\cdot6).$$

Setting $\mu = 2\cdot 2H = 3\cdot 7 . 10^{-24}$ gm., the charge is $5\cdot 10 . 10^{-22}$ electrostatic units per gram. This corresponds to a deficiency of 1 electron in every million tons of matter. Our provisional assumption that there is no appreciable separation of the charges is thus verified. The charge per gram is independent of everything except the molecular weight, and is a practically universal property of hot material at uniform temperature*.

The theory can be applied to the stars although their temperatures are not uniform, provided that the effects of thermal diffusion (§ 194) can be neglected. This would, at any rate, not alter the order of magnitude.

Applying the result to the sun, the total charge is $1\cdot01.10^{12}$ electrostatic units. The potential near the surface is $14\cdot6$ units or 4370 volts and the electric force near the surface is $6\cdot3.10^{-8}$ volts per cm. The electric force, which varies in proportion to gravity in the interior, is absurdly weak, but it stops any diffusion of the electrons outwards.

From $(191\cdot5)$ we obtain

$$m\phi + e\psi = A\phi - Ze\psi = \mu\phi \quad \dots\dots\dots\dots(191\cdot7),$$

so that the resultant force on every particle, whether ion or electron, is the same, viz. $\mu d\phi/dz$. The acceleration of the electron is, of course, enormously greater than the acceleration of the ion under the same mechanical force.

If radiation pressure is considerable a correction is needed. Since the effect is as though gravitation were reduced in the ratio β (so far as the ions are concerned) we take account of it by writing $\beta\phi$ for ϕ. Thus

$$\psi = \mu\beta\phi/e \quad \dots\dots\dots\dots\dots\dots\dots(191\cdot8),$$

and σ is reduced in the same ratio.

192. Consider next material containing two kinds of ions A_1, Z_1 and A_2, Z_2. If s_1, s_2 are their densities (number per cu. cm.) at zero potential, the densities at other points will be

$$s_1 e^{(A_1\phi - Z_1 e\psi)/RT}, \qquad s_2 e^{(A_2\phi - Z_2 e\psi)/RT},$$

* The first investigation of this volume charge appears to have been made by A. Pannekoek, *Bull. Astr. Inst. Netherlands*, No. 19 (1922).

and the density of the electrons will be
$$(s_1 Z_1 + s_2 Z_2) e^{(m\phi + e\psi)/RT}.$$

By differentiation we find the density gradients at $\phi, \psi = 0$ to be
$$\frac{ds_1}{dz} = \frac{s_1}{RT} \left(A_1 \frac{d\phi}{dz} - Z_1 e \frac{d\psi}{dz} \right), \text{ etc. } \quad\ldots\ldots\ldots\ldots(192{\cdot}1),$$

and the gradient of the total charge density is
$$\frac{eZ_1 s_1}{RT} \left(A_1 \frac{d\phi}{dz} - eZ_1 \frac{d\psi}{dz} \right) + \frac{eZ_2 s_2}{RT} \left(A_2 \frac{d\phi}{dz} - eZ_2 \frac{d\psi}{dz} \right)$$
$$- \frac{e(Z_1 s_1 + Z_2 s_2)}{RT} \left(m \frac{d\phi}{dz} + e \frac{d\psi}{dz} \right).$$

Since the resultant charge is insignificant this must vanish; the condition gives
$$e \frac{d\psi}{dz} = \frac{Z_1 s_1 (A_1 - m) + Z_2 s_2 (A_2 - m)}{Z_1 s_1 (Z_1 + 1) + Z_2 s_2 (Z_2 + 1)} \frac{d\phi}{dz}$$
$$= \left\{ \frac{Z_1 s_1 (Z_1 + 1) \mu_1 + Z_2 s_2 (Z_2 + 1) \mu_2}{Z_1 s_1 (Z_1 + 1) + Z_2 s_2 (Z_2 + 1)} - m \right\} \frac{d\phi}{dz} \quad (192{\cdot}2),$$

where μ_1, μ_2 are the average molecular weights for the two kinds of ion
$$\mu_1 = \frac{A_1 + Z_1 m}{Z_1 + 1}, \qquad \mu_2 = \frac{A_2 + Z_2 m}{Z_2 + 1} \quad\ldots\ldots\ldots(192{\cdot}25).$$

We can write (192·2) in the form
$$e \frac{d\psi}{dz} = (\mu_0 - m) \frac{d\phi}{dz} \quad\ldots\ldots\ldots\ldots\ldots\ldots(192{\cdot}3),$$

where μ_0 is a mean between μ_1 and μ_2, each ion being weighted proportionately to $Z(Z+1)$. This is not quite the same weighting as in the average molecular weight of the material μ, the weighting being then proportional to $(Z+1)$. Evidently $\mu_0 > \mu$.

Hence by (192·1) and (192·3)
$$\frac{ds_1}{dz} = \frac{s_1}{RT} \{ A_1 - Z_1 (\mu_0 - m) \} \frac{d\phi}{dz} \quad\ldots\ldots\ldots\ldots(192{\cdot}35),$$

or
$$\frac{d(\log s_1)}{dz} = \frac{1}{RT} \{ (Z_1 + 1) \mu_1 - Z_1 \mu_0 \} \frac{d\phi}{dz} \quad\ldots\ldots\ldots\ldots(192{\cdot}4)$$

by (192·25).

If s is the number of free electrons, we find by setting $A_1 = m$, $Z_1 = -1$ in (192·35)
$$\frac{d(\log s)}{dz} = \frac{\mu_0}{RT} \frac{d\phi}{dz} \quad\ldots\ldots\ldots\ldots\ldots\ldots\ldots(192{\cdot}5).$$

Hence by (192·4) and (192·5)
$$\frac{d}{dz} \left(\log \frac{s_1}{s} \right) = \frac{1}{RT} (Z_1 + 1)(\mu_1 - \mu_0) \frac{d\phi}{dz} \quad\ldots\ldots\ldots(192{\cdot}6).$$

It can easily be shown that this formula applies, however many sorts of ions may be present, μ_0 being the properly weighted mean for them all.

Neglecting thermal diffusion we apply (192·6) to a star. Then by (58·3)

$$\phi = 4\Re T/\mu \quad \ldots\ldots\ldots\ldots\ldots\ldots\ldots(192\cdot7),$$

radiation pressure being neglected for the present since we have not taken account of it in (192·6). We have been reckoning μ in grams but it is convenient at this stage to pass to the usual reckoning in terms of the hydrogen atom; accordingly $\Re$ replaces R in (192·6). Then

$$\frac{d}{dz}\left(\log\frac{s_1}{s}\right) = \frac{1}{\Re T}(Z_1 + 1)(\mu_1 - \mu_0)\frac{4\Re}{\mu}\frac{dT}{dz}.$$

Hence by integration

$$\log\frac{s_1}{s} = 4(Z_1 + 1)\frac{\mu_1 - \mu_0}{\mu}\log T + \text{const}\ldots\ldots\ldots(192\cdot8).$$

The ratio s_1/s represents the abundance of the element at the place considered, since, apart from small changes of μ, the number of free electrons is proportional to the mass. According to (192·8) very few elements will be distributed throughout the star; the heavy elements fall to the centre and the lighter elements rise to the surface. For suppose that $\mu_1 - \mu_0$ is no more than 0·05. Since this must refer to a mean element we can take $Z_1 + 1 = 20$, $\mu = 2$; the abundance then varies as T^2. Even this difference is sufficient to give high concentration to the centre. Taking the molecular weights given in § 176 with $\mu_0 = 2\cdot3$, the abundance varies as the following powers of T

H	He	O	Al	Ti	Fe	Ag	Ba	Sm	Ta	Pb
− 6	− 5	− 8	− 10	− 8	− 4	—	+ 24	+ 36	+ 60	+ 70

193. Radiation pressure greatly modifies these results since it has different effects on the different ions. Radiation pressure is allowed for by multiplying every mass by its own appropriate β. The radiation pressure on the electrons is much smaller than on the ions; but we need not trouble about this as the minute masses of the electrons played only an ornamental part in the investigation of § 192, and apart from mathematical elegance might just as well be dropped. Hence (192·8) is modified to

$$\log\frac{s_1}{s} = 4(Z_1 + 1)\frac{\mu_1\beta_1 - \mu_0\beta_0}{\mu\beta}\log T + \text{const}\ldots\ldots(193\cdot1).$$

Here $1 - \beta_1$ is the ratio of radiation force to gravitation on the ion A_1, and β_0, β are appropriately weighted means. There can be little doubt that the heavier ions perform the most absorption and experience the greatest radiation force, so that β_1 diminishes as μ_1 increases.

This leads to an extraordinary behaviour of the elements. The distribution given at the end of § 192 refers to stars of very small mass in which radiation pressure is unimportant. As the mass increases the heavier elements abruptly leave the centre and come to the surface. The lighter elements—not quite so abruptly—drop from the surface to the centre. Hydrogen lags behind the others, the reversal occurring when $\mu_0\beta_0 = 0\cdot5$, i.e. in extremely massive stars with $1 - \beta_0 > 0\cdot75$. Helium leaves the surface in stars of more than 10 times the mass of the sun— just the stars which show its spectrum most conspicuously. The other light elements reverse at smaller masses.

It would be difficult to reconcile these results with the observed spectra at the surfaces of the stars where light and heavy elements appear together. For some elements the exponent of T is so large as to leave not a single atom anywhere near the surface. If we believed these results we might have to consider important modifications in the theory of the stellar interior—for example, its constitution of heavy elements in small stars and light elements in great stars. We must now point out that these formulae give the ultimate steady state of the material; and the question arises whether the approach to this steady state is sufficiently rapid to effect appreciable separation in the life-time of a star or to overcome the mixing tendencies which may be retarding it.

Thermal Diffusion.

194. It is desirable to give a warning against possible misuse of (191·3) and similar formulae. In a star ϕ is proportional to T by (58·3) so that $e^{(m_1-m_2)\phi/RT}$ has the same value at all parts. We might be tempted to infer that s_1/s_2 is constant so that no separation of the different sorts of atoms occurs. This is very far from true. The formulae (191·1) refer to thermodynamical equilibrium, and there is no justification for employing them even as an approximation in material at non-uniform temperature.

Our procedure is to differentiate these formulae *keeping T constant* because the formulae apply only to uniform temperature. Thus (191·2) gives

$$\frac{d}{dz}(\log s_1) = \frac{m_1}{RT}\frac{d\phi}{dz} \quad\quad\ldots\ldots\ldots\ldots\ldots\ldots(194\cdot1).$$

This gives us the density gradients of the different kinds of atoms required to keep the composition steady when the material is under a pressure gradient but no temperature gradient; that is to say, it gives us the density gradients set up to prevent further pressure diffusion. If now we superpose a temperature gradient this will set up diffusion on its own account known as thermal diffusion. Hence, in general, the required density gradient consists of two parts, the one set up by pressure diffusion, and the other by thermal diffusion.

If thermal diffusion can be shown to be negligible the differential formula (194·1), but not the integral formula, is valid for non-uniform temperature. We then re integrate it *allowing T to vary*.

Thermal diffusion was predicted theoretically by S. Chapman and D. Enskog, and the phenomenon was satisfactorily verified experimentally by F. W. Dootson*. Chapman has also considered its influence on the stratification of the elements in the stars†. He concluded that it was of minor importance compared with pressure diffusion; that it acted in the opposite direction, but could not reduce the general order of magnitude of the stratification. In reviewing Chapman's conclusions in the light of recent knowledge I believe we must take the thermal diffusion to be in the same direction as pressure diffusion, i.e. tending to bring the heavy elements to the centre of the star. In Dootson's experiments the lighter gas became concentrated in the hotter region as was predicted for molecules resembling elastic spheres; but the theory indicates that thermal diffusion diminishes for "softer" models, and vanishes for a law of force varying as the inverse fifth power of the distance. Apparently it changes sign for a still lower force-index, so that with the inverse-square law of force between the atoms the concentration of the heavier atoms would be towards the hot regions. Evidently we have to do with the inverse-square law of repulsion between the charged ions in the interior of a star; owing to this repulsion the ions do not, as a rule, come to close quarters so that no other forces are invoked. It appears then that the effect of the temperature gradient will be to accentuate the tendency of heavy atoms to seek the centre of the star and the lighter atoms to go to the outside‡. We may, however, probably accept Chapman's judgment that the effect of thermal diffusion is unimportant and will not alter the order of magnitude of the concentration already indicated by other causes of diffusion.

Rate of Diffusion of the Elements.

195. According to the theory of gases the coefficient of diffusion of one gas into another is approximately§

$$D = \tfrac{1}{3}\lambda V \qquad \qquad (195\cdot1),$$

where λ is the mean free path and V the velocity of the molecules. The average for the two gases is to be taken weighted in inverse ratio to the number of molecules of each.

We shall attempt to estimate the order of magnitude of D in the stars. The ions whose diffusion we are studying will be deflected mainly by encounters with other ions, the deflections due to encounters with electrons being negligible. We may estimate that a deflection of 90° is a fair

---

* *Phil. Mag.* March, 1917.   † *Monthly Notices*, **77**, p. 539 (1917).
‡ Prof. Chapman confirms this inference.
§ See for instance Jeans, *Dynamical Theory of Gases*, 2nd Ed., p. 326, equation (869).

equivalent to the termination of a free path. For two equal ions the radius of the apparent target giving a 90° deflection is found to be

$$\sigma = \frac{Z^2 e^2}{4 V^2 A_H} = \frac{Z^2 e^2}{12 R T}.$$

Hence the mean free path is

$$\lambda = \frac{1}{\pi \nu \sigma^2} = \frac{A_H}{\pi \rho} \left(\frac{12 R T}{Z^2 e^2} \right)^2 \quad \dots\dots\dots\dots(195\cdot2).$$

It follows that $\qquad\qquad \lambda V \propto \mu T^{\frac{5}{2}}/\rho \quad \dots\dots\dots\dots\dots(195\cdot3),$

which in different parts of the star, and for stars of the same mass, varies as $T^{-\frac{1}{2}}$. Hence the coefficient of diffusion is not much different in different parts of the star. For iron (with two K electrons) at the centre of Capella the numerical results are

$$\lambda = 1\cdot66.10^{-7} \text{ cm.,}$$
$$V = 5\cdot20.10^6 \text{ cm./sec.}$$

Hence $\qquad\qquad D = 0\cdot29 \text{ cm.}^2/\text{sec.} \quad \dots\dots\dots\dots\dots(195\cdot4).$

Results for other elements will be of the same order of magnitude.

It will be seen from a consideration of physical dimensions that it will take an extremely long time to establish a steady state when D is of order unity in c.g.s. units. For the time of relaxation of an unevenness of distribution of wave-length x centimetres will be of order x^2/D seconds (this combination having the dimensions of time). To reach a steady state it is necessary to fill up unevennesses of extent comparable to the radius of the star, say $x = 10^{11}$ cm.; the time required is of order 10^{22} secs., or greater than the largest estimates of the life of a star.

This is scarcely sufficient to prove that no important stratification of the elements occurs in reasonable time; for many elements the steady state involves such an extreme concentration that a relatively small advance towards it would be significant.

196. When the distribution in a star has not reached a steady state there will be a net flow of ions of one kind through a surface perpendicular to r. The coefficient of diffusion D signifies that the mass of molecules of kind 1 passing in this way through 1 sq. cm. per sec. is

$$\delta M_1 = - D \left\{ \frac{d \rho_1}{d r} - \left(\frac{d \rho_1}{d r} \right)_s \right\} \quad \dots\dots\dots\dots(196\cdot1),$$

where the bracketed expression is the difference between the density gradient actually present and the density gradient for a steady state*. The formula is equivalent to

$$\frac{\delta M_1}{\rho_1} = - D \left\{ \frac{d}{d r} \log \rho_1 - \left(\frac{d}{d r} \log \rho_1 \right)_s \right\} \dots\dots\dots(196\cdot2).$$

---

* The steady state is supposed here to be attained by changing $d\rho_1/dr$ without changing ρ_1 at the point considered.

Suppose that initially the element was uniformly distributed in the star so that

$$\frac{d}{dr} \log \rho_1 = \frac{d}{dr} \log \rho = \left(\frac{d}{dr} \log \rho\right)_s .$$

Then

$$\frac{\delta M_1}{\rho_1} = D\left(\frac{d}{dr} \log \frac{\rho_1}{\rho}\right)_s$$

$$= 4D (Z_1 + 1) \frac{\mu_1 \beta_1 - \mu_0 \beta_0}{\mu\beta} \frac{d}{dr} \log T \quad\ldots\ldots(196\cdot3)$$

by ($193\cdot1$), the ratio of s_1/s to ρ_1/ρ being a constant.

To interpret ($196\cdot3$) we substitute

$$4\frac{d}{dr} \log T = \frac{d}{dr} \log P = -\frac{g\rho}{P} = -\frac{GM_r}{r^2} \frac{\mu\beta}{\Re T}.$$

Hence

$$\frac{4\pi r^2 \delta M_1}{M_r \rho_1/\rho} = -\frac{4\pi D (Z_1 + 1)(\mu_1 \beta_1 - \mu_0 \beta_0) G\rho}{\Re T} \quad\ldots(196\cdot4)$$

$$= 1/t.$$

We see from the left-hand side that for an element diffusing outwards t is the time in which the interior would be completely evacuated of atoms of the kind Z_1 if the initial rate of evacuation continued.

For an element diffusing inwards the time t in which the exterior part would be completely drained at the initial rate of evacuation is given similarly by

$$\frac{1}{t} = \frac{4\pi D (Z_1 + 1)(\mu_1 \beta_1 - \mu_0 \beta_0) G\rho}{\Re T} \frac{M_r}{M - M_r} \quad\ldots\ldots(196\cdot5).$$

We have $\Re/G = 1\cdot24.10^{15}$; T/ρ is a minimum at the centre and cannot be much less than 10^7; D is of order unity; $4\pi (Z_1 + 1)(\mu_1\beta_1 - \mu_0\beta_0)$ might perhaps in some cases amount to 300. Hence t is of order 10^{20} seconds or 10^{13} years*.

For an example we take in Capella the region containing the outermost $6\cdot6$ per cent. of the mass and calculate how fast this is losing lead. By § 13

$$T = 1\cdot9.10^6, \qquad \rho = \cdot0012, \qquad M_r/(M - M_r) = 14.$$

We can take $Z_1 + 1 = 70$, $\mu_1 - \mu_0 = 0\cdot6$, $D = 0\cdot3$.

For the moment we neglect radiation pressure which introduces the β factors. Substituting in ($196\cdot5$)

$$t = 9.10^{20} \text{ secs.} = 3.10^{13} \text{ years.}$$

The drain will become slower as it proceeds.

If radiation pressure is taken into account $\mu_1\beta_1 - \mu_0\beta_0$ is less, and the drain is slower; or more probably it is reversed in Capella—the lead coming to the surface.

---

* The very slow rate of diffusion was pointed out by Chapman (*Monthly Notices*, **82**, p. 292, 1922). His numerical illustrations treat the diffusion of hydrogen in detail.

If there were no process counteracting this diffusion we should probably have to allow that in the dwarf stars the time has been sufficient to effect some stratification—especially of the heaviest elements, which in the dwarf stars tend to go to the centre. In § 199 we shall show that there is a mixing process which is likely to annul the slow diffusion.

Viscosity.

197. It is well known that the coefficients for a number of "free-path phenomena" such as diffusion, viscosity, thermal conductivity, electric conductivity are intimately connected.

It is difficult to obtain more than an estimate of the order of magnitude of the free path because the usual formulae of the theory of gases developed for general laws of force break down for inverse-square forces, the integrals diverging. It is necessary to cut off the integrals somewhat arbitrarily at limits beyond which they cease to represent actual processes. Probably the treatment can now be improved by proceeding on the lines of Debye and Hückel's theory (§ 184). We have seen that on the average an ion is surrounded by a shielding negative charge due to its repulsion of other ions, and there seems to be no insuperable difficulty in determining the actual variation of (average) force with distance from the ion; owing to the shielding this is not by any means an inverse-square law, and the difficulty of divergence of the integrals would disappear*.

However, there is as yet little occasion to require in astronomy anything more than the order of magnitude of the coefficients above-mentioned, and (as in § 195) there is no difficulty in reckoning the free path accurately enough for this purpose.

The transport of momentum between adjacent parts of a fluid in non-uniform motion, which is observed as viscosity, is performed mainly by the electrons since these have much longer free paths than the ions. On the other hand, it is chiefly the ions which put an end to the free paths, the deflections of the electrons by one another being comparatively unimportant.

In a simple gas the viscosity η is given by

$$\eta = \rho D,$$

where D is the coefficient of diffusion. For an ionised gas Chapman† gives the formula

$$\eta = \rho D/2Z,$$

where D is now the coefficient of diffusion of the electrons among the

---

* [This investigation has now been carried out by E. Persico, *Monthly Notices*, **86**, p. 93. The results are not much different from Chapman's.]

† *Monthly Notices*, **82**, p. 292.

ions or *vice versa*. This is very much greater than the value of D for ions (195·4); it can be calculated by the same method. Chapman finds for (giant) stellar conditions $D = 100$. Hence for iron the *kinematic viscosity* η/ρ is about 2.

This result is about 100 times the kinematic viscosity of water, so that for hydrodynamical problems we must think of the star as a thick oily liquid. This applies even to the regions of low density because η/ρ, like D, varies only as $T^{-\frac{1}{2}}$ in a single star or in stars of the same mass. The investigation is not intended to apply to photospheric regions; but since the ionisation (though much reduced) still provides large numbers of free electrons, I suppose that even the photosphere will be rather sticky.

The process of thermal conduction in a gas is practically identical with viscosity, being in fact transport of energy instead of transport of momentum. In simple gases the conductivity is $c_v\eta$, where c_v is the specific heat. Since the viscosity is large, the conductivity of heat will be much greater than in ordinary gases. But the temperature gradient in a star is not much greater than in our own atmosphere—in a giant star, much less—so that a millionfold increase of conductivity would make little impression in comparison with the outflow of heat by radiation.

The problem of viscosity in the interior of a star has been fundamentally modified by a result reached recently by J. H. Jeans*. Except in stars of rather small mass the foregoing material viscosity is unimportant compared with viscosity arising from transfer of radiation. Consider motion parallel to the y axis with a velocity V which is a function of x ($V = 0$ at $x = 0$). Let S be an area of 1 sq. cm. in the plane $x = 0$. The radiant energy in a solid angle $d\omega$ making an angle θ with Ox which crosses S in a second is $acT^4 \cos\theta\, d\omega/4\pi$. Its mass is therefore $aT^4 \cos\theta\, d\omega/4\pi c$. It was emitted at an average distance from S equal to $1/k\rho$ and therefore from the stratum $x = -\cos\theta/k\rho$. Hence its y-momentum is

$$- \frac{aT^4 \cos\theta\, d\omega}{4\pi c} \frac{\cos\theta}{k\rho} \frac{\partial V}{\partial x}.$$

Integrating with respect to $d\omega$ the y-momentum passing across S is

$$- \eta_R \frac{\partial V}{\partial x},$$

where
$$\eta_R = aT^4/3k\rho c \qquad \dots\dots\dots\dots\dots\dots(197\cdot1).$$

For example, at the centre of Capella $\eta_R = 95$, and the kinematic viscosity η_R/ρ is 770. At the centre of the sun $\eta_R = 15\cdot3$, $\eta_R/\rho = 0\cdot2$. For the sun this is about three times the material viscosity, and for Capella it is very much greater.

* *Monthly Notices*, 1926, March.

Rotating Stars.

198. We prove first a very beautiful theorem due to H. von Zeipel*.

If a star, rotating as a rigid body with angular velocity ω, is in static equilibrium, the rate of liberation of energy ε at points in the interior is given by

$$\epsilon = \text{const.} \times \left(1 - \frac{\omega^2}{2\pi G\rho}\right) \quad \ldots\ldots\ldots\ldots\ldots(198\cdot1).$$

It is assumed that the physical characteristics of the material (opacity, molecular weight, liberation of subatomic energy, etc.) depend on T and ρ only; this would be true of a star of strictly homogeneous composition.

We take axes rotating with the star and include centrifugal along with gravitational force so that the combined potential is

$$\phi = \phi_0 + \tfrac{1}{2}\omega^2 (x^2 + y^2),$$

where ϕ_0 is the pure gravitational potential. Poisson's equation is then

$$\nabla^2\phi = \nabla^2\phi_0 + 2\omega^2$$
$$= -4\pi G\rho + 2\omega^2 \quad \ldots\ldots\ldots\ldots\ldots(198\cdot2).$$

The surfaces over which ϕ is constant are called *level surfaces*.

From the usual hydrostatic equations

$$\frac{\partial P}{\partial x} = \rho\frac{\partial\phi}{\partial x}, \qquad \frac{\partial P}{\partial y} = \rho\frac{\partial\phi}{\partial y}, \qquad \frac{\partial P}{\partial z} = \rho\frac{\partial\phi}{\partial z},$$

we have $\qquad\qquad\qquad dP = \rho\, d\phi \quad \ldots\ldots\ldots\ldots\ldots(198\cdot3),$

so that $dP = 0$, when $d\phi = 0$. Hence P is constant over a level surface; that is to say, P is a function of ϕ only.

Again by (198·3) $\qquad\qquad \rho = \frac{dP}{d\phi},$

so that ρ is a function of ϕ only.

Since P and ρ are functions of ϕ only, T must be a function of ϕ only; and all other physical characteristics which depend only on the two variables T and ρ defining the statistical state of the material will be functions of ϕ only and constant over a level surface. The gradients of any of these quantities will be normal to the level surface.

The flow of radiation H being along the normal, we have by (71·1)

$$H = -\frac{c}{k\rho}\frac{dp_R}{dn} = -\frac{c}{k\rho}\frac{dp_R}{d\phi}\frac{d\phi}{dn},$$

where dn is along the outward normal to the level surface. We can write

$$\frac{c}{k\rho}\frac{dp_R}{d\phi} = f(\phi) \quad \ldots\ldots\ldots\ldots\ldots(198\cdot41),$$

so that $\qquad\qquad\qquad H = -f(\phi)\frac{d\phi}{dn} \quad \ldots\ldots\ldots\ldots\ldots(198\cdot42).$

---

* *Festschrift für H. v. Seeliger*, p. 144 (1924).

It is to be noticed that $d\phi/dn$ will not be a function of ϕ only unless the distance from one level surface to the next is the same for every point on it. This could not happen in a rotating star.

It is convenient to resolve H into rectangular components

$$H_x = -f(\phi)\frac{\partial\phi}{\partial x}, \qquad H_y = -f(\phi)\frac{\partial\phi}{\partial y}, \qquad H_z = -f(\phi)\frac{\partial\phi}{\partial z} \quad (198\cdot43).$$

It will be seen that H_x represents the net flow across a unit area normal to the x-axis; for the lines of flow cross such an area obliquely at an angle whose cosine is $\dfrac{\partial\phi}{\partial x}\Big/\dfrac{d\phi}{dn}$.

If no additional radiation were being generated the equation of continuity of flow would be

$$\frac{\partial H_x}{\partial x} + \frac{\partial H_y}{\partial y} + \frac{\partial H_z}{\partial z} = 0,$$

but since the rate of generation is $\rho\epsilon$ per unit volume the condition becomes

$$\frac{\partial H_x}{\partial x} + \frac{\partial H_y}{\partial y} + \frac{\partial H_z}{\partial z} = \rho\epsilon \dots\dots\dots\dots\dots\dots(198\cdot5).$$

Now by (198·43) $\qquad -\dfrac{\partial H_x}{\partial x} = f(\phi)\dfrac{\partial^2\phi}{\partial x^2} + \dfrac{\partial}{\partial x}f(\phi)\dfrac{\partial\phi}{\partial x}$

$$= f(\phi)\frac{\partial^2\phi}{\partial x^2} + f'(\phi)\left(\frac{\partial\phi}{\partial x}\right)^2.$$

Hence (198·5) becomes

$$-f(\phi)\nabla^2\phi - f'(\phi)\left(\frac{d\phi}{dn}\right)^2 = \rho\epsilon \quad \dots\dots\dots\dots(198\cdot6),$$

since $(d\phi/dn)^2$ is the square of the resultant force and therefore equal to the sum of the squares of its components $\partial\phi/\partial x$, etc. Then by (198·2)

$$-f(\phi)(-4\pi G\rho + 2\omega^2) - f'(\phi)\left(\frac{d\phi}{dn}\right)^2 = \rho\epsilon \dots\dots\dots(198\cdot7).$$

We have seen that in a rotating star $d\phi/dn$ is not constant over a level surface. But the other quantities in (198·7) are constant over the level surface. Hence (198·7) can only be satisfied if

$$f'(\phi) = 0,$$

so that, integrating $\qquad\qquad f(\phi) = \text{const.} \dots\dots\dots\dots\dots\dots\dots(198\cdot8).$

Accordingly (198·7) becomes

$$\rho\epsilon = \text{const.} \times (4\pi G\rho - 2\omega^2),$$

or $\qquad\qquad\qquad \epsilon = C\left(1 - \frac{\omega^2}{2\pi G\rho}\right)$

which proves the theorem.

The following summary of von Zeipel's analysis will serve to show its extreme generality. The condition of mechanical equilibrium shows that

P and ρ are constant over a level surface and, since in material of homogeneous composition two variables suffice to define the state, all other scalar properties T, μ, k, p_R, ... are constant over a level surface. Vector properties are formed by introducing the factor dn representing normal distance to a neighbouring level surface; this cannot be constant over the surface in a rotating star. Hence we have vectors such as $\mathbf{H}$ and $\mathbf{g}$ whose ratio is constant on a level surface although they themselves are not. The next step is to show that their ratio is constant not only over the level surface but from one surface to the next. The proof depends on the fact that the divergences of $\mathbf{H}$ and $\mathbf{g}$ are scalar quantities $\rho\epsilon$ and $-4\pi G\rho + 2\omega$, which are constant over a level surface. After this step it follows that $\mathbf{H}/\mathbf{g}$ and $\rho\epsilon/(-4\pi G\rho + 2\omega)$ are constant everywhere. The theorem would remain true even if the flow of heat were due to conduction.

For slow rotation (198·1) approximates to the law $\epsilon = $ constant, except in a thin film near the surface where very low density is reached. For the sun, with rotation period about $25\frac{1}{2}$ days, we obtain

$$\epsilon \propto (1 - \cdot 0000195/\rho),$$

so that ϵ is constant to within 10 per cent. in all parts where the density is above ·0002. It is a mathematical curiosity that if we imagine a star with strictly zero rotation the argument breaks down and no limitation is imposed on ϵ. We take this to signify that as ω becomes smaller the condition becomes more and more nearly $\epsilon = $ const., but at the same time the consequences of violating the condition become less serious and deterrent; so that at $\omega = 0$, when the condition becomes exact, the star is able to violate it with impunity.

199. We can scarcely believe that von Zeipel's condition is fulfilled in actual stars. For example, it requires that ϵ shall be negative in the outer parts of a rotating star, that is to say, subatomic energy is absorbed instead of being liberated. It requires that in a slowly rotating star the liberation of energy shall be nearly constant through a wide range of temperature and density; and if the unknown laws of subatomic energy are obliging enough to fulfil this condition, how can they modify themselves so as to provide the right distribution in fast rotating stars? Thus the question is raised, Will anything very awful happen to a star which does not satisfy von Zeipel's condition? At present all we know is that it cannot remain rotating as a rigid body in statical equilibrium.

The angular velocity of the sun's surface varies with the latitude, and no doubt this variation extends into the interior; thus the sun has not a constant ω. It is possible that for the actual distribution of ω in the sun the condition corresponding to (198·1) might be satisfied*. The sun might

---

* The condition will involve $\partial\omega/\partial x$, etc. so that it is not obtained by merely inserting the varying ω in (198·1).

be supposed to have gone on altering its distribution of ω until it reached a state satisfying the condition. Thus we arrive at a definite cause for the non-uniform angular velocity of the sun. This suggestion was made by E. A. Milne.

But this is only one of the ways in which the star could meet the requirement. Non-uniform rotation is equivalent to a superposition on uniform rotation of currents circulating about the axis of rotation. Circulatory currents in other planes will also serve our purpose, and a little consideration will show that the failure of the condition (198·1) tends to set up currents which are primarily in planes through the axis of rotation*.

Suppose that a star in accordance with the ordinary requirements of radiative equilibrium has settled down to a state in which the average temperature over a level surface is maintained constant. There remains the further condition that not only the *average* but the *local* temperature at every point of the level surface is to remain constant. In a non-rotating star this is necessarily satisfied owing to the symmetry; but in a rotating star the further condition leads to von Zeipel's formula. Accordingly, if (198·1) is not satisfied the temperature will begin to rise at the equator and fall at the poles or *vice versa*. This will upset the constancy of pressure over the level surface and a pressure gradient between the equator and the poles will be set up causing a flow of matter. The flow must continue, and take the form of a permanent circulating current; a mere readjustment of the distribution of matter would not bring about equilibrium because no static equilibrium is possible with von Zeipel's condition unsatisfied. Presumably when the current has attained a moderate speed a steady state will be reached because the viscosity of the stellar material is considerable and the fundamental equations of equilibrium will be modified by the addition of viscous stresses. The star will feel its way to a possible steady state of circulation by this method.

Although the primary currents are set up in planes through the meridians the currents will be deflected east and west by the star's rotation, just as similar currents in our own atmosphere are deflected by the earth's rotation. Thus as a secondary phenomenon we shall have different periods of rotation in different latitudes and at different depths. This is a well-known feature of the sun's rotation, and the explanation here provided can scarcely be doubted. It is due to the heat of the interior forcing its way out through a distribution of matter rendered unsymmetrical by rotation, leading to unequal heating along the polar and along the equatorial radius, so that a small permanent circulation is maintained in spite of the opposition of viscosity and thermodynamic dissipation (§ 70).

* H. Vogt, *Astr. Nach.* No. 5342 (Jan. 1925); A. S. Eddington, *Observatory*, **48**, p. 73 (March, 1925).

Whilst the secondary east and west currents are of immediate observational importance, the primary currents in meridian planes are of great interest. In the first place, they will keep the material of the star stirred. The stirring will be slow—far too slow to change the equilibrium from radiative to convective—but rapid compared with the diffusion of the elements discussed in § 196. Thus any tendency of the heavy elements to concentrate at the centre will be frustrated. We shall have occasion to use this argument in discussing subatomic energy: owing to the stirring, when a star divides into two components each component will have the same chemical composition, and there is no chance for the larger component to take more than its share of the heavy elements. This conclusion is subject to one reservation: Bjerknes has pointed out that a circulation of this kind tends to become stratified, so that instead of one circulation between the centre and outside we may have two or three layers of circulation. Each layer will then be thoroughly mixed, but there will be little interchange between consecutive layers.

Another point is that the core of the circulation will probably be a pair of vortices, each vortex being of the form of an anchor ring about the polar axis. This is the postulate of a theory proposed by V. Bjerknes to account for many of the magnetic and periodic properties of sunspots. At any rate, the recognition of an internal circulation of this kind offers a hope of explaining many details of the surface phenomena of the sun which would be difficult to account for in an entirely static star.

It has been urged by B. Gerasimovič* that what I have here called the secondary currents are really the principal currents. The currents in meridian planes would, he considers, not be permanent, whereas a distribution of circulation about the axis of rotation can have secular stability under the dissipative force of viscosity. Admitting that there is a condition of circulation about the axis which does not tend to alter through viscosity, and that there is a condition of circulation about the axis which satisfies von Zeipel's condition (generalised to take account of varying ω), it is very unlikely that these two conditions would coincide. It is just as improbable as that (198·1) would be satisfied in a static state. Therefore I think there is no question of the circulation maintaining itself without motive power; the violation of von Zeipel's condition gives an unequal heating which supplies the motive power for the currents required to restore the condition; and the important point is that the motive power primarily causes currents in the meridian plane†.

* *Observatory*, **48**, p. 148.

† I think that this shows that the circulation in meridian planes will be at any rate sufficient to keep the light and heavy elements from separating. Gerasimovič may be right in holding that this circulation remains small compared with the east and west circulation (owing to the greater friction); in that case the result would not be so favourable to Bjerknes's theory.

The material of the rotating star does not find its state of equilibrium by the methods which the mathematician might employ. Its motto is *solvitur ambulando*. At present we have not got so far as the *solvitur*, but we can speak confidently as to the *ambulando*.

200. The general problem of radiative equilibrium of a rotating star has been treated by E. A. Milne* and H. von Zeipel†. The former adopted the approximation ϵ = const. and the latter adopted the condition (198·1) which we have been discussing. Although (198·1) cannot be accepted with its original interpretation as a law of distribution of the subatomic source of energy in actual stars, we may regard either Milne's or von Zeipel's law of ϵ as a sufficient first approximation on the same footing as our approximation $k\eta$ = const. for non-rotating stars. Presumably the error arising from the inaccuracy of the approximation will be limited as in § 91.

Milne finds that the effect of rotation on the apparent brightness is very small. Imagine a typical star to be set rotating so fast that its equatorial radius is elongated 10 per cent.; then the luminosity will decrease 2·5 per cent.‡ No great stress is to be laid on the precise value, since no allowance was made for the change of k due to the alterations of density and temperature. The significance of the result is that deviations of individual stars from the mass-luminosity curve due to their different speeds of rotation will be very small.

Milne finds further that in the star considered the effective temperature at the poles is 6·4 per cent. above the mean and at the equator 3·2 per cent. below the mean, so that the poles are brighter than the equator. This variation of surface brightness is found more simply in von Zeipel's papers where it is deduced as a simple consequence of (198·8). Since $f(\phi) = C$, we have by (198·42)

$$H = - C \frac{d\phi}{dn} = - Cg \quad \dots\dots\dots\dots\dots\dots(200\cdot1).$$

The analysis breaks down near the actual surface of the star, but we note that, as usual, the surface value of H must be continuous with its value a few thousand kilometres below the surface. Hence

$$H \propto g \quad \dots\dots\dots\dots\dots\dots\dots\dots(200\cdot2),$$

where $g \; (= d\phi/dn)$ is the value of gravity including centrifugal force §.

The variation of brightness over the surface of a rotating star corresponds exactly to the variation of gravity.

* *Monthly Notices*, **83**, p. 118 (1923).
† *Monthly Notices*, **84**, p. 665 (1924).   ‡ *Loc. cit.* p. 139.
§ The result $H \propto g$ for a rotating star was first given in the case of stars of very large mass by Jeans (*Monthly Notices*, **79**, p. 330). He, however, there insisted that the deduction was only applicable if the star had no source of energy other than contraction; and he has abandoned the result (for reasons not stated) in a later paper (*ibid.* **85**, p. 935).

Von Zeipel has also shown that the law $H \propto g$ applies when the star is distorted by tidal forces.

In (200·2) the approximation for ϵ is used in a more specialised way than in a discussion of the total radiation of the star, and it would seem necessary to examine how closely the result is bound up with the accuracy of the approximation before we can be sure that it will apply to actual stars. I daresay it will be found that the approximation still justifies itself, but it is not at all obvious that it is legitimate. The distribution of surface brightness over a tidally disturbed star is of considerable practical importance in the interpretation of the light-curves of eclipsing variables.

CHAPTER XI

THE SOURCE OF STELLAR ENERGY

The Contraction Hypothesis.

201. The energy radiated by the sun into space amounts to $1 \cdot 19 . 10^{41}$ ergs per year. Its present store of heat energy is as follows (§ 103)—

Radiant energy	$2 \cdot 83 . 10^{47}$ ergs
Translatory energy of atoms and electrons	$26 \cdot 9 . 10^{47}$
Energy of ionisation and excitation ...	$< 26 \cdot 9 . 10^{47}$

This constitutes 47 million years' supply at the most. We do not, however, think that this capital is being used for expenditure; it is being added to rather than exhausted.

It is now generally agreed that the main source of a star's energy is subatomic. There appears to be no escape from this conclusion; but since the hypothesis presents many difficulties when we study the details it is incumbent on us to examine carefully all alternatives.

Formerly the contraction theory of Helmholtz and Kelvin held sway. This supposes that the supply is maintained by the conversion of gravitational energy into heat owing to the gradual contraction of the star. The energy obtainable from contraction is quite inadequate in view of the great age now attributed to the sun. It is perhaps worth while to give a revised calculation of the age of the sun according to the contraction hypothesis taking account of two recent conclusions: (1) that the material is a perfect gas and therefore concentrated to the centre more strongly than used to be supposed, and (2) that the sun's rate of radiation cannot have varied very much in the past if its mass has been constant. The gravitational energy lost in contracting from infinite diffusion to the present radius is
$$\Omega = \tfrac{3}{2} GM^2/R = 5 \cdot 66 . 10^{48} \text{ ergs.}$$

Of this, $2 \cdot 97 . 10^{48}$ ergs has been saved in the form of material kinetic energy and radiant energy (as above). An unknown part of the balance $2 \cdot 69 . 10^{48}$ ergs has also been saved as energy of ionisation and excitation. Ignoring this last deduction (which is probably substantial) the balance allows of radiation at the present rate for 23 million years. Allowing for the rather smaller rate of radiation in the past according to the law $L \propto T_c^{\frac{1}{2}} \propto R^{-\frac{1}{2}}$ (equation (98·3)) the age is just doubled.

If we measure the sun's age from the time at which it reached an effective temperature of 3000° the result is 15 million or 19 million years according as we neglect or allow for reduced radiation in the past. These figures are subject to a considerable deduction already mentioned on account of ionisation energy, so that 20,000,000 years is probably a generous estimate of the sun's age on the contraction hypothesis.

202. Biological, geological, physical and astronomical arguments all lead to the conclusion that this age is much too low and that the time-scale given by the contraction hypothesis must somehow be extended. The most direct evidence is given by the determination of the date of formation of terrestrial rocks containing radio-active minerals from the uranium-helium or the uranium-lead ratio of their contents. In this way an age of 1300 million years has been assigned to the oldest sedimentary rocks*. The sun must be still older and its age can scarcely be put at less than 10^{10} years.

The rapidity of evolution required by the contraction hypothesis is most startling when we consider the giant stars. A star of mass $11\cdot5$ would take 31,000 years to develop from type M ($3000°$) to type G ($6000°$) and 72,000 years from type M to type A ($10,500°$); moreover, these figures are subject to deduction on account of ionisation energy.

The Cepheid variables afford direct astronomical evidence against so rapid an evolution. From the numerical results for δ Cephei given in § 134 it will be found that Ω must increase by 1 part in 40,000 per year in order that the balance $\Omega - K - H$ may be sufficient to supply the radiation. The radius must accordingly decrease by 1 part in 40,000 and the density increase by 1 part in 13,000. Since $\Pi\sqrt{\rho}$ is approximately constant the period must decrease by 1 in 26,000 or 17 seconds annually.

The star has been under observation since 1785 and it is impossible that so large a change of period could escape detection. It is doubtful whether there has been any change at all, the observations since 1848 being consistent with a uniform period. E. Hertzsprung† finds an annual decrease of $0^s\cdot106 \pm 0^s\cdot011$, the result depending almost entirely on the trustworthiness of observations by Goodricke and Pigott in 1785. In any case the rate of evolution of δ Cephei is not more than $\frac{1}{150}$ of that given by the contraction hypothesis. There are many other Cepheids which should have shown the large change of period if it had occurred, but the evidence is always negative.

---

* For an account of these and other methods see H. Jeffreys, *The Earth*, Chapter v. On the other hand, arguments by J. Joly, *The Surface-History of the Earth*, Chapter IX, in favour of a lower estimate seem entitled to considerable weight; but even the lowest estimates are much too great for the contraction hypothesis.

† *Observatory*, **42**, p. 338. [Results depending on recent spectrographic observations have been communicated to me by F. S. Jacobsen. These show the period of δ Cephei to be decreasing $0^s\cdot39$ annually, and of η Aquilae *increasing* $0^s\cdot96$ annually.]

This observational result refers to only one particular phase in the life of the star; but if we take it as a general hint that the Kelvin time-scale needs to be multiplied by a factor of at least 150 we arrive at an age of the sun ($> 3.10^9$ years) satisfying modern requirements. Even if the pulsation theory of Cepheids is rejected our argument is probably valid. The law $\Pi \propto \rho^{-\frac{1}{2}}$ is directly deducible from observation without reference to the pulsation theory (Table 25). Moreover, it is inconceivable that a periodicity *intrinsic* in the star should be practically unaffected by large changes of density. If, for example, the period of the light-fluctuation were that of the rotation of the star, as some writers have supposed, the conservation of angular momentum requires that $\Pi \propto \rho^{-\frac{2}{3}}$ so that an even faster change of period would be looked for.

203. In seeking a source of energy other than contraction the first question is whether the energy to be radiated in future is now hidden in the star or whether it is being picked up continuously from outside. Suggestions have been made that the impact of meteoric matter provides the heat, or that there is some subtle radiation traversing space which the star picks up. Strong objection may be urged against these hypotheses individually; but it is unnecessary to consider them in detail because they have arisen through a misunderstanding of the nature of the problem. *No source of energy is of any avail unless it liberates energy in the deep interior of the star.*

It is not enough to provide for the external radiation of the star. We must provide for the maintenance of the high internal temperature, without which the star would collapse. The temperature gradient from the surface to the centre cannot be maintained by supplying heat at the bottom end. If, for example, sufficient heat is developed by meteoric impact to maintain the surface of Capella at 5200°, the temperature throughout the interior will fall gradually to this level and the star will no longer be distended to low density. In fact the evolution of the star goes on unmoved by what is happening at the surface, and if extra heat is generated there it is thrown off as extra radiation (cf. § 143).

We may glance also at the suggestion of a modification of the laws of radiation such that a body radiates only in directions in which there is something to intercept and, as it were, appreciate the radiation. This would economise the heat flowing from the star into space, but it makes no difference to the flow in the interior where in every direction there is matter to intercept the radiation. The suggestion is not helpful because it is the internal flow which decides how much energy is going to be squandered, and it is too late to check the waste by economy at the surface.

Subatomic Energy.

204. Since we are limited to energy liberated in the deep interior of the star, extraneous sources of supply are ruled out, and it is scarcely possible to escape the conclusion that the supply of energy for future expenditure is already hidden in the star. Energy, however, cannot be successfully hidden; it betrays itself by its manifestation as mass. Energy and mass are equivalent, and we know the masses of the stars.

This immediately sets an upper limit to the supply of energy available for radiation for all time (unless the star sweeps up further mass in its progress through space). The mass of the sun $1·985.10^{33}$ gm. when expressed in energy units amounts to $1·785.10^{54}$ ergs. This then is the total store. At the present rate of radiation it would last 15 billion years $(1·5.10^{13})$. If the whole of this supply is going to be used the sun in its later stages will be a star of smaller mass and eke out the supply by radiating less strongly. On the other hand, if the sun started as a star of infinitely large mass its present age must nevertheless be less than 10^{13} years owing to the greater rate of radiation for large masses.

This time-scale is an upper limit because, although the energy is present in the star, we do not know how much of it is utilisable for the purposes of radiation.

This store of energy is, with insignificant exception, energy of constitution of the atoms and electrons or, as it is usually called, subatomic energy. The processes by which subatomic energy might be liberated are—

I. (a) Breaking down of the more complex elements into simpler elements (radio-activity).

(b) Building up of complex elements from simpler elements.

II.   Mutual cancellation of protons and electrons.

It may seem anomalous that energy can be liberated both in the building up and in the breaking down of higher elements, but both cases can occur. Like chemical combination, the combination of protons and electrons in the nucleus is sometimes endothermic and sometimes exothermic. Breaking down of complex nuclei with liberation of energy is familiar in radio-active transformations. The only definitely known example of liberation of energy in the building up of nuclei is in the formation of helium from hydrogen. The helium nucleus contains 4 protons (hydrogen nuclei) bound closely with 2 electrons; this gives it a net electric charge $+ 2e$ in accordance with its atomic number $Z = 2$. The atomic weight $4·00$ comes from the mass of the protons, that of the electrons being insignificant, so that each proton is responsible for a mass $1·000$. But the mass of the uncombined proton as it occurs in the hydrogen atom is $1·008$. This difference is established by the chemically determined atomic weights of hydrogen and helium, and most convincingly by F. W. Aston's measurements with the mass-spectrograph. The formation of helium from hydrogen has thus involved a loss of 0·8 per cent. of the mass; the corresponding energy must have been set free during the process of combination. There can be no doubt that the close approach of the electrons to the protons in the helium nucleus makes their mutual electrostatic energy less than in a state of infinite separation; and it is this loss of field-energy which is betrayed by the measurements of mass. After the first loss of ·008 of the mass when the proton enters into the helium nucleus, the changes of energy in building higher nuclei appear to be much less significant. Aston has found another deviation from the "whole number rule" in the atomic weight of tin; but in proportion to the mass involved the liberation of energy is on a smaller scale.

It appears then that not more than 1 per cent. of the mass is released as free energy by the processes I (b), so that if this is the main source of stellar energy the extreme time-scale is divided by 100, and the life of the sun (past and future) is limited to $1·5.10^{11}$ years. (We are no longer troubled by the possibility of a large change in the rate of radiation since the mass changes no more than 1 per cent.) But this limit would only be attained if the sun originally consisted wholly of hydrogen. An initial proportion of 7 per cent. of hydrogen is necessary for a life of 10^{10} years. We should be reluctant to admit a greater proportion even in the earliest stars*. The time-scale is thus rather cramped, but we cannot definitely say that it is insufficient.

So far as we know, the processes I (a) give much less energy. To maintain a star's energy by the breaking down of elements it is necessary to postulate elements of high radio-activity which are not known to terrestrial experience.

By the third process involving destruction of protons and electrons the whole of the energy might be liberated and the extreme time-scale reached. This hypothesis supposes that when a proton and electron meet they may under exceptional circumstances coalesce; their positive and negative charges cancel and nothing is left but the energy which, released from all constraint, spreads out through the aether as an electromagnetic ripple. Or, instead of considering the two charges, we may fix attention on the field of force between them which involves something of the nature of a tube of discontinuity in the aether; this tube might slip back, healing the discontinuity, and at the same time starting a wave of radiant energy.

If this last source of energy is operating the matter of the star will gradually disappear. The star burns away its mass.

* Cf. § 169, where a mixture of 15 hydrogen atoms to 1 iron atom, or 21 per cent. of hydrogen by mass was considered with the idea of accounting for the opacity of Capella.

We shall have to keep in mind the two forms which the hypothesis of a subatomic source of energy may take—the mild form of transmutation of elements, and the radical form of destruction of matter. The second theory leads to a time-scale at least 100 times longer than the first. Moreover, they lead to essentially different theories of stellar evolution. In the second theory the mass of a star changes to an important degree during its life-time, so that there is an evolution from heavy to light stars—from bright to faint stars. In the first theory the mass remains sensibly constant and there is little scope for evolution, unless indeed there is loss or gain of mass from extraneous causes. These differences afford some hope of eventually deciding between the two theories.

205. The rudiments of the idea that the mass of ordinary matter is an index of the presence of energy which might conceivably be set free, can be traced back to 1881 when J. J. Thomson showed that the electric field of a charged body possesses inertia or mass. The discovery of the electron and the tendency to regard its mass as residing in its electrical field strengthened the belief in large quantities of field energy bound, but perhaps not permanently, in the constitution of matter. How far this conception had advanced by 1900 may be seen for example in J. Larmor's *Aether and Matter*, Appendix E. There the generation of a positive and negative electron by rotating the walls of a tube with respect to an inner core is described; and the possibility that the walls may ultimately slip back annihilating the electrons and releasing the energy is guardedly touched on. The subject of the intrinsic energy of matter was made clearer and more precise by Einstein who showed the identity of mass and energy; that is to say, mass and energy are the modes in which the same underlying condition manifests itself in different types of experiment so that the gram and the erg are as convertible as the yard and the metre. The intrinsic energy of structure of any given mass of matter thus became known, and speculation naturally arose as to whether some or all of it could ever be released and utilised.

Meanwhile, the existence of a store of energy within the atom had been forced on our attention in a more practical way in the phenomena of radioactivity. At one time exaggerated ideas were entertained as to the cosmical importance of this hitherto unrecognised source of energy; it was thought to give an immediate solution of the difficulty as to the age of the sun and earth. In one sense it did extend the age of the earth indefinitely. One of Lord Kelvin's arguments against the long time-scale desired by geologists was based on the temperature gradient below the surface of the earth. Just as in this book we have determined the heat flowing out of a star from the temperature gradient and opacity, so Kelvin determined the heat flowing out of the interior of the earth from the temperature gradient and conductivity of the surface rocks. We now know that this escaping heat is no more than can be reasonably attributed to the release of energy by the radio-active.minerals within, so that it is no measure of the rate of cooling of the earth. Kelvin, however, supposed that it represented the cooling, and calculated backwards to the time when the earth must have been molten. This direct method of setting a limit to the age of the earth's crust is no longer tenable.

But it is not much use extending the age of the earth without extending the age of the sun, and here radio-activity helps very little. It is calculated that if the sun were composed entirely of uranium and its products (in equilibrium proportions) the radio-activity would supply only half the sun's actual rate of radiation; the other half must come from unknown sources.

With regard to the application of these ideas to astronomy there was no temptation to formulate any definite theory so long as the only demand was for an extended time-scale. Some may have speculated on the existence of elements of more potent radio-activity in the stars, uranium and radium on the earth being the last feeble remnants of an expiring process. Others were content to know that an ample store of energy existed in the stars whatever their composition, and there was no pressing occasion to decide in which of the possible ways it was being released.

A more intimate contact with the problem seemed imminent in the first researches on the radiative equilibrium of the stars in 1916. Then we were faced with the question in what manner the source of stellar energy is distributed through the interior. If the source were gravitational energy of contraction the distribution could be settled. But the contraction hypothesis was already becoming obsolete so that allowance had to be made for the source being probably subatomic. But we have shown that it is not necessary in an approximate solution of the problem to make very precise assumptions as to the distribution of the source. Thus the question of the law of release of subatomic energy was shelved for a time.

Reference may here be made to a very interesting discussion by H. N. Russell* in 1919 which indicated some of the conditions which a subatomic source must fulfil in order to satisfy astronomical requirements. This was perhaps the first sign of serious astronomical interest in the subject apart from its bearing on the time-scale.

In 1920 the researches of Aston, establishing the loss of mass occurring when the higher elements are formed from hydrogen, gave a new interest to the subject. It provided a much more powerful source of energy than any known radio-active change. Annihilation of protons and electrons, or the disintegration of unknown elements of intense radio-activity are

* *Pub. Astr. Soc. Pac.* **31**, p. 205 (1919). See also Eddington, *Observatory*, **42**, p. 371 (1919).

speculative hypotheses; these processes may or may not be capable of occurring. But in the formation of helium we have a process which *must* have occurred at some time and place—and where more likely than in the stars where the atoms of primordial matter are for the first time kept in close proximity? The favourable points of this new hypothesis were indicated by J. Perrin* and by the writer† in 1920. But it has also its unfavourable points.

Up to this point the exact nature of the subatomic source has been an interesting but not very pressing problem for astronomers. But the results reached in Chapter VII render the problem one of urgency. For the past 50 years stellar astronomy has been guided by successive theories of evolution. To-day we have no theory of stellar evolution pending the settlement of the laws of subatomic energy. Let us try to see why subatomic energy has now become vital. On the old theory of evolution from type B to M, and on the giant and dwarf theory of evolution from giant M up to B and down to dwarf M, the star's *track of evolution* was fixed by familiar physical laws. The laws of subatomic energy did not guide the star on the magnitude-type diagram; they settled its *rate of progress*. But now there is nothing left but the conditions of liberation of subatomic energy to guide the star; these must determine its track if it is evolving or its halting-place if it is stationary‡.

206. I think that the pure physicist may be inclined to regard our discussions of the details of subatomic energy as airy speculation; if so, he greatly misunderstands the position of the astronomer. It is not a question of unrestrained conjecture remote from observational facts. The astronomer has any amount of facts to build on, and he cannot escape the duty of trying to combine the facts into some sort of order. To measure the rate of radiation of a star is to measure its liberation of subatomic energy; for if these do not approximately balance the result would be evolution on a time-scale comparable with that of Lord Kelvin. Thus the measurement of liberation of subatomic energy is one of the commonest astronomical observations; and unless the arguments of this book are entirely fallacious we have a fair knowledge of the conditions of density and temperature of the matter which is liberating it. Moreover, in the Cepheids we can study the liberation under periodically changing temperature and density. Surely it is permissible to sort these facts into order and consider what laws and theories they may suggest without being held

---

* *Revue du Mois*, **21**, p. 113 (1920).

† *Brit. Assoc. Report*, 1920, p. 45.

‡ On the giant and dwarf theory the line of constant mass was supposed to correspond to the track on or near which most of the stars were found. Now we have learnt that lines of constant mass run in an entirely different direction, so that a star left to the old guiding principle would run off the track.

guilty of vain speculation. If our critic possessed in his laboratory similar fountains of energy whose output he could measure and whose physical state he could calculate, he would not be backward in speculating on the processes occurring.

Unfortunately the facts as yet do not fall into satisfactory order, and we are still groping for a clue. I have no particular theory to advocate in the following sections and the general result of the arguments is entirely inconclusive. But the discussion will bring out the intricacy and difficulty of the subject.

Astronomical Difficulties.

207. Consider the following comparison of Capella and the sun—

1. Capella liberates 58 ergs per gram per second compared with 1·9 liberated by the sun.

2. The density of the sun is 620 times the density of Capella.

3. The temperature of the sun at corresponding points is 4·3 times the temperature of Capella.

The first two are immediate results of observation. The third is a conclusion from the present theory which it is difficult to distrust. Now it is generally believed that the liberation of subatomic energy, if it depends on temperature and density at all, will increase with temperature and density. Why then is there this decreased output in the sun in spite of the apparently more favourable conditions?

Presumably the answer is that the sun is a much older star, and that Capella is drawing on a more prolific source of energy which has become exhausted in the sun. We may note incidentally that (judging from the output) not more than $\frac{1}{30}$ of this original source remains in the sun, so that if the sole supply of energy is the conversion of hydrogen to higher elements the hydrogen must now be pretty well used up in the sun. But the main point is that the interpretation of the astronomical results is likely to be complicated by a third factor in addition to temperature and density, viz. exhaustion of the supply.

Turn now to the two components of Capella. At some epoch a single star divided and the two components started life with material in the same stage of exhaustion. By the mass-luminosity relation the more massive component has radiated more energy per gram and has accordingly suffered greater exhaustion. Yet we find now that the more massive component, with lower temperature, lower density, and more exhausted, is liberating more energy per gram than the fainter. This is a very awkward paradox.

Several points in this last argument require amplification. It has been urged that the massive component will take for its share more of the central region of the original star where the heaviest and most intensely active elements accumulate. But according to § 195 diffusion is so slow that there is no appreciable flow of the heavy elements to the centre. In fact in the parent star of Capella the heavy elements would probably diffuse upwards owing to radiation pressure. It is true that the tendency may be for heavy elements to be *evolved* at the centre; but against this we have the stirring of the star by the circulatory currents caused by its rotation. Presumably the rotation of the parent star must have been rapid since otherwise it would not have divided. This objection might possibly be surmounted by the idea of stratified circulation (§ 199). We may turn, however, to wider pairs and groups such as the Taurus cluster where the primitive material from which the stars separated can have had no very definite central condensation; pairs of stars showing the same anomaly as the two components of Capella can be picked out. Wherever in a coeval group of stars we find the more massive stars with the lower effective temperature the paradox arises; they liberate more energy per gram at lower temperature and density and since they have been doing this through the past their store cannot be less exhausted.

It may be suggested that in the close binaries the stars have not yet reached a steady state so that we are not justified in inferring the amount of liberation of subatomic energy from the radiation of these stars. A star must reach the state of balance in a period of the order of the Kelvin time-scale, that is to say, about 100,000 years for giant stars. If there is anything in this suggestion the anomaly should be conspicuous in the most recently formed binaries; these are presumably the eclipsing variables with separation not much greater than the dimensions of the stars. It appears to be the general rule that in ordinary giant pairs the more massive component has the lower effective temperature (as in Capella); but almost without exception this is reversed in the eclipsing variables, the fainter and less massive component having the lower surface brightness. It is just those stars in which the anomaly would be pardonable which fail to show it at all.

208. The foregoing difficulties arise in a comparison of giant stars with one another and with a star of the main series. We might perhaps hope that an explanation confined to stars of the main series would be a simpler problem to start with. There is the great advantage that effects of temperature in stimulating the liberation of subatomic energy are eliminated since the central temperature is approximately constant along the main series. The first thing that strikes us is the enormous exhaustion effect. The liberation per gram by Krueger 60 is $\frac{1}{8500}$ of the liberation per gram by V Puppis. Moreover Krueger 60 has a much higher density; it is not unnatural to suppose that the rate of liberation is proportional to the density; if so, the falling off of intrinsic potency of the material is 1 : 1,000,000.

It would be difficult to account for this decline as the result of a single process gradually exhausting itself. If the process is a single one the amount of the source remaining will decrease exponentially with the time or perhaps with an acceleration due to the increasing density. Thus the time between V Puppis (680 ergs per gm.) and the sun (2 ergs per gm.) will be much greater than the time between the sun and Krueger 60 (0·08 ergs per gm.). It appears then that the duration of the stage dwarf G to M is much shorter than the preceding stages; but it has always been held that the great abundance of these late dwarf stars shows that this stage occupies the main part of the star's life-history. We do not necessarily suppose that the dwarf stars have all passed through the stage of V Puppis; the point of introducing V Puppis is to show that the source is *capable* of producing 680 ergs per gm. at solar temperature and therefore that less than $\frac{1}{300}$ of it remains in the sun. Thus in any case the solar stage has a much longer history behind than in front of it.

The difficulty can, of course, be met by postulating a number of different sources, so that the exhaustion does not follow the single exponential law. But that concession gives up the hope of interpreting the main series as a simple phenomenon.

An alternative view of the main series was suggested in § 122. There the source is considered practically inexhaustible but it is only tapped at a critical temperature of about 40 million degrees. The idea is that in the giant stage the star uses up various sources of subatomic energy, which (although prolific while they last) are soon exhausted. It then continues to contract until its central temperature reaches 40 million degrees when the main supply of energy is suddenly released; this is perhaps the cancellation of protons and electrons, and the greater part of the star's mass may burn itself away in this stage. A star on the main series must keep just enough of its material above the critical temperature to furnish the supply required; a comparatively small expansion will suffice to decrease the supply to any extent required as the star (by diminishing mass) progresses along the main series. On this view the energy is liberated near the centre of the star and the stellar model approximates to that treated in § 91.

The principal astronomical objection is that such a method of liberation of heat gives the star over-stability. A slight compression of Krueger 60 would make it liberate as much heat as V Puppis. Clearly there would be a great rebound from compression, and oscillations of the star would be maintained and increased. According to § 136 over-stability occurs whenever ϵ increases faster than T^2 so that a discontinuous increase at a critical temperature is fatal. This difficulty of over-stability occurs in most of our attempts at a theory, because the margin between stability and over-stability seems to be very narrow. We have seen that there is one way of meeting it. We can suppose that the dependence of the liberation of energy on density and temperature is not immediate but deferred; that is to say, active material is formed at a rate depending on temperature and density, but it has a life of at least several years and yields up its energy at a rate independent of temperature and density. In that case the liberation of heat will not vary during short period oscillations but will respond to long continued changes of temperature.

But the grave objection to a critical temperature—especially a critical temperature so low as 40,000,000°—is that there is nothing in our current physical knowledge of atoms and electrons and radiation to render it probable. In particular the radiation at this temperature consists of X rays of a very ordinary kind and the electrons have speeds such as are common in laboratory experiments. Only after a very exhaustive elimination of alternatives would we venture to recommend so revolutionary a hypothesis.

Physical Difficulties.

209. If the astronomical evidence afforded more definite guidance for a formulation of the laws of liberation of subatomic energy, we should still, I suppose, have to submit the resulting theories to the censorship of the mathematical physicist. It may save waste of time in looking in hopeless directions if we know in advance the kind of theory which the physicist would condemn as intolerable. But his own position contains difficulties and contradictions and it is doubtful if he is justified in exercising any rigid censorship.

The difficulty is that from the physicist's point of view the temperature of the stars is absurdly low. He regards the stars as practically at absolute zero, because in regard to nuclear processes 40 million degrees is a small quantity which it is scarcely worth while to take notice of. If liberation of subatomic energy occurs freely on the stars, why not on the earth?

As regards laboratory conditions, electrons and ions of far higher energy than would correspond to 40 million degrees can be studied. If concentration of energy is required, the stars have the advantage; nevertheless a concentration equivalent to $1\frac{1}{2}$ million degrees has been reached by Kapitza and by Anderson. It is to be remarked, however, that the radiation released by the subatomic processes would be extremely penetrating, and even if released in the laboratory would be difficult to catch and measure.

The absence of release in the interior of the earth could perhaps be explained by the comparative fixity of the electrons. Yet there must be considerable numbers of free electrons, as is shown by the thermoelectric emission from hot metals.

The difference of temperature between terrestrial and stellar conditions seems quite inadequate to account for any appreciable stimulation of transmutation or annihilation of matter; and this is the chief ground on which censorship of our theories is likely. For example, it is held that the formation of helium from hydrogen would not be appreciably accelerated at stellar temperatures, and must therefore be ruled out as a source of stellar energy. But the helium which we handle must have been put together at some time and some place. We do not argue with the critic who urges that the stars are not hot enough for this process; we tell him to go and find *a hotter place*.

Indeed the formation of helium is necessarily so mysterious that we distrust all predictions as to the conditions required. The attention paid to temperature, so far as it concerns the *cookery* of the helium atom, seems to neglect the adage "First catch your hare...." How the necessary materials of 4 mutually repelling protons and 2 electrons can be gathered together in one spot, baffles imagination. One cannot help thinking that this is one of the problems in which the macroscopic conception of space has ceased to be adequate, and that the material need not be at the same place (macroscopically regarded) though it is linked by a relation of proximity more fundamental than the spatial relation.

According to one line of thought we should only expect liberation of subatomic energy on a large scale if the electrons had great speed; it is not very clear how the fast electrons are expected to operate, but there is always the chance that if the electron were endowed with enough energy it might do something surprising. At stellar temperatures the mean speed is small compared with β rays, so that there is not much chance of a surprise. There must be some electrons in a Maxwellian distribution with speeds considerably in excess of the mean, but this makes no great difference. So far as temperature speed is concerned there will be in *the whole of the sun* only one electron or ion with an energy as high as $5 . 10^{-7}$ ergs; compare this with the energy of the fastest β particles $30 . 10^{-7}$ ergs, or of the fastest α particles $130 . 10^{-7}$ ergs. It would seem that there are no particles in a star of energy great enough to provoke subatomic processes except, of course, those shot out by the processes themselves.

210. If local electric fields are formed by circulation in the interior of a star as they are in our atmosphere, it is possible that the electrons may acquire speeds higher than the temperature speeds and so work more damage. In this connection reference must be made to an idea brought forward by C. T. R. Wilson*. Ordinarily the maximum energy which a particle can acquire in an electric field corresponds to the drop of potential in its own free path. If we start with a slow-moving β particle in our

* *Proc. Camb. Phil. Soc.* 22, p. 534 (1924).

atmosphere its speed will increase by the electrical acceleration until it happens to ionise an atom; that will cause a discontinuous drop followed by an increase of speed until the next ionisation occurs. Even if the net result is at first an acceleration, the frequency of the ionisations increases with the speed so that the brake becomes more powerful and a limiting speed is reached. But for fast-moving particles the conditions are different; the ionising power increases with speed only up to a certain point and then falls. If the speed of the particle passes this critical point it can go on increasing indefinitely since the brake offers less and less resistance. Wilson suggests that in thunderstorms these runaway particles may occur; and picking up practically the whole energy of the potential drop (about 10^9 volts) they will surpass in energy anything else that is known*.

Although it is not clear that anything of this kind could occur in the interior of a star, it gives food for reflection. If local fields, such as occasion terrestrial thunderstorms, exist in the stellar interior an electron going fast enough to get a good start will proceed with ever-diminishing chance of capture or deflection as its speed increases under the influence of the field; so that its free path is greatly extended and it can pick up almost unlimited energy. It is difficult to admit local fields of strong intensity in a star owing to the high conductivity of the ionised material. So far as we can judge the electron would have to start with very high speed in order to gain rather than lose energy. Numerical calculations are not at all encouraging. Still if a few high-speed electrons started the liberation of subatomic energy, this energy would itself send off other high-speed electrons, and in certain circumstances the action instead of dying out might be regenerative and maintain or multiply the number of runaway particles. If anything of this kind is going on the influence of temperature and density becomes incalculable, and other factors, more especially rotation which is likely to be concerned in causing local fields, may have to be taken into consideration. We leave this suggestion as a conceivable alternative, but assume it to have been rejected in the arguments which follow.

Dependence on Temperature and Density.

211. In the foregoing sections we have indicated that the physicist has difficulty in admitting that the rate of liberation of energy can depend to an appreciable extent on temperature because stellar temperatures are trivial from his point of view. Those who have maintained this attitude have, I think, been mainly influenced by the known characteristics of radio-activity. Disintegration of radium is a spontaneous event involving the atom as an isolated system, so that density is irrelevant. It could be

* For comparison, the energy set free by annihilation of a proton and electron corresponds to 9.10^8 volts.

stimulated by a field of γ radiation of the same frequency as the γ rays emitted in the disintegration; the amount of this stimulation can be calculated from Einstein's equation. By (38·5) the emission at temperature T is to the emission at temperature zero in the ratio $(1 - e^{-h\nu/RT})^{-1}$, where ν is the frequency of the γ rays. At stellar temperatures the increase is quite insignificant.

This argument does not settle the question because it is limited to one mode of release of energy—and that not the mode which an astronomical theory is likely to propose. We shall first explain why the astronomer feels bound to insist on a variation with temperature and density.

If the rate of liberation of energy were independent of ρ and T the stars would be unstable. For then the energy generated E would be incapable of alteration by any expansion or contraction of the radius. The energy radiated L is determined by the mass and (to a comparatively small extent) by the radius. Suppose that by exhaustion of the source or by slight disturbance E becomes less than L. Then the energy of the star diminishes at the rate $L - E$, so that it contracts. By hypothesis this does not affect E, but L increases according to the law $L \propto R^{-\frac{1}{2}}$. Thus the deficit becomes worse and the star contracts indefinitely*.

We here assume that $L \propto R^{-\frac{1}{2}}$ or at least as a negative power of R. It will be remembered that this depends on the exponent n in the law $k \propto \rho/T^n$ being greater than 3—a condition which although probable both from theory and observation is not established as certainly as we could wish (§ 150). But if n were less than 3 it would scarcely overthrow the argument. The quantities E and L are governed by entirely different laws; each has an observed range of 1,000,000 : 1 in the stars; and evidently they would not be equal in a star unless it had some means of adjusting them to agreement. Taking $n = 3\frac{1}{2}$ we have shown above that the adjustment is not made by L changing towards E because it would actually change away from E. If $n = 2\frac{1}{2}$, L changes towards E but it cannot change by a factor greater than 4 without going beyond known stellar conditions. Thus in either case the main adjustment must be made by E changing towards L.

In order to give the star stability E must increase as the star contracts so as to oppose the contraction, i.e. it must increase with ρ or T or with both. This condition was first pointed out by H. N. Russell. The threatened instability is with respect to a rather long time-scale and is not catastrophic. Unless the star keeps E and L closely balanced it will change density at

---

* This argument has been criticised by J. H. Jeans (*Monthly Notices*, **85**, p. 792). He objects that since the star with $E < L$ is changing its energy it is not legitimate to apply equilibrium equations. He further states that when $E < L$ the star expands. It seems to be sufficient to point out in reply that $E = 0$ corresponds to the Kelvin contraction hypothesis.

a rate comparable with the Kelvin time-scale ($E = 0$) and the subatomic energy will fail to achieve the purpose for which it was introduced.

The danger of over-stability must again be recalled; E has to increase with contraction but not much faster than T^2 or the star will be set oscillating. It seems unlikely that a plausible law can be found between such narrow limits; so that we prefer to suppose that there is a lag of a few months up to a thousand years in the response of E to the changed conditions. The response must be rapid enough to save a giant star from collapse.

The second reason for denying that E is independent of ρ and T is that the assumption would make L/M solely a function of the age of the material. It supposes that the material has gone on degenerating at a rate independent of physical conditions past and present so that its stage of exhaustion is determined solely by its age. The question what zero the age is to be reckoned from remains unanswered. We cannot fit the astronomical facts into so cast-iron a rule, as was shown in § 207. It is true that the admission of a dependence on ρ and T has not helped us far forward in reconciling the facts; but it does leave us free to explore further instead of coming to a blank wall of contradiction.

The result that E increases with contraction of the star sometimes enables us to eliminate one of the variables ρ and T in a comparison. For example, imagine the material of Capella to be slowly compressed until it reaches the temperature of the sun. Then since $\rho \propto T^3$ the density becomes $\frac{1}{8}$ that of the sun. We have now the comparison that at the same temperature the material of Capella emits *more than* 30 times as much energy per gram at a density $\frac{1}{8}$ that of the sun.

Since the dependence on T may be very complicated, whilst the dependence on ρ is expected to be fairly simple we can get a clearer idea of the exhaustion of the solar material in this way.

212. We shall try to classify the possible ways in which we think that ϵ (the liberation of energy per gram) might depend on ρ and T.

To begin with, a nucleus must be concerned in the emission. If nothing else is concerned the emission by the nucleus is independent of the statistical state of the system and ϵ is independent of ρ and T. (It is possible that the structure of the nucleus may be modified by temperature and density, that is to say, nuclei of different kinds may be evolved in different physical conditions; but in that case we regard the emission as a consequence of the event which creates the radio-active nucleus, and it falls under one of the succeeding alternatives.)

If, in addition, something extraneous to the nucleus is concerned, this may be (1) a bound electron, (2) a free electron, (3) the field of radiation. Two nuclei may also be concerned although their repulsion tends to keep them apart; somehow or other the assemblage of four hydrogen nuclei in the helium atom must be contrived, but this is too mysterious a problem for us to tackle.

(1) If an electron bound to the nucleus is concerned, the law may be very complex. For instance, the condition might be that the electron describes an ellipse which grazes the nucleus at pericentron. This involves excitation in a high quantum orbit and depends in a complicated manner on T and ρ according to the formulae in Chapter III.

(2) If a free electron is concerned the law seems to be $\epsilon \propto \rho T^{-\frac{1}{2}}$, for this expresses the frequency with which electrons hit the nucleus (§ 170)*. The decrease with T is due to the tracks of fast electrons being less bent towards the nucleus. The nature of the collision cannot be appreciably affected by temperature, because the kinetic energy of the electron when in contact with the nucleus is due almost entirely to the potential there of the order 3,000,000 volts; the extra 1000 volts (variable according to T) which represents the initial energy cannot make much difference. Hence, for similar nuclei, the emission will be simply proportional to the frequency of collision. Exhaustion effects can be provided for by supposing that in some nuclei the protons are better guarded from attack than in others.

(3) If radiation is concerned it presumably acts by stimulating the emission as provided for in Einstein's equation, and the stimulation is quite inappreciable. It must not be overlooked that there is no logical justification for applying Einstein's equation to a process involving the annihilation of matter; for that equation implies that the converse process (creation of matter) can occur and that it accords with the second law of thermodynamics. Either of these propositions may be denied without striking too heavily at our sense of the fitness of things.

213. Since our arguments seem to lead to a deadlock, and no suggested way of escape appears very inviting, we must hold all the inferences under suspicion for the present. But one point seems to have emerged clearly. No theory will fit the astronomical facts unless it admits of exhaustibility of the source of energy.

At first sight the exhaustibility of the source seems opposed to the hypothesis that it is due to annihilation of protons and electrons, for it is difficult to see why protons and electrons should ever get tired of destroying one another. But the argument may be turned the other way. If we agree that the sun's low rate of supply is due to exhaustion, we are almost forced to suppose that a star changes mass considerably as it grows older. For suppose that the sun has always had its present mass and therefore practically its present rate of radiation. There must have been a time when its material was fresh like that of Capella, and the sun

* A speculation which evades the law $\epsilon \propto \rho T^{-\frac{1}{2}}$ has been mentioned in § 210.

must have been in this stage much longer than Capella since (owing to low mass) it could only use up the supply at $\frac{1}{30}$ the rate. To slow down ϵ to the value balancing radiation it must have been greatly expanded as compared with its present dimensions. Why then do we not find stars of mass 1 in this early long-enduring diffuse state? The answer seems to be that the numerous stars now of mass 1 were not born with mass 1 but with the higher masses which *are* found in a diffuse state. The star cannot radiate any considerable fraction of its mass without annihilating matter, so that this process (rather than transmutation of elements) seems to be indicated; though it is, of course, conceivable that there are other ways by which a star can lose mass as it grows older.

The theory of annihilation of matter is more fertile in astronomical consequences than the other forms of the subatomic theory, and for this reason alone it seems worth while to follow it up in detail. We shall not be greatly concerned with *how* the annihilation is accomplished; but it may perhaps be well to have a scheme in mind. I do not think it is done by free electrons directly hitting protons in the nucleus and performing a joint suicide, because this seems to lead to the cast-iron law $\epsilon \propto \rho T^{-\frac{1}{2}}$ and (since there is no time-lag) to over-stability*. It is preferable to suppose that the process consists in evolving certain kinds of nuclei which are self-destroying. The destruction occurs spontaneously some time after the formation of the nucleus. Perhaps also at the same time refractory nuclei are evolved so that the star gradually accumulates some material safe from annihilation; the purpose of introducing the last conception is to provide a residuum to pass on to the white dwarf stage. We suppose that very little mass is lost in the giant stage, the earlier subatomic processes being either transmutation of elements or a small scale rehearsal of the great development which appears to set in at 40,000,000°.

Radiation of Mass†.

214. In § 14 we concluded that radiation pressure was concerned in limiting the amount of matter gathered together to form a star, the actual masses of stars falling within the range in which radiation pressure rises from insignificance to predominance. It is now desirable to scrutinise the figures more closely. If we are right in believing that the mass of a star is gradually burnt away, the proper masses to consider in this connection are those of stars in the earliest most diffuse stage. The clear separation

* This law, however, is only just beyond the dividing line, and perhaps a more accurate calculation would negative the over-stability.

† Any radiation is radiation of mass. But by the hypothesis of "radiation of mass" we mean the hypothesis that a large proportion of the star's mass is lost in this way during its life-time.

of giants and dwarfs in types K and M shows that there is a lower limit of mass below which stars are rarely if ever formed:

For example, we take the statistics given in Adams and Joy's determination of spectroscopic parallaxes of 500 stars*. Omitting one or two outliers the giant stars of type M are comprised within a range $- 0^{m}\cdot5$ to $+ 2^{m}\cdot5$ visual, corresponding to $- 2^{m}\cdot3$ to $+ 0^{m}\cdot7$ bolometric. The masses according to Table 14 are therefore between 11·5 and 3·5 in terms of the sun as unit. Below this there is a clear interval with no M stars until we reach the dwarfs beginning at absolute magnitude $9^{m}\cdot5$ visual, corresponding to mass 0·5. Stellar masses between 0·5 and 3·5 are extremely common, but none are found in the M stage. If stars were born with these masses they would have to pass through the M stage on their way to the less diffuse condition in which we find them. It seems fair to conclude that 3·5 is ordinarily the lower limit of the mass of a star at birth, and that lower masses can only occur after the star has already reached considerable age and density.

We can perhaps improve on the above limits by using later and more abundant material. We shall take the giant stars of types G 8 to K 2 in a list of 1600 spectroscopic parallaxes†. The number of stars is greater and the various reductions are better determined than for the M type; the loss of mass before reaching this stage must be very small. The mean magnitude of 287 stars is $+ 1^{m}\cdot01$ and the observed average deviation is $\pm 0^{m}\cdot69$‡. Allowing for the probable error of the determinations the actual average deviation is found to be $\pm 0^{m}\cdot59$. The mean magnitude corresponds to mass 3·6 and to $1 - \beta = 0\cdot25$. The average deviation corresponds roughly to a factor 1·22 in mass and to $\pm \cdot043$ in $1 - \beta$.

So far as we can judge the spread in magnitude is a Gaussian distribution. If that is so, we obtain the following table where the first column gives the percentage of stars brighter than the magnitude in the second column.

Table 40.

Giant Stars G 8—*K* 2.

Percentage	Vis. Mag.	Mass	$1 - \beta$
5	− 0·21	5·5	·35
15	+ 0·24	4·7	·31
50	+ 1·01	3·6	·25
85	+ 1·78	2·8	·20
95	+ 2·23	2·4	·17

* *Astrophys. Journ.* **46**, p. 334.
† Adams, Joy and Burwell, *Astrophys. Journ.* **53**, p. 13.
‡ Eddington and Douglas, *Monthly Notices*, **83**, p. 115.

This does not give the exact proportion of stars born with masses within the assigned limits, because the number found between $G\,8$ and $K\,2$ depends also on the rate of evolution at this stage which is likely to depend on the mass.

215. It appears then that initially the ratio of radiation force to gravitation is usually between 0·17 and 0·35—the former representing a value too feeble to prevent the aggregation of material round a stellar condensation, and the latter being so high as decisively to prevent accumulation under ordinary circumstances. These values seem to be of the right magnitude for the effect attributed to them. We can make a comparison with centrifugal force which creates instability when its maximum value reaches $\frac{1}{3}$ of gravitation.

The foregoing results are for molecular weight 2·11 which probably applies nearly enough to stars in a visible stage. We may ask, how have the stars tided over the period when they were of extremely low density and low temperature? Ionisation would then be less, molecular weight and radiation pressure would be considerably greater. I think the answer is that radiation pressure does not in itself break up the mass, but only renders it more liable to break up under other disturbances. Probably the peril to the star does not become serious until it is moderately condensed—until for example its rate of rotation has increased by contraction. The existence of so many close binaries shows that stars which have weathered the earlier stages become disrupted at higher concentration, so that the critical period for a star must not be placed too early in its history.

We conclude that the relation of stellar masses to the critical range of values of radiation pressure favours the view that a star loses mass with advancing age, since the accordance is much closer if the original lower limit of mass is that of the diffuse giants (about 2·4) than if it is that of stars of all ages (about 0·2).

216. The rate of loss of mass by radiation is given by

$$\frac{dM}{dt} = -\frac{L}{c^2} \quad \dots\dots\dots\dots\dots\dots\dots(216 \cdot 1).$$

If the effective temperature remains constant we have by (99·2)

$$L \propto M^{\frac{7}{5}}(1-\beta)^{\frac{3}{2}} \quad \dots\dots\dots\dots\dots\dots(216 \cdot 21),$$

or, if the central temperature remains constant, by (99·1)

$$L \propto M\,(1-\beta)^2/\beta \quad \dots\dots\dots\dots\dots\dots(216 \cdot 22).$$

Since the second condition is fulfilled on the main series we shall employ it. It will make the early giant stages relatively too short by a factor 2 or 3, but that is scarcely important in the present estimates of duration. By (216·1) and (216·22)

$$dt = -C \frac{\beta}{(1-\beta)^2} \frac{dM}{M} \quad \text{.....................}(216\cdot3),$$

where C is a constant. We have seen (§ 204) that for the sun

$$-M \Big/ \frac{dM}{dt} = 1\cdot5 . 10^{13} \text{ years}$$

and $1 - \beta = \cdot05$. Hence $C = 4\cdot0 . 10^{10}$ years.

Differentiating the fundamental quartic (84·6)

$$-2 \frac{dM}{M} = \frac{d\beta}{1-\beta} + \frac{4d\beta}{\beta}.$$

Hence
$$dt = \tfrac{1}{2}C \frac{4-3\beta}{(1-\beta)^3} d\beta \quad \text{.....................}(216\cdot4),$$

so that, integrating $\quad \delta t = \tfrac{1}{4}C\delta \left(\dfrac{1}{(1-\beta)^2} + \dfrac{6}{1-\beta} \right)$ ....(216·5).

We obtain from (216·5) the following table—

Table 41.
Duration of Stages of Evolution.

Abs. Bol. Mag.	Mass	Duration (10^{10} years)
< - 5·0	∞ to 35	3·8
- 5·0 to - 2·5	35 to 10	6·5
- 2·5 to 0·0	10 to 3·7	21·4
0·0 to + 2·5	3·7 to 1·73	93
+ 2·5 to + 5·0	1·73 to 0·92	521
+ 5·0 to + 7·5	0·92 to 0·53	3630
+ 7·5 to + 10·0	0·53 to 0·31	28100
+ 10·0 to + 12·5	0·31 to 0·18	219000

217. If the stellar system is a mixture of stars of all ages and if the stars run through the whole course, the number of stars in any range should be proportional to the duration of the range. Thus the numbers in the last column should represent the luminosity function, i.e. the frequency of stars within the given limits of absolute magnitude. The figures in the early part of the table will be much too high since very few stars start at the largest masses, but at mass 2·5 nearly all the competitors have started, so that below + 2·0 we may expect agreement with the luminosity function. Since the fainter stars are increasingly red due allowance for the average difference of visual and bolometric magnitude should be made in any comparison.

Unfortunately we have not much observational knowledge as to the course of the luminosity function beyond $+ 8^m$; but in the range from $0 \cdot 0$ to $+ 7 \cdot 5$, the figures 93, 521, 3630 represent about the right rate of increase; and it is now agreed by Seares, Luyten, Malmquist and others that there is evidence of an increasing number of fainter stars.

The enormous difference of age of the giant and dwarf stars is very striking. The table shows that a star of mass 2 cannot be older than 10^{12} years however great the mass with which it originally started; and a star of mass $0 \cdot 5$ must be at least $40 . 10^{12}$ years old unless it is one of the very exceptional stars starting below mass $2 \cdot 5$. This does not apply to the components of double stars which skip a great many billion years by the fission. In certain cases this essential difference of age may create a difficulty. For example, in a compact system, such as a globular cluster, we can scarcely expect to find a mixture of greatly different ages. It is therefore interesting to note that globular clusters are suspected not to have their full complement of faint stars. "Shapley believes he has recorded the faintest stars existing in the globular cluster M 22 and there are indications that the lower limit of brightness has also been approached in the Hercules cluster M 13. In both of these systems stars of solar brightness appear to be relatively infrequent."* If this is substantiated it is strong evidence for the hypothesis of diminution of stellar mass, for in the globular clusters we seem to have an ideal opportunity of studying coeval stars.

I believe that Shapley's later opinion does not stress so much the lack of dwarf stars in globular clusters. He has pointed out to me that such a system as the Taurus cluster seems fatal to the theory of radiation of mass; for there we certainly have dwarfs and giants together. The presence of the giants sets a limit to the age of the system, and within this time limit the numerous dwarfs cannot have been evolved from appreciably higher masses by radiation of mass.

On the other hand, Hertzsprung has pointed out to me that in the Taurus cluster, Praesepe, and other coeval groups there is strong support for Shapley's original statement that stars of solar brightness have not by any means their usual relative abundance, and that there appears to be a definite lower limit of brightness of the cluster stars. It certainly looks as though the fainter stars are missing because the cluster has not existed for a time sufficient to evolve them. The situation is that qualitatively the clusters confirm the theory of radiation of mass in a rather striking way, whilst quantitatively they contradict it brusquely. Perhaps in the crude stages of a theory qualitative evidence is more significant than quantitative.

The argument in § 214 that the dwarf stars are evolved from stars of

* *Mount Wilson Report*, 1920, p. 343.

larger mass seems too strong to be overthrown. If the evidence of the Taurus cluster and similar coeval groups compels us to give up the theory of radiation of mass, we must presumably find some other method by which a star can change its mass. Some attention is given to this alternative in Chapter XIII, §§ 266–7; but it does not seem likely to provide an escape from our difficulty.

218. It has been pointed out by H. Vogt* that if the components of a double star radiate away their masses the mass ratio must tend to approach unity as the system grows older. In proportion to its mass the heavier star loses more than the light star. Data for 93 stars collected by Vogt tend to confirm this effect, the average mass ratio progressing towards unity for the systems considered to be furthest advanced in evolution. Allowance must be made for selection effects especially when it is remembered that the earlier systems are generally spectroscopic and the later systems visual binaries; but we see no reason why dwarf systems of types K and M with large mass ratio should escape observation and we think that Vogt has made out a fair case.

By a discussion of 342 double stars (the mass ratio being inferred from the differences of luminosity) G. Shajn† has shown very conclusively that in giant systems the component with higher effective temperature has, in general, the smaller mass, whilst in dwarf systems it has the larger mass, the difference of mass increasing with the difference of spectrum. The two cases are combined in the statement that the less massive component is further advanced in the Russell-Hertzsprung scheme of evolution‡. A similar phenomenon is shown in globular clusters where the most luminous

Table 42.

Mass Ratio and Difference of Type.

Giants			Dwarfs		
Diff. of Spectrum	Mass ratio	No. of Systems	Diff. of Spectrum	Mass ratio	No. of Systems
0·0–0·4	0·88	78	0·0–0·4	0·88	65
0·5–0·9	·72	12	0·5–0·9	·85	16
1·0–1·4	·66	33	1·0–1·4	·70	15
1·5–1·9	·62	20	1·5–1·9	·63	12
2·0–2·4	·45	18	2·0–4·5	·35	4
2·5–2·9	·56	9			
3·0–4·5	·37	9			

* *Zeits. für Physik*, **26**, p. 139. † *Monthly Notices*, **85**, p. 245.

‡ As stated in § 207 the close eclipsing binaries almost without exception follow the opposite rule. These may be recently formed systems which have not yet reached a balance of L and E.

(most massive) stars are in the earliest diffuse stages. The uniformity appears to indicate evolutionary progress. But it has always been difficult to understand why the smaller mass should evolve more rapidly than the greater; every circumstance seems to be against it. Although it does not radiate away its source of energy so fast, yet after the same lapse of time it has reached higher temperature and density as though it were endeavouring to stimulate a failing supply.

Table 42 exhibits Shajn's results. In the column "Difference of Spectrum" 0·1 represents one-tenth of a type.

219. The effect of radiation of mass on the orbits of binary stars has been discussed by J. H. Jeans and W. M. Smart*. For simplicity, consider two equal masses. A star does not receive any kick from its own radiation†; consequently the orbit is the same as that of a star of constant mass under the attraction of a centre of force of gradually diminishing strength. The equation of the orbit is thus

$$\frac{d^2u}{d\theta^2} + u = \frac{\mu}{h^2},$$

where h is constant and μ diminishes with the time according to the same law as the masses. Since

$$h^2 = \mu a \, (1 - e^2),$$

where a and e are the elements of the instantaneous ellipse, we have

$$Ma \, (1 - e^2) = \text{const.}$$

The latus rectum of the orbit increases in proportion as the mass diminishes.

In studying binary stars it is difficult to resist the impression that there is an evolution of wide pairs from close pairs. The relations of type, separation and eccentricity suggest that the components recede from one another in the course of time. But no cause is known which can increase the separation to more than a limited extent. Radiation of mass does not help very much. The latus rectum of a system with masses now equal to the sun cannot have increased more than tenfold unless the masses were originally more than 10 times the sun's mass—a very rare occurrence. Since a tenfold increase by no means meets requirements, the discussion affords no particular support for the theory of radiation of mass.

Jeans further points out that the law that the separation of the stars increases in proportion as the masses diminish, is roughly true of more complicated systems, e.g. clusters. If the stellar system consisted wholly of dwarf stars we could argue that its linear dimensions must have expanded, say fivefold, since these were first formed as giants. The presence

---

* *Monthly Notices*, **85**, pp. 2, 423.

† Note that angular momentum is lost by the system. Each component can be compared to a ship firing guns equally fore and aft; the velocity is unaffected, but momentum is reduced by the loss of the shells.

of many giant stars in the system complicates the problem, since it becomes impossible to treat it as a single coeval cluster.

Jeans considers that his cosmogonic theories requirs, or at least render desirable, a greater concentration of the stars in the early history of the stellar system; he had indeed postulated this in some of his investigations before the foregoing explanation of the expansion of the system was proposed. In particular, he welcomes the very long time-scale and the closer concentration of the stars in the past as rendering more probable the event which he is forced to postulate as the origin of the solar system, viz. the close approach of another star to the sun. This provoked the subtle reply that since we know that this event occurred within the last 10^{10} years, there is not much gain in rendering it more probable in a distant past when it did not occur. To this it may fairly be answered that the 10^{10} years is the interval between the event itself and a direct consequence of the event (viz. the evolution of beings capable of speculating on it) and does not in any way serve to date it in the evolution of the universe. But the argument is double-edged; as the time relation between the event and its consequence does not date it, so the place relation between the event and its consequence does not locate it; and, if we locate neither time nor place —if we consider the probability of the event happening not to the sun 10^{10} years ago, but somewhere in the stellar system at some time—it already becomes highly probable without an extension of time limit by the aid of the hypothesis of radiation of mass.

220. We attempt to sum up the arguments for and against the hypothesis of radiation of mass, i.e. radiation of a considerable fraction of a star's mass during its life-time.

1. Unless we admit the hypothesis the time-scale is somewhat cramped though it cannot be definitely shown to be inadequate.

2. It appears to account satisfactorily for the relative numbers of stars between different limits of brightness.

3. It appears that very few stars are born with masses below 2·5, so that most dwarf stars must have lost a great part of their original mass. The radiation of mass is a natural explanation of this loss though perhaps not the only explanation.

4. On this hypothesis the age of dwarf stars of types G to M is vastly greater than the maximum possible age of a giant star. The presence of giants and dwarfs together in clusters of coeval stars is a most serious objection to the theory. On the other hand dwarfs of small mass although present are not so overwhelmingly abundant as in ordinary regions of the stellar system.

5. It has certain consequences of interest in the evolution of double

stars; but nothing very favourable or unfavourable to the theory has been found, except that it predicts correctly that the mass ratio progresses towards unity as the evolution advances.

6. The uniformity of the main series comprising the great majority of the stars suggests that there is a simple mode of liberation of energy tapping an enormous store, in contrast to the rapidly exhausted supplies used during the giant stage.

7. Great difficulties arise in relating the rate of liberation of energy to temperature, density, and exhaustion of the source; but since these affect every proposed source of subatomic energy there must presumably be some way out of them.

Transmutation of Hydrogen.

221. We sum up similarly the reasons for and against the transmutation of hydrogen into helium or higher elements as the main source of stellar energy.

(1) It is the only process *known* to occur or to have occurred which would be capable of providing sufficient energy, and is therefore less speculative than other suggestions.

(2) Unless the initial proportion of hydrogen in a star is unduly large the length of life of the star is only barely sufficient.

(3) If the low value of ϵ in the sun as compared with Capella and V Puppis is held to be due to exhaustion—and it seems impossible to explain it otherwise—the sun must very nearly have exhausted its stock of hydrogen and its future life will be short. The hypothesis thus extends the Kelvin time-scale where extension is least needed, viz. in the early infrequent types, and does not extend it sufficiently for the dwarf G to M stages which include the great majority of the stars.

(4) The transmutation of elements is virtually a single source of energy, since there is very little further release of energy after helium has been formed. The phenomena of giant stars and the main series seem to indicate that at least two sources are tapped successively.

(5) Part of the attraction of the hypothesis is lost if it is not accepted in its complete form—that the formation of the elements (hydrogen nuclei being reckoned as unformed primordial matter) begins with the condensation into stars. Besides the occurrence of advanced elements (Ti, Zr, etc.) in very early stars and of light elements (He, C) in the diffuse nebulae, the evidence of the theory is strongly against admitting a large proportion of hydrogen in early stars.

(6) We should say that the assemblage of 4 hydrogen nuclei and 2 electrons to form the helium atom was impossible if we did not know

that it had occurred. This is perhaps in favour of the hypothesis, since the difficulties of detailed application become of minor importance. We can scarcely prescribe limits to what can be performed by a process, before we see how the process can be possible at all.

(7) Apart from effects depending on the presence of hydrogen in early stars, the theory leads to no interesting astronomical consequences. In particular the change of mass is insignificant; and unless the star can gain or lose mass from other causes there is no evolution from bright to faint classes of stars.

No. (5) may be explained a little further. We have shown that admixture of a large proportion of hydrogen considerably lowers the radiation pressure $(1 - \beta)$ and the brightness of the star. The lowered value of $1 - \beta$ would altogether spoil the general agreement between the masses of stars and the critical range of radiation pressure. In fact radiation pressure would lose most of its importance in this subject. Further, since the proportion of hydrogen must on this hypothesis diminish with the age of the star, the luminosity would be lowered by a variable factor and we should not have the uniform relation of luminosity and mass which the observations appear to confirm. It was shown in § 168 that a proportion of 20 per cent. of hydrogen in Capella would bring the astronomical opacity into agreement with Kramers' theory. But this is no improvement, since the sun and other late stars with very little hydrogen left (according to No. (3)) would remain outstanding. Whatever cure is suggested for the discrepancy of Kramers' theory it should be one that is applicable to all stars alike.

The hypothesis that the source consists of unknown elements of intense radio-activity requires no long discussion. Since radio-activity is independent of density and (practically) of temperature the stars would be unstable. In other respects it is an arbitrary hypothesis which can be adjusted to fit any facts we like—assuming a sufficient variety of these provided sources. It seems objectionable to have to postulate an initial supply of complex unstable elements dating before the beginning of the star's life and formed presumably in the nebula; it is more reasonable to suppose that the ordinary radio-active elements are synthesised in the stars and are therefore a source of loss, not of gain, of available energy.

Mode of Conversion of Subatomic Energy.

222. If an atom of helium is formed from hydrogen at a single process the energy released must be a quantum. Since the energy represents ·032 of the mass of a hydrogen atom the radiation will be of frequency ν given by the relation

$$·032_H c^2 = h\nu.$$

The frequency is $7 \cdot 3 . 10^{21}$ and the corresponding wave-length

$$\lambda = \cdot 00041 \text{ Å}.$$

If there is a succession of processes the frequencies of the quanta will be smaller but of the same order of magnitude.

We may also assume that if an electron and proton annihilate one another the released energy constitutes a quantum. This conclusion is not strictly justified unless there exists some counter process by which radiation can spontaneously generate electrons and protons—an assumption carrying us into realms of speculation that are perhaps better avoided. If the counter process exists a state of equilibrium can be reached, and by the second law of thermodynamics the distribution of radiation in this state must be the same as that given by all other interactions of matter and radiation; accordingly Planck's law holds and the radiation must be bound and released in single quanta. But I suppose that those who have imagined a reformation of waste radiation into matter have done so rather with a view to evading the consequence of the second law of thermodynamics that the world is running down, and it is not very logical to apply the second law to a process intended to get round it.

Assuming that the quantum relation holds it gives for the annihilation of an electron and proton

$$Hc^2 = h\nu,$$

so that

$$\lambda = \cdot 0000131 \text{ Å}.$$

To justify either of these theories of the source of stellar energy we must satisfy ourselves that the star contains the necessary mechanism for transforming this high-frequency radiation into a normal form of energy. Until recently this constituted a difficulty. Being so far above the K frequency of any material its chance of ionising an atom is exceedingly small. The second of the two quanta above calculated would probably travel right through the star—and to the end of the world—with nothing to absorb it and utilise it. This difficulty has been resolved by the discovery of the Compton effect in the scattering of radiation (§ 52). Although the scattering coefficient diminishes for radiation of very high frequency, it does not fall off with great rapidity as the absorption coefficient does. The subatomic radiation will be scattered after a path short compared with the radius of the star. The Compton effect increases the wave-length by $\cdot 024 (1 - \cos \theta)$ Ångströms whenever the radiation is scattered through an angle θ, the increase being independent of the original wave-length. The first considerable deflection will accordingly bring the energy down to γ ray status and after that there is no difficulty in its further transmutation. The greater part of the energy is, however, no longer in the scattered ray but has been handed over to the electron which scattered it. This recoils with enormous energy, which it proceeds to distribute through the material by the ordinary processes of collision. There is thus suitable mechanism for the conversion of the released energy into utilisable form.

Penetrating Radiation from Interstellar Space.

223. The wave-length 0·0004 Å of the radiation released in the formation of helium from hydrogen is much shorter than that of known γ rays, and the radiation should be distinguished by greater penetrating power. A very penetrating radiation is known to exist in our atmosphere, apparently entering it from outer space. It has been suggested that this may originate from the transmutation of elements in the stars and nebulae.

The penetrating radiation can be detected in the following manner. An ionisation chamber is surrounded by a shield of heavy metal sufficiently thick to protect it from all ordinary radiation outside, and the rate of production of the ions is measured. Whilst there may be a constant production of ions due to radio-activity of the inner part of the walls, any change in the rate must be attributed to radiation from outside which has succeeded in penetrating through the walls. Experiments are made at different altitudes, in ice caverns and below the surface of mountain lakes and the change in the quantity of radiation penetrating the walls is measured. It appears that the radiation travels downwards from the sky because the ionisation is reduced according to the amount of atmosphere, ice or water above the apparatus.

The absorption properly so called of this radiation must be exceedingly small and practically it can only be stopped by scattering. Once scattered it is done with, since it loses its penetrating power by the Compton effect. Hence there is no backward scattered beam of penetrating radiation, and the intensity diminishes downwards according to the usual exponential law of absorption.

Scattering depends only on the number of electrons in the material, which is practically proportional to the mass. It is convenient to keep in mind that the stopping power of the whole atmosphere is roughly equivalent to 10 metres of water or ice or to 1 metre of lead. Such a screen is sufficient to reduce the intensity considerably, but not to exclude the radiation entirely.

In this provisional discussion we follow the results of W. Kohlhörster whose experiments were made on the Jungfrau. It should be stated, however, that R. A. Millikan, who has experimented at high altitudes in the United States, has obtained somewhat different results and I understand that he is not in agreement with Kohlhörster's conclusions. It is not for us to judge which is right; but since our only reason for treating of this radiation is its supposed extra-terrestrial origin we must tentatively follow the authority whose experiments appear to demonstrate extra-terrestrial origin*.

Kohlhörster compared the ionisation when the apparatus was exposed in the open and in an ice cavern whose roof cut off the radiation from above. He found that the intensity did not depend on the altitude of the sun. Hence the sun is not the source of the radiation. Maxima were found to occur when the Milky Way crosses the zenith; the greatest depth of the stellar system is then overhead.

It must be realised that there is no possibility of the radiation coming from matter at a high temperature—high in the astronomical sense. All the matter of the universe at temperature much above 100,000° is securely tucked away behind screens of stopping power much greater than a metre of lead, and none of its penetrating radiation can escape into the open. Hence our choice is between the photospheric layers of the stars, the bright and dark gaseous nebulae, and the general unaggregated matter diffused through space. As regards temperature there is not much to choose between these; the temperature of diffuse matter in space is probably above 10,000°. The chief theoretical objection to nebular origin is the low density which, one might suppose, would hinder the collection of material for atomic combination.

224. To examine further the question of nebular or stellar origin, consider a column of 1 sq. cm. section extending to the limits of the stellar system. Let σ be the mass contained in it with the proviso that only the first kilogram is to be counted since that would effectively screen any radiation emitted behind it. The limit will operate if the column intersects a star, but in general not otherwise. Divide the integral of σ with respect to solid angle into four portions corresponding to (1) the sun, (2) the stars, (3) bright and dark nebulae, (4) apparently clear regions. If all matter liberated the radiation equally the amount due to each of these sources would be proportional to their respective shares of $\int \sigma d\omega$.

It is not very certain in what order of importance the four sources would be placed by this criterion but I should be inclined to adopt the order (3), (1), (4), (2). There can be little doubt that (2) comes last. The amount of matter diffused through space is likely to be comparable with the mass of the stars and it all counts in (4), whereas only a thin surface-film of each star counts in (2). The sun occupies $\frac{1}{200,000}$ of the sky so that if the radius in a clear region meets more than $\frac{1}{200,000}$ kg. per sq. cm.

---

* [More recently Millikan has announced the results of a reinvestigation of the penetrating radiation by himself and H. Cameron in the summer of 1925. He is convinced of its extra-terrestrial origin. The absorption (scattering) coefficient is found to be 0·18–0·3 per metre of water (*Proc. Nat. Acad. Sci.* **12**, p. 48 (1926)).]

(4) will be more important than (1); the density of interstellar matter may be somewhere about this limit. Dark and diffuse nebulae occupy large tracts of the sky and must be considerably denser than ordinary interstellar matter so that (3) ranks above (4) and perhaps above (1). We take it that the empirical relation of the intensity of the penetrating radiation to the position of the Milky Way shows that it is unnecessary to consider sources outside our own galactic system.

Owing to the uncertainty in placing (1) we cannot say whether the absence of dependence on the altitude of the sun means that the sun is deficient as a source of penetrating radiation compared with the nebulae or whether it is accounted for by a smaller integral of $\sigma d\omega$. The integral for the stars is to that for the sun roughly in the proportion of starlight to sunlight so that it is very unlikely that the stars contribute much. It has been suggested that the younger stars are responsible for this radiation; if so, their emission must be exceedingly fierce; moreover, we should only receive the radiation from the surface layers which are at low density and temperature—conditions not so widely differing from the sun as to suggest greatly enhanced activity.

This then points to the nebulae as the source of the radiation, assuming it to be extra-terrestrial. If, further, we consider that its penetrating power proves that it is of a frequency too high to come from other than subatomic sources, we must regard it as a sign of subatomic processes (evolution of elements?) occurring in the nebulae. That is why we have considered the phenomenon here as possibly of astronomical significance. All our preconceptions tend to regard the nebulae with their exceedingly low density and (relatively) low temperature as most unfavourable for subatomic transformations of this intense kind. But our preconceptions have certainly had little success in explaining stellar evolution, and we are very ready to remodel our ideas if sufficient evidence is forthcoming. If we admit that evolution of the elements occurs in diffuse matter it becomes easier to understand the occurrence of helium and some other elements in the diffuse nebulae, of calcium and sodium in interstellar space, and of rather advanced elements in the reversing layers of the youngest stars.

A numerical calculation, whilst uncertain in its details, will give an idea of the cosmical magnitude of the phenomenon. Divide the mass of the universe into two portions, viz. M_1 which *might* be the source of the radiation and M_2 which *cannot* be the source. Approximately M_1 is the mass of the nebulae and diffuse matter and M_2 the mass of the stars; a thin shell from each star should be transferred from M_2 to M_1 but this can be neglected. Let ϵ_1 and ϵ_2 be the average rates of liberation of subatomic energy in M_1 and M_2. Then $M_2\epsilon_2$ represents the total radiation of the stars. We shall find (§ 256) that at an average point in space $M_2\epsilon_2$

gives a total flux of $7\cdot7.10^{-13} \times 3.10^{10} = \cdot023$ ergs per sq. cm. per sec. Hence the flux of penetrating radiation derived from M_1 is

$$\cdot023 \frac{M_1 \epsilon_1}{M_2 \epsilon_2} \text{ ergs/cm.}^2 \text{ sec.}$$

The quantum for the formation of helium is $4\cdot8.10^{-5}$ ergs, and in any case the penetrating power of the radiation shows that its quantum is of this order of magnitude. Hence the flux is

$$500 \frac{M_1 \epsilon_1}{M_2 \epsilon_2} \text{ quanta/cm.}^2 \text{ sec.}$$

Since this flux is considerably reduced in passing through our atmosphere, we take the reciprocal of the absorption coefficient to correspond to 5 km. of air. Then the amount absorbed in 1 cu. cm. per sec. is

$$10^{-3} \frac{M_1 \epsilon_1}{M_2 \epsilon_2} \text{ quanta.}$$

For such penetrating radiation the stoppage is not by true absorption but by scattering. Nearly all the energy is transferred to the scattering electron, which becomes a high speed β particle and creates a large number of ions before it is brought to rest. The total number of ions resulting from one such scattering will be well over 100,000.

In the terrestrial experiments the ionisation observed is of the order 3 or 4 ions per cu. cm. per sec. I do not know whether it is fair to take the number produced in a small vessel as equal to the number in free air; if so, this would indicate that $M_1 \epsilon_1$ is of the order $\frac{1}{100} M_2 \epsilon_2$. Since M_1 is not likely to exceed M_2 this indicates that ϵ_1 is at least $\frac{1}{100} \epsilon_2$. Accordingly, the rate of liberation of subatomic energy in the nebulae though probably less than in an average star is not of greatly different order of magnitude.

We have here followed up (without necessarily endorsing) the theory that the ionisation chamber experiments reveal a penetrating radiation of frequency higher than any known γ rays, coming to us from outer space. It leads to astronomical conclusions of great interest, which in themselves seem to us entirely reasonable. It seems to be established that (up to considerable altitudes) the radiation is coming downwards and therefore its source is either in the upper atmosphere or extra-terrestrial. If we felt certain that radiation of such extraordinary energy could only be produced by subatomic transformations we might, in discussing celestial *versus* terrestrial origin, prefer the hypothesis of celestial origin as the less sensational of the two. But there is the Wilson effect (explained in § 210) to be reckoned with; the high frequency radiation might be caused by "runaway" electrons in the earth's atmosphere without involving unknown subatomic changes. The decision as to origin depends on the more detailed experimental results—rate of change with altitude, and relation to the altitude of the Milky Way. It would be outside our province to judge critically the trustworthiness of these results.

CHAPTER XII

THE OUTSIDE OF A STAR

225. The fundamental equation (71·2) for the radiative flow of energy fails when the radiation is not enclosed by matter at approximately uniform temperature; in particular, the analysis breaks down at the photosphere where radiation is escaping freely into outer space.

The approximations used in the preceding Chapters relate to matter at a temperature of some millions of degrees. In addition to a re-examination of the fundamental equation, physical approximations of a different kind will be needed in the treatment of the cool outer layers. A higher standard of approximation is generally desirable, since observational comparisons are more abundant and more direct. There is so little in our previous work that can safely be applied to the outside of a star that the simplest course is to begin *de novo*.

Take the axis of x upwards along the vertical, so that $-x$ is the depth below the surface. We shall be concerned with depths small in comparison with the radius and therefore neglect the curvature of the surface. Let $J(\theta) \, d\omega/4\pi$ be the flow per sq. cm. per sec. of radiation travelling in directions within an infinitesimal solid angle $d\omega$ at an inclination θ to the vertical. Consider a cylinder of unit cross-section with its axis in the direction θ, the element of length along the cylinder being

$$ds = dx \sec \theta.$$

Then the flow $J(\theta) \, d\omega/4\pi$ will in the length ds lose by absorption

$$(J(\theta) \, d\omega/4\pi) \, k\rho \, ds$$

and gain by emission $(j \, d\omega/4\pi) \, \rho \, ds$. Here j is the emission per gm. per sec., of which $j \, d\omega/4\pi$ is in directions within $d\omega$. Hence we have

$$\frac{dJ(\theta)}{ds} = - k\rho J(\theta) + j\rho,$$

or

$$\cos \theta \frac{dJ(\theta)}{dx} = - k\rho J(\theta) + j\rho \quad \dots\dots\dots\dots(225\cdot1)$$

a formula equivalent to (74·1).

Let τ be the "optical depth" below the surface defined by

$$\tau = \int_x^0 k\rho \, dx \quad \dots\dots\dots\dots(225\cdot21),$$

so that

$$d\tau = - k\rho \, dx \quad \dots\dots\dots\dots(225\cdot22).$$

Then by (225·1)

$$\cos \theta \frac{dJ(\theta)}{d\tau} = J(\theta) - \frac{j}{k} \dots\dots\dots\dots(225\cdot3).$$

Multiply this first by $d\omega$ and integrate over a sphere, then by $d\omega \cos\theta$ and integrate over a sphere; we obtain

$$\frac{dH}{d\tau} = J - \frac{j}{k} \qquad \text{......................(225·41)},$$

$$\frac{dK}{d\tau} = H \qquad \text{..............................(225·42)},$$

where

$$J = \frac{1}{4\pi}\int J(\theta)\,d\omega, \qquad H = \frac{1}{4\pi}\int J(\theta)\cos\theta\,d\omega, \qquad K = \frac{1}{4\pi}\int J(\theta)\cos^2\theta\,d\omega$$
$$\text{......(225·5)}.$$

We are here considering how the net flow per sq. cm. H, established by the liberation of energy through the whole interior, makes its way out through the last few thousand kilometres; hence H is to be taken as constant. Then by (225·41)

$$j = kJ \qquad \text{..............................(225·6)},$$

and by (225·42)

$$K = H\tau + \text{const.} \qquad \text{.....................(225·7)}.$$

The foregoing analysis is essentially the same as in § 74.

First Approximation.

226. *Approximate* treatments for the outer layers of a star have been developed by Schwarzschild, Jeans, Lindblad, Milne and others*. The following approximation appears to be most natural from our point of view. We set

$$\left. \begin{array}{l} J(\theta) = \quad \text{a constant} \quad = J_1 \text{ for } \theta < \dfrac{\pi}{2} \\[2mm] J(\theta) = \text{another constant} = J_2 \text{ for } \theta > \dfrac{\pi}{2} \end{array} \right\} \quad \text{......(226·1)}.$$

(The constancy is as regards θ, J_1 and J_2 being functions of τ.) The approximation consists in ignoring direction except for the broad distinction of inwards and outwards.

Substituting for $J(\theta)$ in (225·5) we have†

$$J = \tfrac{1}{2}(J_1 + J_2), \qquad H = \tfrac{1}{4}(J_1 - J_2), \qquad K = \tfrac{1}{3}J \ ...(226·2).$$

Hence by (225·42)

$$\frac{dJ}{d\tau} = 3H,$$

so that

$$J = 3H\tau + \text{const.}$$

The constant is determined from the condition that at the boundary

---

* Our approximations and formulae are usually equivalent to those given by Milne, except that the second approximation in § 230 is on different lines.

† The average value of $\cos\theta$ over a hemisphere is $\pm\tfrac{1}{2}$, and of $\cos^2\theta$ is $\tfrac{1}{3}$.

$(\tau = 0)$ there is no inflowing radiation, and hence $J_2 = 0$; then by (226·2) $J = 2H$. Accordingly
$$J = H(2 + 3\tau) \quad\dots\dots\dots\dots\dots\dots(226\cdot3).$$

The energy-density is J/c and the effective temperature T of the radiation is therefore given by
$$J/c = aT^4 \quad\dots\dots\dots\dots\dots\dots\dots(226\cdot4),$$
by the definition of effective temperature in § 29. Hence
$$acT^4 = H(2 + 3\tau) \quad\dots\dots\dots\dots\dots(226\cdot5).$$

The effective temperature T_0 of the radiation at the boundary is then given by
$$acT_0{}^4 = 2H \quad\dots\dots\dots\dots\dots\dots(226\cdot61).$$

The effective temperature of the *star* T_e is by (31·1)
$$acT_e{}^4 = 4H \quad\dots\dots\dots\dots\dots\dots(226\cdot62).$$

Hence
$$T_e = 2^{\frac{1}{4}}T_0 = 1\cdot189T_0 \quad\dots\dots\dots\dots\dots(226\cdot7).$$

Other approximations by Jeans and Milne give this factor as 1·278 and 1·232 respectively. Our second approximation in § 230 gives 1·230. It is important to have found that the whole outer atmosphere of a star is at a temperature not greatly less than the photospheric temperature, so that the material is not exposed to radiation differing widely in quality from that which would be present in thermodynamical equilibrium. For this reason a judicious application of the results of thermodynamical equilibrium is often permissible in dealing with the outside of a star.

In particular, the material will take up approximately the same temperature T as the radiation, and the results (226·4)–(226·7) will be taken to refer to the temperature of the material* and the effective temperature of the radiation indiscriminately.

By (225·6) and (226·3)
$$j = kH(2 + 3\tau) \quad\dots\dots\dots\dots\dots(226\cdot8).$$

227. Accepting the first approximation (226·8) as giving with sufficient accuracy the emission j at different depths we can calculate how the intensity of the emergent radiation varies with direction.

A ray travelling at an angle θ to the vertical has to traverse an optical thickness $\tau \sec \theta$ before emergence and is reduced by absorption to the fraction $e^{-\tau \sec \theta}$ of its original intensity. Considering an oblique cylinder of unit cross-section, a length $ds \; (= dx \sec \theta)$ gives an emission within solid angle $d\omega$ equal to $\rho \, dx \sec \theta . j \, d\omega/4\pi$ which is reduced before emergence to
$$j \frac{d\omega}{4\pi} \rho \, dx \sec \theta \, e^{-\tau \sec \theta} = -H \frac{d\omega}{4\pi} \sec \theta \, (2 + 3\tau) \, e^{-\tau \sec \theta} \, d\tau \quad (227\cdot1),$$

---

* By temperature of material not in thermodynamic equilibrium I mean the temperature corresponding to the mean speed of its molecules.

by (226·8). Hence integrating, the total amount emerging is

$$H \frac{d\omega}{4\pi} \sec\theta \int_0^\infty (2 + 3\tau)\, e^{-\tau\sec\theta}\, d\tau \quad\ldots\ldots\ldots\ldots\ldots\ldots(227\cdot15)$$

$$= H \frac{d\omega}{4\pi} \int_0^\infty (2 + 3z\cos\theta)\, e^{-z}\, dz \quad (z = \tau\sec\theta)$$

$$= H \frac{d\omega}{2\pi} (1 + \tfrac{3}{2}\cos\theta) \quad\ldots\ldots\ldots\ldots\ldots\ldots\ldots(227\cdot2).$$

This is called the "law of darkening" since it gives the variation of brightness over the apparent disc of the star. As we approach the edge we view the surface by more and more oblique rays. Between the centre $(\theta = 0)$ and the limb $\left(\theta = \dfrac{\pi}{2}\right)$ the brightness changes in the ratio $\tfrac{5}{2} : 1$ or very nearly 1 magnitude. This (approximate) theoretical formula is in close agreement with observations of the solar disc.

The total amount of radiation emerging from unit area of the star (not of the *disc*) is obtained by multiplying (227·2) by the factor $\cos\theta$ for foreshortening and integrating over a hemisphere. The result is H—as it should be*.

The effective temperature of a particular region on the disc is given by

$$acT_e{}^4 = 2H (1 + \tfrac{3}{2}\cos\theta) \quad\ldots\ldots\ldots\ldots\ldots(227\cdot3).$$

This follows from (227·2) because for this point of the disc we see only the radiation emerging in the direction θ, and compare it with a black body giving the same flow *in all directions*.

Hence at the centre of the disc $acT_e{}^4 = 5H$, so that the effective temperature at the centre is $(\tfrac{5}{4})^{\frac{1}{4}}$ or $1\cdot0574$ times the effective temperature for the star as a whole, e.g. the effective temperature at the centre of the solar disc is $6070°$ against $5740°$ for the integrated radiation of the sun.

The effective temperature of the integrated disc is the same as that of a region where $\cos\theta = \tfrac{2}{3}$.

The Spectral Energy Curve.

228. The average depth τ_m from which the emergent radiation has come is

$$\tau_m = \int_0^\infty \tau (2 + 3\tau)\, e^{-\tau\sec\theta}\, d\tau \div \int_0^\infty (2 + 3\tau)\, e^{-\tau\sec\theta}\, d\tau$$

$$= \cos\theta (1 + 3\cos\theta) \div (1 + \tfrac{3}{2}\cos\theta).$$

By (226·5) the temperature T_m at τ_m is given by

$$acT_m{}^4 = 2H \{1 + \tfrac{3}{2}\cos\theta (1 + 3\cos\theta)/(1 + \tfrac{3}{2}\cos\theta)\}$$

$$= 2H \frac{1 + 3\cos\theta + \tfrac{9}{2}\cos^2\theta}{1 + \tfrac{3}{2}\cos\theta} \quad\ldots\ldots\ldots\ldots\ldots(228\cdot1).$$

* The early approximations of Schwarzschild and Jeans do not satisfy this check. See Milne, *Monthly Notices*, **81**, p. 364.

On the other hand, the intensity of the emergent radiation corresponds to an effective temperature given by (227·3)

$$acT_e^4 = 2H \left(1 + \tfrac{3}{2} \cos \theta\right) \quad \dots\dots\dots\dots\dots(228\cdot2).$$

The ratio T_m/T_e is 1·08 at the centre (cos $\theta = 1$) and falls to unity at the limb. We might perhaps expect the quality of the light (distribution in wave-length) to correspond to the mean temperature of its origin. In that case T_m/T_e will be the ratio of the effective temperature judged by quality of the radiation to the effective temperature judged by quantity. This, however, is a lazy way of handling the problem and it is not surprising that the result fails to accord with observation. The proper course is to find the spectral distribution of the emergent radiation by treating each wave-length separately using its own proper value of j and k.

The chief published investigations of the theory of the spectral distribution of the emergent radiation are by E. A. Milne[*] and B. Lindblad[†]. Reference may be made to these to supplement the present account in matters of detail.

The observed spectral energy-curve of the sun is shown by the broken line in Fig. 5 (p. 328). It is derived from Abbot's measurements as combined by Lindblad. The ordinate is proportional to the amount of energy emitted within a fixed range of wave-length $d\lambda$. (In our previous theoretical work we have generally considered a fixed range of frequency $d\nu$.) When plotted in this way the maximum ordinate of the black-body curve is given by (102·3)

$$\lambda_{\text{max.}}\, T = 0\cdot288 \text{ cm. deg.} \quad \dots\dots\dots\dots\dots(228\cdot3).$$

The dotted curve (constant absorption coefficient) in the figure, although not precisely the black-body curve, is barely distinguishable from it on the scale of the diagram, so that the difference of the two curves is practically the deviation of the sun's radiation from a black-body.

Three causes may contribute to this deviation—

(a) What we see is a superposition of radiation from layers at different temperatures, and the spread of temperature distorts the black-body curve.

(b) Since the absorption coefficient is different for different wave-lengths we see farther into the sun in some wave-lengths than in others and so receive radiation from a hotter stratum.

(c) The conditions in the radiating layers are beginning to deviate from thermodynamical equilibrium and deviations from Planck's Law may arise at the source of the radiation.

---

[*] *Monthly Notices*, **81**, p. 375 (1921); *Phil. Trans.* **223** A, p. 201 (1922).

[†] *Uppsala Universitets Årsskrift*, 1920, No. 1; *Nova Acta Reg. Soc. Sci.Upsaliensis*, Ser. 4, Vol. 6, No. 1 (1923).

If $j_\nu \, d\nu$ is the emission (per gm. per sec.) between frequencies ν and $\nu + d\nu$, and k_ν is the absorption coefficient for frequency ν, then as in (227·1) the emergent radiation is

$$d\nu \frac{d\omega}{4\pi} \int j_\nu \rho \, dx \sec \theta \, e^{-\tau_\nu \sec \theta}$$

$$= - \, d\nu \frac{d\omega}{4\pi} \int (j_\nu / k_\nu) \, d\tau_\nu \sec \theta \, e^{-\tau_\nu \sec \theta} \quad \dots\dots\dots\dots (228\cdot 4),$$

where
$$\tau_\nu = \int_x^0 k_\nu \rho \, dx.$$

The relation between absorption and emission coefficients is by (77·15)

$$j_\nu = c k_\nu I \, (\nu, T) \quad \dots\dots\dots\dots\dots\dots (228\cdot 5),$$

where as usual $I \, (\nu, T)$ denotes Planck's energy distribution. Hence denoting the emergent radiation by $H \, (\nu, \theta) \, d\nu \, d\omega / 4\pi$, we have from (228·4)

$$H \, (\nu, \theta) = c \int_0^1 I \, (\nu, T) \, d \, (e^{-\tau_\nu \sec \theta}) \quad \dots\dots\dots\dots (228\cdot 6).$$

The use of the equilibrium formula (228·5) is perhaps open to criticism considering that in the problem of spectral energy distribution we have to aim at rather high accuracy. The molecular velocities will correspond to temperature T, but the state of ionisation and excitation of the material will be slightly different owing to its exposure to non-equilibrium radiation. Thus the material may not have the normal absorbing and emitting power to which the equation (228·5) refers. We reserve this point (cause (c) above) for later consideration.

229. We take the three causes of deviation in order—

(a) *Spread of Temperature.*

As the effect of variation of k_ν is not to be considered at present, we take $k_\nu = k$, $\tau_\nu = \tau$. The formula (228·6) gives the following rule: Divide the range of $e^{-\tau \sec \theta}$ into a large number of equal parts. Calculate the temperatures $T_1, T_2, T_3 \dots$ at the middle of each part. Take a cu. cm. of equilibrium radiation at each of these temperatures; the simple mean gives the constitution of the emergent radiation.

Table 43 has been calculated in this way. The first part of it refers to $\theta = 0$, and ten equal ranges of $e^{-\tau}$ are taken so that the temperatures $T_1, T_2 \dots$ correspond to $e^{-\tau} = 0\cdot 95,\ 0\cdot 85,\ \dots$. The temperatures are calculated from (226·5) and (226·62) which give

$$T^4 = T_e^4 \, (\tfrac{1}{2} + \tfrac{3}{4}\tau) \quad \dots\dots\dots\dots\dots (229\cdot 1),$$

the sun's effective temperature T_e being taken as 5740°. The next three columns give

$$(e^{h\nu/RT} - 1)^{-1} \quad \dots\dots\dots\dots\dots (229\cdot 15),$$

for three different frequencies; this represents the intensity $I \, (\nu, T)$ for frequency ν so far as it depends on T.

At the foot of the table the means of these intensities are taken. By the above rule this gives the intensity of the emergent radiation. The black-body temperature corresponding to this emergent intensity is deduced by the converse application of (229·15). Besides the equivalent black-body temperatures for the three wave-lengths, we give the equivalent black-body temperature 6039° for the whole intensity. This is deduced from the mean value of τ by (229·1). It is not quite the same as the actual effective temperature of the centre of the sun's disc (6068°) because we have, so to speak, left out a little bit of the sun in replacing the integral by the sum of 10 terms; but it is evidently proper to use the exact result for the distribution under discussion rather than the actual value for the celestial object which it approximately represents*. Finally, the intensities for a black-body at 6039° are given in the last line of the table, so that a comparison with the mean intensities gives the deviation from the black-body law arising from the spread of temperature. It is seen that these deviations are quite small.

The second part of the Table gives similar results for a region near the sun's limb. Since the spread of temperature is proportionately smaller, the deviations from black-body radiation are smaller.

Table 43.

Effect of Spread of Temperature of Radiating Layers.

		Centre of Disc				Sec $\theta = 3$		
$e^{-\tau}$	τ	T	Int. $\lambda 4157$	Int. $\lambda 6235$	Int. $\lambda 12470$	T	Int. $\lambda 4157$	Int. $\lambda 12470$
·95	·0513	4920°	·00091	·0095	·107	4850°	·00083	·104
·85	·1625	5100	·00116	·0111	·117	4920	·00091	·107
·75	·2877	5280	·00147	·0131	·128	4990	·00101	·111
·65	·4308	5470	·00185	·0153	·140	5060	·00109	·116
·55	·5979	5660	·00230	·0177	·152	5150	·00125	·121
·45	·7985	5880	·00285	·0205	·165	5250	·00142	·125
·35	1·0498	6110	·00359	·0239	·180	5360	·00163	·133
·25	1·3863	6390	·00459	·0283	·199	5500	·00193	·142
·15	1·8971	6760	·00617	·0347	·224	5700	·00239	·154
·05	2·9958	7390	·00954	·0467	·268	6070	·00341	·177
Mean	·9658	—	·00344	·0221	·168	—	·00159	·129
Eff. temp.	6039°	—	6070°	5987°	5924°	5326°	5342°	5290°
B.B. int.	—	—	·00334	·0228	·176	—	·00156	·132

* It will be noticed that most of the intensity comes from the deeper partitions, and for exact calculation we should naturally sub-divide these. The purpose of the table, however, is to enable us to find our bearings with regard to the problem. If the calculations are worth pursuing further, recourse may be had to the analytical treatment of the integral (228·6) developed in Milne's researches (*loc. cit.*).

The maximum ordinate of the spectral energy curve occurs near 5900 A. Table 43 shows that the intensity is here rising faster than the black-body curve as we go towards the violet; hence the maximum ordinate will be displaced in this direction. Milne has calculated that the displacement amounts to 4·3 per cent., so that the effective temperature calculated from (228·3) is 4·3 per cent. higher than that calculated from the total intensity of the radiation. This is actually in good agreement with observation; but reference to Fig. 5 shows that the accordance is accidental; the trivial shift in the position of the maximum ordinate (inappreciable on the scale of the diagram) achieves no real advance in explaining the sun's deviation from a black body.

By (227·2) the contrast in brightness between the centre and the selected point near the limb (sec $\theta = 3$) is 0·6 for the integrated spectrum. By Table 43 it is

$$\tfrac{159}{344} = 0\cdot46 \text{ for } \lambda 4157; \qquad \tfrac{129}{168} = 0\cdot77 \text{ for } \lambda 12470.$$

This is mostly accounted for by the difference of effective temperatures 5326° and 6039°, a decrease of temperature having more effect on the violet than on the red. According to Milne the observed contrast in all wave-lengths agrees very closely with that predicted by this theory. He considers this agreement to be very unwelcome; it is premature because we have yet to take account of the variation of the absorption coefficient. The close connection between centre-limb contrast and variation of k_ν is shown by the occurrence of $\tau_\nu \sec \theta$ in (228·6); to double k_ν/k is equivalent to transferring to a new point on the disc where $\sec \theta$ is doubled. When

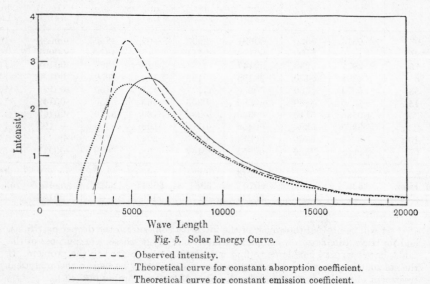

Fig. 5. Solar Energy Curve.

－－－－－－　Observed intensity.
....　Theoretical curve for constant absorption coefficient.
————————　Theoretical curve for constant emission coefficient.

we introduce variations of the absorption coefficient in order to account for the difference between the broken curve and dotted curve in Fig. 5, we shall necessarily alter the centre-limb contrast and presumably make it less accordant with observation.

The predicted energy-curve allowing for the spread of temperature but not allowing for any variation of k_ν with ν is shown by the dotted curve in Fig. 5. It is based on Milne's calculations.

(b) Variation of k_ν.

By (228·5) if k_ν is constant j_ν varies with ν, and *vice versa*. There is no known physical hypothesis that suggests constancy of k_ν, but the hypothesis that j_ν is independent of ν is plausible.

On Kramers' theory of absorption as developed for X rays in the interior of a star we found that j_ν was independent of ν up to the guillotine limit (§ 157). It is a wide extrapolation to extend this to optical frequencies; but since the general principles of optical and X ray absorption are the same, we shall adopt the hypothesis tentatively. We may say at once that it will not bring about the desired agreement with the observed energy curve of the sun; but it is a proper first step to exhibit divergences from a curve which has a physical meaning rather than from a curve which corresponds to a purely mathematical abstraction with no physical interpretation.

From the analysis in § 157 it follows that if j_ν is independent of ν

$$\frac{k_\nu}{k} = \frac{105}{128} \frac{\beta}{\alpha} \frac{e^x - 1}{x^3} \quad \dots\dots\dots\dots\dots(229\cdot2),$$

where $x = h\nu/RT$, $\beta = 1\cdot151$, $\alpha = 1\cdot0823$. The mean coefficient k in the present discussion is evidently the coefficient of opacity k_2 of § 157. From (226·5) and (226·61)

$$d\tau = \frac{8}{3} \frac{T^3 dT}{T_0^4} = \frac{8}{3} x_0^4 \frac{dx}{x^5},$$

where $x_0 = h\nu/RT_0$. Hence

$$\tau_\nu = \int \frac{k_\nu}{k} d\tau = \frac{35}{16} \frac{\beta}{\alpha} x_0^4 \int_{x_0} \frac{e^x - 1}{x^8} dx \quad \dots\dots\dots(229\cdot3).$$

Having tabulated the integral of $(e^x - 1)/x^8$ we can calculate the values of x (and therefore T) for any optical depth τ_ν and then proceed as in Table 43.

The calculation would be long and it is doubtful if the labour of an accurate computation would be justified. A short method will give sufficient accuracy for our purpose. Although x varies as we descend in the star we shall be content to calculate k_ν/k for a mean value $x_e = h\nu/RT_e$ and treat it as constant. By (228·2) and (226·5) the effective temperature is the temperature at an optical depth given by $\tau \sec \theta = 1$. The effective temperature for a particular frequency ν will also correspond very nearly to the same depth provided that $\tau_\nu = \tau$ (the small divergences being those exhibited in Table 43); but if τ_ν is different the condition $\tau \sec \theta = 1$ is evidently replaced by

$$\tau_\nu \sec \theta = 1 \quad \text{or} \quad \tau = \cos \theta . k/k_\nu$$

so that the intensity corresponds to temperature T_ν, where

$$acT_\nu^4 = H (2 + 3 (k/k_\nu) \cos \theta).$$

Since Fig. 5 refers to the integrated light of the solar disc we must take $\cos \theta = \frac{2}{3}$; and accordingly the equivalent temperature for frequency ν will be given by $\qquad T_\nu^4 = \frac{1}{2} (1 + k/k_\nu) T_e^4 \ldots\ldots\ldots\ldots\ldots(229\cdot4).$

We can now by Planck's law calculate the change in intensity due to our seeing down to a layer of temperature T_ν instead of T_e and multiply the ordinates of the dotted curve in the ratio found. The result is shown by the continuous curve in Fig. 5.

At first sight this curve for constant j_ν seems to deviate more from the observed spectral energy curve than the curve for constant k_ν did. But even if that is so, we must emphasize that it is the deviation from this new curve that requires a physical explanation rather than the deviation from the first curve which was merely a mathematical auxiliary. The new curve has the advantage that it accounts better for the falling off of the solar curve at short wave-lengths*. The high peak of the observed curve is still unaccounted for; assuming that this is due to less emission† in the wave-lengths concerned, the general opacity k will be reduced and hence T_ν for other frequencies will be reduced according to (229·4). Thus the deviation on the right-hand side of the figure is likely to right itself automatically when the high peak is accounted for.

We have calculated the effect of changes of k_ν on the energy-curve. By the converse process we can calculate what variation of k_ν would be necessary to account for the observed curve. Values of k_ν obtained in this way by Milne are tabulated in the second column of Table 44. The values which correspond to constant j_ν, obtained from (229·2), are given in the third column. By division we obtain the values of $1/j_\nu$ given in the fourth column. (The unit in each column is arbitrary.)

The last column indicates that the whole deviation of the observed curve is accounted for by a regular decrease in the emission with decreasing

---

* H. H. Plaskett (*Pub. Dominion Observatory*, **2**, p. 242) considers that the diminished intensity at short wave-lengths in Abbot's curve is due to the large number of absorption lines, and that the intensity *between* the lines agrees with the black-body curve. This conclusion was also reached by Fabry and Buisson (*Comptes Rendus*, **175**, p. 156 (1922)) from measurements at five places free from absorption lines in the region 2920–3940 Å. If this is correct we must emphasize that the agreement is quite unexpected and unexplained.

† Note that increased brightness indicates decreased emission.

wave-length. This seems a very reasonable explanation. We might expect some such modification of Kramers' formula for emission when account is taken of the finite size of the ions responsible for the radiation of optical frequencies. It may be remarked that between wave-lengths 3000 and 12,000 the emission is due mainly to capture of electrons in excited orbits; electron switches without capture would give longer waves, and capture in normal orbits would give shorter waves. The reduction of the emission cannot be attributed to the guillotine effect of occupied orbits; it is, perhaps, due to the fact that for these close approaches the atom with one or two electrons missing cannot be treated as equivalent to a point charge.

Table 44.

Analysis of the Observed Solar Energy Curve.

λ	k_ν (obs.)	k_ν (calc.)	$1/j_\nu$
3230	1·97	4·89	2·48
3860	1·09	2·35	2·16
4330	·81	1·65	2·03
4560	·69	1·44	2·08
4810	·68	1·27	1·87
5010	·70	1·16	1·66
5340	·70	1·03	1·48
6040	·71	·87	1·22
6700	·76	·78	1·03
6990	·77	·76	·98
8660	1·16	·70	·61
10310	1·36	·72	·53
12250	1·02	·79	·77

Against this interpretation of the observed energy curve there is the objection raised by Milne that his values of k_ν in Table 44 are not supported by the centre-limb contrast which agrees much better with a nearly constant k_ν. Milne concludes "with considerable assurance that the departure of the sun's energy spectrum from that of a black body is not due to a varying general absorption in the layers contributing to the radiation." It depends on how closely we can trust the observed values of the centre-limb contrast. If Milne is right, we must turn to cause (c).

(c) *Deviation from equilibrium conditions.*

There is the possibility that owing to its exposure to non-equilibrium radiation the material may not have the normal absorbing and emitting power for its temperature and density so that j_ν/k_ν is not given by (228·5). The radiation is richer in the high-frequency constituents which are capable of ionising normal atoms; the ionisation may therefore be greater than the equilibrium value. For the most part emission by capture can only be performed by ionised atoms*, so that if the number of ions is increased 10 per cent. j_ν is increased 10 per cent. There will also be some further increase due to the greater abundance of free electrons. At the same time k_ν diminishes. In fact the equilibrium ionisation attains just the value required to bring j_ν and $ck_\nu I\ (\nu, T)$ into agreement; if greater ionisation occurs, then $j_\nu > ck_\nu I\ (\nu, T)$.

The emergent intensity is seen from (228·4) to be directly proportional to j/k_ν. We can therefore see at once the excess of j_ν/k_ν required to give the observed curve. If the excess ionisation is more or less the same at all depths the intensities at the centre and limb are multiplied by the same factor, so that the contrast-ratio is unaffected and Milne's requirement is satisfied. The non-equilibrium conditions are too complicated to allow a prediction as to what part of the spectrum would be most affected by the excess ionisation but there is no reason to think that any difficulty arises on this point.

I should scarcely have expected the change of ionisation to be sufficiently great to explain the observed curve—at least 15 per cent. seems to be required in order to represent the high peak.

At present we cannot decide on a definite conclusion. The whole investigation leaves one with a sense not so much of puzzlement over the deviations of the sun from a black-body as of surprise that it should approach a black-body so nearly as it does.

It should be added that the observational data to which we have trusted are not entirely confirmed by recent investigators, and it is possible that we have been laying too much stress on some of the features of Abbot's curve.

Second Approximation to the Temperature Distribution.

230. The emergent radiation (227·2) is $J\ (\theta)\ d\omega/4\pi$ for the level $\tau = 0$, so that

$$J\ (\theta) = 2H \left(1 + \tfrac{3}{2} \cos \theta\right) \quad \text{for } \tau = 0,\ \theta < \frac{\pi}{2}.$$

For $\theta > \dfrac{\pi}{2}$, $J\ (\theta)$ is zero at this level. Hence by (225·5)

$$J = \frac{1}{4\pi} \int J\ (\theta)\ d\omega = \tfrac{7}{4}H \dotfill (230\text{·}1).$$

This should now replace our original boundary condition $J = 2H$ which corresponds to the approximation in which $J\ (\theta)$ is supposed to be constant over the hemisphere. Hence in place of (226·61) and (226·62) we now have

$$acT_0{}^4 = \tfrac{7}{4}H, \qquad acT_e{}^4 = 4H,$$

so that

$$T_e = (\tfrac{16}{7})^{\frac{1}{4}}\, T_0 = 1\text{·}230T_0 \dotfill (230\text{·}2).$$

---

* Capture of electrons can be effected by neutral atoms, but their efficiency is likely to be much less. The negatively charged atoms H_, C_, O_, etc. are well known in positive ray experiments.

Note that the ratio T_e/T_0 depends solely on the law of darkening, so that for the sun it could be deduced at once from the observed law of darkening without reference to the theory of the temperature distribution in the interior.

By the same method we can find $J(\theta)$ at any level τ_1. Making the appropriate modifications of (227·15) we have

$$J(\theta) = H \sec\theta \int_{\tau_1}^{\infty} (2 + 3\tau) e^{-(\tau - \tau_1)\sec\theta} \, d\tau \qquad \left(\theta < \frac{\pi}{2}\right),$$

$$J(\theta) = H \sec\theta' \int_0^{\tau_1} (2 + 3\tau) e^{-(\tau_1 - \tau)\sec\theta'} \, d\tau \qquad \left(\theta' = \pi - \theta < \frac{\pi}{2}\right).$$

Hence performing the integration

$$J(\theta) = H(2 + 3\cos\theta + 3\tau_1) \qquad \left(\theta < \frac{\pi}{2}\right) \quad (230\cdot31),$$

$$J(\theta) = H\{(2 - 3\cos\theta')(1 - e^{-\tau_1 \sec\theta'}) + 3\tau_1\} \qquad \left(\theta' < \frac{\pi}{2}\right) \quad (230\cdot32).$$

Substitute these values in (225·5) so as to obtain the values of J, H and K. We give separately the parts corresponding to the outward radiation (J_+) and inward radiation (J_-). The results are—

$$\left.\begin{aligned}
&J_+ = H\left(\tfrac{7}{4} + \tfrac{3}{2}\tau\right), \qquad J_- = H\left(\tfrac{1}{4} + \tfrac{3}{2}\tau - U_2(\tau) + \tfrac{3}{2}U_3(\tau)\right), \\
&\qquad J = H\left(2 + 3\tau - U_2(\tau) + \tfrac{3}{2}U_3(\tau)\right), \\
&H_+ = H\left(1 + \tfrac{3}{4}\tau\right), \qquad H_- = H\left(-\tfrac{3}{4}\tau + \tfrac{1}{2}\tau\left(U_2(\tau) - U_3(\tau)\right)\right), \\
&\qquad H = H\left(1 + \tfrac{1}{2}\tau\left(U_2(\tau) - U_3(\tau)\right)\right), \\
&K_+ = H\left(\tfrac{17}{24} + \tfrac{1}{2}\tau\right), \qquad K_- = H\left(-\tfrac{1}{24} + \tfrac{1}{2}\tau - U_4(\tau) + \tfrac{3}{2}U_5(\tau)\right), \\
&\qquad K = \tfrac{1}{3}H\left(2 + 3\tau - 3U_4(\tau) + \tfrac{9}{2}U_5(\tau)\right)
\end{aligned}\right\} \quad (230\cdot4),$$

where

$$U_r(\tau) = \int_1^{\infty} \frac{e^{-\tau y}}{y^r} \, dy \quad\ldots\ldots\ldots\ldots\ldots\ldots\ldots(230\cdot5).$$

231. Consider now how these results are to be used for a second approximation to the temperature distribution. Equation (225·42) is rigorous and H is constant, so that

$$K = \tau H + \text{const.} \quad \ldots\ldots\ldots\ldots\ldots(231\cdot1).$$

Formerly we set $K = \tfrac{1}{3}J$ the factor $\tfrac{1}{3}$ coming from the mean value of $\cos^2\theta$ over a sphere. We can now replace this by the ratio of K to J given in (230·4), which is the mean value of $\cos^2\theta$ properly weighted according to the distribution of the radiation in regard to direction as determined in (230·31) and (230·32). Hence

$$J = 3f(\tau H + \text{const.}),$$

where

$$f = \frac{2 + 3\tau - U_2(\tau) + \tfrac{3}{2}U_3(\tau)}{2 + 3\tau - 3U_4(\tau) + \tfrac{9}{2}U_5(\tau)} \quad\ldots\ldots\ldots\ldots(231\cdot2).$$

The constant has already been determined since $J = \tfrac{7}{4}H$ at the boundary, so that

$$acT^4 = J = fH\left(\tfrac{17}{8} + 3\tau\right) \quad\ldots\ldots\ldots\ldots\ldots(231\cdot3),$$

since the boundary value of f is found to be $\frac{14}{17}$. This replaces the first approximation $acT^4 = J = H(2 + 3\tau)$.

It will be noticed that we do not use the "revised" value of H from (230·4); that would be a retrograde step. That H is constant and equal to a given boundary value is the essential condition of the problem. The fact that, calculating from the first approximation to the temperature distribution, we do not exactly reproduce a constant H indicates the failure of the first approximation to fulfil the conditions of the problem; and if the "revised value" is $H + \Delta H$, ΔH is a measure of the error of the first approximation.

The functions $U_r(\tau)$ are calculated by the reduction formula

$$(r - 1)\, U_r(\tau) = e^{-\tau} - \tau U_{r-1}(\tau),$$

and $U_1(\tau)$ is a tabulated function.

In Table 45 the second column gives the value of f calculated from (231·2), the third column gives the ratio of the second approximation to T^4 from (231·3) to the first approximation from (226·5). The fourth column gives $\Delta H/H$ as defined above.

Table 45.

Second Approximation to Temperature Distribution.

τ	f	$T_{(2)}{}^4/T_{(1)}{}^4$	$\Delta H/H$
0	·8235	·875	·0000
$\frac{1}{8}$	·9188	·967	+ ·0176
$\frac{1}{4}$	·9497	·993	+ ·0241
$\frac{1}{2}$	·9755	1·010	+ ·0263
1	·9915	1·016	+ ·0194
∞	1·0000	1·000	·0000

The main interest of the investigation is that the second approximation makes so slight an amendment to the distribution given by the first approximation. We could without much difficulty examine the effect of this amendment on the law of darkening (227·2) but it is evident that the correction would be trivial*.

The first approximation will be sufficiently accurate for most purposes, and we shall use it throughout the rest of this Chapter.

The Photosphere†.

232. The photosphere is the region in which the heat and light directly reaching us is emitted. We shall take two levels τ_1 and τ_2 between which

---

* The chief effect is a slight extra dimming near the limb, where the radiation comes from small depth τ and would in the limit be reduced to $\frac{7}{8}$ of the intensity given by the first approximation.

† The investigation of conditions in the sun's photosphere is resumed in § 251 and reference should be made to that section for the definitive conclusions.

80 per cent. of the heat is emitted, 10 per cent. being above τ_1 and 10 per cent. below τ_2, and regard these conventionally as the upper and lower boundaries of the photosphere.

To find τ_1 and τ_2 we must insert these as limits in the integral in (227·15)

$$\sec \theta \int (2 + 3\tau) e^{-\tau \sec \theta} d\tau = \int (2 + 3z \cos \theta) e^{-z} dz$$
$$= - e^{-z} (2 + 3 \cos \theta + 3z \cos \theta)$$
$$\dots\dots(232\cdot1).$$

It is then easy to determine the values of $z = \tau \sec \theta$ between which (232·1) increases by any given fraction of its total increment from $z = 0$ to ∞.

For the *centre of the disc*—
Setting $\cos \theta = 1$ we find
$$\tau_1 = 0\cdot25, \qquad \tau_2 = 3\cdot4 \dots\dots\dots\dots(232\cdot2).$$
By (226·5) the temperatures at these levels are
$$T_1 = 0\cdot911 T_e, \qquad T_2 = 1\cdot322 T_e \dots\dots\dots(232\cdot3),$$
where T_e is the effective temperature of the star; or if T_e' is the effective temperature of the centre of the disc
$$T_1 = 0\cdot86 T_e', \qquad T_2 = 1\cdot25 T_e'.$$

For the *integrated disc*, or for a region of the disc where $\cos \theta = \frac{2}{3}$—
We find
$$\tau_1 = 0\cdot134, \qquad \tau_2 = 2\cdot21 \dots\dots\dots\dots(232\cdot4),$$
and the temperatures are
$$T_1 = 0\cdot880 T_e, \qquad T_2 = 1\cdot212 T_e \dots\dots\dots\dots(232\cdot5).$$

It will be seen that the range of temperature in the photosphere is determined without any knowledge of the law of variation of the absorption coefficient k.

233. The hydrostatic equation $dP = - g\rho dx$ continues to be valid at the outside of a star so that
$$d (p_G + p_R) = - g\rho dx.$$
But since the radiation pressure is not strictly isotropic p_R is here the vertical component of the pressure. The pressure of radiation in a vertical direction is K/c (cf. the definition of p_R' in (74·2)). Hence by (225·42)
$$dp_R = dK/c = Hd\tau/c = - k\rho Hdx/c,$$
so that
$$dp_R = \frac{kH}{cg} (dp_G + dp_R) \dots\dots\dots\dots(233\cdot1),$$
which is the same as (81·4) for the stellar interior.

Conformably with the first approximation we set $p_R = \frac{1}{3}aT^4$. The exact value is $\frac{1}{3}aT^4/f$, where f is given in Table 45; but it would not be proper to introduce f without attending to the other modifications involved in a second approximation.

Let
$$1 - \beta' = \frac{kH}{cg} \quad \ldots\ldots\ldots\ldots\ldots(233\cdot2).$$

Then $(233\cdot1)$ becomes

$$\tfrac{1}{3}a\beta' dT^4 = (1 - \beta') \Re d\, (\rho T/\mu) \quad \ldots\ldots\ldots\ldots(233\cdot3).$$

Suppose that β' (and therefore k) is constant. Then by integration

$$T^4 - T_0{}^4 = \frac{3\Re\,(1 - \beta')}{a\mu\beta'} \rho T \quad \ldots\ldots\ldots\ldots(233\cdot4).$$

This is similar to $(84\cdot1)$ except that the constant of integration is no longer negligible. Of course β' will not have the same value as β in the stellar interior.

Owing to the constant of integration $(1 - \beta')/\beta'$ no longer represents the ratio of p_R to p_G; but it represents dp_R/dp_G, which is what is commonly *meant* by the ratio of radiation pressure to gas pressure, i.e. the ratio of the forces exerted by these pressures on a given piece of material. It has sometimes been thought that, since p_R/p_G tends to infinity at the boundary, radiation pressure becomes of enormous importance in the equilibrium of the extreme layers of the star; this is a fallacy because the force depends on the gradient of the pressure and not on its absolute value.

By $(226\cdot5)$ and $(226\cdot61)$

$$T^4 - T_0{}^4 = 3\tau H/ac \quad \ldots\ldots\ldots\ldots(233\cdot5).$$

Hence by $(233\cdot4)$
$$\frac{\rho_1 T_1}{\rho_2 T_2} = \frac{\tau_1}{\tau_2} \quad \ldots\ldots\ldots\ldots(233\cdot6).$$

Inserting the values $(232\cdot4)$ and $(232\cdot5)$ for the limits of the photosphere (integrated disc) we find
$$\rho_2 = 12\cdot0\rho_1.$$

By $(233\cdot4)$ and $(233\cdot5)$

$$p_G = \frac{\Re}{\mu} \rho T = \frac{a\beta'}{3\,(1 - \beta')} \frac{3\tau H}{ac}$$

$$= \frac{\beta'}{1 - \beta'} \frac{H}{c} \tau \quad \ldots\ldots\ldots\ldots(233\cdot7).$$

According to Milne (§ 248) the value of $1 - \beta'$ for the outer part of the sun is roughly $0\cdot1$. We have for the sun $H/c = 2\cdot08$. Hence for the limits of the solar photosphere $(232\cdot4)$

$$(p_G)_1 = 2\cdot50, \qquad (p_G)_2 = 41\cdot3 \text{ dynes per sq. cm.},$$

that is to say, the pressure in the solar photosphere is round about 10^{-5} atmospheres.

Also
$$-g\,dx = \frac{dP}{\rho} = \frac{\tfrac{1}{3}a\,dT^4}{1 - \beta'} \frac{3\Re\,(1 - \beta')}{a\mu\beta'} \frac{T}{T^4 - T_0{}^4} \text{ by } (233\cdot4)$$

$$= \frac{4\Re}{\mu\beta'} \frac{T^4 dT}{T^4 - T_0{}^4} \quad \ldots\ldots\ldots\ldots\ldots\ldots\ldots\ldots(233\cdot8).$$

Hence integrating

$$\text{const.} - x = \frac{\Re T_0}{\mu \beta' g} \left\{ \frac{4T}{T_0} + \log_e \frac{T - T_0}{T + T_0} - 2 \tan^{-1} \frac{T}{T_0} \right\} \dots (233 \cdot 9).$$

For μ we guess the value 20 since the ionisation is low; $g = 2 \cdot 74 . 10^4$ on the sun; hence with the values of T in $(232 \cdot 5)$

$$x_1 - x_2 = 2 \cdot 70 . 10^6 \text{ cm.}$$

To sum up—at an average point on the sun's disc ($\cos \theta = \frac{2}{3}$) the thickness of the layer furnishing 80 per cent. of the whole radiation is 27 kilometres. In this zone the temperature increases from 5050° to 6950° and the density increases twelvefold. The pressure increases sixteenfold, and in the middle its value is about 10^{-5} atmos.

In a giant star the thickness of the photosphere will be greatly increased on account of the much smaller value of g $(233 \cdot 9)$. The pressure is only altered to a moderate extent according to the value of $\beta'/(1 - \beta')$.

These preliminary results will be revised in § 251; but their general character is not much altered.

Absorption Lines.

234. Line absorption is caused by the excitation of an atom from one state to another. In this process radiation of a definite frequency ν to $\nu + \delta\nu$ is absorbed and if the atom is free from disturbance the width $\delta\nu$ of the absorption line is small. The explanation of the appearance of absorption lines in stellar spectra is not quite so obvious as we might think at first, because absorption is closely linked with emission.

Here are two rough (and contradictory) arguments—

(a) Consider radiation proceeding outwards. It excites atoms and is accordingly absorbed; but the excited atoms subsequently relapse and emit radiation of the same frequency. The emission, however, occurs in all directions equally so that only half of it goes to reinforce the outward beam. Hence absorption followed by emission is equivalent to simple absorption with coefficient $\frac{1}{2}k$, and the intensity in the range ν to $\nu + \delta\nu$ falls off exponentially giving a very dark line.

(b) In light of frequency ν to $\nu + \delta\nu$ we can only see a very small depth into the star since it is highly opaque to this radiation. But the region we do see has a temperature not less than T_0 the boundary temperature, so that the intensity of the radiation in the line should not be less than that corresponding to T_0. Since the surrounding spectrum has an intensity corresponding to $T_e = 1 \cdot 23 T_0$ the contrast is very limited.

The first argument is nearer the truth than the second; but we have the uncomfortable feeling that more attention should be paid to the subsequent adventures of the radiation emitted backwards. I think it is a not uncommon idea that the Fraunhofer spectrum is caused by a cloud of cooler matter which cuts out the photospheric radiation at frequencies for which it is opaque and substitutes the less intense radiation proper to its own temperature; this is argument (*b*). It seems best to examine the whole question by an analytical investigation, tracing the formation of absorption lines—under idealised conditions it is true, but not too unlike the actual conditions.

We assume the radiation to have the equilibrium constitution with the necessary exception at the absorption line which is being studied*. We set J' for the flow of radiation of frequency ν to $\nu + d\nu$ in the absorption

---

* There is no *self-contradiction* in assuming equilibrium constitution of the radiation right up to the boundary of a star; by making the emission coefficient j a suitable function of ν and T we can construct an ideal star conforming to this condition. In actual stars, however, the region above the photosphere is traversed by radiation which is beginning to deviate appreciably from equilibrium constitution, and it may fairly be asked whether our assumption does not differ so much from the actual conditions as to make the results misleading. I think it can be shown that our discussion represents fairly well the *typical conditions* of formation of actual absorption lines. We may divide the assumption into two parts in so far as it relates to (*a*) radiation contiguous to the absorption line, (*b*) more remote parts of the spectrum. The latter part seems to be a fair approximation, no more harmful in this connection than in §§ 241–243; it is employed in most standard investigations of the outer layers of a star. But the part (*a*) is more risky; in particular an incorrect assumption as to the density of the contiguous spectrum directly affects calculations of the contrast ratio or blackness of absorption lines. But this error is not systematic; the actual radiation is richer in high frequencies and poorer in low frequencies than the equilibrium radiation substituted for it, so that lines in the blue and in the red are affected in opposite ways. There is in fact an intermediate region of the spectrum where the assumption is substantially correct; its location can be found as follows. According to observation the radiation at the boundary is approximately equilibrium radiation for temperature T_e except that its density is reduced to $\frac{1}{2}$ by lack of inflowing components; thus the density is

$$\tfrac{1}{2}C\nu^3/(e^{h\nu/RT_e} - 1) \text{ instead of } C\nu^3/(e^{h\nu/RT_0} - 1),$$

where $T_0 = T_e \sqrt[4]{\tfrac{1}{2}}$. The constitution below the surface cannot be determined without a detailed knowledge of the emission laws, but presumably it follows the same kind of relation, i.e. approximately

$$\theta C\nu^3/(e^{h\nu/RT_e} - 1) \text{ instead of } C\nu^3/(e^{h\nu/RT} - 1),$$

where $T = T_e \sqrt[4]{\theta}$. The condition that the two expressions become equal is found to be $h\nu/RT_e = 3\cdot6$ to $3\cdot9$ for $\theta = \frac{1}{2}$ to 1. For the sun the corresponding wave-lengths are 6900 to 6400 Å. Our results should be fairly correct for absorption lines near this part of the spectrum. This region can be shifted to any part of the observed spectrum by choosing a star of appropriate temperature.

Part (*a*) of the assumption is employed when we set the ordinary continuous emission $j\rho ds$ equal to $kJ\rho ds$ (below). By (225·41) the more general expression is $j = k (J - dH/d\tau)$. Although $dH/d\tau$ vanishes for the whole radiation it does not in general vanish when (as here) the symbols refer to radiation of a particular frequency. There would thus be an additional term $- kdH/d\tau$ on the right of (234·1). Unless this is got rid of either by assuming equilibrium constitution or by choosing the region of the spectrum discreetly, the analysis becomes intractable. The assumption is also invoked in calculating the emission due to excitation by inelastic collisions.

line and J for the flow in the same range at practically identical frequency just outside the line; similarly for the other symbols.

The radiation J' will suffer the ordinary continuous absorption $kJ'\rho ds$ and in addition the absorption $(k' - k) J'\rho ds$ of energy employed in exciting atoms. Most of the latter will be re-emitted with the same frequency; but a certain fraction ϵ will be transferred to translatory energy by superelastic collisions and lost to that particular frequency*. Additional emission will be given by atoms excited by inelastic collisions; the amount of this is found from the condition that it balances the amount

$$\epsilon (k' - k) J'\rho ds$$

lost by the converse process when J' has its equilibrium value J. Its amount is accordingly $\epsilon (k' - k) J\rho ds$. Further, there will be the ordinary continuous emission $kJ\rho ds$ for the temperature. The total emission is thus

$$\rho ds \{(1 - \epsilon) (k' - k) J' + \epsilon (k' - k) J + kJ\}.$$

Hence the equation corresponding to (225·1) is

$$\cos \theta \frac{dJ' (\theta)}{\rho dx} = - k'J' (\theta) + (1 - \epsilon) (k' - k) J' + \epsilon (k' - k) J + kJ \quad (234\cdot1).$$

Multiply by $d\omega/4\pi$ and integrate, also by $d\omega \cos \theta/4\pi$ and integrate; we obtain

$$\left. \begin{aligned} \frac{dH'}{\rho dx} &= \{k + \epsilon (k' - k)\} (J - J') \\ \frac{dK'}{\rho dx} &= - k'H' \end{aligned} \right\} \quad \ldots\ldots\ldots\ldots(234\cdot2).$$

By the usual first approximation we set $K' = \frac{1}{3}J'$. Let

$$p^2 = 3 \{k + \epsilon (k' - k)\}/k' \quad \ldots\ldots\ldots\ldots\ldots(234\cdot3),$$
$$d\tau' = - k'\rho dx.$$

Then (234·2) becomes
$$3 \frac{dH'}{d\tau'} = p^2 (J' - J) \quad \ldots\ldots\ldots\ldots(234\cdot41),$$

$$\frac{dJ'}{d\tau'} = 3H' \quad \ldots\ldots\ldots\ldots\ldots\ldots(234\cdot42),$$

so that
$$\frac{d^2J'}{d\tau'^2} = p^2 (J' - J) \quad \ldots\ldots\ldots\ldots(234\cdot5).$$

Setting $k' = k$ in (234·5) we have

$$\frac{d^2J}{d\tau^2} = 3 (J - J) = 0 \quad \ldots\ldots\ldots\ldots(234\cdot6).$$

* Transfers may also occur to or from other lines of the same spectrum, but we cannot very well follow this up. By ignoring it we determine the intensity of the *spectrum* rather than of one particular *line* in it, since these interchanges will not alter the sum of the intensities in the lines.

235. First suppose that ϵ and k'/k are constant so that

$$p^2 = \text{const.}, \qquad d\tau'/d\tau = \text{const.}$$

Then by (234·6) $d^2J/d\tau'^2 = 0$ so that (234·5) becomes

$$\frac{d^2}{d\tau'^2}(J' - J) = p^2(J' - J) \quad \dots\dots\dots\dots\dots(235\cdot1).$$

The solution is $\qquad\qquad J' = J + Ae^{-p\tau'} \quad \dots\dots\dots\dots\dots(235\cdot21),$

the negative sign being taken because J' must approach the equilibrium value J at great depths. Differentiating we have

$$\frac{dJ'}{d\tau'} = \frac{dJ}{d\tau}\frac{d\tau}{d\tau'} - pAe^{-p\tau},$$

or by (234·42) $\qquad\qquad 3H' = 3H\frac{k}{k'} - pAe^{-p\tau'} \quad \dots\dots\dots\dots\dots(235\cdot22).$

Following the first approximation the boundary condition at $\tau' = 0$ is

$$J = 2H, \qquad J' = 2H' \dots\dots\dots\dots\dots(235\cdot3).$$

Hence multiplying (235·21) by $\frac{3}{2}$ and subtracting (235·22)

$$0 = 3H(1 - k/k') + A(\tfrac{3}{2} + p).$$

This determines A and the results become

$$\left.\begin{aligned} J' &= J - \frac{3H(1 - k/k')}{p + \frac{3}{2}}e^{-p\tau'} \\ H' &= H\left(\frac{k}{k'} + \frac{p(1 - k/k')}{p + \frac{3}{2}}e^{-p\tau'}\right) \end{aligned}\right\} \quad \dots\dots\dots(235\cdot4),$$

with $J = H(2 + 3\tau)$ and $H = \text{const.}*$

The value of H'/H at $\tau' = 0$ measures the blackness of the absorption line that will be observed.

236. Next suppose that the atoms giving the special absorption do not extend to the surface. To illustrate this we suppose that k'/k is constant as before when $\tau > \tau_1$, but $k' = k$ for $\tau < \tau_1$.

Then equations (235·21) and (235·22) hold for $\tau > \tau_1$, and at τ_1 we must fit on continuously a solution of the form

$$\left.\begin{aligned} J' &= J - 2B\left(\cosh\tau\sqrt{3} + \frac{\sqrt{3}}{2}\sinh\tau\sqrt{3}\right) \\ H' &= H - \frac{2}{\sqrt{3}}B\left(\sinh\tau\sqrt{3} + \frac{\sqrt{3}}{2}\cosh\tau\sqrt{3}\right) \end{aligned}\right\} \quad (\tau < \tau_1) \quad (236\cdot1),$$

which satisfies (235·1) and the boundary conditions (235·3). In this outer region $p = \sqrt{3}$ and $\tau = \tau'$.

---

* It can be shown from (234·6) that the equation $J = H(2 + 3\tau)$, originally proved only for the integrated radiation, is valid for the present application. (This is, however, a consequence of the initial assumption of equilibrium constitution of the radiation, and is not a general theorem.)

By the continuity at τ_1

$$Ae^{-p\tau_1} + 2B\left(\cosh\tau_1\sqrt{3} + \frac{\sqrt{3}}{2}\sinh\tau_1\sqrt{3}\right) = 0,$$

$$-pAe^{-p\tau_1} + 2\sqrt{3}B\left(\sinh\tau_1\sqrt{3} + \frac{\sqrt{3}}{2}\cosh\tau_1\sqrt{3}\right) = 3H\left(1 - k/k'\right),$$

which gives

$$B = \frac{\frac{3}{2}H\,(1 - k/k')}{(p + \frac{3}{2})\cosh\tau_1\sqrt{3} + \sqrt{3}\,(\frac{1}{2}p + 1)\sinh\tau_1\sqrt{3}} \quad \ldots(236\cdot2).$$

Also by (236·1) we have at the boundary

$$H' = H - B \ldots\ldots\ldots\ldots\ldots\ldots(236\cdot3).$$

237. Thirdly, let the absorbing material be near the surface and not extend below τ_1' so that $k' = k$ when $\tau' > \tau_1'$. The appropriate solutions are

$$\left.\begin{aligned} J' &= J + Ae^{-\tau'\sqrt{3}} \\ H' &= H - \frac{1}{\sqrt{3}}Ae^{-\tau'\sqrt{3}} \end{aligned}\right\} \quad (\tau' > \tau_1') \ldots\ldots\ldots\ldots(237\cdot1),$$

$$\left.\begin{aligned} J' &= J - 2B\cosh p\tau' + \frac{3}{p}\left(H\left(1 - k/k'\right) - B\right)\sinh p\tau' \\ H' &= H\frac{k}{k'} - \frac{2p}{3}B\sinh p\tau' + \left(H\left(1 - k/k'\right) - B\right)\cosh p\tau' \end{aligned}\right\} \quad (\tau' < \tau_1')$$

$$\ldots\ldots(237\cdot2).$$

The latter values satisfy $J = 2H$, $J' = 2H'$, at $\tau' = 0$.

From the continuity at $\tau' = \tau_1'$ we have by eliminating A

$$B = \frac{H\frac{\sqrt{3}}{2}\left(1 - \frac{k}{k'}\right)\left(\cosh p\tau_1' + \frac{\sqrt{3}}{p}\sinh p\tau_1' - 1\right)}{\left(1 + \frac{\sqrt{3}}{2}\right)\cosh p\tau_1' + \left(\frac{3}{2p} + \frac{p}{\sqrt{3}}\right)\sinh p\tau_1'} \quad \ldots(237\cdot3).$$

At the boundary (237·2) gives

$$H' = H - B.$$

238. Certain general conclusions can be drawn from the formulae in the last three sections. Since p is not less than $\sqrt{(3k/k')}$, when p is a small quantity of the first order k/k' will be a small quantity of the second order. Thus to the first order the boundary value of H'/H in (235·4) is

$$H'/H = \tfrac{2}{3}p \ldots\ldots\ldots\ldots\ldots\ldots(238\cdot1).$$

Hence by (234·3)

$$\frac{k}{k'} + \epsilon - \frac{k}{k'}\epsilon = \frac{3}{4}\left(\frac{H'}{H}\right)^2 \ldots\ldots\ldots\ldots\ldots(238\cdot2).$$

This requires that both k/k' and ϵ shall be less than $\frac{3}{4}(H'/H)^2$.

To obtain a line of blackness $1 : 10$ $(H'/H = \frac{1}{10})$ we must have—

Firstly, $\epsilon < 1/133$. Such a line can only be formed in gas at low pressure where superelastic collisions are infrequent and transform less than 1 per cent. of the energy of excitation.

Secondly, $k'/k > 133$. Very high absorption coefficients are required. The element producing the line can scarcely be expected to constitute more than 1 or 2 per cent. of the whole material; k is probably of the order 100 to 1000; so that the absorption coefficient of the pure element for the monochromatic radiation must be 10^6 or 10^7.

If the material does not extend to the surface but stops say at $\tau_1 = 0.2$ we find from (236·2) that for $p = 0$

$$\frac{H'}{H} = 1 - \frac{1}{\cosh \tau_1 \sqrt{3} + \dfrac{2}{\sqrt{3}} \sinh \tau_1 \sqrt{3}} = 0.32 \quad \ldots\ldots(238\text{·}3),$$

so that however intense the absorption below $\tau_1 = 0.2$ the blackening is not more than 1 : 3. The filling up of the line is caused by the photospheric emission above $\tau_1 = 0.2$, but this emission is about double the emission from the same stratum in neighbouring parts of the spectrum. This is because the material of high opacity which backs it acts very much like a mirror. It stops radiation of the frequency of the absorption line from going deeper into the star, so that it all has to come outwards.

Finally, consider a thin layer of material of great opacity near the boundary. From (237·3) we find that when $p\tau_1' \to 0$

$$\frac{H'}{H} = \left(1 + \frac{3\tau_1'}{2 + \sqrt{3}}\right)^{-1} \quad \ldots\ldots\ldots\ldots\ldots\ldots\ldots(238\text{·}4).$$

This holds only when $p\tau_1'$ is small and τ_1 then is much smaller. As τ_1 increases, the value must tend to the limit (238·1).

The main points which emerge are that very high absorption coefficients are required to give strong blackening of the lines and that the blackness increases as the square root of k'. Also greater contrast than 1 : 3 cannot be produced by absorption below $\tau = 0.2$ however strong. For this reason we think that the *reversing layer*, i.e. the region which is most effective in determining the darkness of the absorption lines, should not be placed much lower than $\tau = 0.2$.

Estimates of the blackness of observed absorption lines are at present rather contradictory. Kohlschütter and Shapley obtain a contrast of 1 : 3 or 4 in the strongest lines; Schwarzschild about 1 : 10; H. H. Plaskett 1 : 10 for faint lines*.

It is clear that we must be able to detect lines with a contrast-ratio of less than 1 : 2; otherwise the double spectra in spectroscopic binaries could never be observed. The usual estimate is that a line just becomes observable when the intensity in it is $\frac{7}{8}$ of the intensity of the surrounding spectrum.

The theoretical difficulties increase if very high contrast is insisted on, since that may involve impossibly high absorption coefficients. The difficulty

---

* C. H. Payne, *Stellar Atmospheres*, p. 51.

is aggravated for "subordinate lines" which are absorbed by only a small proportion of the atoms present. On the other hand any degree of contrast can be admitted in the H and K lines and a few other prominent lines which belong to the *chromosphere* rather than the reversing layer and are formed under conditions different from those laid down in § 234.

Emission Lines.

239. The spectra of certain stars contain bright lines superposed on the continuous spectrum. The Balmer series of hydrogen and the enhanced lines of iron are specially liable to this reversal, some of the lines appearing bright instead of dark in a spectrum which would otherwise be considered normal. The phrase "star with peculiar spectrum" usually has reference to bright lines. In type O bright lines are fairly common, the stars with this feature being called Wolf-Rayet stars; but emission lines occur also in other types. We shall not here consider the bright lines in long-period variables where the phenomenon is evidently associated with the varying physical conditions and is not so mysterious as in an apparently static star; nor do we consider such phenomena as dark lines with bright centres where the brightness is not compared with the regular photospheric background.

It is very difficult to account for a bright line in a static star. We can scarcely attribute it to special abundance of the atom or ion concerned since that is already invoked to explain strong absorption lines.

To contribute to an emission line of frequency ν an atom must emit without having previously absorbed this frequency. The double process of absorption followed by emission adds nothing to the amount of radiation of frequency ν present; it merely helps to equalise the flow in all directions, so that the *outward* flow is at any rate not strengthened by it. There are only three ways in which emission can occur without previous absorption of the same frequency—

(1) The atom may be brought by a collision into the state necessary to emit.

(2) It may be brought to the required state by absorption or emission of other lines of its spectrum.

(3) It may capture an electron in an excited orbit.

As regards (1), since the emitting material must clearly be in front of the photosphere the speeds of the electrons correspond to a temperature near T_0, or at any rate less than T_e. By collision they excite normal atoms and de-excite excited atoms, and would by themselves just maintain the number of excited atoms corresponding to equilibrium at their temperature. To give a line showing bright against the photosphere there must be many more excited atoms present. Excitation and de-excitation no longer balance, because the latter is increased proportionately to the greater number of atoms ready to be de-excited. Consequently the electron collisions on balance reduce the excited atoms without letting them emit their energy as radiation and tend to wash out the emission line.

If the motion of the electrons is purely a temperature motion they cannot assist the formation of emission lines; but if they have extraneous velocities greater than the random temperature velocities (about 500 km. per sec.) then they may be able to perform more excitation than de-excitation. Currents in the stellar atmosphere could scarcely have sufficient speed. But a disturbed (cyclonic) state of the atmosphere might establish local and temporary electric fields—thunderstorms—under which the electrons would acquire high speeds, the free path at the low density being fairly long. If there is no other way out we may have to suppose that bright line spectra in the stars are produced by electric discharges similar to those producing bright line spectra in a vacuum tube, and depend entirely on disturbed conditions in the atmospheres of the stars which show them*.

Explanation (2) seems to postulate a much wider deviation from thermodynamical equilibrium than we can admit in the stars. It requires that a bright line at ν shall be accompanied by a dark line at ν_1, the latter representing the absorption which raises the emitting atom to, or above, the required state. But since no such effect occurs in thermodynamical equilibrium there is only the difference in strength of the ν_1 radiation at temperature T_e and T_0 respectively available for this extra excitation. Similar considerations apply to explanation (3), the dark line at ν_1 being replaced by continuous absorption beyond the head of the principal series.

Again, since the process of absorbing in certain lines and emitting in other lines does not alter the total energy in the lines, a bright line which has, say, 6 times the intensity of the continuous spectrum would (roughly speaking) have to be compensated by 5 wholly black lines—or more, if the dark lines are relegated to the unobservable part of the spectrum where the intensity is weak.

* Another possible source of high-speed electrons is radio-active disintegration. In order to account for magnetic storms it seems necessary to postulate streams of negative and positive charges issuing from the sun. It is usually supposed that these are α and β particles emitted with high velocity from uranium, etc., though it is difficult to believe that the heavy radio-active substances rise sufficiently high in the photosphere to give free exit to the emitted particles. The cause of the emission may perhaps be radiation pressure (§ 254) or C. T. R. Wilson's phenomenon (§ 210). The difficulty is to account for the escape of positively charged particles; unless charges of both signs are leaving the escape is immediately stopped by an electrostatic field.

High-speed electrons will also be produced by the penetrating radiation (§ 223) which, whatever its origin, must be supposed to occur in stellar atmospheres as it does in our own atmosphere.

These arguments are not affected by postulating an extended chromosphere—within reasonable limits. If the extension is comparable with or greater than the radius of the star the appendage is more naturally described as a nebulosity surrounding the star. An emission spectrum is then more intelligible. For example, the integrated spectrum of a planetary nebula with its central star would show bright lines; this must still be explained by the process (2), but the process is afforded more scope by the great deviation from thermodynamical equilibrium in the more distant part of the nebula.

We conclude provisionally that bright lines in the spectrum of a static star indicate that either (a) the star is greatly disturbed by "thunderstorms," or (b) it is a nebulous star.

Spectra and Temperature.

240. After the first use of spectroscopy for identifying the elements present in a star, the most important advance was the discrimination of "enhanced" lines, i.e. lines which are strengthened in the spark spectrum compared with the arc spectrum. This leads naturally to the use of spectra as a clue to the physical conditions (as well as the chemical conditions) in the outside of a star; without going further than the empirical relations we can decide that in certain stars the conditions are akin to those prevailing in the electric arc, in others to the spark. This progress was mainly due to Sir Norman Lockyer and A. Fowler.

It is now known that the arc lines are usually due to un-ionised atoms and the spark lines to ionised atoms. The spectra not only of singly ionised but of doubly and trebly ionised atoms can now be disentangled. For example, the well-known H and K lines of calcium are due not to neutral Ca but to the singly ionised atom Ca_+. Calcium is divalent, that is to say, it has only two moderately loose electrons; hence the next stage Ca_{++} is a very compact ion difficult to disturb. But for the quadrivalent element silicon Fowler has identified the spectra of doubly and trebly ionised atoms in the stars*.

A very fertile line of investigation was initiated when M. N. Saha† first brought together the observational indications of the state of ionisation in the outside of the stars and the modern thermodynamical theory of ionisation. By Saha's theory all the details of stellar spectra become quantitatively connected with the temperature and pressure in the reversing layer. From the historical point of view it is to be remarked that the thermodynamical theory of ionisation was at that time regarded as a bold and tentative generalisation admitting of no terrestrial test. It is due to

* _Proc. Roy. Soc._ **103** A, p. 413.
† _Phil. Mag._ **40**, pp. 472, 809 (1920); _Proc. Roy. Soc._ **99** A, p. 135 (1921).

the tests applied by Eggert in the interior of a star and especially by Saha in the exterior that it has gained credence. As shown in Chapter III the theory appears to be logically inevitable, but it is easier to perceive the inevitability of a conclusion when one is already persuaded by experiment of its truth.

The ionisation depends mainly on the temperature, but also to some extent on the pressure or strictly the electron pressure; and the conclusions depend on the pressure adopted for the layer where the spectral absorption takes place. But Saha showed in a general way that the spectrum varies with the photospheric temperature in the manner corresponding to the theoretical degree of ionisation. For example, it is calculated that calcium will not be ionised in the coolest stars; these show mainly the lines of the neutral atom. At somewhat higher temperature ionisation begins, and as soon as a reasonable proportion of ionised atoms is present the spectrum of Ca_+ appears. In the sun both kinds of atoms should be plentiful, and in fact both spectra are prominent. At still higher temperature ionisation is nearly complete; the Ca spectrum disappears, leaving only Ca_+. At very high temperatures Ca_+ disappears, the atoms being now all reduced to Ca_{++}.

241. There is an important difference of behaviour of *principal* and *subordinate* lines of a spectrum. The former are absorbed by the atom or ion in its normal state, the latter in an excited state. The conditions for obtaining abundance of ions in an excited state are rather critical. On the one hand the fraction excited is increasing with temperature according to Boltzmann's formula $e^{-x/RT}$; on the other hand the atoms capable of this excitation are disappearing owing to the increasing ionisation. The atom in fact has to juggle with its electron without dropping it; and the increasing stimulation of temperature ultimately defeats itself because so many of the electrons are dropped.

If we arrange the stars in temperature sequence and trace along the sequence the changes in intensity of the spectral lines, a subordinate line rises to a fairly sharp maximum and drops again. A principal line on the other hand has a very flat maximum, and persists with nearly the same intensity for a long range of temperature, since it requires a considerable change of condition before one stage of ionisation gives way to the next.

At the maximum of a subordinate line the number of atoms in the required excited state is found to be of the order 10^{-3} to 10^{-5} of the whole number of atoms of the element*. At the maximum of a principal line practically all the atoms are in the appropriate absorbing condition, i.e. unexcited atoms in the proper stage of ionisation. The material for production of a principal line is thus about 10,000 times as abundant as the

* Fowler and Milne, *Monthly Notices*, **84**, p. 510.

material for a subordinate line. By (238·2) to produce a blackening of 1 : 5, k'/k must be at least 33. For a subordinate line this absorption is due to say 10^{-4} of the whole number of atoms of the element, which in turn will constitute say $\frac{1}{30}$ of the whole mass present. Hence material constituted wholly of the excited atoms should have k' equal to $10^7 k$, if the subordinate lines are of the above blackness. If following Milne we take $k = 10^3$, we are led to values of k' of the order 10^{10} for line absorption. Monochromatic absorption coefficients are certainly very high, but it is doubtful whether they can be quite so high as this. Perhaps, however, the subordinate lines do not attain so deep a blackness; I think also that Milne's value of k should be reduced.

A comparison of principal and subordinate lines should take account of the linkage in the formation of the lines. Consider a principal line formed by an atom going from state 1 to state 3, and a subordinate line formed by the atom going from state 2 to state 3. We should expect the principal line to darken the more rapidly, because of the much greater amount of absorbing material in state 1 than in state 2. But the emission in either line depends only on the number of atoms in state 3; and so long as there is energy in the subordinate line raising atoms to state 3, these will emit in both lines indiscriminately so that the principal line cannot become fully dark. There appears to be a tendency to equalise the two lines owing to this linkage of emission. But I am not sure whether that is really so. Suppose that not merely this one line but all the principal lines became entirely black; then there would be no radiation capable of exciting normal atoms, and hence no atoms in state 2 except a few produced by collision. The subordinate absorption line could not be formed at all, owing to lack of material. The question seems to be too complex to be decided here.

242. Saha's theory has dominated all recent progress in the observation and interpretation of stellar spectra. This is a highly specialised subject involving not only the collation of a great amount of astronomical and terrestrial spectroscopic data but the theory of series in optical spectra which, starting from principles similar to those involved in X ray spectra, has been elaborated in great detail. To pursue this subject would lead us far from our main purposes, and we shall here only touch on the fringe of these researches.

The most precise mathematical development of Saha's theory is due to R. H. Fowler and E. A. Milne*. Instead of determining the temperature at which a line should just appear or disappear (which involves estimates of the abundance of atoms or ions required to produce detectable absorption) they calculated the conditions for which the line should reach maximum intensity.

* *Monthly Notices*, **83**, p. 403; **84**, p. 499; **85**, p. 970.

The number of atoms in a state to absorb a given line varies with temperature and density. Fowler and Milne take as their two variables the temperature T and the electron pressure P_e; the latter is presumably about half the total gas pressure since we may expect about 1 free electron per atom in photospheric conditions*. Keeping P_e fixed we can trace how the proportion of atoms in the required state changes with T, and determine the temperature for which it is a maximum. If P_e is rightly chosen this should be the temperature at which the line reaches maximum intensity, and the spectral class of observed maximum intensity can thus be correlated with temperature. Conversely if we know the temperatures of the different spectral classes we can determine the value of P_e for the reversing layer.

The formulae for determining the number of atoms in a given state of ionisation when the electron density is given have been developed in § 47; the proportion of these in any given excited state is also known by Boltzmann's formula. By differentiating with respect to T the temperature of maximum abundance of the given state can be found. We do not give the formulae here explicitly, since for practical computation simplifications appropriate to the particular conditions considered are introduced, and we are not here concerned with the technique of practical computation†.

The following examples are taken from Fowler and Milne's calculations—

(1) H. Balmer Series. Maximum in type A 0 = 10,500° on temperature scale usually adopted. Temperatures of maximum abundance of hydrogen atoms in a state to absorb the Balmer series are—

$$P_e = 1{\cdot}3 . 10^{-4} \text{ atmos.,} \qquad T = 10,000°,$$
$$P_e = 7{\cdot}2 . 10^{-4}, \qquad T = 11,000,$$
$$P_e = 3{\cdot}1 . 10^{-3}, \qquad T = 12,000.$$

(2) Mg_+. $\lambda4481$. Maximum in type A 0 = 10,500°—

$$P_e = 0{\cdot}8 . 10^{-4}, \qquad T = 10,000,$$
$$P_e = 5{\cdot}2 . 10^{-4}, \qquad T = 11,000,$$
$$P_e = 1{\cdot}1 . 10^{-3}, \qquad T = 12,000.$$

(3) Mg. $\lambda5711$, 5528, 4703, 4352. Maximum "between sun and sunspot" = 5500°—

$$P_e = 2{\cdot}4 . 10^{-5}, \qquad T = 5,000,$$
$$P_e = 1{\cdot}6 . 10^{-4}, \qquad T = 5,500,$$
$$P_e = 7{\cdot}8 . 10^{-4}, \qquad T = 6,000.$$

(4) Ca_+. H and K lines. Maximum in type K 0 = 4300°—

$$P_e = 9{\cdot}9 . 10^{-7}, \qquad T = 5,000,$$
$$P_e = 5{\cdot}0 . 10^{-5}, \qquad T = 6,000.$$

* Some elements will not be ionised, others may be doubly ionised.

† Reference may be made to Fowler and Milne, *Monthly Notices*, **83**, pp. 408–410.

(5) He$_+$. $\lambda 4686$. Still increasing in the hottest type O—

$$P_e = 5 \cdot 1 . 10^{-6}, \qquad\qquad T = 30,000,$$
$$P_e = 1 \cdot 1 . 10^{-4}, \qquad\qquad T = 35,000.$$

(6) He. $\lambda 5876, 4471, 4026$. Maximum in type $B\,2$—

$$P_e = 5 \cdot 9 . 10^{-6}, \qquad\qquad T = 14,000,$$
$$P_e = 1 \cdot 2 . 10^{-4}, \qquad\qquad T = 16,000,$$
$$P_e = 4 \cdot 0 . 10^{-4}, \qquad\qquad T = 17,000.$$

In types M to A where the temperature scale is fairly well known the results are used to determine P_e in the reversing layer. Having discovered in this way the general order of magnitude of P_e, we can use the results of examples (5) and (6) to extend the temperature scale to types B and O.

243. Many other examples will be found in the papers quoted, and the general body of evidence is that *ordinarily P_e* is about 10^{-4} atmospheres. This then may be taken to be the average pressure in the reversing layer. (Of course, the pressure cannot be just the same through the whole series of stars, but as mentioned in § 233 the range is moderately small.) But certain lines give much lower pressures (e.g. Ca$_+$ in example (4)) and are evidently formed at high levels where the pressure is of the order 10^{-7} to 10^{-8} atmospheres.

Fowler and Milne remark that it is the principal lines of the elements that give the exceptionally low pressures. Their view is that, since atoms in a state to absorb a principal line are about 10^4 times as abundant as those absorbing subordinate lines, a comparatively thin layer suffices to produce full absorption; hence in the wave-length of the principal line we can see only a little way into the star, and the high level and low pressure are accounted for. We do not think this explanation can be correct. If the material is considered to be so superabundant that it prevents us seeing down to the ordinary reversing layer, abundance ceases to be a matter of primary concern. So long as we have enough to form a practically opaque screen in front of the region from which nearly all the photospheric radiation comes, i.e. in front of the reversing layer, variations of abundance will scarcely affect the appearance of the line. Further, if Fowler and Milne's view were true the spectral types at which the line just appears and disappears would still be determined by the reversing layer conditions, and not by the high level pressure which determines the maximum.

It seems more likely that the clue to this deviation is given by Milne's work on the chromosphere (§ 252). The elements which show the deviation are subject to strong selective radiation pressure—which is associated with the occurrence of strong principal lines in the intense part of the general spectrum.

The radiation pressure supports the atoms above the photosphere in the chromosphere; elements not subject to the strong radiation pressure do not rise to this level. Thus the difference of pressure is accounted for. Whilst this explanation also lays stress on the fact that the elements with strong principal lines show the deviation (since it is the absorption by these lines which makes them ascend to the chromosphere), it does not assume complete opacity above the photosphere—which was the objection to Fowler and Milne's explanation.

It is rather doubtful at present what the observed "intensity" of a line should be taken to signify. In the foregoing it has been supposed to be a measure of the blackness. Actually our information depends almost wholly on eye estimates of intensity, which presumably combine blackness and breadth. Now breadth depends on entirely different considerations from blackness. It would seem that photometric measurements of blackness at the centres of the lines are essential for a proper application of the theory, and the present use of eye estimates is a very uncertain makeshift.

What is the temperature referred to in these investigations? The absorbing material is in front of the photosphere and presumably nearer to the boundary temperature T_0 than to the effective temperature T_e. The molecular speeds and the *density* of the radiation will correspond to a temperature near to T_0; but the *quality* of the radiation corresponds to T_e or indeed to a temperature rather higher. The ionising power of the radiation depends on its intensity for high frequencies, and this will be more nearly represented by T_e than by T_0. Probably T in the foregoing results may be considered to correspond fairly nearly to T_e.

Molecular Spectra.

244. In the reversing layers of cooler stars chemical compounds can exist and the molecules give rise to band spectra. For diatomic molecules such as cyanogen, CN, the structure of the bands has been unravelled, and a satisfactory theory of the distribution of intensity in the bands has been developed. So far as we are aware the only attempt to use the band spectra as a clue to the physical conditions in the reversing layer is contained in a paper by R. T. Birge*.

The cyanogen band observed in the solar spectrum near 3883 Å is composed of five overlapping series. Each series starts from a missing line labelled $m = 0$ and runs in both directions; the positive ("P") branch runs towards the red, the successive lines being denoted by $m = +1$, $+2, \ldots$; the negative ("R") branch runs towards the violet and is denoted

* *Astrophys. Journ.* **55**, p. 273.

by $m = -1, -2, \ldots$. The lines are not equally spaced; the separation in the positive branch (in CN) diminishes continually, becomes zero, and finally negative so that a head of the band is formed where the series doubles back on itself. In other compounds it may be the negative branch that inverts.

The state of the molecule is characterised by two or more quantum numbers, of which one, m, corresponds to angular momentum (equivalent to n' in §§ 42, 51). We shall call the remaining quantum number or numbers n. The band as a whole is due to a transition between two states n_1 and n_2, and the individual lines correspond to different values of m. In accordance with Bohr's selection principle the only possible transitions are those in which m changes by $+1$ or -1; a change $+1$ on emission gives the positive branch and -1 gives the negative branch. The numbering of the lines will be best understood by reference to the converse absorption; absorption with change from m to $m-1$ units of angular momentum gives the line numbered $+m$ and with change from m to $m+1$ units gives the line $-m$. It should be understood that the main change of energy is determined by the transition from n_1 to n_2 which has nothing to do with angular momentum, and can be visualised as a difference in closeness of binding of the two atoms; but since by the selection principle this transition cannot occur without a consequential jump of m, there is a small additional gain or loss of energy which varies with the starting value of m and gives rise to the line structure of the band. It is found that the two branches have similar intensity curves; this shows that the two possible transitions $\Delta m = \pm 1$ are equally probable.

It can probably be assumed that the molecular absorption coefficient is independent of m; that is to say, the rotation of the molecule will not appreciably affect its chance of absorbing a quantum from the radiation around it. The whole band occupies only a small length of spectrum; and were it not that frequency is observable with extremely high accuracy we should scarcely have thought of distinguishing molecules with different velocities of rotation. In that case the absorption in the lines $\pm m$ will be simply proportional to the number of molecules in the state (m, n_1). In equilibrium this number depends on the temperature, since by Boltzmann's formula it is proportional to $\exp(-\chi_{m, n_1}/RT)$. It would seem that measures of relative intensity in a band spectrum—especially the value of m for which the intensity is a maximum—are remarkably favourable for determining the temperature. Isolated atomic lines can only be compared from one star to another and their intensity depends on density as well as temperature. But in band spectra the evidence is obtained by differential comparisons of the successive lines in the band; density affects the absolute intensity (by dissociation of molecules) but not the relative intensity.

245. By the usual quantum condition, viz.

$$\int p\, dq = mh,$$

we have for quantisation of angular momentum

$$J\omega \, . \, 2\pi = mh \, \ldots\ldots\ldots\ldots\ldots\ldots\ldots(245\cdot1),$$

where J is the moment of inertia of the molecule.

The rotational energy is

$$\tfrac{1}{2}J\omega^2 = \frac{m^2h^2}{8\pi^2J} \, \ldots\ldots\ldots\ldots\ldots\ldots\ldots(245\cdot2).$$

Accordingly if J_1 and J_2 are the moments of inertia of the molecule in the states n_1 and n_2, the frequency of the line $+ m$ is given by

$$h\nu_{+m} = \text{const.} + \frac{(m-1)^2\, h^2}{8\pi^2J_2} - \frac{m^2h^2}{8\pi^2J_1} \, \ldots\ldots(245\cdot31),$$

and of the line $- m$ by

$$h\nu_{-m} = \text{const.} + \frac{(m+1)^2\, h^2}{8\pi^2J_2} - \frac{m^2h^2}{8\pi^2J_1} \, \ldots\ldots(245\cdot32).$$

These formulae give a parabolic spacing of the lines ($\nu = A + Bm + Cm^2$) which agrees well with observation. We can determine J_1 from observation since by (245·31)

$$h\nu_0 - h\nu_{+2} = 4h^2/8\pi^2J_1,$$

or

$$\Delta\nu = h/4\pi^2J_1 \, \ldots\ldots\ldots\ldots\ldots\ldots(245\cdot4),$$

where $\Delta\nu$ is the spacing between consecutive lines at $m = +1$.

Considering molecules in a state n_1 (i.e. ready to absorb); the number with angular momentum corresponding to m will be proportional to

$$q_m e^{-\chi_m/RT} \, \ldots\ldots\ldots\ldots\ldots\ldots(245\cdot5),$$

where by (245·2), $\chi_m = m^2h^2/8\pi^2J_1$, and q_m is the weight of states corresponding to m. For a diatomic molecule the vector of angular momentum is restricted to the plane perpendicular to the line joining the two atoms so that for reasonably large values of m the weight q_m is proportional to $m*$. (Compare § 42, where each value of n' represents $n' + 1$ orbits corresponding to the possible values of n''.)

Since then $q_m \propto m \propto \chi_m^{\frac{1}{2}}$, the number of molecules in state m is proportional to

$$\chi_m^{\frac{1}{2}} e^{-\chi_m/RT},$$

which is a maximum when $\chi_m/RT = \tfrac{1}{2}$, or

$$\frac{m^2h^2}{8\pi^2J_1} = \tfrac{1}{2}RT \, \ldots\ldots\ldots\ldots\ldots\ldots(245\cdot6).$$

Hence by (245·4)

$$m_{\text{max.}} = \sqrt{\frac{RT}{h\Delta\nu}} \, \ldots\ldots\ldots\ldots\ldots\ldots(245\cdot7).$$

---

* Representing the angular momentum by a point in the plane, the classical weight of a range of values is proportional to the area (since the components of momentum are Hamiltonian coordinates, § 48). In the quantum theory the weight of the annulus between $(m \pm \tfrac{1}{2})\, h/2\pi$ is appropriated to the quantised circle $mh/2\pi$, and its area is nearly proportional to m.

For the CN band which is most easily observable $\Delta \nu/c = 3 \cdot 704$. Hence
$$m_{max.} = 0 \cdot 434 \sqrt{T}.$$
At the centre of the sun's disc we should expect the temperature of the reversing layer to be about $5200°$ (T_1 in $(232 \cdot 3)$); at any rate it cannot be lower than $T_0 = 4660°$. The corresponding values of m are

$$m_{max.} = 31 \cdot 2 \text{ and } 29 \cdot 6.$$

Birge was not able to observe directly the maximum intensity in the solar spectrum, but by an indirect procedure (which is not very fully explained) he arrived at a much lower temperature $4000°$[*]. The difference seems inexplicable; even granting that the region in the sun has no definite temperature (the radiation corresponding in quality to $5740°$ and in density to $4660°$) it is difficult to see how any criterion could give a temperature lower than both. Further investigation seems to be required.

Width of Absorption Lines.

246. Whilst some lines in stellar spectra are extremely sharp, others may be of considerable width. In some stars the lines of the Balmer series of hydrogen extend over 30 Ångström units on each side of the centre of the line. In the solar spectrum the H and K lines of Ca_+ extend 10 Å on each side[†].

Broadening of the lines can be produced by the disturbing effects of neighbouring atoms on the absorbing atom; these interfere with its perfect periodicity so that its quantum states are not entirely sharp. Broadening from this cause is usually referred to as *pressure broadening* though the name is now scarcely adequate. It is closely associated with the Stark effect of electric fields since the disturbing causes are electrical.

Other conceivable causes of broadening are (a) Doppler effect of atomic velocities due to temperature, (b) Doppler effect of ascending and descending currents, (c) Doppler effect of rotation of the star, (d) Stark effect of regular electric fields, (e) Compton scattering by free electrons with different velocities, (f) Rayleigh scattering by atoms and ions, (g) great depth of the absorbing layer enhancing the importance of slight broadening due to other causes. Most of these have at one time or another been advocated as the main cause of width in stellar lines; but we do not think the arguments will stand scrutiny. It is doubtful if they would have been proposed had not the operation of "pressure broadening" in stellar conditions been deemed inadequate.

---

[*] Birge's clue was that in a certain part of the band the relative intensities of the lines corresponded to that of a 4-ampere arc, and was at any rate intermediate between the furnace spectrum and the 13-ampere arc. The temperatures of these terrestrial sources of comparison were deduced from the observation of $m_{max.}$.

[†] C. H. Payne, *Stellar Atmospheres*, p. 51.

It has sometimes been urged against pressure broadening that we do not get anything like so much broadening in a vacuum tube when the pressure is equal to that now assigned to the reversing layer of a star. For example, the Balmer series is quite sharp in a vacuum tube at a pressure of 10^{-4} atmospheres. But this comparison overlooks the great difference due to the ionisation of stellar material. The ion or electron is the centre of a disturbing field of far wider extent than the neutral atom's field which can scarcely come into play except at collision; and the broadening effect is of a much higher order of magnitude. Although ions and free electrons are produced in a vacuum tube, their abundance is insignificant compared with photospheric conditions.

As an example we consider the H_β line of hydrogen which corresponds to a transition between a 4-quantum and a 2-quantum orbit. In the 4-quantum orbit the period is $0.97 \cdot 10^{-14}$ sec. The average duration of the 4-quantum state is about 10^{-8} sec. or 10^6 periods. Hence we should expect the quantisation in this state to be sharp to about 1 part in a million. Roughly speaking the purity of the H_β line emitted or absorbed by undisturbed atoms should correspond to the purity of the spectrum from a grating with a million lines. This can be modified by the disturbance of other atoms or electrons in two ways: (1) the average duration of the excited state may be shortened by frequent collisions, (2) general irregular disturbance may shorten the stretches over which the phase of the periodicity is approximately preserved—just as the resolving power of the grating is impaired (1) by reducing the number of lines, (2) by irregularity of ruling. Numerical calculation seems to indicate that in photospheric conditions the process (2) is the more important. The problem has been discussed by Russell and Stewart*.

Let σ be the total number of electrons and (singly charged) ions per cu. cm., and let r_0 be a length such that $\frac{4}{3}\pi\sigma r_0^3 = 1$. Then if we draw a sphere of radius r_0 round a given atom this sphere will on the average contain one disturbing charge. The more distant charges will by their imperfect symmetry also produce disturbing fields, but the order of magnitude of the resultant field will be not very different from that due to the nearest charge.

For singly ionised material at $10,000°$ and 10^{-4} atmospheres pressure, we have
$$\sigma = 7.4 \cdot 10^{13}, \qquad r_0 = 1.48 \cdot 10^{-5} \text{ cm.}$$

The field due to a charge e at distance r_0 is

$$2.18 \text{ electrostatic units.}$$

Since the nearest charge is within r_0 the average disturbing field will be larger. Russell and Stewart calculate the average to be 2.7 times larger

* *Astrophys. Journ.* 53, p. 197 (1924).

THE OUTSIDE OF A STAR

or about 6 electrostatic units. The Stark effect of a steady field of 6 units resolves H_β into components extending over 0·7 Å. The observed width of the line should be greater—say 2 to 3 Å—since the Stark components will be shifting about over a wider range owing to the fluctuations of the field. The actual width of H_β in stars corresponding to the assumed conditions is about 15 Å.

I do not think that the fluctuating Stark effect is in itself sufficient to account for the great widths often observed. It seems likely that another point is involved. In the foregoing conditions the average speed of the electrons is 6·2.10⁷ cm. per sec. so that the electron traverses a distance r_0 in 2·4.10⁻¹³ secs. or 24 periods of the 4-quantum orbit. Some electrons will approach much closer and some will have greater speeds so that there will be a considerable amount of disturbance which changes completely in the course of 3 or 4 periods. Now the Stark effect represents the disturbance by a steady field, which during one half-revolution counteracts to a large extent the change of phase produced by it in the other half-revolution; the theory of the effect is based on the "adiabatic hypothesis" that the field is established slowly in comparison with the time of revolution. The quickly fluctuating field should give much larger effects, and it seems possible that the great width of the lines is produced in this way.

Continuous Absorption.

247. Although the general flow of heat through the photosphere is to some extent dammed back by line absorption and emission, the main obstruction is likely to be continuous absorption and emission, just as in the deep interior.

Our formula for the continuous absorption coefficient at temperatures of some million degrees was (158·2)

$$\frac{\mu k T^{\frac{7}{2}} (1+f)}{\rho} = 0·668 \frac{R b^2 c}{H^2 a u_0} \frac{Z^2}{A} \quad \ldots\ldots\ldots\ldots(247·1).$$

The theory of continuous optical absorption at photospheric temperatures must be fundamentally the same as that of continuous X ray absorption at high interior temperatures; but we should scarcely expect the formulae derived under the simplifications permissible at high temperature to apply to the photosphere. Milne*, however, has found reason to believe that, whether by coincidence or by actual appropriateness, this extreme extrapolation of (247·1) gives results not far from the truth.

We apply (247·1) to a typical photospheric region with

$$T = 6000°, \qquad p_G = 200 \text{ dynes/cm.}^2$$

* *Monthly Notices*, **85**, p. 768.

The material is taken to be calcium which is found to be singly ionised in these conditions so that

$$Z = 20, \qquad A = 40, \qquad \mu = 20, \qquad f = 1.$$

The result is
$$k = 2 \cdot 00 . 10^3 \qquad \dots \dots \dots \dots \dots \dots (247 \cdot 15).$$

Milne gives $k = 7 \cdot 8 . 10^3$, the difference being due to his neglect of Rosseland's correction. We might feel inclined to adopt a value 10 times larger than (247·15), since the theoretical result is only $\frac{1}{10}$ of the observed value in the deep interior. As Milne's value corresponds to a convenient compromise we shall adopt it in this section, so that

$$k_0 = 7800 \qquad \dots \dots \dots \dots \dots \dots (247 \cdot 16),$$

k_0 denoting the value of k for the standard temperature and pressure defined above.

Since
$$\frac{p_G}{p_R} = \frac{3 \Re}{a} \frac{\rho}{\mu T^3} \dots \dots \dots \dots \dots \dots \dots (247 \cdot 2),$$

the absorption law $k \propto \rho / \mu T^{\frac{7}{2}}$ can be written

$$k \propto \frac{p_G}{p_R} T^{-\frac{1}{2}} \qquad \dots \dots \dots \dots \dots \dots (247 \cdot 3).$$

At $6000°$, $p_R = 3 \cdot 30$ dynes/cm.^{2} Hence determining the constant from (247·16)

$$k = 129 \frac{p_G}{p_R} \left(\frac{T}{6000} \right)^{-\frac{1}{2}} \qquad \dots \dots \dots \dots \dots (247 \cdot 4).$$

248. To determine the value of k in the outer part of the sun Milne adopts a procedure equivalent to the following. The fundamental equation (233·1) gives

$$dp_G = \left(\frac{cg}{kH} - 1 \right) dp_R \qquad \dots \dots \dots \dots \dots (248 \cdot 1).$$

Integrating this on the assumption that k can be treated as constant and neglecting the constant of integration, we have

$$p_G = \left(\frac{cg}{kH} - 1 \right) p_R \qquad \dots \dots \dots \dots \dots (248 \cdot 15).$$

Hence by (247·4)
$$\frac{k}{129} \left(\frac{T}{6000} \right)^{\frac{1}{2}} = \frac{cg}{kH} - 1 \dots \dots \dots \dots \dots (248 \cdot 2).$$

Setting for the sun $T = 6000°$, $cg/H = 1 \cdot 319 . 10^4$, we have

$$\frac{k}{129} = \frac{13190}{k} - 1,$$

whence
$$k = 1241.$$

For approximate calculation the term -1 in (248·2) is unimportant so that

$$k^2 = \frac{129cg}{H} \left(\frac{T}{6000} \right)^{-\frac{1}{2}} \qquad \dots \dots \dots \dots \dots (248 \cdot 3),$$

and $k \propto T^{-\frac{1}{4}}$. Hence the result is consistent with the original assumption that k can be treated as constant for a considerable range of temperature.

The ratio of radiation force to total force is determined by

$$1 - \beta' = \frac{kH}{cg} = \frac{1241}{13190} = 0 \cdot 094.$$

This is the source of the value $0 \cdot 1$ used in § 233; and the general reasonableness of the results there found is considered as evidence that our extrapolation of the law for k has given a value of the right order of magnitude.

The value of $1 - \beta$ in the deep interior of the sun is $\cdot 05$, so that apparently radiation pressure becomes more important at the photosphere. But this conclusion lays too much stress on the accuracy of the extrapolated value of k and the only legitimate conclusion is that $1 - \beta$ and $1 - \beta'$ are of the same order of magnitude.

249. We may inquire a little further into the reason for the slowness of the variation of k. The absorption law $(247 \cdot 3)$ may be written

$$k = C p_G / p_R^{\frac{2}{3}} \quad \dots\dots\dots\dots\dots\dots\dots(249 \cdot 1),$$

where C is a constant. Imagine that we are integrating equation $(248 \cdot 1)$ starting from the outside. Having reached a certain point let us continue the solution assuming that k remains constant. Call this solution A. Now take p_G and p_R from solution A, determine k from $(249 \cdot 1)$, and make a new solution B from $(248 \cdot 1)$ with this value of k. If k is *decreasing* (as usually happens), dp_G/dp_R is increased so that p_G/p_R gradually becomes larger than in solution A. The new value of k found by inserting solution B values in $(249 \cdot 1)$ is accordingly *increased*, and the next solution C will move back towards A, and so on.

For example, in § 233 on the assumption of k constant we found (solution A) at the limits of the photosphere

$$T_2/T_1 = 1 \cdot 38, \qquad \rho_2/\rho_1 = 12 \cdot 0,$$

whence
$$k_2/k_1 = 3 \cdot 9.$$

In solution B we should accordingly suppose that k increases between the two levels in the ratio $3 \cdot 9 : 1$; but this gives great over-correction, and the next solution moves back towards solution A. Probably a quite small change of k in this range would give the necessary adjustment.

The absorption coefficient has a natural tendency to steady its own value. Physically the explanation is that if as we go inwards we find material that is specially absorbent, the increased outward force of radiation pressure will support more of its weight and so check the natural increase of density downwards and (through the dependence of k on ρ) k falls again towards its normal value. This effect is well illustrated by Milne's formula $(248 \cdot 3)$ where k varies as $T^{-\frac{1}{4}}$, or if anything less rapidly, instead of the anticipated variation as $T^{-\frac{1}{2}}$.

250. If the method of § 248 is applied to the conditions in the reversing layer the neglect of the constant of integration will introduce inaccuracy which seems likely to be serious. Near the bottom of the photosphere this "end correction" will have practically disappeared, and k and $1 - \beta$ will have settled down to Milne's values; but we are chiefly interested in regions where they can scarcely have begun to recover from the boundary disturbance.

The following method should give a good approximation for the outer layers down to about $\tau_1 = 0.25$, which we have taken as the top of the photosphere for the centre of the disc (§ 232)*. In this region T lies between $0.84T_e$ and $0.91T_e$ so that we shall treat it as an isothermal region so far as k and p_G are concerned.

Introduce a quantity v defined by

$$\frac{kH}{cg} = \frac{p_G}{v} \qquad \qquad \text{......................(250·1)}.$$

Since in the isothermal region k and p_G are both proportional to ρ, we have v constant. Then (248·1) becomes

$$dp_G = \left(\frac{v}{p_G} - 1 \right) dp_R,$$

or

$$\frac{p_G dp_G}{v - p_G} = dp_R \qquad \qquad \text{................................(250·2)}.$$

Integrating we obtain

$$- v \log (1 - p_G/v) - p_G = \delta p_R = \tfrac{1}{3}a \, (T^4 - T_0{}^4)$$
$$= H\tau/c \qquad \text{......................(250·3)}$$

by (226·5). In most cases p_G/v is small and the equation can be written

$$\frac{1}{2} \frac{p_G{}^2}{v} + \frac{1}{3} \frac{p_G{}^3}{v^2} + \dots = \frac{H\tau}{c} \qquad \text{..................(250·4)}.$$

In Table 46 the first column gives an assumed gas pressure at the conventional upper limit of the photosphere $\tau = 0.25$. The second column gives v deduced from (250·3). The third column gives the value of k at this point deduced from (250·1). The last column gives the corresponding

Table 46.

Absorption Coefficient for Sun's Reversing Layer.

p_G	v	k	k_0
1	1·69	7820	840000
10	102·5	1286	13810
100	9700	135·9	146·0
1000	963000	13·7	1·47

* An alternative treatment is given by Milne, *loc. cit.* § 9.

value of k_0, i.e. k for the standard conditions $T = 6000°$, $p_G = 200$ for comparison with (247·16).

It will be seen that a very rough knowledge of k_0 would suffice to give a reasonably close value of p_G for the level considered; but since estimates of k_0 depend on risky theoretical speculation, we prefer to proceed in the converse way. The discussion of the intensities of spectral lines by Fowler and Milne (§ 242) indicated that they are usually produced where the pressure is rather above 100 dynes per sq. cm. or 10^{-4} atmospheres. Their location cannot be much below the level $\tau = 0·25$, because even at the centre of the disc $\frac{1}{10}$ of the photospheric radiation comes from above this level, and for the disc as a whole nearly $\frac{1}{5}$ is above this level. We judge therefore that the results for $p_G = 100$ dynes/cm.² should be accepted. This gives in round numbers

$$k_0 = 150,$$

as compared with 7800 adopted by Milne and the value 2000 derived in (247·15).

There is no theoretical objection to be urged against this lower value. Extrapolation of a theoretical formula is not the same thing as extrapolation of a theory; and so far as we can judge the value 150 really corresponds better with Kramers' theory.

In deriving the value 2000 we assumed $Z = 20$; but unless the electron penetrates inside the ion during its encounter the actual charge influencing it will be $Z = 1$ or 2 since few atoms in the reversing layer are more than doubly ionised. Taking $Z = 2$, k_0 is thereby divided by 100. Allowing for various minor adjustments the value $k_0 = 150$ is about as likely a prediction from Kramers' theory as we can make.

We verify as follows that the electron does not enter the ion deeply. Setting $\lambda = 5000$ Å, $T = 5740°$, $Z = 2*$ in (155·2), we find $\gamma = 1·5$ for $\sigma = 1·00 . 10^{-7}$ cm. Now the main part of the emission comes from electrons for which γ is in the neighbourhood of 1·5, and these are aimed to pass at the above distance σ from the centre. From (153·7) we find that the eccentricity of these orbits is 1·09, and the closest approach to the centre is then calculated to be $2·1 . 10^{-8}$ cm. This will not quite clear the ion which has a radius $2·3 . 10^{-8}$ cm.; but the penetration is too slight to have much effect.

251. Adopting the third line of Table 46 for $\tau = 0·25$, we have

$$k_0 = 146·0, \qquad p_G = 100, \qquad v = 9700, \qquad k = 135·9.$$

If we were to solve (250·3) with this value of v and with $\tau = 3·4$, so as to find the conditions at the bottom of the photosphere, we should obtain

---

* This is intended to apply to singly or doubly ionised calcium equally, because in the former case the approaching electron penetrates within the orbit of the valency electron.

$p_G = 365$, $k = 497$. But it is clear that the approximation has broken down, because the increase of k in the ratio $1 : 3.65$ will be more than compensated by a decrease in the ratio $1 : 5.38$ due to the temperature factor $T^{-\frac{9}{2}}$ ignored in the approximation. Accordingly for the stretch $\tau = 0.25$ to 3.4 it will be much better to pass over to Milne's approximation $k = $ const. Recomputing k by the method of § 248 with the value $k_0 = 146$ now adopted we find at 6000°

$$k = 177 \dots\dots\dots\dots\dots\dots(251.1).$$

It will be seen that $\tau = 0.25$ is a very suitable place to join the two approximations since they give roughly the same value of k at the junction.

We shall now revise the calculations of § 233 as to the solar photosphere*. Using $k = 177$ we have

$$1 - \beta' = kH/cg = .0134 \dots\dots\dots\dots(251.2),$$

so that (contrary to Milne's conclusion) radiation pressure is relatively less important in the photosphere than in the deep interior ($1 - \beta = .05$). It should be understood however that the accuracy of our determination of k is not sufficient to justify any great confidence in this amendment. As already explained, radiation pressure, although it becomes larger in actual amount than gas pressure near the boundary of the star, is less important as a sustaining force. If any material is supported by radiation pressure it must be through selective line absorption and not through continuous absorption.

By integrating (248.1) between the limits $\tau = 0.25$ to 3.4

$$(p_G)_2 - (p_G)_1 = \frac{\beta'}{1 - \beta}\{(p_R)_2 - (p_R)_1\} = \frac{\beta'}{1 - \beta'}\frac{H}{c}(\tau_2 - \tau_1) = 483 \ (251.3),$$

so that at the two limits of the photosphere

$$(p_G)_1 = 100, \qquad (p_G)_2 = 583 \dots\dots\dots\dots(251.41).$$

By (232.3) $$T_2 = 1.45T_1 \dots\dots\dots\dots\dots(251.42).$$

By (251.41) and (251.42) $$\rho_2 = 4.02\rho_1 \dots\dots\dots\dots\dots(251.43).$$

Hence by the absorption law

$$k_2 = 1.10k_1 \dots\dots\dots\dots\dots(251.44),$$

showing that the assumed constancy of k is a good approximation for this range.

Equation (251.3) can be written in the form

$$p_G = \frac{\beta'}{1 - \beta'}\frac{H}{c}(\tau + 0.403) \dots\dots\dots\dots(251.5),$$

the constant being determined from the value of $(p_G)_1$. (If we had not

---

* The calculations in this section refer to the photosphere at the centre of the disc whereas those in § 233 refer to the integrated disc; so they are not quite comparable. I have here chosen the central photosphere for the reason that it falls wholly in the region covered by one approximation.

allowed for the diminishing value of k between $\tau = \cdot 25$ and 0 the constant would have been zero.) By $(226\cdot5)$

$$\tfrac{1}{3}aT^4 = \frac{H}{c}\left(\tau + \tfrac{2}{3}\right).$$

Hence

$$p_G = \frac{a\beta'}{3\,(1-\beta')}\,(T^4 - T_0'^4)\dots\dots\dots\dots(251\cdot6),$$

where $T_0'^4 = 0\cdot396T_0^4$.

Since $(251\cdot6)$ is the same as $(233\cdot4)$ with T_0' replacing T_0, we deduce as in $(233\cdot9)$

$$\text{const.} - x = \frac{\Re T_0'}{\mu g\beta'}\left\{4\,\frac{T}{T_0'} + \log_e\frac{T - T_0'}{T + T_0'} - 2\tan^{-1}\frac{T}{T_0'}\right\}\quad(251\cdot7).$$

This gives for the thickness of the sun's photosphere

$$x_1 - x_2 = 17\cdot0 \text{ km.,}$$

or about half the thickness given by the former discussion.

No doubt the actual photosphere will be more extended owing to its non-homogeneous composition. The different elements may sort themselves out to some extent according to their atomic weights and to the force of radiation pressure on them.

Consider next a giant star with the same effective temperature as the sun but with a smaller value of g. Comparing the stars at corresponding levels of τ, we have $k \propto p_G$ since the temperatures are the same. Hence by $(250\cdot1)$ v is proportional to g. So long as p_G is small compared with v, $(250\cdot4)$ gives

$$p_G = \sqrt{(2H\tau v/c)}\dots\dots\dots\dots\dots(251\cdot8),$$

so that at the reversing layer $(\tau = 0\cdot25)$

$$p_G \propto \sqrt{v} \propto \sqrt{g}.$$

For example, if g has $\frac{1}{100}$ of its value on the sun, $v = 97$ and, by Table 46, p_G at the reversing layer is slightly under 10.

The result $p_G \propto \sqrt{g}$ for stars of the same effective temperature was originally given by Milne as the result of the theory of § 248. By $(248\cdot3)$ approximately $k \propto \sqrt{g}$, and for the same temperature $k \propto p_G$.

We can now compare the effective temperatures of giant and dwarf stars of the same spectral type*. The result must depend on the criteria actually used in fixing the spectral types of stars. Following Milne we take this to correspond on the average to the state of ionisation with regard to ionisation potentials of the order 8 volts, or $\psi = 1\cdot27 \cdot 10^{-11}$ ergs. Then by $(174\cdot2)$ the same spectra will appear if

$$\frac{T_1^{\frac{5}{2}}e^{-\psi/RT_1}}{(p_G)_1} = \frac{T_2^{\frac{5}{2}}e^{-\psi/RT_2}}{(p_G)_2}\dots\dots\dots\dots(251\cdot91)$$

where the suffixes 1 and 2 now refer to the reversing layers of two different stars.

* E. A. Milne, *Monthly Notices*, **85**, p. 782.

Since $H \propto T^4$ and $k \propto p_G/T^{\frac{9}{2}}$

$$v \propto gT^{\frac{1}{2}}$$

by (250·1). Hence at the reversing layer by (251·8)

$$p_G \propto g^{\frac{1}{2}}T^{\frac{9}{4}}$$

so that (251·91) becomes

$$T_1^{\frac{1}{4}}e^{-\psi/RT_1}/g_1^{\frac{1}{2}} = T_2^{\frac{1}{4}}e^{-\psi/RT_2}/g_2^{\frac{1}{2}} \quad \ldots\ldots\ldots\ldots (251\cdot92),$$

or approximately $\quad \left(\dfrac{1}{2} + \dfrac{2\psi}{RT}\right)\delta\left(\log T\right) = \delta\left(\log g\right) \ldots\ldots\ldots\ldots (251\cdot93).$

Using the values of g for the sun and Capella this gives $T_1/T_2 = 1\cdot105$. The effective temperatures are in the same ratio as the reversing layer temperatures, hence they are respectively: Sun 5740°, Capella 5200°.

It is generally considered that the observed difference of temperature is of about this amount. In fact the temperature 5200° for Capella used throughout this book was an estimate from the observations, there being no theory available when the choice was made.

The Chromosphere.

252. We have seen that the thickness of the photosphere of the sun may be estimated at 15 km.; above this the density continues to diminish rapidly but there is no definite outer boundary to the distribution. In this region the conditions are practically isothermal, and the density therefore falls off exponentially with the height according to the well-known law for an isothermal atmosphere. The density decreases fourfold in the 15 km. of photosphere, and it will continue to decrease at about this rate so that 150 km. higher it should be inappreciable.

Now the flash spectrum observed at many eclipses shows that sufficient material to produce bright lines extends far above this limit. According to Evershed the H and K lines of calcium reach to a height of 8000 km.; Mitchell has traced them even to 14,000 km. Some of the hydrogen lines extend to 8500 km. above the limb. How is this material supported?

It seems impossible that there can be any steady electric field, other than the weak field described in § 191 which prevents the electrons from diffusing apart from their ions. And indeed an electric field could not well support a material atmosphere which must necessarily contain almost identical numbers of positive and negative charges. The only possible explanation seems to be that this material is supported by radiation pressure. It consists of atoms on which the radiation pressure is exceptionally strong, so that they are driven out from the photosphere and kept balanced at high level. The theory here described is due to E. A. Milne[*].

Why are certain elements selected to form this chromosphere

* *Monthly Notices*, **84**, p. 354; **85**, p. 111.

rather than others? For intense radiation pressure the atom or ion must have a *principal* line in the region of the spectrum in which the stellar radiation is strong; it can then absorb the radiation strongly. A subordinate line is no use because very few atoms are in a state to absorb it at any one moment. Further, the principal line must be a long way from the head of its series; that is to say, the stellar radiation must be able to excite the atom but not to ionise it. For at the low densities concerned an atom which once lost its electron would have small chance of recapturing one; and as it would meanwhile be unable to absorb, it would fall back into the photosphere. These conditions are well fulfilled by the H and K lines of Ca_+ which correspond to excitation of the odd electron from its normal 4_1 orbit to two 4_2 orbits (which differ only slightly from one another and need not here be discriminated).

253. In the highest part of the chromosphere only the H and K lines have been observed so that it is a fair approximation to take the material as constituted wholly of Ca_+ with the necessary complement of free electrons; it is also assumed that the only processes are the transitions from 4_1 to 4_2 orbits and back again*. Let n_1 be the number of atoms at any moment in the normal state and n_2 the number in the excited state; then the ratio n_1/n_2 is given by Einstein's equation (36·3)

$$a_{12} n_1 I (\nu_{12}) = b_{21} n_2 + a_{21} n_2 I (\nu_{12}) \ldots\ldots\ldots\ldots(253\cdot1).$$

There is no thermodynamical equilibrium, and this equating of direct and reverse transitions is only permissible because of the special postulates above which exclude any other transitions.

Now $I (\nu_{12})$ is not the black-body intensity for temperature T_e; it is modified in two ways. Consider for simplicity atoms at the top of the chromosphere. The radiation travelling in directions in the inward hemisphere is missing, hence the intensity is reduced to $\frac{1}{2}$ the full intensity. Further, ν_{12} being in the midst of an absorption line, we must multiply by the ratio r between the intensity in the line and the intensity just outside the line. It will be possible to determine r by photometric measurements of the intensity in the H and K lines in the observed spectrum. The equation accordingly is

$$a_{12} n_1 . \tfrac{1}{2} r I (\nu_{12}, T_e) = b_{21} n_2 + a_{21} n_2 . \tfrac{1}{2} r I (\nu_{12}, T_e) \ldots\ldots(253\cdot2).$$

Using the values of the atomic constants found in (38·25) and (38·4), we obtain

$$\frac{n_1}{n_2} = \frac{q_1}{q_2} \left(1 + \frac{C\nu_{12}{}^3}{\tfrac{1}{2} r I (\nu_{12}, T_e)} \right)$$

$$= \frac{q_1}{q_2} \left(1 + \frac{e^{h\nu_{12}/RT_e} - 1}{\tfrac{1}{2} r} \right) \quad \ldots\ldots\ldots\ldots(253\cdot3).$$

* Actually certain other transitions are bound to occur. The necessary modification of the theory is discussed by Milne in *Monthly Notices*, **86**, p. 8.

We write $q_2/q_1 = q$. There are two 4_1 orbits and six 4_2 orbits (four belonging to the K line and two to H); hence $q = 3$.

It is found that e^{hv_{12}/RT_e} is large so that we have with sufficient accuracy

$$n_2/n_1 = \tfrac{1}{2}qre^{-hv_{12}/RT_e}.$$

In this form the result is easily seen to be the appropriate modification of Boltzmann's formula. If the n_2 atoms were excited by full radiation at temperature T_e we should have $n_2/n_1 = qe^{-hv_{12}/RT_e}$; but n_2 is reduced proportionately to the diminished intensity of the radiation, so long as n_2 is small compared with n_1.

Let t_1 be the average duration of a normal state, t_2 of an excited state. Then

$$t_2/t_1 = n_2/n_1 = \tfrac{1}{2}qre^{-hv_{12}/RT_e} \quad\dots\dots\dots\dots\dots(253\cdot4).$$

The atom will be excited $(t_1 + t_2)^{-1}$ times per second and absorb $hv_{12} . (t_1 + t_2)^{-1}$ ergs per second. For each erg absorbed $1/c$ units of momentum will be absorbed; this momentum is in all directions over the outward hemisphere and the average component in the radial direction will be $1/2c$. (Allowing for the law of darkening the result should strictly be $4/7c$.) For equilibrium this outward momentum must balance the momentum communicated by gravity, viz. A_Hg, A being the atomic weight of calcium. Hence

$$A_Hg = \frac{hv_{12}}{2c\,(t_1 + t_2)},$$

or

$$t_1 + t_2 = \frac{hv_{12}}{2cA_Hg} \quad\dots\dots\dots\dots\dots\dots(253\cdot5).$$

By (253·4) and (253·5) to our order of approximation

$$t_2 = \frac{qrhv_{12}}{4cA_Hg}\, e^{-hv_{12}/RT_e} \quad\dots\dots\dots\dots\dots(253\cdot6).$$

Inserting numerical values for the sun the results are

$$t_2/t_1 = r \times 3\cdot54.10^{-3},$$
$$t_1 + t_2 = 4\cdot6.10^{-5},$$

so that

$$t_2 = r \times 16\cdot2.10^{-8}.$$

Since r is necessarily less than unity an upper limit to the duration of the excited state giving the H and K emission is $16\cdot2.10^{-8}$ seconds. (If this limit were exceeded there could be no calcium chromosphere on the sun.) By accurate measurement of the residual intensity at the centre of the H and K lines we could determine definitely this physical constant of the calcium atom. Provisionally r is believed to be about $0\cdot1$ so that

$$t_2 = 1\cdot6.10^{-8} \text{ secs.}$$

Values of t_2 have been determined in the laboratory by experiments on canal rays for some elements (but not for Ca_+) and these give results of the order 10^{-8} secs.; so that the astronomical determination is probably near the truth.

254. We now consider what happens as we descend in the chromosphere still assuming that Ca$_+$ is the only material present. The investigation of § 226 is immediately applicable and we have

$$H' = \text{const.} \\ J' = 2H' \left(1 + \tfrac{3}{2}\tau'\right) \Big\} \quad \text{......................(254·0),}$$

where H', J', τ' refer to monochromatic radiation of frequency ν_{12}. The law of darkening towards the limb (for the residual radiation at the centre of the absorption line) can be worked out as before and the same result (227·2) is obtained as for the photospheric radiation as a whole*. This is believed to be confirmed by observation.

The resultant outward force of radiation pressure is proportional to $H'n_1$ and the weight to be supported is proportional to $n_1 + n_2$. Hence, since H' is constant, the ratio of radiation force to gravity varies with depth as $n_1/(n_1 + n_2)$. A correction however is required on account of the momentum of the "stimulated emission." Whilst the spontaneous emission is symmetrical in all directions, the stimulated emission is in the direction of the stimulating radiation; the radiation pressure is accordingly reduced in corresponding proportion. It will be seen from (253·2) and (253·3) that the stimulated is to the spontaneous emission in the proportion $(e^{h\nu_{12}/RT_\theta} - 1)/\tfrac{1}{2}r : 1$ or approximately n_2/qn_1. Hence the radiation pressure is reduced approximately in the ratio $n_1 - n_2/q : n_1$. Writing then

$$\frac{\text{radiation force}}{\text{gravity}} = (1 + \sigma)\,\frac{n_1 - n_2/q}{n_1 + n_2} = (1 + \sigma)\Big/\left(1 + \frac{q+1}{q}\frac{n_2}{n_1}\right) \text{ approx.}$$

$$\text{................(254·1),}$$

the constant σ is determined by the condition that this ratio must be unity at the top of the chromosphere where the gas pressure vanishes. Since $q = 3$ and n_2/n_1 for the top of the chromosphere is $3·54.10^{-3}r$, this gives
$$\sigma = 4·72.10^{-3}r.$$

Now n_2/n_1, so long as it is small, is proportional, not to H', but to J' and therefore to $1 + \tfrac{3}{2}\tau'$. Hence

$$(q + 1)\,n_2/qn_1 = \sigma\,(1 + \tfrac{3}{2}\tau') \quad \text{................(254·2).}$$

By (254·1) and (254·2)

$$\frac{\text{radiation force}}{\text{gravity}} = \frac{1 + \sigma}{1 + \sigma + \tfrac{3}{2}\tau'\sigma} = 1 - \tfrac{3}{2}\tau'\sigma \text{ approximately.}$$

* Not the law of darkening for the neighbouring portion of the continuous spectrum which introduces other considerations (§ 229). Hence the contrast or "blackening" will not be strictly constant over the disc.

The deficit $\frac{3}{2}\tau'\sigma$ must be made up by gas pressure; hence

$$-\frac{dp_G}{dx} = \tfrac{3}{2}\tau'\sigma g\rho \quad\dots\dots\dots\dots(254\cdot3),$$

or

$$\frac{dp_G}{d\tau'} = \tfrac{3}{2}\tau'\sigma g/k',$$

where k' is the monochromatic coefficient of absorption.

In integrating this equation we can neglect the slight variation of k' due to the inert ions present. Hence

$$p_G = \tfrac{3}{4}\sigma g\tau'^2/k',$$

$$\rho = \frac{3\mu\sigma g\tau'^2}{4\Re k'T} \quad\dots\dots\dots\dots(254\cdot4).$$

Then

$$d\tau' = -k'\rho dx = -\frac{3\mu\sigma g\tau'^2}{4\Re T}dx.$$

Since T is practically constant* we have by integration

$$\tau' = \frac{4\Re T}{3\mu\sigma g(x+x_0)} \quad\dots\dots\dots\dots(254\cdot51),$$

where x_0 is a constant of integration. Hence by (254·4)

$$\rho = \frac{4\Re T}{3\mu k'\sigma g(x+x_0)^2}\dots\dots\dots\dots(254\cdot52).$$

The value of x_0 can be found roughly. By (226·2)

$$\tfrac{1}{2}(J_1' - J_2') = 2H', \qquad \tfrac{1}{2}(J_1' + J_2') = J' = 2H'(1+\tfrac{3}{2}\tau'),$$

so that

$$J_1' = 4H'(1+\tfrac{3}{4}\tau')\dots\dots\dots\dots(254\cdot61).$$

For radiation just outside the H and K lines the absorption in the chromosphere is negligible, so that the boundary values apply, viz.

$$J_1 = 4H \quad\dots\dots\dots\dots(254\cdot62).$$

By the definition of r, $H' = rH$; hence J_1' will be equal to J_1 at a depth τ_0' given by

$$r(1+\tfrac{3}{4}\tau_0') = 1,$$

so that

$$\tau_0' = \tfrac{4}{3}(1-r)/r \quad\dots\dots\dots\dots(254\cdot63).$$

Clearly the chromosphere cannot have greater depth than this, for the outflowing radiation in the absorption lines cannot have greater intensity than the surrounding spectrum. Hence τ_0' should be an upper limit to the optical thickness of the chromosphere. The theory is, however, somewhat of an extrapolation since in the lower part of the chromosphere other ions besides Ca_+ will be present and the simple conditions will no longer

---

* If the only exchange of energy between molecular speeds and radiation is by the scattering of the free electrons, the whole radiation of the sun is equally effective and the chromosphere takes up the uniform temperature T_0. There may, however, be some conversion of the radiation ν_{12} into molecular speeds; in that case the speeds will increase according to the intensity of ν_{12} and the chromosphere will be slightly hotter towards its base.

be valid. However, taking τ_0' to give the base of the chromosphere and measuring x from the base, we have by (254·51) and (254·63)

$$x_0 = \frac{\Re Tr}{\mu \sigma g \,(1-r)} \quad\dots\dots\dots\dots\dots\dots(254\cdot7).$$

Inserting $\sigma/r = \cdot00472$, $\mu = 20$, $1 - r = 0\cdot9$, $T = 5740°/1\cdot23$, $g = 2\cdot74 \cdot 10^4$, we find

$$x_0 = 1650 \text{ km.}$$

All the constants required in this calculation are very well determined, and the only uncertainty is that above-mentioned as to the conditions where the chromosphere merges into the photosphere. By (254·52)

$$\rho \propto (x + x_0)^{-2},$$

so that at a height of 8200 kilometres the density is $\frac{1}{36}$ the density at the base. The density of the *emitting atoms* $(\rho n_2/n_1)$ is proportional to $\rho \,(1 + \frac{3}{2}\tau')$, which up to 8000 km. is nearly proportional to $(x + x_0)^{-3}$. Thus in the same range the emission per unit volume in the chromosphere is reduced to $\frac{1}{150}$. The problem of how the brightness of the chromosphere as seen at the limb of the sun will vary with the density is very complicated, and the solution does not seem to have been attempted. It is therefore impossible to say how nearly the decrease in density agrees with the observed decrease of brightness.

As Milne has pointed out, the comparatively slow decrease of density in the chromosphere is evidence that radiation pressure supports nearly the whole mass. If gas pressure played more than the very subordinate rôle assigned to it in the above discussion the law of decrease of density would be exponential and ρ would become insignificant at a small height above the photosphere. It is easy to see how the balance is attained. In the final state of the chromosphere no more atoms can be supported at the top, because the screen of calcium atoms below has reduced the H and K radiation to an intensity too weak to give support; no more can be added at the bottom, the pressure of the radiation sent back from the chromosphere towards the interior presses them down. Until the back pressure attains the equilibrium amount atoms will be driven from the photosphere into the chromosphere by the forward pressure of the radiation of H and K frequency in the photosphere.

The monochromatic absorption coefficient for Ca_+ can be obtained from the value of t_2 (the life of an excited ion) found in (253·6); but an assumption must be made as to the width of the H and K lines. We adopt as a rough guess a combined width $\Delta\lambda = 1$ Å. It is remarkable that all previous results are independent of $\Delta\lambda$. Let n_1 and n_2 be the numbers of ions in the two states in a cubic centimetre in equilibrium at a *low* temperature T^*. By taking a low temperature we can set $(e^{h\nu/RT} - 1)$

---

* Since k' and t_2 are atomic constants we find the relation (254·83) between them by a purely thermodynamical argument without reference to the chromospheric conditions.

equal to $e^{h\nu/RT}$ and neglect stimulated emission. Then the emission per cu. cm. per sec. is

$$\frac{n_2}{t_2} h\nu = \frac{q n_1 h\nu e^{-h\nu/RT}}{t_2} \quad \ldots\ldots\ldots\ldots\ldots(254\cdot81),$$

and this will also be equal to the absorption. The radiation of H and K frequency traversing the cubic centimetre per second is

$$cI(\nu, T) \,\Delta\nu = 8\pi h\nu^3 \Delta\nu e^{-h\nu/RT}/c^2.$$

Hence by division, the absorption coefficient per cu. cm. is

$$\frac{q n_1 c^2}{8\pi t_2 \nu^2 \Delta\nu} \quad \ldots\ldots\ldots\ldots\ldots(254\cdot82),$$

and the coefficient per gram is

$$k' = \frac{q\lambda^2}{8\pi A H t_2 \Delta\nu} \quad \ldots\ldots\ldots\ldots\ldots(254\cdot83).$$

For $\lambda = 3950$ Å, $\Delta\lambda = 1$ Å, we find $\Delta\nu = 1\cdot92.10^{11}$, and hence

$$k' = 9\cdot0.10^8.$$

The mass M of a column of 1 sq. cm. section extending from the base to the top of the chromosphere is

$$M = \int \rho \, dx = \tau'/k' \quad \ldots\ldots\ldots\ldots\ldots(254\cdot9).$$

Taking the base to be given by (254·63)

$$\tau_0' = 4(1-r)/3r = 12,$$
so that $\qquad M = 1\cdot33.10^{-8}$ gm./cm.^{2}

The same result can also be found (without previously calculating k') by equating the weight of the column to the difference of radiation pressure at its extremities due to radiation in the range $\Delta\lambda$.

The density is of order 10^{-17} gm. per cu. cm. and the free path must be very great. Milne, treating the particles as neutral, finds a free path of 6000 km.; in that case the gas pressure can scarcely be said to "support" the matter of the chromosphere, but it replaces the falling particles by projecting fresh ones into the region. Probably, however, when account is taken of the charges of the particles the free path is not so formidable.

The equilibrium of a calcium atom at the top of the chromosphere is unstable. Although the value of g and the intensity of the radiation both fall off according to the inverse-square law as the distance increases, the radiation force diminishes less rapidly than gravity. This is because the absorbing power of a given mass of material is proportional to the number of *unexcited* atoms present; the proportion of excited atoms is always small, but there is a slight loss of efficiency because of them. With increasing distance from the star the efficiency increases towards unity, so that radiation force gains slightly in comparison with gravity. Presumably there is some escape of atoms from the top of the chromosphere but it is doubtful whether they can travel far. Ultimately the calcium atom will be doubly ionised (by starlight if not by sunlight); it will then drop back since it has small chance of picking up another electron when outside the chromosphere.

Milne has also pointed out that a calcium atom receding from the sun under radiation pressure experiences a rapidly increasing acceleration. Owing to the Doppler effect of its growing velocity its individual absorption shifts farther and farther from the centre of the solar H and K lines. At first it is, so to speak, balanced on the summit of the dark lines; but it topples off into a clear region and experiences the full force of undimmed solar radiation.

Abundance of the Elements.

255. In Saha's early researches the spectral types at which a line first appears and finally disappears were connected with the physical conditions at which the proportion of atoms in the right stage of ionisation becomes appreciable. Owing to the difficulty of assigning numerical significance to the word "appreciable," Fowler and Milne preferred to work with maximum intensity rather than marginal appearance. But just because the marginal appearance involves extraneous factors and is unsuitable for the main purpose, it may yield interesting information as to these factors. In particular it involves the abundance of the element since *ceteris paribus* if the atoms are ten times more abundant the required proportion in the proper state of ionisation is ten times smaller.

Although the reservation *ceteris paribus* covers a multitude of individual peculiarities of the elements and their spectra, a first clue to the relative abundance may be obtained on the hypothesis that the number of atoms required to give a spectrum at the limit of visibility is the same for all kinds of atoms.

This hypothesis is not so wild as we might suppose at first. Observation is limited to a rather narrow range of spectrum so that the energy-constants are roughly the same for all the lines studied. The absorption coefficient is mainly determined by the time taken to relapse from an excited state; this in turn is supposed to be connected with the classical radiation in the excited orbit which cannot be greatly different for the different orbits producing optical spectra. The series of lines in the spectra of the same element are of widely different intensities, and in comparing the abundance of elements by this method care must be taken to choose comparable lines of comparable importance as representative of the spectrum. If the element is represented only by weak lines in the visual region we might be misled.

This method of calculating abundance of the elements is due to C. H. Payne and the results in Table 47 are taken from her book*. They corre-

* *Stellar Atmospheres*, p. 187.

spond to the simple theory that if $1/n$ is the fraction of atoms in the appropriate absorbing condition when the line just becomes visible then the abundance of the element is proportional to n.

Table 47.

Stellar Abundance of the Elements.

Z	Element	Abundance	Z	Element	Abundance
14	Si	5·7	22	Ti	·43
11	Na	5·7	25	Mn	·36
12	Mg	4·2	24	Cr	·29
13	Al	3·6	19	K	·11
6	C	3·6	23	V	·05
20	Ca	2·9	38	Sr	·002
26	Fe	2·5	54	Ba	·005
30	Zn	0·57	3	Li	·0000

Other elements which are probably abundant are O, S, N, Ni, but quantitative determination is not yet possible. Information is not obtainable as to P, Cl, F, Zr which are terrestrially abundant. Miss Payne considers that there is a fairly close parallelism shown between stellar abundance and terrestrial abundance.

A study of this table does not suggest any need for amending the view expressed in § 173 that the mean molecular weight should be taken to correspond to a predominance of elements in the neighbourhood of Fe with some admixture of lighter elements. But this evidence is not to be stressed very much. The abundance here determined depends on the ability of the element to rise to the upper part of the photosphere and may not be typical even of the photosphere itself. The heavy elements are likely to be badly handicapped in showing themselves.

CHAPTER XIII

DIFFUSE MATTER IN SPACE

The Temperature of Space.

256. The total light received by us from the stars is estimated to be equivalent to about 1000 stars of the first magnitude. Allowing an average correction to reduce visual to bolometric magnitude for stars of types other than F and G, the heat received from the stars may be taken to correspond to 2000 stars of apparent bolometric magnitude 1·0. We shall first calculate the energy-density of this radiation.

A star of absolute bolometric magnitude 1·0 radiates 36·3 times as much energy as the sun or $1·37.10^{35}$ ergs per sec. This gives $1·15.10^{-5}$ ergs per sq. cm. per sec. over a sphere of 10 parsecs $(3·08.10^{19} \text{cm.})$ radius. The corresponding energy-density is obtained by dividing by the velocity of propagation and amounts to $3·83.10^{-16}$ ergs per cu. cm. At 10 parsecs distance the apparent magnitude is equal to the absolute magnitude; hence the energy-density $3·83.10^{-16}$ corresponds to apparent bolometric magnitude 1·0.

Accordingly the total radiation of the stars has an energy-density

$$2000 \times 3·83.10^{-16} = 7·67.10^{-13} \text{ ergs/cm.}^3$$

By the formula $E = aT^4$ the effective temperature corresponding to this density is

$$3°·18 \text{ absolute.}$$

In a region of space not in the neighbourhood of any star this constitutes the whole field of radiation, and a black body, e.g. a black bulb thermometer, will there take up a temperature of $3°·18$ so that its emission may balance the radiation falling on it and absorbed by it. This is sometimes called the "temperature of interstellar space."

It is possible, however, for matter which has strong selective absorption to rise to very much higher temperature. Attention was called to the possible astrophysical importance of this effect by C. Fabry*. Radiation in interstellar space is about as far from thermodynamical equilibrium as it is possible to imagine, and although its density corresponds to $3°·18$ it is much richer in high-frequency constituents than equilibrium radiation of that temperature. It is convenient to exhibit this by stating for each wave-length λ an equivalent temperature T_λ such that the actual density

* *Astrophys. Journ.* **45**, p. 269.

for wave-length λ is equal to that of equilibrium radiation at temperature T_λ. The following results are found—

Table 48.

Equivalent Temperatures of Radiation in Space.

λ	T_λ
600 Å	4707°
2000	1750
4000	967
6000	690

The source of the radiation was taken to be as follows—5 per cent. from stars at 18,000°, 10 per cent. 12,000°, 20 per cent. 9,000°, 40 per cent. 6,000°, 25 per cent. 3,000°. The total density was taken at the round figure 10^{-12} ergs per cu. cm.

Suppose, for example, that we are dealing with material capable of absorbing and emitting only in wave-length 600. It is unaffected by the presence or absence of radiation of other wave-lengths. It therefore behaves as though it were in a field of equilibrium radiation of temperature $T_\lambda = 4707°$ and takes up this temperature. This is an idealised illustration, and in actual matter no one process of energy transfer could be isolated so completely; indeed the notion of temperature is scarcely applicable unless a more general exchange is occurring. In natural material there will be a number of absorption and emission processes each striving to bring the temperature to the T_λ corresponding to the wave-length of the radiation concerned in it; and it is not possible to predict the result of the conflict without careful inquiry.

257. Apart from direct astronomical evidence it is unlikely on general grounds that interstellar space is entirely void. Matter may escape from stars by radio-active emission, by radiation pressure or by the ordinary loss of high-speed molecules. Terrestrial magnetic storms are usually ascribed to some kind of corpuscular emission from the sun. At the same time space is continually being swept by the passage of stars which will pick up the atoms lying in or near their tracks; but it appears that the spring-cleaning of space takes at least 10^{16} years so that it is unlikely that a steady balance of gain and loss has yet been reached.

To fix ideas we shall consider a density of 1 atom per cubic centimetre. This density is probably about the maximum admissible, but it is more instructive to discuss an upper rather than a lower limit. We take a mean atomic weight 10, since perhaps light elements are likely to preponderate. The mass in a sphere of 5 parsecs radius is then $128 \times \odot$. This volume would contain about 50 luminous stars, most of them of mass less than $\frac{1}{2}\odot$. Thus the assumed density gives a greater proportion of diffuse matter than aggregated stellar matter. Dynamical studies of stellar motions lead to the conclusion that the mass of invisible matter cannot exceed in any large ratio the mass of the luminous stars; it has in fact generally been concluded that it is not greater.

For a density of 1 atom per cu. cm. and atomic radius 10^{-8} cm., the mean free path is $5 \cdot 6 . 10^9$ km.

We have yet to decide whether this matter takes up a high or a low temperature, but provisionally we shall assume a temperature of 10,000°. The mean speed for atomic weight 10 is then $4 \cdot 6$ km. per sec.; hence the duration of the free path is 40 years. But we shall find later that the inter-stellar gas is ionised so that the attractions and repulsions of the electric charges will modify the free path. We assume single ionisation, and regard a deflection of 90° or more as constituting an encounter; the results are then:

Free path of atoms.—Length $7 . 10^8$ km. Duration 5 years.

Free path of electrons.—Length $1 \cdot 8 . 10^8$ km. Duration $3\frac{1}{2}$ days.

The collisions are sufficiently frequent to ensure that the material is a genuine gas with atomic velocities distributed according to Maxwell's law. The term temperature can be applied with its ordinary significance as a measure of the energy of the random motions*.

Energy is transferred from stellar radiation to this diffuse matter in four ways—

(a) Line absorption by the atoms.

(b) Ionisation of the atoms.

(c) Scattering by free electrons.

(d) Switches of electron orbits at encounter with atoms.

Energy is radiated from the matter by the four converse processes. The processes (a) and (b) involve high-frequency radiation and therefore tend to raise the temperature to a high value of T_λ. The process (c) is independent of wave-length and tends to reduce the temperature to $3° \cdot 18$. The fourth process requires closer examination.

(a) Line absorption has practically no effect on the temperature of the material. An atom absorbs a quantum and is thereby raised to an excited state, but there is no mechanism for converting the energy so acquired into translatory energy; all the atom can do is to retain it for about 10^{-8} sec. and then by re-emission restore it to the field of radiation.

Dense material can be heated by line absorption through the mechanism of *superelastic collisions*. An excited atom collides with an electron (or perhaps another atom) and the energy of excitation is released so as to cause an explosive rebound. Thus the energy passes from radiation *via*

* We prefer not to use the term *temperature of matter* except in this sense.

excitation into kinetic energy of translation. The transfer continues until the temperature is raised to the equilibrium value at which it is balanced by the converse transfer by *inelastic collisions*. But when the free path lasts for several days conversion by this method is so slow as to be negligible compared with other processes.

(b) The light of the stars expels electrons from the metals used in photoelectric cells in observatories and it must have a similar effect on matter in space*. The electrons are expelled with a velocity given by the quantum law
$$\tfrac{1}{2}mV^2 = h\nu - h\nu_1,$$
where $h\nu_1$ is the energy of ionisation. The elements affected will be chiefly those with low ionisation potential round about 5 volts such as Na, K, Rb, Ca, Ba, Al, etc. For 5 volts λ_1 $(= c/\nu_1)$ is 2468 Å. The mean velocity of expulsion of electrons should correspond to a temperature somewhat higher than T_{λ_1}, say 2000°, since all radiation between 0 and λ_1 is concerned in the ionisation. This is an example of a high effective temperature of the radiation in space *for a particular purpose*; evidently the absence of the proper proportion of radiation with wave-length greater than λ_1 is quite immaterial†.

It is possible that the actual conditions are even more extreme. A small proportion of the stellar radiation is capable of removing a second electron from the above-mentioned elements—at any rate from the divalent and trivalent elements. Recovery of an electron must be very slow and the dissociation may be rapid enough to keep the element as a rule doubly ionised. In that case the first ionisation potential of 5 volts will not be concerned and the transfer by ionisation will be operated by the still higher frequencies above the second ionisation potential—leading to higher values of T_λ.

We have thus a continually renewed supply of free electrons with speeds appropriate to a temperature of some thousands of degrees. These will mix with the atoms and by encounters tend to bring them to their own temperature. But the electron will suffer some loss of energy in its life-time and it is important to discover whether its initial energy of expulsion is at all comparable with its average energy. Ultimately the atoms will reach the average, not the initial, temperature of the electrons. Within reasonable limits it does not matter how slow is the transfer from the electrons to the atoms because we know of no process by which the atoms can waste the energy handed over to them. Note that the electrons take the lead in this adjustment, because the electron is continually going

---

* It should, however, be realised that the circumstances are not *precisely* the same. Less work is required to expel the electrons from a metallic film than from isolated atoms of the same element.

† At the end of this section it is shown that this argument does not contain the *whole* truth of the matter.

back to fetch more energy whilst the atom is passive. The shorter the life of the electron the more favourable is the chance of high temperature, since there is less opportunity for loss of initial energy and all loss is wiped out when the next life begins.

(c) One source of loss of energy of the free electrons is scattering. Let us (very liberally) estimate the life of a free electron at 10 years. In that time the energy flowing through a square centimetre amounts to 9.10^6 ergs (for energy-density 10^{-12}). To scatter this radiation completely it would be necessary to place the electrons contained in 5 gm. of matter as a screen (the coefficient of electron scattering being $\frac{1}{5}$ by (53·5)). The screen contains $1·5.10^{24}$ electrons, so that each electron scatters 6.10^{-18} ergs of stellar radiation or 2.10^{-28} units of momentum in 10 years. Even if the whole of this momentum were in a direction opposed to the motion of the electron its speed would be retarded less than 1 cm. per sec. The process (c) is evidently negligible.

(d) Between expulsion and final capture an electron makes many encounters with atoms and is liable to undergo the switches described in § 159. Switches involving loss of energy will occur in any case; switches involving gain of energy will be dependent on the presence of radiation available for absorption. The radiation concerned in switches is of lower frequency than the radiation which first expels the electrons from the atoms and determines their initial temperature; and interstellar radiation is relatively less rich in such frequency. Hence the gains of energy of the electron will by no means balance its losses, and in fact we cannot expect any appreciable part of the losses to be recovered.

In § 159 we divided the spectrum emitted by electrons of given speed into two parts (α) due to switches, and (β) due to capture. The former represents the loss of energy during the lives of the electrons; from the latter we can compute the amount retained and given up on capture. As usual let $h\nu_0 = \frac{1}{2}mV^2$, and let us consider the spectrum β' formed by multiplying the intensities in spectrum β by ν_0/ν. Since spectrum β represents the whole energy emitted on capture, spectrum β' represents the kinetic energy given up on capture; because the electron has only the kinetic energy $h\nu_0$ to lose, although it radiates $h\nu$ by falling to an orbit of negative energy. By Kramers' theory the intensity Q is constant up to the guillotine limit; hence the total intensities of the spectra are

$$(\alpha) \quad Q\nu_0,$$

$$(\beta') \quad Q \int_{\nu_0}^{\nu_1} \frac{\nu_0}{\nu} \, d\nu = Q\nu_0 \log \frac{\nu_1}{\nu_0},$$

where ν_1 is the guillotine limit. Hence

$$\frac{\text{kinetic energy lost by electron}}{\text{kinetic energy retained until capture}} = \frac{1}{\log (\nu_1/\nu_0)}.$$

For temperatures of two or three thousand degrees and atoms ionised down to 5–10 volts, $\log \nu_1/\nu_0$ is about 2–3. (The precise value is not of much importance; it is clear that in any case it is of order unity.) Hence the electrons preserve more than half their initial energy, and their average temperature is not much less than their initial temperature which we have already estimated at 2000° at least.

To sum up—the processes (a) and (c) have negligible effect on the temperature. The process (b) continually furnishes electrons at high temperature; and although this is appreciably toned down by process (d) the order of magnitude is still roughly that of process (b). Diffuse matter in space will accordingly rise to a temperature of the order 2000°. It is scarcely necessary to add that this conclusion is entirely provisional as there may be important gaps in our present knowledge.

Recently I have come to the conclusion that 2000° may be an underestimate. The following is an attempt to calculate more specifically the "initial temperature" of the electrons expelled from the atoms. To simplify the conditions we suppose that the stars are all black bodies with the same effective temperature T, so that the energy-density of interstellar radiation between ν and $\nu + d\nu$ is proportional to

$$\frac{\nu^3 d\nu}{e^{h\nu/RT} - 1} \quad \ldots\ldots\ldots\ldots\ldots\ldots\ldots(257\cdot1).$$

We are thus dealing with *evenly diluted* radiation. Suppose also that all the atoms have the same ionisation potential ν_0 (in frequency units). Let the absorption coefficient follow the law

$$k \propto \nu^{-3-s} \quad (\nu > \nu_0) \quad \ldots\ldots\ldots\ldots\ldots(257\cdot2).$$

On Kramers' theory $s = 0$, but we retain s as a precaution. By (257·1) and (257·2) the amount of radiation absorbed between ν and $\nu + d\nu$ can be set equal to

$$\frac{C d\nu}{\nu^s \left(e^{h\nu/RT} - 1\right)},$$

and the number of quanta absorbed is

$$\frac{C d\nu}{h\nu^{s+1} \left(e^{h\nu/RT} - 1\right)}.$$

Hence the average quantum absorbed is

$$h\bar{\nu} = \int_{\nu_0}^{\infty} \frac{h\, d\nu}{\nu^s \left(e^{h\nu/RT} - 1\right)} \div \int_{\nu_0}^{\infty} \frac{d\nu}{\nu^{s+1} \left(e^{h\nu/RT} - 1\right)} \quad \ldots\ldots(257\cdot3).$$

In our applications $h\nu_0/RT$ will be large so that we can replace $(e^{h\nu/RT} - 1)$ by $e^{h\nu/RT}$. Hence (257·3) becomes

$$\frac{h\bar{\nu}}{RT} = \int_{x_0}^{\infty} x^{-s} e^{-x} dx \div \int_{x_0}^{\infty} x^{-s-1} e^{-x} dx \quad \ldots\ldots\ldots\ldots(257\cdot4),$$

where $x_0 = h\nu_0/RT$. If E is the average initial energy of an electron after expulsion and T_0 the corresponding initial temperature, we have

$$\tfrac{3}{2}RT_0 = E = h\bar{\nu} - h\nu_0.$$

Hence by (257·4) we find

$$T_0 = \tfrac{2}{3}T \frac{1 - 2\,(s+1)\,x_0^{-1} + 3\,(s+1)\,(s+2)\,x_0^{-2} - \cdots}{1 - (s+1)\,x_0^{-1} + (s+1)\,(s+2)\,x_0^{-2} - \cdots} \quad (257·5).$$

For large values of x_0 the initial temperature approximates to $\tfrac{2}{3}T$, the next approximation being

$$T_0 = \tfrac{2}{3}T \left(1 - \frac{s+1}{x_0}\right).$$

Afterwards the mean temperature tends to rise above this initial value, because the slowest electrons are weeded out most quickly by capture. If this cause operated alone the average temperature would become equal to T. But we have seen that some fraction of the initial energy ($\tfrac{1}{4}$ to $\tfrac{1}{2}$) is gradually lost by the process (d). The conclusion is that the temperature of interstellar matter will be between $\tfrac{2}{3}T$ and T.

In considering a suitable average value to adopt for T it must be remembered that we are only concerned with radiation of short wave-length capable of ionising the atoms, and therefore the hottest stars must be given most weight. I therefore suggest a temperature about 10,000° for interstellar matter. The interesting point is that when ionisation alone is operating the enfeeblement of the radiation makes no difference to the temperature assumed by diffuse matter; T_0 depends on the relative intensities for different frequencies and not on the absolute intensity. For example, diffuse matter round about the orbit of Neptune should be cooler than the average; the sun, by liberating large numbers of slow-moving electrons *cools* the interstellar material in its neighbourhood.

The weak point of the investigation is that we have assumed the radiation of the stars to follow the black body law at very short wave-lengths—an assumption which has little theoretical or observational justification (§ 229). Numerical results must therefore be uncertain. I do not think there is any thermodynamical principle that forbids interstellar material attaining a temperature higher than the effective temperatures of the stars if there happened to be absorption bands in stellar spectra so placed as to cut down the number of expulsions with small energy.

Fixed Calcium Lines.

258. In certain spectroscopic binaries the absorption lines H and K of calcium are found not to partake of the orbital motion shown by the other spectral lines. Evidently these lines do not arise in the atmosphere of either component; they are formed either in an envelope surrounding the whole system or during the passage of the light through interstellar

space to the observer. The material at a considerable distance from either component must be of very low density, and the exceptionally sharp and narrow appearance of the "fixed calcium lines" is in keeping with this.

The detection of fixed calcium lines in binary stars may be compared with the detection of telluric lines in the solar spectrum; certain lines are found not to partake of the sun's rotation, and these have been imprinted on the spectrum during the journey of the light to us, viz. in our own atmosphere.

The phenomenon is shown only by the very hottest "early type" stars, viz. those of types O to B 3. It might, however, exist undetected in cooler stars, the fixed lines being masked by stronger and wider absorption lines in the atmospheres of the components.

The question whether the calcium cloud producing this absorption is attached to the star or is a free cloud in space can be settled by measuring the radial velocity. The test is not an easy one because the early type stars have usually low individual velocities; but an investigation by J. S. Plaskett appears to be conclusive*. He measured the calcium velocity and the ordinary stellar velocity (determined from the lines of normal behaviour) of 40 stars earlier than B 3, the investigation not being restricted to spectroscopic binaries. In a number of cases considerable differences ranging up to 50 km. per sec. were found, indicating that the cloud could not be attached to the star. Moreover, after correcting the calcium velocities for solar motion it was found usually that the cloud had little, if any, velocity referred to the standard of reference of stellar velocities—the so-called "mean of the stars." This uniformity of motion (or rest) of the calcium cloud indicates that it is a continuous cloud extending through all parts of the stellar universe explored in the investigation. Presumably it is of the nature of the diffuse matter in space imagined in the last two sections; inequalities of motion have been smoothed out in the course of time by diffusion and collision of the atoms.

The D lines of sodium also appear fixed in these early type stars and must therefore be produced in the cloud. No doubt other elements may be present but are not in a condition to produce prominent lines in the visible region of the spectrum. It is evident that only lines of a principal series are likely to be seen, since in the weak field of radiation the proportion of atoms excited at any one moment must be exceedingly small.

It is noteworthy that the H and K lines are produced by singly ionised calcium and the spectrum of the un-ionised element does not appear although it has strong principal lines that might have been observed. We deduce therefore that practically all the calcium is ionised. On the other hand, the D lines are absorbed by sodium atoms which are un-ionised and unexcited. Some difficulty has been felt with regard to the absence of

* *Pub. Dom. Obs. Vict.* 2, p. 287.

un-ionised calcium and presence of un-ionised sodium, since the ionisation potential for sodium is lower than for calcium and we should naturally expect the sodium to become ionised first in accordance with (174·2). But the expectation applies only when no second stage ionisation of either element is occurring, and owing to the low second potential for calcium the reversal might even have been anticipated. The following explanation has been given by R. H. Fowler.

The valency electrons of an element are detached by fairly low ionisation potentials; after they have been removed there is a sharp rise to the next ionisation potential required to detach an electron of the compact inner group. We may suppose 'that the stellar radiation traversing space contains constituents of sufficiently high frequency (emanating chiefly from the B and O stars) to ionise the valency electrons, but practically no constituents of the much higher frequency required to break into the next group. At the low density electron captures are rare; consequently the atoms are usually in the state of having lost all their valency electrons but with their inner groups complete. These compact ions give no absorption in the visible region since their principal lines are far in the ultraviolet. From time to time one of them will capture an electron and hold it for some considerable time*, since the ionising radiation is very weak; thus the next most common state is that of an ion with one valency electron. Since calcium is divalent and sodium monovalent, this places singly ionised calcium and neutral sodium on the same footing as regards chance of absorbing. Neutral calcium would only occur through the improbable coincidence of two electron captures in quick succession, so that its spectrum is not to be expected.

259. The question now arises whether, granting that there is a cloud extending through interstellar space, the fixed lines are produced uniformly during the transit of the light from the star to the earth or only in the neighbourhood of the star.

The reason for wishing to restrict the production of the lines to the neighbourhood of the star is that, if the star is absolved from all complicity, the phenomenon should be the same for all types of stars, the intensity of the fixed lines depending only on the distance traversed by the light. Since the phenomenon is detected only in the hottest stars of types O to B 3 the idea has been put forward that the presence of an intensely hot star stimulates the part of the cloud in its neighbourhood to perform the absorption. This would explain admirably the fixed calcium lines, the calcium being ionised by the high-frequency radiation and so brought to a condition to absorb the H and K lines. But the fixed sodium

---

* I.e. time enough for it to be excited a number of times, since many quanta of excitation frequency will come along before a quantum of the ionisation frequency arrives.

lines cannot be explained in this way because they are absorbed by neutral unexcited atoms which require no preparatory stimulation. This is a fatal objection to the theory. Moreover, we see no reason why the lines of un-ionised calcium should not be imprinted on the light as it traverses the regions where the atoms are supposed to be unstimulated.

Another possibility is that calcium and sodium do not exist in great quantity in the general cloud, but only in the neighbourhood of the hottest stars which eject them by selective radiation pressure or otherwise. After ejection the atoms are caught up in the cloud so that they have the motion of the cloud and not of the star. This view presents great difficulties when we attempt to consider it quantitatively. Remembering that the star is moving through the cloud, it cannot very well prepare a screen ahead of it. At any rate, the fixed lines should be stronger in receding stars than in approaching stars, and if the suggestion were seriously entertained this correlation should be looked for.

It appears then that we must turn to the alternative theory that the fixed lines are produced uniformly by absorption in interstellar space. They must accordingly be present in every type of star which is sufficiently distant, although it may be impracticable to detect them. Plausible reasons can be given why they have hitherto failed to appear. Below $B\,3$ it is presumed that H and K begin to be prominent in the spectrum of the star proper, and the fixed lines could only be distinguished if the star had large velocity. From $B\,3$ to $B\,8$ the velocities are generally very small. Stars of lower types are generally not sufficiently remote to give the general space-absorption a fair chance, and the increasing multitude of lines in the spectrum makes the detection difficult in the lowest types. Stars with the necessary requirement of very great distance and large velocity can perhaps be found, and it may be that they will give decisive evidence for or against the theory; we do not know of any test of this kind yet tried*.

It would seem that a valuable test could be obtained if an attempt were made to correlate the intensity of the fixed lines with the distances of the stars of types O–$B\,3$. If these stars were grouped according to estimated distance a distinct relation should be found; and it is even possible that if the test proved satisfactory it would furnish a method of determining large stellar distances. Exceptions must however be expected,

---

* [The star 66 Eridani, type $B\,9$, mag. 5·2, affords evidence distinctly unfavourable to the theory. It is a spectroscopic binary with both spectra visible and the calcium lines follow the orbital motion. The relative velocity of the two components amounts to 220 km. per sec. so that there would be plenty of room for fixed lines to appear *between* the stellar lines, but none are observed (Frost and Struve, *Astrophys. Journ.* **60**, p. 313). I can only suggest that its distance, estimated at 150 parsecs, might be insufficient to give the interstellar absorption a chance, but the excuse is not very satisfactory to me.]

because if the star's light traverses a diffuse nebula (with density perhaps 10,000 times that of the interstellar cloud) the calculation is altogether upset.

In some binaries the calcium lines show a radial velocity variable in the same period as the other lines but with smaller amplitude. It seems obvious that this is the result of a blend of the fixed calcium lines with the calcium lines of the star itself. Some writers, however, have attributed it to motion of a calcium envelope, supposed to surround the whole system, which follows with reduced amplitude the motion of the bigger component towards and away from us. The suggestion disregards altogether the dynamics of the problem; obviously the motion of the principal star could not communicate displacement to a distant rare medium without great lag of phase.

A word may be added as to the method of production of the lines. We have already seen that the atoms which have performed the line absorption cannot get rid of their energy except by radiating it again. But the absorbed radiation is taken out of the ray travelling from the star to the earth and the emitted radiation is sent out indiscriminately in all directions; if any of it meets the eye of the observer it is not coming from the direction of the star but is part of the general light of the sky. As there is no thermodynamic equilibrium it is not necessary that the emission should be qualitatively the exact inverse of the absorption—the atom may be excited in one step and return to its normal state by several intermediate steps. In fact the emission will usually be in lower frequencies than the absorption owing to the relative deficiency of the field of radiation in low frequencies.

260. According to Milne's theory of the chromosphere (254·83) the monochromatic absorption coefficient for H and K light is of the order 10^9, so that moderately dark lines will be produced by 10^{-9} gm. or $1·5.10^{13}$ atoms of Ca_+ per sq. cm. Assuming that fixed lines of this intensity occur in stars distant 500 parsecs ($1·5.10^{21}$ cm.), there must be 1 atom of Ca_+ in 10^8 cu. cm. The un-ionised atoms are presumably much rarer since their principal lines do not appear, but there may be any number of doubly ionised atoms. Judging by terrestrial abundance calcium might be expected to form rather more than 1 per cent. of the whole material.

The fixed calcium lines may thus be considered to give a lower limit of about 10^{-6} atoms per cu. cm. for the density of interstellar matter. There is rather a wide gap between this and the upper limit of 1 atom per cu. cm. fixed by dynamical considerations; but this will be closed up if most of the calcium is doubly ionised. Another clue to the density is obtained by considering the general scale of the local condensations occurring in it—the diffuse and dark nebulae. Since the investigation of the temperature of diffuse matter applies also to the nebulae, we take the conditions to be isothermal with $T = 10,000°$. Then by (63·4) with $\mu = 10$, $\beta = 1$

$$r = 3·14.10^8\rho_0^{-\frac{1}{2}}z,$$

or if r is measured in parsecs

$$r = (10^{20}\rho_0)^{-\frac{1}{2}}z \quad\dots\dots\dots\dots\dots\dots(260·1).$$

Take, for example, the unit of z to be 1 parsec; the density then diminishes from ρ_0 at the centre of the nebula to $\frac{1}{8}\rho_0$ at 5 parsecs from the centre and $\frac{1}{40}\rho_0$ at 10 parsecs distance (Table 7). I suppose that this corresponds very well to the size of typical nebular aggregations. Accordingly by (260·1)

$$\rho_0 = 10^{-20}.$$

Even if the scale of the nebula is 3 times larger or smaller ρ_0 is only changed by a factor 9, so that the central density of the nebulae is rather well determined if this theory is valid. At 150 parsecs distance from any one nebula we probably reach the general average conditions of interstellar space undisturbed by exceptional attracting masses. By Table 7 the density has there fallen to $10^{-4}\rho_0$. This then indicates a density 10^{-24} or about $\frac{1}{16}$ of the upper limit which we have been adopting. This last result happens to be nearly independent of the determination of ρ_0; and it seems impossible to strain the data so as to give a result near the lower limit of 10^{-6} atoms per cu. cm.

We judge therefore that the interstellar medium is much denser than would be necessary to give the fixed calcium lines if all the calcium were in the state of Ca_+. It is probable therefore that most of the calcium is doubly ionised—a conclusion favourable to Fowler's argument (§ 258).

A rough determination of the state of ionisation of the diffuse matter can be made in the following way. Assume as in § 257 that all the stars have the same effective temperature T—approximately the same as the temperature of the interstellar matter. Then the radiation in space is evenly diluted equilibrium radiation, that is to say, the density for frequency ν to $\nu + d\nu$ is $\quad I(\nu, T)\,d\nu/\delta,$

where $I(\nu, T)$ is the equilibrium intensity and δ is a constant "factor of dilution." The degree of ionisation is determined by equating the number of captures to the number of expulsions. The former number is proportional to the density of the electrons and the latter to the density of the radiation. If the radiation density and the electron density are both multiplied by the same factor δ the balance will be unaltered. This multiplication brings the radiation up to its equilibrium density; hence we have the rule—

The conditions of ionisation in interstellar material are the same as in material of density $\rho\delta$ in thermodynamical equilibrium at temperature T.

Equilibrium radiation at $10,000°$ has a density 76 ergs per cu. cm.;

hence the density of interstellar radiation being $7 \cdot 7 \cdot 10^{-13}$, we have $\delta = 10^{14}$. With $\rho = 10^{-24}$ we have $\rho\delta = 10^{-10}$, and the problem reduces to finding the ionisation in equilibrium conditions for density 10^{-10} and temperature $10,000°$. By $(174 \cdot 2)$ we find

$$\psi_0/RT = 19 \cdot 8, \qquad \psi_0 = 17 \text{ volts.}$$

The second ionisation potential of calcium is $11 \cdot 8$ volts. The proportion of calcium remaining in the Ca_+ state is then

$$e^{(\psi - \psi_0)/RT} = \cdot 0025,$$

the rest being doubly ionised.

The second ionisation potential for sodium is 30–35 volts so that there is practically no double ionisation. The first ionisation potential is $5 \cdot 1$ volts; hence we find that 1 atom of sodium in 1,000,000 is neutral. If the abundance and the absorption coefficients for sodium are the same as for calcium this is barely sufficient to produce the fixed D lines*. Calcium's first ionisation potential is 1 volt higher and the corresponding divisor is 300,000. We can now readily understand why neutral calcium is less abundant than neutral sodium (as the observations indicate); our results are

$$\frac{Ca}{Ca_+} = \frac{1}{300,000}, \qquad \frac{Ca_+}{Ca_{++}} = \frac{1}{400}, \qquad \frac{Na}{Na_+} = \frac{1}{1,000,000},$$

so that there is an extra divisor of 400 due to the second stage ionisation occurring in calcium but not in sodium.

Any minor numerical discrepancies will probably disappear when we take account of the spread of effective temperatures of the stars. This makes the radiation richer in high frequencies and poorer in low frequencies, so that the second stage ionisation is more intense and the first stage less intense than in the foregoing results. This may well reduce the proportion of Ca_+ atoms to $\frac{1}{10}$ and increase the proportion of Na atoms to 10 times the above figures. All the results then become satisfactorily consistent.

Absorption of Light in Space.

261. Distances of celestial objects up to about 50 parsecs can be determined by the trigonometrical method. By the use of mean parallactic motions and mean cross-motions the determination of *average* distances of groups of objects can be extended to perhaps 400 parsecs. Beyond this we are almost entirely dependent on an optical method; if the absolute magnitude of a star is supposed to be known independently, then it is a simple calculation to find at what distance it must be situated in order to give the observed apparent magnitude.

---

* Terrestrially sodium atoms are about 4 times as abundant as calcium atoms; moreover the fixed D lines are weaker than H and K. Allowing for this we still require a rather higher absorption coefficient—which is perhaps not unlikely.

This optical method of finding distances assumes that there is no appreciable loss of light by absorption or scattering during the journey across space. The direct evidence for this assumption is very limited. Some check is afforded by the general agreement of spectroscopic and trigonometrical parallaxes, but this gives an upper limit to the absorption too high to be of much service. The evidence which is usually quoted as indicating an almost perfect transparency of interstellar space is H. Shapley's demonstration that the light from the stars in globular clusters (at a distance of the order 10,000 parsecs) shows no appreciable reddening; it is assumed that absorption without reddening is unlikely.

According to modern ideas Shapley's result does not really carry us much farther. We shall presently show that the reddening by diffuse matter is small in proportion to the absorption so that the absence of detectable reddening is no proof of absence of dimming.

The weakness of the position is apparent when we consider the possible causes of dimming of a distant object. These are—

1. Obstruction by particles large compared with the wave-length of light (meteoric matter).

2. "Rayleigh scattering" by atoms, ions or particles comparable with the wave-length of light.

3. Scattering by free electrons.

4. Continuous absorption by gaseous material.

Line absorption, discussed in §§ 258, 259, has insignificant effect on the general brightness of the star and cannot occur without betraying itself in the spectrum.

Of these only the Rayleigh scattering definitely causes reddening. It is proportional to the inverse fourth power of the wave-length, so that blue light is eliminated from the transmitted beam faster than red. But we might almost have rejected Rayleigh scattering without observational test for reddening; to produce appreciable effect a vast quantity of interstellar material is required which would be irreconcilable with dynamical studies of stellar velocities.

The causes (1) and (3) act independently of wave-length and would not produce reddening. No. (4) is likely to be selective but whether it would make the light redder or bluer cannot be foretold.

We have seen reason to believe that most elements lose their valency electrons in interstellar space; and in any case the fixed calcium lines constitute observational evidence that calcium is ionised. Hence the material contains free electrons. We shall consider whether the electron scattering can produce appreciable dimming of the stars. If there were 500 free electrons per cu. cm., a column of 1 sq. cm. section and length

1000 parsecs would contain $1 \cdot 5 . 10^{24}$ electrons—the number contained in 5 gm. of matter. Light traversing this column would be reduced in intensity in the ratio e^{-1} or roughly 1 magnitude. An absorption of 1^m per 1000 parsecs is just large enough to be of serious importance in stellar investigations in the galactic system. There is no reason to suppose that the diffuse cloud extends much beyond the galactic system—its motion determined by Plaskett shows that it is associated with our local system in particular—so that we must not assume that the absorption extends equally to the globular clusters; but anything seen outside our system would be dimmed at least one magnitude, and this would give important corrections to the deduced distances of globular clusters and spiral nebulae.

But a density of 500 free electrons per cu. cm. is much greater than we can admit. We have seen that 1 atom per cubic centimetre is about the maximum possible, and since it would not be more than doubly or triply ionised, there cannot be more than 2 or 3 electrons per cu. cm. We can probably conclude safely that electron-scattering in interstellar space is too small to cause appreciable dimming of even the most distant objects. There is perhaps a small risk in neglecting it in the determination of the distance of the Andromeda nebula (300,000 parsecs); but even if the matter were supposed to continue with undiminished density through intergalactic space, the required correction would not alter the order of magnitude of the distance of the nebula.

If dimming by electron-scattering is of cosmical importance at all, it must be in local regions of the sky, where the interstellar matter is more condensed.

When a gas is ionised the electron scattering (which does not redden) is very much larger than the Rayleigh scattering (which reddens), so that the combined result is absorption without appreciable reddening. We have above us a column of air containing about 1000 gm. per sq. cm. If this were fully ionised, the electron scattering would reduce the light of a star overhead by $1000/5 = 200$ magnitudes; if singly ionised, the reduction would be 28 magnitudes. The Rayleigh scattering which is not appreciably different for ionised air and the actual atmosphere is, of course, trifling in comparison.

We might tentatively use observations of reddening as a test whether nebulous material is ionised or not. If there is absorption with reddening the number of free electrons must be small; if there is no detectable reddening the material must be considerably ionised. The only difficulty is that we cannot be sure that the absorption is not produced in some quite different way, e.g. by meteoric matter. Measurements of reddening by obscuring patches and gaseous nebulae have been attempted, but it is too early yet to state any firm conclusions.

262. Continuous absorption (as distinct from scattering) is produced by the two causes studied in connection with the interior of a star.

(*a*) Ionisation of atoms.

(*b*) Switches of electron orbits at encounter with atoms.

To these we may possibly have to add a third cause not operative in the stellar interior.

(*c*) Dissociation of molecules into atoms.

(*a*) Absorption by ionisation affects only radiation of frequency above that corresponding to the ionisation potential. For absorption of yellow light which contributes most to visual brightness the ionisation potential would have to be as low as 2·2 volts. This is below any known ionisation potential. An excited atom can be ionised by light of lower frequency but the proportion of excited atoms must be extremely small.

(*b*) This must be extremely small owing to the rareness of encounters.

(*c*) It is unlikely that combination of atoms into molecules occurs in interstellar space, because the atoms are ionised and their positive charges tend to keep them apart when they meet; their chemical attraction is given no chance. We may, however, provisionally examine what happens if the combination is possible. The energy-density in space (10^{-12}) corresponds to about 1 visual quantum in 3 cu. cm., or roughly 1 quantum per molecule (or potential molecule) for our estimate of maximum material density. By a synchronised effort the molecules could just extinguish all the starlight lying about; after this they could do nothing for 40 years—the time until the atoms suffered their next encounter and had a chance of recombining. Extinction once in 40 years spread over a light track means that a star distant 13 parsecs (40 light years) would be dimmed in the ratio $1/e$ or 1 magnitude. This is a quite serious absorption. But we have been dealing with extreme upper limits and cannot really expect anything like so high an efficiency. It is fairly safe to conclude that molecular absorption, if it occurs, is not great enough to produce appreciable effects.

As regards obstruction by meteoric matter we have no evidence to guide us. The meteoric matter encountered by the earth is generally supposed to have originated in the solar system and there is no reason to think that anything of the kind exists in interstellar space. We have the impression (perhaps not too well founded) that the primordial state of matter is gaseous, and that meteors or meteor dust must be the débris of some former aggregation of matter. Obstruction by meteor dust is rather more economical of mass than other forms of absorption or scattering—a consideration often of importance; and although we do not favour the hypothesis of absorption from this cause it is not to be set aside altogether.

Returning to the question whether the usual assumption of perfect transparency of space (apart from specially obscured regions) is justified, we must answer that we think it is; the only serious risk in this conclusion is that it neglects the possibility of absorption by meteor dust.

Dark Nebulae and Diffuse Nebulae.

263. We now consider diffuse nebulae such as the Orion Nebula which show bright line emission spectra, and dark nebulae which appear as obscuring patches in the sky hiding the light of the stars behind. Whilst it may not always be possible to discriminate correctly between an obscuring patch and an actual lacuna in the distribution of the stars, there are many cases where the existence of dark nebulosity is undoubted. Dark and diffuse nebulae are closely connected and grade into one another insensibly; sometimes a diffuse nebula is continued as an obscuring patch; sometimes part of a dark nebula is faintly luminous where the proximity of bright stars gives the necessary stimulation.

It is now generally agreed that the luminosity of a diffuse nebula is stimulated by the radiation of the stars contained in it; it is often described as a fluorescence. The dependence of the nebular light on the stellar radiation is well shown by Hubble's Variable Nebula, where the stimulating star is a variable and accordingly the nebula itself is variable. The idea is that the atoms in the nebula are excited by absorbing the radiation coming from the stimulating star or stars, and emit their characteristic bright line spectrum as they relapse.

Consider for example the lines of the Balmer series (H_a, H_β, etc.) which appear in the diffuse nebulae. The wave-length of the radiation required to raise the normal hydrogen atom to the required state is 1025·5 Å for H_a ranging up to 911·5 A for the highest members of the series. As this is far in the ultra-violet the hot stars will be much more rich in the required radiation than cool stars. Accordingly luminous nebulae showing the hydrogen lines are generally found surrounding groups of B type stars. The dark nebulae may be considered to be precisely similar intrinsically, but lacking stars hot enough to stimulate them. It may be remarked, however, that it is possible for opacity to be stimulated by radiation—the radiation, for example, liberating more free electrons and thus providing absorbing mechanism. I do not suppose that the opacity of ordinary dark nebulae is a stimulated opacity; but an examination of the photographs of Hubble's Variable Nebula strongly suggests that the dark patches of obscuration which appear and disappear in certain regions of it are governed by a varying stimulus from the associated star.

Since the state of the nebula is far removed from thermodynamic equilibrium, the emission is not generally in the same wave-lengths as the absorption. The energy of emission of the Balmer series is in fact derived from absorption in the principal series of hydrogen. Dark lines of the latter series will cross the spectrum of the stimulating stars but they are in the far ultra-violet beyond the region which can be observed*. Probably the Orion Nebulă is nearly transparent to Balmer radiation in spite of the fact that it is emitting it, so that the brightness is a direct measure of the gross emission—a very unusual simplification. (This may be contrasted with the chromosphere, where the brightness is by no means a measure of the number of emitting atoms since there is high internal absorption.) Probably a great deal of interesting information as to the density of the hydrogen distribution and the probabilities of transition between the different quantised states of the atom, etc. could be obtained from absolute measures of the emission of the Orion Nebula.

We naturally assume that the diffuse and dark nebulae are local condensations of the general cloud of interstellar matter revealed by the fixed calcium lines. It is, however, by no means easy to account quantitatively for the great opacity of the dark nebulae. Most theories lead to an extravagantly high mass, as has been pointed out by A. Pannekoek. We may take as typical the dark nebula in Taurus studied by Pannekoek†. He found an obscuring patch of area 140 square parsecs, which in general reduced the light of the stars behind it by 2 magnitudes. Interpreting the darkening as Rayleigh scattering he found a mass of at least $4.10^9 \times \odot$. Adopting electron scattering the required mass is less, but the difficulty is not wholly removed. To reduce by 2^m we require 10 gm. per sq. cm. of fully-ionised material or say 200 gm. per sq. cm. of singly-ionised material. The whole mass is then $140 \times 200 \times (3.10^{18})^2 = 2 \cdot 5.10^{41}$ gm. = 120 million suns. If the depth is taken as 12 parsecs (corresponding to the transverse dimensions) the density is 5.10^{-18} gm. per cu. cm. or 500 times our estimate of ρ_0 in § 260. A star approaching this nebula would, under its gravitational attraction, acquire a velocity of 300 km. per sec. at the boundary and 350 km. per sec. on reaching the centre. The mass is clearly too high. To avoid abnormal stellar velocities the mass should be divided by 100. Accepting reduction by a factor $\frac{1}{100}$, the density is about 1000 times our assumed density of ordinary interstellar matter, and the mass is 2 gm. per sq. cm. It is doubtful if 2 gm. per sq. cm. can give the observed opacity in any other way than by solid obstruction, e.g. by particles like sand. The problem of the masses of the dark nebulae is fraught with difficulty, and we do not venture to suggest any conclusion.

* Our upper atmosphere is practically opaque to radiation of wave-length less than 2850 Å, and even the solar spectrum cannot be observed beyond this limit.

† Proc. Akad. van Wetenschappen, Amsterdam, 23, p. 720 (1920).

Planetary Nebulae.

264. Planetary nebulae are similar to diffuse nebulae in many respects, but they are of more regular shape, they surround a single star, and they are of much smaller absolute dimensions. They give bright line spectra accompanied by a certain amount of continuous spectrum. There is not much difference between the spectra of diffuse and planetary nebulae, the latter differing among themselves quite as much as they differ from the diffuse nebulae.

The central star is always faint, a great deal of its light being doubtless lost through the continuous absorption of the nebula. The spectrum is very rich in ultra-violet light, and the stars capable of supporting this nebulous appendage are probably limited to type O.

The *annular nebulae* are a characteristic and interesting type of planetary nebulae.

Spectroscopic measurements of radial velocity have demonstrated the rotation of several planetary nebulae including the Ring Nebula in Lyra. It is not a rigid body rotation, but diminishes outwards as orbital revolution would do. It may be assumed that rotation plays an essential part in the phenomenon. It looks as though the nebulous matter cannot have been expelled from the central star (by radiation pressure or otherwise) since this would not possess enough angular momentum. But on the other hand, in the Novae we observe matter, which certainly seems to be expelled from a star, acquiring rotation or at any rate large transverse velocity. The fact is that rotation of celestial objects is altogether mysterious, and we really know no adequate cause for the almost universal prevalence of rapid rotation*.

The observed spectrum points to a high degree of ionisation. The elements detected are H, He, He_+ and probably C_{+++}; in addition, there are numerous unidentified lines including the prominent doublet of nebulium. Ca_+ is not shown so that presumably calcium is triply ionised. On the other hand, the occurrence of the He spectrum shows that helium is not doubly ionised. As the second ionisation potential of helium is

* [The view that the nebula consists of matter left behind in the course of stellar condensation seems to be inadmissible, because a tenuous structure of this kind could not be propelled through the interstellar cloud at 100 km. per sec. without suffering rapid change and dissipation. We feel bound therefore to admit replenishment both of the material and of the angular momentum by emission from the central star. Failing any other explanation we may perhaps invoke the magnetic field of the star. If ionised material is streaming out in the equatorial plane the ions will acquire angular momentum of one sign and the electrons angular momentum of the opposite sign about the magnetic axis of the star. A weak field of the same order as the sun's general magnetic field is quite sufficient to produce the required transverse velocity. This explanation might apply also to the transverse velocities observed in Novae. It is difficult to develop a detailed explanation on these lines and the idea is at present a vague conjecture.]

54 volts, we consider that the elements in general are ionised down to a level of 40–50 volts. Bearing in mind the high temperature of the central star, this is about the value predicted by the method of § 260.

The inferences in the last paragraph are based on the argument (§ 258) that in highly diffuse material not only will the spectrum of the ion ordinarily present appear but also that of the next lower ionisation. For example the ion He_+ will after excitation emit its proper spectrum. But it is also able to capture an electron; the captured electron does not necessarily occupy the lowest orbit in the first instance but it will soon come down to the lowest orbit in one or more steps and emit the spectrum of neutral He in so doing.

The fact that so large a proportion of the nebular lines are unidentified is evidence that the conditions of ionisation are more extreme than those generally attained in a vacuum tube.

It is a natural suggestion that the nebula should be regarded as an extended chromosphere. There is, however, little real resemblance. Whether radiation pressure is concerned in the phenomenon or not, it can scarcely be the main support of the nebula as it is of the chromosphere. The hydrogen is mainly ionised in the nebula and the solitary hydrogen nuclei are unabsorbent, so that they could not be supported. It seems evident that the chief support of the nebula must be rotation.

265. Two possible lines of explanation of the annular form of many of these nebulae are open. It may be that the limits of the annulus mark the places where the conditions for emission of the light concerned cease to exist; or it may be that the annulus represents an actual condensation of the element concerned. In either case an observational result of great interest is the variation of size of the annulus as studied in different kinds of monochromatic light. When viewed through a prism a number of monochromatic images of the nebula are seen—one for each of the chief emission lines in the spectrum. These images are rings of different sizes, the nebulium rings being noticeably large and He_+ noticeably small.

It may well happen that as we go away from the star the ionisation rises to a maximum and then declines. At small distances the density is too great, and at large distances the high frequency radiation is reduced by absorption in the nebula. It is, however, difficult to explain the hydrogen annulus in this way since ionisation of the hydrogen would seem to be wholly disadvantageous.

With regard to the other explanation Milne's investigation showed that a chromosphere must necessarily stand on a base and cannot float above the star detached from it (§ 254). But the nebula differs from the chromosphere in two essential respects: firstly, it has the additional support of rotation; secondly, it is transparent to much of its own radiation.

In the calcium chromosphere the back-thrust of the radiation from the higher part on the atoms of the lower part was of great importance; the *net* flow of radiation outwards was the same at all heights so that the force of radiation pressure was practically constant in all parts. In the nebula the radiation absorbed is re-emitted mostly in wave-lengths to which the nebula is transparent and there is less back-thrust. Consequently the force of radiation pressure decreases along the radius according to the ordinary absorption law. This seems to permit a stable annular distribution; a particle falling from the midst of the nebula would be sent back again by the increased radiation pressure; a particle moving towards the outside would fall back under the reduced radiation pressure.

I doubt, however, whether these considerations as to the behaviour of radiation pressure are of much importance because, as already stated, the hydrogen which is conspicuous in planetary nebulae is not likely to be much influenced by it.

Accretion of Stellar Mass.

266. A star travelling through the diffuse matter in interstellar space must sweep up the atoms in and near its track and thereby gain mass.

If we neglect the encounters of the atoms with one another the problem is very similar to that of the capture of an electron by hitting the nucleus. Let V be the relative velocity of the star and the cloud and R the radius of the star; we have first to find the radius σ of the apparent target corresponding to a true target R. Conservation of angular momentum and of energy gives

$$\sigma V = RV',$$
$$V'^2 - V^2 = 2GM/R,$$

V' being the velocity of the atom as it grazes the star. Eliminating V',

$$\frac{\sigma^2}{R^2} = 1 + \frac{2GM}{RV^2} \qquad \ldots\ldots\ldots\ldots\ldots\ldots(266 \cdot 1).$$

In practical cases $2GM/RV^2$ is large so that with sufficient accuracy

$$\sigma^2/R^2 = 2GM/RV^2.$$

Hence the amount of matter swept up per second is

$$dM/dt = \pi\sigma^2 V\rho = 2\pi GMR\rho/V \quad \ldots\ldots\ldots\ldots(266 \cdot 2),$$

ρ being the density of the diffuse cloud.

As in § 257 we adopt a density of $1 \cdot 66 \cdot 10^{-23}$ corresponding to 1 atom per cu. cm. of atomic weight 10. For the sun $V = 2 \cdot 10^6$, so that

$$dM/dt = 4 \cdot 8 \cdot 10^8 \text{ gm. per sec.}$$

The loss of mass by radiation is

$$L/c^2 = 4 \cdot 2 \cdot 10^{12} \text{ gm. per sec.}$$

We add for comparison the corresponding results for V Puppis and Krueger 60 adopting $V = 8$ and $V = 50$ km. per sec. respectively, which are about the average velocities for stars of their class.

Star	dM/dt	L/c^2	Ratio
V Puppis	$1\cdot8\cdot10^{11}$	$2\cdot9\cdot10^{16}$	165000
Sun	$4\cdot8\cdot10^{8}$	$4\cdot2\cdot10^{12}$	8800
Krueger 60	$1\cdot9\cdot10^{7}$	$4\cdot7\cdot10^{10}$	2500

Probably R ought to have been taken greater than the photospheric radius of the star. I suppose that if an atom from space encountered the solar corona it would be tangled up with it sufficiently to be captured by the sun. But allowing for all uncertainties it seems clear that the loss of mass by radiation cannot be compensated by accretion in any ordinary type of star.

267. Loss of mass by escape of atoms has been considered by a number of writers. According to E. A. Milne* the loss from a star by reason of thermal velocities is quite negligible for all elements. There seems to be some possibility of escape of the chromospheric atoms acted upon by intense radiation pressure; but calculations are not as yet very definite†.

But in any case it is difficult to believe that the loss by escaping atoms can be at all comparable with the loss of mass by radiation. The radiation of the sun carries away a mass of $6\cdot10^{-11}$ gm. per sq. cm. per sec. We have found (§ 254) that the average density of the calcium chromosphere is of order 10^{-17} gm. per cu. cm.; so that the whole chromosphere would have to move steadily outwards at 60 km. per sec. in order to carry away as much mass as the radiation does!

The radiation of mass of the sun is equivalent to the escape of a billion calcium atoms per second from each square centimetre of its surface.

It seems then that change of mass of a star by radiation far outweighs any material accretion or loss. If that is so, the calculation of the duration of stages of evolution in Table 41 must be accepted as definitive. As already explained grave difficulties then arise as to the coexistence of giants and dwarfs in the same cluster; it seems almost necessary to throw over the idea of any important advance in evolution in the life-time of the clusters, and it then becomes a question whether there is any point in retaining the idea for stars in general. Somewhere in the present tangle of evolution and sources of energy I have been misled; and my guidance of the reader must terminate with the admission that I have lost my way.

* *Trans. Camb. Phil. Soc.* **26**, p. 483 (1923).

† The problem is discussed by M. C. Johnson, *Monthly Notices*, **85**, p. 813 (1925)·

To recall Kelvin's classic phrase, there are two clouds obscuring the theory of the structure and mechanism of the stars. One is the persistent discrepancy in absolute amount between the astronomical opacity and the results of calculations based either on theoretical or experimental physics. The other is the failure of our efforts to reduce the behaviour of subatomic energy to anything approaching a consistent scheme. Whether these clouds will be dissipated without a fundamental revision of some of the beliefs and conclusions which we have here regarded as securely established, cannot be foreseen. The history of scientific progress teaches us to keep an open mind. I do not think we need feel greatly concerned as to whether these rude attempts to explore the interior of a star have brought us to anything like the final truth. We have learned something of the varied interests involved. We have seen how closely the manifestations of the greatest bodies in the universe are linked to those of the smallest. The partial results already obtained encourage us to think that we are not far from the right track. Especially do we realise that the transcendently high temperature in the interior of a star is not an obstacle to investigation but rather tends to smooth away difficulties. At terrestrial temperatures matter has complex properties which are likely to prove most difficult to unravel; but it is reasonable to hope that in a not too distant future we shall be competent to understand so simple a thing as a star.

APPENDIX I

PHYSICAL AND ASTRONOMICAL CONSTANTS

Physical Constants.

		Number	Logarithm
H	Mass of hydrogen atom	$1\cdot662.10^{-24}$	$\overline{24}\cdot2206$
m	Mass of electron = $H/1845$	$9\cdot01.10^{-28}$	$\overline{28}\cdot9546$
e	Charge of electron in electrostatic units	$4\cdot77.10^{-10}$	$\overline{10}\cdot6789$
b	$\frac{3}{2}\times$ radius of electron = e^2/mc^2	$2\cdot81.10^{-13}$	$\overline{13}\cdot4494$
u_0	Arithmetic mean speed of electron at $1°$ abs.	$6\cdot23.10^5$	$5\cdot7944$
c	Velocity of light	$3\cdot00.10^{10}$	$10\cdot4769$
R	Boltzmann's constant = $\frac{1}{8}\pi m u_0^2$	$1\cdot372.10^{-16}$	$\overline{16}\cdot1374$
$\Re$	Gas constant = R/H	$8\cdot26.10^7$	$7\cdot9168$
a	Coefficient of Stefan's law = $\frac{8}{15}\pi^5 R^4/c^3h^3$	$7\cdot64.10^{-15}$	$\overline{15}\cdot8832$
h	Planck's constant	$6\cdot55.10^{-27}$	$\overline{27}\cdot8161$
G	Constant of gravitation	$6\cdot66.10^{-8}$	$\overline{8}\cdot8235$
	Loschmidt's number (molecules per cu. cm. at $273°\cdot1$ and 10^6 dynes)	$2\cdot67.10^{19}$	$19\cdot4263$
	Rydberg's constant = $2\pi^2 e^4 mH/ch^3 (H+m)$	$109678\cdot3$	$5\cdot0401$

Astronomical Constants.

		Number	Logarithm
The Sun.	Mass (gm.)	$1\cdot985.10^{33}$	$33\cdot2978$
	Radius (cm.)	$6\cdot951.10^{10}$	$10\cdot8421$
	Mean density (gm./cm.³)	$1\cdot4109$	$0\cdot1495$
	Gravity at surface (cm./sec.²)	$2\cdot736.10^4$	$4\cdot4371$
	Total radiation (ergs/sec.)	$3\cdot780.10^{33}$	$33\cdot5775$
	H/c at surface (ergs/cm.³)	$2\cdot08$	$0\cdot3171$
	Effective temperature (deg. abs.)	5741	$3\cdot7590$
	Absolute bolometric magnitude	$4\cdot85$	—
Astronomical unit (cm.)		$1\cdot494.10^{13}$	$13\cdot1744$
Parsec (cm.)		$3\cdot08.10^{18}$	$18\cdot4888$
Sidereal year (sec.)		$3\cdot156.10^7$	$7\cdot4991$
Light ratio for 1 magnitude		$2\cdot512$	$0\cdot4000$

Miscellaneous Factors.

	Number	Logarithm
hc/e^2	861	$2\cdot9352$
hc/R	$1\cdot431$	$0\cdot1556$
$4\pi cG$	25100	$4\cdot3996$
$\frac{4}{3}\pi$	$4\cdot189$	$0\cdot6221$
Napierian base	$2\cdot7183$	$0\cdot4343$

If electric potential (X), wave-length (λ), temperature (T) and electron velocity (V) and energy (W) are connected by

$$eX = hc/\lambda = \tfrac{3}{2}RT = \tfrac{1}{2}mV^2 = W,$$

we have the relations

5 volts = 2468 Ångströms = 38,650 degrees = $1\cdot329.10^8$ cm. per sec.
= $7\cdot95.10^{-12}$ ergs.

1293 volts = 9·54 Ångströms = 10,000,000 degrees = $2\cdot138.10^9$ cm. per sec.
= $2\cdot058.10^{-9}$ ergs.

APPENDIX II

REFERENCES

The two lines of investigation which are brought together in the present theory of the equilibrium of a star originate in two classical papers—

1. J. HOMER LANE. On the Theoretical Temperature of the Sun. *Amer. Journ. of Sci. and Arts*, Series 2, Vol. **4**, p. 57 (1870).
2. K. SCHWARZSCHILD. Ueber das Gleichgewicht der Sonnenatmosphäre. *Göttingen Nachrichten*, 1906, p. 41.

The latter paper develops the theory of radiative equilibrium in a form appropriate to the outer layers of a star.

Investigations up to the year 1907 are brought together in

3. R. EMDEN. Gaskugeln: Anwendungen der Mechanischen Wärmetheorie. (B. G. Teubner, Leipzig and Berlin, 1907.)

which contains important developments by Emden himself. The most relevant portions are here summarised in §§ 54–63. Schwarzschild's work, which had newly appeared, is described by Emden, p. 330, but the book is in the main a study of convective equilibrium.

Two further references of historic interest may be added—

4. R. A. SAMPSON. On the Rotation and Mechanical State of the Sun. *Memoirs R.A.S.* **51**, p. 123 (1894).
5. I. BIALOBJESKY. Sur l'Équilibre Thermodynamique d'une Sphère Gazeuse Libre. *Bull. Acad. Sci. Cracovie*, May, 1913.

The first definitely postulates radiative equilibrium rather than convective equilibrium in the sun's interior. The second takes account of radiation pressure and demonstrates its importance in investigations of the internal equilibrium of a star.

For other early papers the references in Emden's *Gaskugeln* should be consulted.

My own investigations originated in an attempt to discuss a problem of Cepheid variation. The line of thought is indicated in an article (published a year later)

6. A. S. EDDINGTON. The Pulsation Theory of Cepheid Variables. *Observatory*, **40**, p. 290 (1917).

The problem was to find if possible some cause maintaining the mechanical energy of pulsation against loss by dissipative forces—some method by which mechanical energy could be automatically extracted from the abundant supplies of heat at different temperatures in the star without violating the second law of thermodynamics. This might happen if the material of the star acted as the working substance of a simple thermodynamic engine (§ 137), or if the radiation pressure varied in the manner necessary to perform mechanical work.

The equations developed for this study naturally laid stress on the opacity (which must serve as the valves of the engine), the transport of heat by radiation, and on radiation pressure. None of these were treated in the investigations of the stellar interior then customary; so that before discussing the small oscillations the conditions of the steady state had to be investigated anew. The Cepheid problem was laid aside for a time, and attention paid to the equilibrium problem. The sequence of papers which have followed is—

7. On the Radiative Equilibrium of the Stars. *Monthly Notices*, **77**, p. 16 (1916).
8. Further Notes on the Radiative Equilibrium of the Stars. *Monthly Notices*, **77**, p. 596 (1917).
9. On the Radiative Equilibrium of the Stars. A Correction. *Monthly Notices*, **79**, p. 22 (1918).
10. On the Conditions in the Interior of a Star. *Astrophysical Journ.* **48**, p. 205 (1918).
11. On the Pulsations of a Gaseous Star and the Problem of the Cepheid Variables, Parts I and II. *Monthly Notices*, **79**, pp. 2, 177 (1918–19).
12. Das Strahlungsgleichgewicht der Sterne. *Zeitschrift für Physik*, **7**, p. 351 (1921).
13. On the Absorption of Radiation inside a Star. *Monthly Notices*, **83**, p. 32 (1922).
14. Applications of the Theory of the Stellar Absorption-Coefficient. *Monthly Notices*, **83**, p. 98 (1922).
15. The Problem of Electron Capture in the Stars. *Monthly Notices*, **83**, p. 431 (1923).
16. The Absorption of Radiation inside a Star. Second Paper. *Monthly Notices*, **84**, p. 104 (1924).
17. On the Relation between the Masses and Luminosities of the Stars. *Monthly Notices*, **84**, p. 308 (1924).
18. A Limiting Case in the Theory of Radiative Equilibrium. *Monthly Notices*, **85**, p. 408 (1925).
19. Electrostatic Forces in a Star and the Deviations from a Perfect Gas. *Monthly Notices*, **86**, p. 2 (1925).

Answers to various criticisms by J. H. Jeans are given in *Monthly Notices*, **78**, p. 113; **85**, p. 403. Minor references are—*Scientia*, **23**, p. 9 (1918); *Brit. Assoc. Report*, 1920, p. 34; *Proc. Royal Institution*, Feb. 23, 1923; *Festschrift für H. von Seeliger*, p. 25 (1924). The following relate to side-problems—

20. Cepheid Variables and the Age of the Stars. *Observatory*, **41**, p. 379 (1918).
21. The Sources of Stellar Energy. *Observatory*, **42**, p. 371 (1919).
22. Circulating Currents in Rotating Stars. *Observatory*, **48**, p. 73 (1925).

As a guide to papers 7–19 it is to be noted that the absorption coefficient was supposed to be independent of density up to 1921, the modern view of the absorption process being adumbrated (but not generally employed) in No. 12. This is the most important modification that the theory has undergone since ionisation was introduced in No. 8. Nos. 10 and 12 were intended to summarise results up to date, the former in elementary form and the latter fairly exhaustively. No. 9 gives a rather important numerical correction to the formulae of Nos. 7 and 8, and the error is set right in all succeeding papers. Nos. 13–15 adopt the theory of nuclear capture of electrons, but much of the work is applicable also to Kramers' theory of capture adopted afterwards. Rosseland's correction to the opacity (§ 77) appeared subsequently to No. 17, so that the present book is my first opportunity of presenting the theory with attention to this important point. The conclusion that dwarf stars are in the state of a perfect gas appears first in No. 17. The theory of Cepheids in Chapter VIII is mainly contained in No. 11, but all numerical results have been revised in accordance with the later theory of the absorption coefficient. The chief additions are in §§ 131, 135–138.

Investigations hitherto unpublished are contained in §§ 64–66, 90, 122, 157, 160, 192, 193, 196, 229, 230, 231, 234–238, together with most of Chapters XI and XIII.

Molecular Weight.

The numerical results are very sensitive to changes in the adopted molecular weight. In No. 7 this was taken to be 54. In consequence of arguments for strong ionisation urged convincingly by Jeans, it was reduced to 2 (or, having regard to correction No. 9, to 2·8) in No. 8. At first it was only intended that Nos. 7 and 8 should indicate the two limits between which the results must lie, but gradually the latter came to be regarded as approximately correct. The first thermodynamical study of ionisation in the stellar interior is

23. JOHN EGGERT. Ueber den Dissoziationszustand der Fixsterngase. *Physikalische Zeitschrift*, **20**, p. 570 (1919).

This appeared to indicate a molecular weight 3·3, or perhaps higher; and in some of the author's subsequent papers values of 3·5, 4, 4·5 have been used tentatively. It was shown by

24. E. A. MILNE. Statistical Equilibrium in relation to the Photoelectric Effect and its Application to the Determination of Absorption Coefficients. *Phil. Mag.* **47**, p. 209 (1924).

that more refined calculation indicated much stronger ionisation, the same conclusion being reached by the author a few weeks later (No. 16). There has consequently been a reaction to low values $\mu = 2 \cdot 1$ or $2 \cdot 2$. The latest calculations are given in

25. R. H. FOWLER and E. A. GUGGENHEIM. Applications of Statistical Mechanics to determine the Properties of Matter in Stellar Interiors. *Monthly Notices*, **85**, p. 939 (1925).

but I understand that Mr Fowler is not yet satisfied and believes that in the smaller stars μ is to be increased appreciably.

Absorption Coefficients.

The following additional references are of fundamental importance—

26. H. A. KRAMERS. On the Theory of X Ray Absorption and on the Continuous X Ray Spectrum. *Phil. Mag.* **46**, p. 836 (1923).

27. S. ROSSELAND. Note on the Absorption of Radiation within a Star. *Monthly Notices*, **84**, p. 525 (1924).

The first contains the physical theory of absorption here accepted as most satisfactory; the second points out the distinction between absorption and opacity which we have called "Rosseland's correction." Other papers are

28. S. ROSSELAND. The Theory of the Stellar Absorption Coefficient. *Astrophys. Journ.* **61**, p. 424 (1925).

29. J. WOLTJER, *Junior*. Line Absorption and Absorption Coefficients inside a Star. *Bull. Astr. Inst. Netherlands*, No. 82 (1925).

30. E. A. MILNE. The Stellar Absorption Coefficient. *Monthly Notices*, **85**, p. 750 (1925).

Connected with the same subject is

31. R. H. FOWLER. On Statistical Equilibrium and the Mechanism of Ionisation by Electronic Impacts. *Phil. Mag.* **47**, p. 257 (1924).

I may here acknowledge indebtedness to Dr C. D. Ellis who guided me among the literature and helped me to a working knowledge of X-ray absorption, etc. when the astronomical researches led in that direction.

Electrical Forces and Diffusion in the Interior.

The subject is treated by

32. S. CHAPMAN. Convection and Diffusion within Giant Stars. *Monthly Notices,* 77, p. 541 (1917).

33. S. CHAPMAN. Diffusion and Viscosity in Giant Stars. *Monthly Notices,* 82, p. 292 (1922).

34. S. ROSSELAND. Electrical State of a Star. *Monthly Notices,* 84, p. 720 (1924).

35. E. A. MILNE. Dissociative Equilibrium in an External Field of Force. *Proc. Camb. Phil. Soc.* 22, p. 493 (1925).

36. S. ROSSELAND. On the Distribution of Hydrogen in a Star. *Monthly Notices,* 85, p. 541 (1925).

The section of the book dealing with this subject (§§ 191–196) was written before the last three papers appeared; they were available for the final revision. Circulating currents are suggested in No. 22, and in

37. H. VOGT. Zum Strahlungsgleichgewicht der Sterne. *Astronomische Nachrichten,* No. 5342 (1925).

The theorem leading to this inference is contained in

38. H. VON ZEIPEL. Zum Strahlungsgleichgewicht der Sterne. *Festschrift für H. von Seeliger,* p. 144 (1924).

A criticism by Jeans is answered by von Zeipel in *Monthly Notices,* 85, p. 678.

Rotating Stars.

Detailed investigations are given by

39. E. A. MILNE. The Equilibrium of a Rotating Star. *Monthly Notices,* 83, p. 118 (1923).

40. H. VON ZEIPEL. The Radiative Equilibrium of a Rotating System of Gaseous Masses. *Monthly Notices,* 84, pp. 665, 684, 702 (1924).

The Outside of a Star.

The classical papers are (in addition to reference No. 2)

41. A. SCHUSTER. Radiation through a Foggy Atmosphere. *Astrophys. Journ.* 21, p. 1 (1905).

42. M. N. SAHA. On a Physical Theory of Stellar Spectra. *Proc. Roy. Soc.* 99 A, p. 135 (1921).

Chapter XII is based in large measure on E. A. Milne's researches. We divide our selected references under the headings (a) Photosphere, (b) Chromosphere, (c) Reversing Layer.

(a) *Photosphere.*

43. K. SCHWARZSCHILD. Ueber Diffusion und Absorption in der Sonnenatmosphäre. *Berlin. Sitzungsberichte,* 1914, p. 1183.

44. J. H. JEANS. The Equations of Radiative Transfer of Energy. *Monthly Notices,* 78, p. 28 (1917).

45. E. A. MILNE. Radiative Equilibrium in the Outer Layers of a Star. *Monthly Notices,* 81, p. 361 (1921).

46. E. A. MILNE. Radiative Equilibrium and Spectral Distribution. *Monthly Notices,* 81, p. 375 (1921).

47. E. A. MILNE. The Effect of a strong Absorption Line. *Monthly Notices,* 81, p. 510 (1921).

48. E. A. MILNE. The Relation between the Spectral Energy Curve and the Law of Darkening of the Disc towards the Limb. *Royal Soc. Phil. Trans.* **223** A, p. 201 (1922).

49. R. LUNDBLAD. The Radiation and Temperature of the External Photospheric Layers. *Astrophys. Journ.* **58**, p. 113 (1923).

50. B. LINDBLAD. Radiative Equilibrium and Solar Temperature. *Nova Acta Upsaliensis*, Ser. 4, **6**, No. 1 (1923).

51. E. A. MILNE. Absorption Coefficients and the Pressure of Radiation in the Photospheric Layers of a Star. *Monthly Notices*, **85**, p. 768 (1925).

(b) *Chromosphere.*

52. E. A. MILNE. An Astrophysical Determination of the Average Life of an Excited Calcium Atom. *Monthly Notices*, **84**, p. 354 (1924).

53. E. A. MILNE. The Equilibrium of the Calcium Chromosphere. *Monthly Notices*, **85**, p. 111 (1924); **86**, p. 8 (1925).

(c) *Reversing Layer.*

54. A. PANNEKOEK. Ionisation in Stellar Atmospheres. *Bull. Ast. Inst. Netherlands*, No. 19 (1922).

55. R. T. BIRGE. The Quantum Theory of Band Spectra and its Application to the Determination of Temperature. *Astrophys. Journ.* **55**, p. 273 (1922).

56. R. H. FOWLER and E. A. MILNE. The Intensities of Absorption Lines in Stellar Spectra and the Temperatures and Pressures in the Reversing Layers of Stars. *Monthly Notices*, **83**, p. 403 (1923).

57. R. H. FOWLER and E. A. MILNE. The Maxima of Absorption Lines in Stellar Spectra. *Monthly Notices*, **84**, p. 499 (1924).

58. H. N. RUSSELL and J. Q. STEWART. Pressures at the Sun's Surface. *Astrophys. Journ.* **59**, p. 197 (1924).

59. P. A. M. DIRAC. The Effect of Compton Scattering by Free Electrons in a Stellar Atmosphere. *Monthly Notices*, **85**, p. 825 (1925).

60. R. H. FOWLER. Notes on the Theory of Absorption Lines in Stellar Spectra. *Monthly Notices*, **85**, p. 970 (1925).

61. C. H. PAYNE. Stellar Atmospheres. *Harvard Observatory Monographs*, No. 1 (1925).

The last-mentioned monograph contains in addition to Miss Payne's own researches a full survey and discussion of existing knowledge of reversing layer problems. We have avoided entering on this part of the subject beyond the elementary principles. Any detailed study requires a knowledge of the series relations in optical spectra for which reference should be made to

62. A. FOWLER. Report on Series in Line Spectra. *Physical Society*, 1922.

Nebulous Matter.

Chapter XIII does not for the most part follow any published theory. The general ideas originated in private discussions with S. Rosseland to whom I am considerably indebted. Existence of interstellar matter was at that time hypothetical, but a month later observational evidence of a diffuse cloud in space was announced by

63. J. S. PLASKETT. The H and K Lines of Calcium in O-type Stars. *Monthly Notices*, **84**, p. 80 (1923).

Use has been made of

64. A. PANNEKOEK. Further Remarks on the Dark Nebula in Taurus. *Proc. Kon. Akad. Amsterdam*, **23**, p. 720 (1920).

Theories of planetary nebulae are discussed in

65. J. H. JEANS. The Mechanism and Structure of Planetary Nebulae. *Monthly Notices*, **83**, p. 482 (1923).
66. B. P. GERASIMOVIČ. On the Radiative and Mechanical Equilibrium of Spherical Planetary Nebulae. *Astr. Nach.* No. 5382 (1925).

Lick Observatory Publications, Vol. 13 (1918) is the main source of observational data for the nebulae.

Subatomic Energy.

On the astronomical side of the problem we have found most helpful

67. H. N. RUSSELL. On the Sources of Stellar Energy. *Pub. Astr. Soc. Pac.* **31**, p. 205 (1919).
68. H. N. RUSSELL. The Problem of Stellar Evolution. *Nature*, **116**, p. 209 (1925).

Miscellaneous.

The long series of papers by J. H. Jeans in the *Monthly Notices* from 1917 onwards can only be dealt with here by a general reference. Some of the criticisms brought by Jeans against the theory as developed in this book would, if justified, be of a very vital character and opposition develops at the very beginning.

We shall not enumerate papers primarily concerned with observations or statistical discussions of observational data. These and other researches auxiliary to the theory are referred to in footnotes to the pages of the text to which they are relevant. A few not quoted in the text are added here—

69. F. W. SEARES. The Masses and Densities of the Stars. *Astrophys. Journ.* **55**, p. 165.
70. A. BRILL. Der Physikalische Zustand der Sterne. *Zeits. für Physik*, **31**, p. 717 (1925).
71. W. RABE. Die absolute Helligkeit der Zwergsterne als Funktion der Temperatur und Masse. *Astr. Nach.* No. 5389–90 (1925).

A monograph dealing with the theory generally but with special reference to ionisation, opacity and the electrical state of the stars has been received during proof-reading—

72. S. ROSSELAND. On the Internal Constitution of the Stars. *Norske Videnskaps-Akademi, Oslo*, 1925, No. 1.

Another late paper carrying a little farther the investigations of Chapter XIII is

73. A. S. EDDINGTON. Diffuse Matter in Interstellar Space (Bakerian Lecture). *Proc. Roy. Soc.* **111** A, p. 424.

INDEX

Abbot, C. G., 325

Absolute magnitude, 13; of sun, 14, 149. *See* Luminosity

Absorption, of radiation, 3, 20, 21, 47, 217; of light in space, 384

Absorption coefficient, for terrestrial X-rays, 22, 236; relation to emission coefficient, 50, 54, 105; astronomical determination of, 118, 146; law of variation, 121, 202, 219, 229, 248; in photosphere, 355; monochromatic, 368

Absorption edges, 70

Absorption lines, 238; formation of, 337; broadening of, 353; fixed lines, 377

Abundance of the elements, 369

Accretion of mass by stars, 391

Adams, W. S., 2, 160, 171, 172, 307

Adiabatic changes, 35; equilibrium, 97; pulsations, 186

Adiabatic principle, 72, 355

Aetherial heat, 18

Age, of sun, 289; of earth, 290

Aitken, R. G., 150, 155

Albedo of stars, 211

Algol, 209

Amplitude of pulsations, 185, 195

Anderson, J. A., 12, 300

Annihilation of protons and electrons, 293

Aston, F. W., 293, 295

Astronomical constants, values of, 395

Atom, structure of, 10

Atomic absorption coefficient, 54, 236

Atomic numbers of elements, 10, 252

Balancing, principle of detailed, 45

Band spectra, 350

Betelgeuse, 6

Bialobjesky, I., 397

Binary hypothesis of Cepheids, 184

Binary stars, 11, 152, 161; mass ratios of, 160; change of mass, 311, 312

Birge, R. T., 350

Bjerknes, V., 286

Black body, 39; sun's deviation from, 325

Blackness of absorption lines, 340, 342, 347, 350

Bohr atom, 60, 72

Bolometric magnitude, 13; reduction to visual magnitude, 138

Boltzmann's constant, 51

Boltzmann's formula, 49; inapplicable to free electrons, 263

Boundary conditions, 95, 116, 127, 211

Boundary temperature of stars, 323, 332

Bright line spectra, 343

Broadening of spectral lines, 353; in Cepheids, 206

Buisson, H., 330

Calcium, in chromosphere, 362; in interstellar space, 378; ionisation of, 345, 349, 382

Cameron, H., 318

Campbell, W. W., 11, 147

Canonical variables, 58

Capella, 11, 14, 85, 145

Capture of electrons, 23, 218, 221, 230, 245

TV Cassiopeiae, 214

Cell of unit weight, 68

Central temperature of stars, formulae for, 85, 136; minimum value, 91; numerical values, 136, 151, 182; constancy on main series, 177, 299

δ Cephei, 146, 199, 290

Cepheid variables, 157, 180, 290

o Ceti, 206, 208; companion of, 173

Chapman, S., 277, 279, 280

Chemical constitution of stars, effect of, 2, 10, 243; assumptions as to, 250, 370

Chromosphere, Milne's theory of, 362

Circulating currents in rotating stars, 285; tendency to die out, 99

Classical theory, of emission, 223; of electron scattering, 77

Classification of spectra, 2

Cloud, interstellar, 378

Clusters, masses of stars in, 162; variables in, 181; giant and dwarf stars in, 310

Coeval stars, difficulty arising from, 310, 392

Collisions, inelastic and superelastic, 339, 373

Companion of Sirius, 171

Composition. *See* Chemical constitution

Compressibility of a gas, 165

Compton effect, 76, 316

Condensations in interstellar medium, 381

Conduction of heat, 97, 281

Constants, list of natural, 395

Contraction hypothesis, 5, 289

Contrast. *See* Blackness

Contrast, centre-limb, 328, 331; in chromosphere, 365

Convection currents, 98, 285

Convective equilibrium, 9, 97

Conversion of subatomic energy, 315

Correspondence principle, 53, 64, 230, 241, 263

Currents, circulating, 98, 285

Cyanogen bands, 350

Dark nebulae, 387

Darkening at the limb, 212; law of, 324

Debye and Hückel's theory, 264, 280

Decay of pulsations, time of, 199

Delaunay's canonical variables, 58

Dense stars, 130; gas laws in, 165

Density, of photosphere, 336, 360; of chromosphere, 368; of interstellar matter, 372 382; of nebulae, 382

Density of stars, 5, 8; ratio of central to mean density, 84; mean densities of stars, 136; high density possible, 170
Destruction of matter, 293
Detailed balancing, principle of, 45
Deviations from perfect gas, 260; in ionised gas, 263; in stars, 131, 165
Diameter. *See* Radius
Dielectric constant, 237
Diffuse matter in space, 371
Diffuse nebulae, 387
Diffusion, coefficient of, 277; thermal, 276; of electrons, 273
Dilution, factor of, 382
Disorganisation of energy, 30
Displacement law (Wien's), 39
Dissipation of energy in Cepheids, 198
Distribution, of elements in a star, 275, 298; of subatomic sources, 122
Dootson, F. W., 277
Double stars. *See* Binary stars
Doublets, 74
Douglas, A. V., 307
Duration of stages of evolution, 309
Dwarf stars, 7, 130; white dwarfs, 170
Dynamical parallaxes, 158, 161

Earth, age of, 290
Eclipsing variables, 156, 208
Effective temperature, of radiation, 37; of a star, 2, 120, 135, 140, 323; of radiation in space, 371
Eggert, J., 346, 399
Einstein's equation, 46, 56
Einstein's theory of gravitation, 6, 172; identity of mass and energy, 294
Electric charge in a star, 272
Electrons, 10; orbits of, 58; K and L groups, 69; capture of, 24, 218, 221, 230, 245; scattering by, 74, 77, 316, 385; free, 64, 263; runaway, 302; destruction of, 293
Electrostatic energy and pressure, 264; correction to ionisation, 257
Elements, atomic numbers and energy levels of, 252; stellar abundance of, 369
Emden, R., 5, 81
Emission coefficient, 24, 47, 218, 329; relation to absorption coefficient, 50, 54, 105; theories of, 223, 229, 245
Emission lines, 343
Enclosure, 35, 39, 100
Energy, of a polytrope, 86; of a star, 141; of a white dwarf, 172; of the sun, 289, 292; of ionisation, 269
Energy, subatomic, 292
Energy and mass, 27, 294
Energy levels in atoms, 252, 257
Energy-density of equilibrium radiation, 38; relation to pressure, 29
Enhanced lines, 345
Enskog, D., 277
Entropy, 30
Equilibrium of a star, 9, 79; stability of, 142

Equilibrium radiation, 36
66 Eridani, 380
Escape of atoms, 368, 392
Evenly diluted radiation, 376, 382
Evershed, J., 362
Evolution of stars, 7, 174, 296, 309
Exchanges, principle of, 35, 45
Excited atoms, 45, 66, 238, 259, 346; life of, 364
Excluded volumes, 259
Exhaustion of subatomic sources, 297, 299

Fabry, C., 330, 371
Fixed calcium lines, 377
Flow of heat, 100, 321; variable, 197
Fowler, A., 73, 345
Fowler, R. H., 194, 220, 256, 266, 347, 379
Free electrons, 64, 263
Free path, 222, 277, 280, 368, 373
Frequency. *See* Wave-length

Gas, deviations from perfect, 131, 165; theory of, 260, 263
Gas-constant, 8
Gas-sphere, 79; polytropic, 80; isothermal, 89; tables, 82, 90
Gerasimovič, B., 286
Giant and Dwarf theory, 2, 119, 163
Giant stars, 5, 176; masses of, 307; lower effective temperature, 361
Gravitation opposed by radiation pressure, 17
Gravity on Capella, 15; on the sun, 395
Guggenheim, E. A., 256, 266
Guillotine, 231, 256; factors, 233
Güssow, M., 181
Gyllenberg, W., 207

Hamiltonian equations, 59, 67
Hartree, D. R., 257
Heat, aetherial and material, 19; irreversible flow of, 32; radiometer measurement of, 138, 206; sun's store of, 289
Helium, formation of, 292, 296, 301, 314, 315, 317
Helmholtz, H. L. F., 289
Hertzsprung, E., 7, 139, 152, 158, 161, 164, 180, 290, 310
Hubble's variable nebula, 387
Hyades, 158
Hydrogen, exceptional behaviour of, 10, 244, 276, 315; quantisation of, 58; transmutation of, 293, 296, 301, 314
Hypothetical parallaxes, 158, 161

Initial temperature of electron gas, 376
Inner quantum number, 74
Inside of a star, 19
Insight, 102
Interferometer, 6, 12, 171
Interstellar space, 371; calcium cloud in, 378
Invariance of weights, 68
Inverse square forces, 168

Ionisation, 10; equation determining, 65, 66; applied to stars, 251, 254; energy of, 142, 269; in Cepheid variables, 204; in reversing layer, 345; in interstellar medium, 382
Ionisation potentials, 252, 257, 383
Ions, size of, 166, 359; diffusion of, 273
Iron, ionisation potentials of, 257
Irreversible processes, 32
Isothermal gas-sphere, 89, 92, 382

Jeans, J. H., 3, 10, 203, 281, 287, 303, 312, 322
Joy, A. H., 160, 307

K electrons, 23, 69, 217, 252
Kelvin, 5, 289, 294
Kohlhörster, W., 317
Kohlschütter, A., 2, 342
Kramers, H. A., 223, 225, 229
Krueger 60, 150
Kulenkampff, H., 234, 238, 249

L electrons, 23, 69, 217, 252
Lane, H., 4, 7, 163
Laplace, 6
Larmor, J., 294
Leavitt, H. S., 181
Light, absorption of, 383
Light curve of variables, 147, 180, 205, 208, 210
Light ratio for 1 magnitude, 14
Lindblad, B., 322, 325
Lindemann, F. A., 10
Line absorption and emission, 111, 238; formation of absorption lines, 337, 381; intensity of, 342, 350; width of, 353; emission lines, 343
Lockyer, J. N., 6, 345
Long period variables, 206
Luminosity of stars, relation to mass, 151; relation to spectral type, 175; relation to period in Cepheids, 181; relation to heat radiation, 138
Luminous efficiency, 13, 138, 213

Magnetic field of star, 389
Magnitude, 13, 14. See Absolute magnitude, Bolometric magnitude, Luminosity, Mass-luminosity relation
Main series, 151, 176, 177, 210, 215, 299
Mass, relation to energy, 27, 292, 294; distribution in a polytrope, 86; of chromosphere, 368; of nebulae, 388
Masses of stars, determined by radiation pressure, 16, 118, 308; method of determining, 12; large masses, 148; initial masses, 307; change of, 176, 306, 312, 391; principal formulae involving, 135
Mass-absorption coefficient, 22, 100
Mass-luminosity relation, theory of, 116, 118, 135; table of, 137; curve, 153; agreement with observation, 158; applied to Algol, 210

Mass-ratios in binary stars, 160, 311
Mathematicians, 102
Maxwell's equations, 57
Maxwell's law, proof of, 51; for electrons with negative energy, 64
McDiarmid, R. J., 214
McLaughlin, D. B., 214
Merrill, P. W., 12, 207
Metastable orbit, 74
Michelson, A. A., 12
Millikan, R. A., 318
Milne, E. A., 287, 322, 325, 330, 347, 349, 355, 361, 362
Minimal problems (central pressure and temperature), 90
Molecular weight, 10; probable values of, 253, 258, 259; variation of, 128; determined by observation, 159; effect of change, 255
Molecules, absorption by, 386; band spectra of, 350; quantisation of, 352
Multiplets, 74

Nebulae, 387; penetrating radiation from, 319
Nebulium, 389
Negative absorption, 50
Nernst, W., 3
Newall, H. F., 10, 11
Nicholson, S. B., 206
Novae, 389
Nuclear capture, 245
Nucleus of atom, 10

Opacity, 3, 21; distinguished from absorption, 109; inversely proportional to luminosity, 118; astronomical measurement of, 146; law of variation, 121, 219, 229, 237, 248; variation with temperature, 202, 221, 303; of dark nebulae, 388
Optical depth, 321
Optical spectra, 72
Orbits of binary stars, 11; photometric orbits, 148, 209
Orbits of electrons, 58, 71; of large quantum number, 61, 241; hyperbolic, 224, 229, 245
Oscillation. See Pulsation
Over-stability, 201, 299

Pannekoek, A., 273, 388
Parallax of Capella, 13; dynamical parallaxes, 158, 161
Parsec, 395
Pauli, W., 70, 76
Payne, C. H., 141, 369, 401
Pease, F. G., 208
85 Pegasi, 160
Penetrating radiation, 317
Perfect gas, 5, 8, 84, 116; deviations from, 131, 167, 260, 263; of high density, 165
Period of pulsation, 192
Period-luminosity relation in Cepheids, 181
Perrin, J., 296

Persico, E., 280
Perturbation of electron orbits, 71
Pettit, E., 206
Photometric orbits, 148, 209
Photosphere, 334, 360
Planck's constant, 46, 395
Planck's law, 21, 49, 53, 55
Planetary nebulae, 389
Plaskett, H. H., 330, 342
Plaskett, J. S., 148, 156, 214, 378
Plummer, H. C., 185
Point-source of energy, solution for, 124
Polytropic gas-sphere, 80; tables, 82; incomplete, 94; applicable to stars, 117, 128
Potential, gravitational, 79; at centre of star, 83, 85
Potential energy of polytrope, 86; of a star, 141
Poynting vector, 57
Pressure, 79; at centre of a star, 85, 91; in reversing layer, 349; in photosphere, 360; electrostatic correction to, 266, 269; broadening of lines by, 353
Pressure of radiation, 15; theory of, 27; numerical value, 38; ratio to whole pressure, formulae, 117, 129; tables, 117, 137; determines stellar masses, 16, 118, 308; stress components of, 105, 335; in outer layers, 357, 360; in chromosphere, 362; escape of atoms by, 368
Principal lines, 74, 346, 349, 363
Procyon, 152; companion, 155
Protons, destruction of, 293
Pseudo-Cepheids, 181
Pulsation, of Cepheids, 180; criticisms, 185; adiabatic theory of, 186; period of, 192; limit to amplitude, 194; maintenance of, 200; of long period variables, 206
V Puppis, 147

Quanta, 41, 46; general conception of, 57
Quantisation, of hydrogen-like ion, 58; of molecules, 352; lack of sharpness, 60, 354
Quantum numbers, 59, 70, 72
Quartic equation, fundamental, 117, 129

Radiation, 27; equilibrium of, 35; temperature of, 37; Stefan's law, 38; Wien's law, 39; Planck's law, 55; flow of, 101, 322; from accelerated electron, 77, 223; penetrating, 317
Radiation of stars (total), 114; relation to opacity, 118; relation to mass and radius, 134; relation to luminosity, 138. See also Luminosity, Absolute magnitude, Mass-luminosity relation
Radiation pressure. See Pressure of radiation
Radiative equilibrium, 9, 97; equation of, 101, 107, 322
Radiative viscosity, 281

Radio-activity, 294, 315, 344
Radiometer, 138
Radius, of Cepheids, 182; of long period variable, 208; of sun, 395
Radius of star, 2; interferometer measures, 6; method of calculating, 13; method for Algol, 210
Rayleigh scattering, 384, 385
Reflection effect in eclipsing variables, 210, 213
Refractive index, 38, 237
Relativity, 6, 173
Reversible processes, 32
Reversing layer, 342; pressure in, 349, 359
Rigour of proofs, 102
Ring nebula, 389
Ritter, A., 5
Rosseland, S., 109, 238, 243, 264, 401
Rosseland's correction, 112, 247, 356, 398
Rotating stars, brightness of, 287; currents in, 285; von Zeipel's theorem, 282
Rotation, of Algol, 210; of planetary nebulae, 389
Runaway electrons, 302, 320
Russell, H. N., 7, 148, 160, 163, 177, 295, 303, 354
Rutherford, E., 220

Saha, M. N., 345, 347
Sampson, R. A., 9
Scattering by electrons, 74, 243, 384; coefficient of, 76
Schuster, A., 400
Schwarzschild, K., 9, 322, 342
Seares, F. H., 174
Selection principle, 71, 73, 351
Series in spectra, 74
Shajn, G., 160, 311
Shapley, H., 8, 146, 181, 310, 342, 384
Shielding of nuclear field by electrons, 67, 71, 264
Shinjo, S., 203
Silicon, spectra of, 345
Sirius, companion of, 171
Size of atoms and ions, 165, 262, 359
Smart, W. M., 312
Sodium, fixed lines of, 378, 383
Sorting demon, 37
Source of stellar energy, 289; relative distribution of, 122, 295; point-source, 124
Space, interstellar, 371; temperature in, 371, 377; density in, 372, 382; ionisation in, 383; absorption of light in, 383; penetrating radiation from, 318
Specific heats, ratio of, 9, 35; for radiation, 10, 29; for stellar material, 270; in Cepheids, 157, 190, 203; limit of stability, 142
Spectra, X-ray, 70, 230, 234; optical, 72; molecular, 350. See also Absorption. Emission, Spectral type
Spectral energy curve, 324

Spectral type, 2; Saha's theory of, 345; temperature scale, 141; magnitude statistics, 175; progression in Cepheids, 181, 208; range, 186; comparison of giants and dwarfs, 361
Stability of a star, 142, 303
Stark effect, 353, 355
Stationary calcium lines, 377
Stebbins, J., 209
Stefan's law, 38
Stewart, J. Q., 354
Stimulated emission, 50, 303, 365
Strömberg, G., 207
Subatomic energy, 292
Subordinate lines, 343, 346
Sun, 149; astronomical constants for, 395; darkening at the limb, 324, 328; spectral energy curve, 328; photosphere, 336, 360; height of chromosphere, 362, 367
Superelastic collisions, 339, 373
Superperfect gas, 267
Surface-brightness and effective temperature (table), 139
Switches of orbits, 229, 375

Target for electron capture, 221, 245
Temperature, inside a star, 14, 84, 120, 136; mean temperature, 88, 94; in outer layers, 323; second approximation, 332; in interstellar space, 371, 377. See also Central temperature, Effective temperature
Temperature-gradient in Capella, 15
Tensors, 57, 69
Thermal diffusion, 276
Thermodynamical equilibrium, 44, 47; application to outside of a star, 323, 338

Thermometric temperature, 32
Thomson, J. J., 294
Thunderstorms, stellar, 344
Time, direction of progress, 44
Time-scale, 290, 293, 309
Transmutation of hydrogen, 292, 296, 314

Valency electrons, 72, 379
Valve of heat engine, 200, 202
Van der Waals' equation, 131, 167, 259, 262
Variable stars, Cepheid, 157, 180, 290; eclipsing, 156, 208; long period, 206
Velocity curves of Cepheids, 180, 205
Virial, 260
Viscosity, 280
Vogt, H., 285, 311
Volts, conversion to ergs and Ångströms, 396

Wave-length of maximum energy, 140, 325; of energy levels, 252; of subatomic emission, 316; changed by scattering, 76; conversion to volts, 396
Weights of atomic states, 49, 61, 67, 230; for calculating opacity, 112
White dwarfs, 170, 306
Width of absorption lines, 353, 367
Wien's law, 39, 48
Wilson, C. T. R., 301, 320
Woltjer, J., 203, 238, 240

X-rays, 21; spectra, 70, 230, 234; absorption coefficients, 22, 217, 236

von Zeipel, H., 162, 282, 287
Zonal harmonics, 105